Prehistory of the Eastern Sahara

FRED WENDORF

Department of Anthropology
Southern Methodist University
Dallas, Texas

ROMUALD SCHILD

Institute for the History of Material Culture
Polish Academy of Sciences
Warsaw, Poland

ACADEMIC PRESS
A Subsidiary of Harcourt Brace Jovanovich, Publishers
New York   London   Toronto   Sydney   San Francisco

ACADEMIC PRESS, INC.
111 Fifth Avenue, New York, New York 10003

United Kingdom Edition published by
ACADEMIC PRESS, INC. (LONDON) LTD.
24/28 Oval Road, London NW1 7DX

Library of Congress Cataloging in Publication Data

Wendorf, Fred.
    Prehistory of the eastern Sahara.

    Bibliography: p.
    Includes index.
    1. Man, Prehistoric––Egypt––Western Desert.
2. Egypt––Antiquities. 3. Western Desert––Antiquities.
I. Schild, Romuald, joint author. II. Title.
GN865.E3W46   932   79–8865
ISBN 0–12–743960–9

PRINTED IN THE UNITED STATES OF AMERICA

80 81 82 83   9 8 7 6 5 4 3 2 1

Prehistory of
the Eastern Sahara

To Gertrude Caton-Thompson

Contents

1
Introduction

2
The Bir Sahara-Bir Tarfawi Area

3
Gebel Nabta and Vicinity

4

The Northern Oases: The Kharga and Dakhla Areas

5

Miscellaneous Investigations

6

Paleoenvironment of the Western Desert of Egypt

7

Human Exploitation of the Western Desert

8

Some Thoughts on the Origin of Food Production in Northeast Africa

APPENDIX
1

The Quaternary Sediments of the Southern Western Desert of Egypt: An Overview

RUSHDI SAID

APPENDIX
2

A Study of Stylistic Variability and Continuity in the Nabta Area

ANGELA E. CLOSE

APPENDIX
3

Ceramics of the Western Desert

K. MORGAN BANKS

APPENDIX
4

Contributions to the Archaeozoology of Egypt

ACHILLES GAUTIER

APPENDIX
5

Vegetation of the Nubian Desert (Nabta Region)

M. NABIL EL HADIDI

APPENDIX
6

Geological Evidence of Pluvial Climates in the Nabta Area of the Western Desert, Egypt

C. VANCE HAYNES

APPENDIX
7

Discussion of Radiocarbon Dates from the Western Desert

HERBERT HAAS AND C. VANCE HAYNES

APPENDIX
8

Intrasite and Intersite Spatial Analyses at Bir Tarfawi

HAROLD J. HIETALA AND RICHARD E. LARSON

APPENDIX
9

Biometrical Analysis of the Early Neolithic Human Mandible from Nabta Playa (Western Desert of Egypt)

MACIEJ HENNEBERG, JANUSZ PIONTEK, AND JAN STRZAŁKO

APPENDIX
10

A Scanning Electron Microscope Study of Cereal Grains from Nabta Playa

ANN STEMLER AND RICHARD FALK

List of Contributors

Numbers in parentheses indicate the pages on which the authors' contributions begin.

K. MORGAN BANKS (299)
Department of Anthropology
Southern Methodist University
Dallas, Texas 75275

ANGELA E. CLOSE (291)
Department of Anthropology
Southern Methodist University
Dallas, Texas 75275

RICHARD FALK (393)
Department of Botany
University of California, Davis
Davis, California 95616

ACHILLES GAUTIER (317)
Laboratorium voor Paleontologie
Rijksuniversiteit Ghent
Ghent, Belgium

HERBERT HAAS (373)
Department of Geology
Southern Methodist University
Dallas, Texas 75275

M. NABIL EL HADIDI (345)
Department of Botany
Faculty of Science
Cairo University
Giza, Egypt

C. VANCE HAYNES (353, 373)
Department of Anthropology
University of Arizona
Tucson, Arizona 85721

MACIEJ HENNEBERG (389)
Department of Anthropology
A. Mickiewicz University
Fredry 10,61-701
Poznan, Poland

HAROLD J. HIETALA (379)
Departments of Anthropology and Statistics
Southern Methodist University
Dallas, Texas 75275

RICHARD E. LARSON (379)
Department of Geology
Southern Methodist University
Dallas, Texas 75275

JANUSZ PIONTEK (389)
Department of Anthropology
A. Mickiewicz University
Fredry 10,61-701
Poznan, Poland

RUSHDI SAID (281)
Geological Survey of Egypt
Cairo, Egypt

ANN STEMLER (393)
Department of Biology
DeAnza College
Cupertino, California 95014

JAN STRZAŁKO (389)
Department of Anthropology
A. Mickiewicz University
Fredry 10,61-701
Poznan, Poland

Preface

This book describes the major results of a long-term multidisciplinary study of the Pleistocene and Early Holocene environments of the Western Desert of Egypt and the human exploitation of these environments. The area studied is today one of the driest and least hospitable on earth, with virtually no rainfall, extremely high temperatures during much of the year, and seemingly devoid of all life except near widely scattered wells or oases. While primarily designed as a study in prehistory and paleoecology, this book will be of interest to anyone concerned with arid lands, with their environments, and with past human responses to hyperaridity. It will also be useful to those interested in the prehistory of North Africa, and the origins of Egyptian civilization. The logistical problems of working in the eastern Sahara are such that information of the kind given here has previously been unobtainable.

Following a brief description of the research methods and the modern environment, the main body of the book is concerned with the presentation of data from five widely separated localities. For each locality the lithostratigraphic sequence is given first, followed by a detailed consideration of the associated archaeology. These data are then used to reconstruct both the environmental sequence of the Western Desert and the pattern of human exploitation of the area, and to compare these with data available from elsewhere in North Africa. The final chapter deals with the origin of food production in northeast Africa, and the implications that the early occurrence of this phenomenon in the eastern Sahara has for theories concerning the "causes" of food production. Finally, the book concludes with 10 appendixes wherein the reader may find more detailed data on the regional geology, the ceramics, stylistic and locational studies, faunal and floral remains, human skeletal material, and the radiocarbon dates discussed in the preceding body of the book.

THE COMBINED PREHISTORIC EXPEDITION

From 1962 to 1965, much of the archaeological interest of the world was focused on Nubia, along the Nile Valley in northern Sudan and southern Egypt, where an international effort was being made to save the heritage soon to be lost behind the new Aswan High Dam and the Aswan Reservoir. One of the groups involved in that effort was the Combined Prehistoric Expedition, a largely informal organization of scholars from Belgium, Egypt, England, Poland, and the United States, bound by a common interest in the prehistory of the Nile Valley and supported by funds from their own institutions, as well as the United States Department of State and the National Science Foundation.

By 1966 work on the Aswan Reservoir had been terminated. The rising waters of Lake Nasser had already covered most of the archaeological sites along that portion of the Nile, and the final reports on the salvage studies at the prehistoric sites excavated by the Combined Prehistoric Expedition were nearing completion (Wendorf 1968). Discussions among the members of the expedition indicated a desire to continue the informal cooperative arrangement and to extend their research interests beyond this portion of Africa, particularly since there was almost no information on the prehistory of the Nile Valley north of Aswan and Kom Ombo or south of the Aswan Reservoir. The prehistory of the adjacent desert was also largely unknown; however, there was little interest in that area, because a preliminary project by the expedition to one portion of the area, Dungul Oasis, had been disappointing, since almost all the sites found there had been destroyed by deflation.

The group decided to stay in the Nile Valley and to divide into two parties. The first, headed by J. L. Shiner, went south along the Nile to near Dongola and from there up the Atbara almost to the Ethiopian frontier. Unfortunately, the 1967 war and personal illness terminated this project after the first season (Marks *et al.* 1967; Shiner *et al.* 1971). The second portion of the expedition went north from Aswan toward the Mediterranean in what was essentially a survey, regarded as the first phase of a long-range research program (Wendorf and Schild 1976b). Three seasons were spent on this survey (1967, 1968, and 1969). It was a difficult time in the relations between Egypt and the United States, but political problems never seriously affected the expedition because of the support given our project at the highest levels of government by Dr. Rushdi Said, a member of Parliament, then advisor to President Nasser and later Vice Minister for Mining and Mineral Resources and Director of the Geological Survey of Egypt.

In 1969, however, new security regulations were imposed in Egypt that severely restricted the movement of all foreigners, and even the good offices of Dr. Said could not help us. Unable to work in Egypt, the expedition shifted its activities to Ethiopia, first with a disappointing survey near Lake Tana, and then in the Rift Valley lake district, south of Addis Ababa. We spent three seasons there—1971, 1972, and 1973 (Wendorf and Schild 1974).

In the spring of 1972, with the support of Dr. Said and his associate, Dr. Bahay Issawi, the expedition was again given permission to work in Egypt, but not in the Nile Valley because of the security-sensitive areas concentrated there. With some misgivings because of our Dungul experience, we chose to go to Dakhla, a large, occupied oasis west of Kharga and far from any military installations. This was the first of six seasons' work in the desert. In 1973 we worked at Bir Sahara; in 1974, at Bir Tarfawi; in 1975, at Nabta; in 1976, at Kharga; and in 1977, at Nabta again. This book gives the major results of our investigations and relates them to data from both the Nile Valley and other parts of the Sahara. Needless to say, our fears that the archaeology of the Western Desert would be extremely limited and of little interest proved to be unfounded; there are numerous archaeological sites in the desert, reflecting a long and complicated history of exploitation.

All the projects of the Combined Prehistoric Expedition in Egypt since 1967 have been sponsored by three organizations: the Geological Survey of Egypt; the Institute for the History of Material Culture, Polish Academy of Sciences; and Southern Methodist University (SMU). At first these cooperative arrangements were based only on oral agreements; however, in 1976 formal contracts were concluded between SMU and the other two organizations. These contracts served to codify the existing arrangements and to detail the financial agreements and publication responsibilities.

Acknowledgments

We view these projects as true cooperative efforts by the three sponsoring organizations. Each institution, and individual, brought to the project some unique resource or facility that, together with the others, made this research possible. The Geological Survey of Egypt, however, must receive a special acknowledgment. Not only did the Geological Survey provide the sponsorship needed for permits to work in the Western Desert and much of the equipment used by the expedition, particularly the heavy trucks and jeeps, but it also assigned some of its best technical and professional people to work with us. The Geological Survey staff have in every instance performed their tasks with keen enthusiasm and high competence; beyond that, they have gracefully accepted our strange ways, made us feel welcome, and extended their hands in friendship. In particular we wish to thank Dr. Galal Moustafa, who succeeded Dr. Rushdi Said as Director of the Geological Survey, for his continued interest in and support for these cooperative activities.

It is appropriate also to acknowledge the support of our own organizations, both of which have contributed substantially to this endeavor. They made it possible for us to be absent from our regular posts for several months each year, provided research space and facilities for us and our students, and assisted in the publication of the results. We wish to thank Dr. Withold Hensel, Director of the Institute for the History of Material Culture, for his long support of the Combined Prehistoric Expedition. Dr. Willis M. Tate, until recently president of Southern Methodist University, and his successor, Dr. James H. Zumberge, also have taken a keen interest in the work and have always offered encouragement and assistance when needed.

In most years the expedition field staff numbered more than 40 people, clearly too numerous a group to acknowledge individually here. We can, however, recognize the professional staff who worked in the field. Their names and sponsoring organizations are as follows:

1972 Geological Survey of Egypt: B. Issawi
Polish Academy of Sciences: R. Schild, J. Lech
Southern Methodist University: F. Wendorf, T. M. Ryan, F. A. Servello
Egyptian Department of Antiquities: A. S. Hindi

1973 Geological Survey of Egypt: R. Said, B. Issawi
Polish Academy of Sciences: R. Schild, M. Kobusiewicz
Southern Methodist University: T. R. Hays, O. Henderson, R. Morrison, T. M. Ryan, F. Wendorf
Egyptian Department of Antiquities: A. S. Hindi

1974 Geological Survey of Egypt: R. Said, M. M. Said, R. A. Osman, M. I. Tawakol, El. S. Zaghloul
Polish Academy of Sciences: R. Schild, M. Kobusiewicz
Southern Methodist University: C. V. Haynes, P. Jeschofnig, H. Mosca, T. M. Ryan, M. Wendorf, F. Wendorf
University of Ghent: A. Gautier
Egyptian Department of Antiquities: A. A. El Shennawi

1975 Geological Survey of Egypt: R. Said, M. El Hinnawi, R. Osman
Polish Academy of Sciences: R. Schild, M. Kobusiewicz
Southern Methodist University: C. V. Haynes, H. Mosca, F. Wendorf

University of Cairo: N. El-Hadidi

Egyptian Department of Antiquities: A. A. El Shennawi

1976 Geological Survey of Egypt: R. Said, M. El Hinnawi, R. Osman, K. Abu Zeid, M. Selim

Polish Academy of Sciences: R. Schild

Southern Methodist University: J. A. Attebury, H. Mosca, F. Wendorf

University of Arizona: C. V. Haynes

University of Ghent: A. Gautier

Egyptian Department of Antiquities: A. El Fatah

1977 Geological Survey of Egypt: R. Said, M. El Hinnawi, R. Osman

Polish Academy of Sciences: R. Schild, M. Kobusiewicz, H. Wieckowska

Southern Methodist University: J. A. Attebury, A. E. Close, K. M. Banks, F. Wendorf

University of Arizona: C. V. Haynes

University of Cairo: N. El Hadidi

Egyptian Department of Antiquities: A. S. Hindi

Throughout this period the expedition has benefited from the continued support of the National Science Foundation and the Foreign Currency Program of the Smithsonian Institution. We wish to acknowledge and express our profound thanks to the staffs of both organizations for the understanding and patient assistance extended to us during this long period of research activity. We hope these results justify the confidence they have expressed in us by their support. We also wish to acknowledge and express our thanks for the assistance given to us by the Egyptian Department of Antiquities. The several inspectors of the Department of Antiquities who participated in the field portions of our project have been named in the preceding list.

The superb illustrations of the artifacts are by Mrs. Lucile R. Addington of the Department of Anthropology, Southern Methodist University.

Finally, we wish to thank Dr. Angela E. Close for her assistance in the assembly and editing of this volume.

1
Introduction

The Western Desert of Egypt is an area totally devoid of people and lacking in roads or trails (Figure 1.1). Previous studies of the geology and archaeology in this area have generally been only exploratory in nature, limited to quick glimpses or at most a few days' work by one or two people, usually as a side interest during the initial modern Egyptian and European exploration of the area. The investigations described in this volume are significantly different, not only in scope but also in methods and goals. It was our intention to bring prehistorians, geologists, paleontologists, hydrologists, and botanists together in a detailed and coordinated study of several widely separated localities within the Western Desert. Our goal was to document both the environmental changes that have affected this area during the Quaternary and the human adaptations that have occurred here. This goal required a sizable technical and labor staff, easy mobility, and logistical support of a magnitude not available to previous workers. The assembling of these resources was made possible through the joint efforts of the three organizations that sponsored the Combined Prehistoric Expedition: the Geological Survey of Egypt; the Institute for the History of Material Culture, Polish Academy of Sciences; and Southern Methodist University. It is fair to say that none of them could have done it alone.

Only two earlier projects in this area were comparable in their scope and goals. The first projects resulted in Caton-Thompson's (1952) and Gardner's magnificent pioneer studies at Kharga. There were, however, many important differences from our project, the most important being their ability to utilize local resources for food, water, and labor. Sustained and systematic work away from the occupied oases on the north edge of the Western Desert, and thus for most of this vast area, requires a radically different kind of organization from that at Kharga.

The second project in the Western Desert that might be comparable to the present study was the 1963 work at Dungul Oasis, conducted by the Combined Prehistoric Expedition (Hester and Hoebler 1969). This was, however, only a single season's effort, and in many respects it was more limited in its goals. Its primary aim was to investigate the desert fringe beyond the Nile Valley for comparison with the data obtained during the archaeological salvage campaign in the Aswan Reservoir.

PREVIOUS INVESTIGATIONS IN THE WESTERN DESERT

Because of the limited water resources in the Western Desert, the area south of the northern oases of Kharga and Dakhla has not supported a permanent population in modern times. The scarcity of water and the proximity of the more easily traveled Nile also kept major trade routes to central Africa from crossing the area. The region was, therefore, rarely entered by those eighteenth and nineteenth century explorers who first opened up much of the Sahara to the Europeans. The Western Desert, of course, was not unknown to the ancient Egyptians, who stationed garrisons at Kharga and Dakhla (see Bates 1914; Caton-Thompson 1952: 45–53), maintained active quarries near Dungul

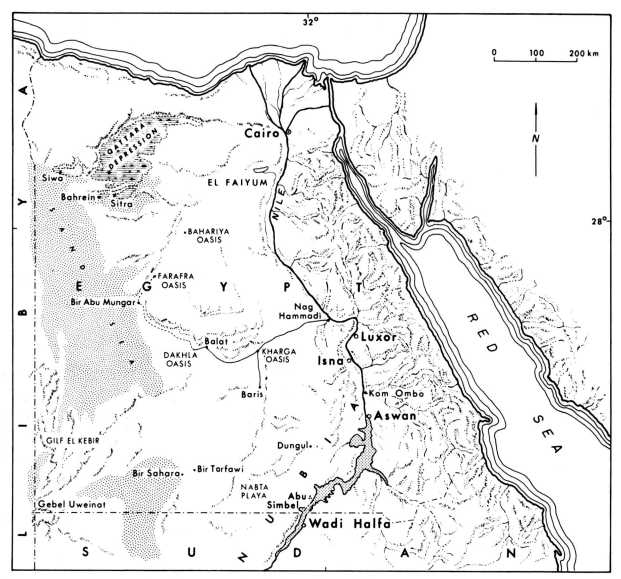

FIGURE 1.1. *Map of Egypt showing location of areas discussed in text.*

(Murray 1939), hunted in the area, and explored much of it in their quest for minerals. The Persians, Greeks, and later the Romans all were present at Kharga, and constructed extensive irrigation systems there. There is, however, no direct evidence that any of these non-Egyptian groups made use of the desert itself.

In the mid-nineteenth century routes through or adjacent to the Western Desert were used by Arab merchants and slavers. The most important of these routes was the Darb el Arbain ("40 days' road"), which went from Kharga south to Bir Kiseiba, then to Selima Oasis in the Sudan, and from there to Wadi Laqiya and El Fasher in Darfur. In 1793 W. G. Browne used the Darb el Arbain to go from Assuit to Darfur, and the route gave Europeans their first view of this area (Browne 1799). The route is still used today, mostly by smugglers who bring illegally mined natron into Egypt from the Sudan. Thousands of camel skeletons mark the route, a stark testimony to its long use and many hazards.

A second route apparently went from the village of Mut at Dakhla south to Bir Tarfawi, and then to Merga and El Fasher (Ball 1927: 122). This was not as frequently used as the Darb el Arbain because of the greater distance between wells, but apparently it was active until around AD 1800. The third trade route connected Dakhla with Kufra, but the precise placement of the "road" is not known. It is believed to have passed Abu Ballas ("pottery hill") and then skirted the north edge of the Gilf el Kebir. It also fell into disuse before the period of modern exploration began, probably because of hostility between Egypt and the Senussi of Kufra.

The first scientific interest in the area was the Gerald Rohlfs' expedition of 1873–1874, which went from the Nile

Valley to Farafra Oasis, south from there to Dakhla, then west into the Sand Sea, and north to Siwa. The expedition was trying to reach Kufra, but it was unable to cross the Sand Sea. This was the first multidisciplinary study of the Western Desert, and the scientific team included three natural scientists and a photographer (Abel 1975; Rohlfs 1875). The expedition was sponsored by the Egyptian Court, and one of its major goals was to investigate a legendary old riverbed of the Nile that supposedly crossed that area. It was hoped that the old riverbed might be a suitable place for an irrigation development, and also that it might yield evidence of ancient man. The old river, of course, was not found, but the expedition did take several archaeological collections, mostly of Pharaonic age.

The Geological Survey of Egypt was founded in 1896, and thereafter it sponsored most of the subsequent explorations of the Western Desert. One of the first employees of the Geological Survey was H. J. L. Beadnell, who in 1898 went to Farafra and Dakhla, and in 1910 published a paper on dune formations in the Libyan Desert. Beadnell continued to work in the desert until 1930; it was he who dug the deep wells at Bir Sahara and Bir Messaha in 1927 and 1928 (Beadnell 1931). Another leading figure was W. J. Harding-King (1913, 1918, 1925), who made several significant contributions to desert geomorphology. J. Ball (1927) was another important member of this early group and perhaps the most influential; he was the long-time director of the Desert Survey Department. It was he who (with Lieutenant Moore) discovered Abu Ballas in 1917 and went southwest from there almost to the Gilf el Kebir. In the company of Prince Kemal el Din (1928), Ball made several trips across the area in the 1920s, discovering the Gilf el Kebir and continuing to Uweinat. The 1920s and 1930s saw an enormous increase in activity in the Western Desert. The entire area was traversed several times by different groups, and the first detailed topographic maps were made. Most of these early explorers had a keen interest in both the Quaternary geology and the prehistoric archaeology of the area. Hassanein Bey (1924, 1925), who made the first trip to Kufra and Uweinat, also was the first to report rock drawings in the same area. A few paintings were also found there by Prince Kemal el Din (Kemal el Din and Breuil 1928), but it was H. W. G. Penderel (1934), P. A. Clayton (1933a and 1933b), and Count L. E. de Almasy (1942) who are credited with the discovery of the spectacular mass of rock paintings at Uweinat and along the Gilf el Kebir.

No history of this early work in the Western Desert would be complete without a mention of Bagnold (1931, 1933, 1939), and his work on the physics of windblown sand (Bagnold 1941). Archaeological investigations were also included as an important part of the work by the Bagnold group at Uweinat and the Gilf el Kebir. O. H. Myers accompanied the 1938 expedition and excavated three sites at these localities, one of which was Acheulian, and the other two were Neolithic. In addition, H. A. Winkler (1938–1939) made the first systematic study of the rock art

of the area. Unfortunately, because of World War II, many of the results of these investigations were never published in detail (McHugh 1975). Nevertheless, a reasonably good, general picture of the prehistoric occupation of the desert areas emerged from these preliminary studies. They showed heavy use of the desert during the Acheulian and Middle Paleolithic periods and numerous Mesolithic and Neolithic settlements (Sandford 1933). There was no evidence of the Late Paleolithic.

Caton-Thompson (1952) did her monumental study of prehistoric sites at Kharga during two seasons; the first, in the winter of 1930–1931, and the second, during the winter of 1931–1932. Most of this work was focused at several fossil spring vents on a series of low ridges northeast of the modern village of Kharga, but some important studies were also done at sites in wadi deposits near the Eocene scarp, and rather less at sand pans on the adjacent Eocene plateau. These excavations and the accompanying paleoenvironmental and stratigraphic studies by E. W. Gardner provided our first comprehensive reconstruction of the prehistory of the Western Desert.

Two major pluvial epochs were defined. The first, tentatively dated to the early and middle Pleistocene, had no associated archaeological remains. The second pluvial epoch contained four subevents, each separated from the others by erosional episodes, and each associated with a different archaeological complex. The first subevent ranges from Upper Acheulian to a developed Middle Paleolithic called Upper Levalloisian. Other Middle Paleolithic complexes were placed in the decline of the second pluvial, of which the latest was the Aterian. Two microlithic complexes, the "Epi-Levalloisian" and the "Bedouin Microlithic," and, finally, the "Peasant Neolithic," complete the sequence (Caton-Thompson 1952: 22–53).

Unfortunately, the usefulness of this sequence is somewhat limited, because almost all of the Middle Paleolithic excavated collections from Kharga are extremely small, often less than 50 pieces, reflecting the work's emphasis upon spring vents. It is therefore difficult to evaluate the changes in lithic typology and technology suggested for the Kharga sequence, and to compare these with Middle Paleolithic developments elsewhere. It was for this reason that the Combined Prehistoric Expedition spent a season at Kharga in 1976, and, with her approval, reworked several of Caton-Thompson's sites. The results, however, were very discouraging and certainly no better than those of Caton-Thompson. The stratigraphy of the spring vents proved to be extremely complex; most of them had been active more than once, and the consequent enlarging, contracting, and shifting of the spring eye resulted in considerable mixture of the associated archaeological materials. Only vents of Terminal Paleolithic and Neolithic age yielded any hope of preserved artifact patterning in the surrounding sediments.

No further study of the Western Desert was made after 1939 until the Nubian Salvage Campaign in 1963, although the area was intensively used during World War II, particularly by the British Army and the Long-Range Desert Group (W. B. K. Shaw 1945). Two separate groups connected with the Nubian Salvage Campaign worked in the Western Desert during that period. One was sponsored by Yale University (Butzer 1964; Reed 1964); the other, by the Combined Prehistoric Expedition (Hester and Hoebler 1969). In both instances, these studies were undertaken to provide comparative data for the prehistoric materials recovered from the Aswan Reservoir. The Yale project was limited to a brief survey of Kurkur Oasis, west of Aswan. The project sponsored by the Combined Prehistoric Expedition was focused at Dungul oasis, at the foot of the Eocene scarp about 125 km north and slightly west of Abu Simbel, but extensive surveys were also made in the playa areas below the scarp to the south and west as far as Bir Sheb. The sequence of alluvial, spring tufa, and playa deposits in this area is believed to record a complex series of environmental changes from Late Pliocene to the present. In many respects, the sequence closely parallels that proposed for Kharga by Caton-Thompson, yet there are important differences. At Dungul and Kurkur there were two major moist episodes represented by tufa accumulations preceding the earliest evidence of man, which was Late Acheulian. Subsequently, there were four moist episodes with intervening periods of aridity, and five different cultural complexes: an undifferentiated Middle Paleolithic, Khargan, Aterian, Libyan, and Oasis C-Group. Unfortunately, most of the sites were surface scatters, and only the last two groups could be confidently related to the stratigraphic sequence or to an absolute chronology. Perhaps the most significant conclusion to emerge from this work was that the desert had been extensively used during several intervals in the past, and that from the Middle Paleolithic onward there were significant differences between the developments in the desert and those in the adjacent Nile Valley.

FIELD METHODS

In most parts of the Western Desert there is no readily available drinking water; there is no food, no local supply of labor, no repair facilities, no fuel, and no shelter. All these things had to be provided to sustain a long-range program of investigation (Figure 1.2). Water could sometimes be obtained by digging shallow wells, but their loca-

FIGURE 1.2. *View of Combined Prehistoric Expedition camp at Bir Sahara (1973).*

FIGURE 1.3. *Staff and vehicles used by the Combined Prehistoric Expedition, 1973 season.*

tions were often some distance from both our work and suitable places to camp. In these situations the water was transported in a water tanker. When the water was nearby, large water cans, filled daily or whenever needed, were sufficient.

Fuel had to be brought from the nearest depot, either Aswan or Kharga. Since the expedition usually operated from 8 to 13 vehicles (Figure 1.3), and they were often driven for long distances each day, a gasoline tanker usually accompanied the party. Other supplies of gasoline and diesel fuel were brought in barrels and stored a short distance

FIGURE 1.4. *Water tanker used for camp supplies at Nabta camp.*

from camp. Supplementary dumps and emergency fuel supplies were often placed in more distant localities when work was under way in those areas.

Besides the water and gasoline tankers (Figure 1.4), the expedition had one or two large lorries to transport the tents and other camp gear (Figure 1.5). Smaller pickup trucks were used to transport the workers each day from camp to the excavation areas, and they were also used to haul supplies when small parties were dispatched to set up "flying camps" and to work at distant locations. Most of these trucks were equipped with four-wheel drive, and carried sand tracks to facilitate movement through occasional soft, sandy areas. The Geological Survey also provided two or three jeeps, which were used by their personnel in their geological investigations, and by other crew members for most survey work. Finally, through the good offices of the National Geographic Society, the expedition had three Volkswagen 181s, which were used as light reconnaissance vehicles (Figure 1.6).

The base camp consisted of some 30 large canvas tents (Figure 1.7). One tent, larger than the others, served as a combination dining and laboratory facility; another was for the kitchen, and each scientist either had a tent to himself or shared a tent. There were also tents for the camp servants, others for the drivers and mechanics, and still others for the workers. Several toilets were erected around the camp periphery. The equipment in the individual tents was simple: a cot, a small wooden table and a chair, a

FIGURE 1.5. *Geological Survey of Egypt drivers and mechanics do major overhaul while in the desert.*

FIGURE 1.7. *Typical camp scene. Ducks were the major source of meat for the expedition.*

FIGURE 1.6. *View of Combined Prehistoric Expedition camp at Nabta Playa, 1975 season, showing Volkswagen 181s used as light reconnaissance vehicles.*

wooden box for clothing and personal equipment, a small water can, and a plastic basin for washing. Our workers were skilled in setting up and dismantling the camp, and the whole thing could be taken down and packed on the lorries in 2 to 3 hours' time. The camp was managed by the staff of the Geological Survey, which also provided the key support personnel, the cook, the guides, and the drivers and mechanics on a partial cost reimbursement basis.

Camp routine followed long-established patterns of other Geological Survey camps. Breakfast was at 7:30 each morning, departure for work was at 8:00, and return was between 4:30 and 5:00 each evening. Dinner was at 7:00. There was no electricity, so after dinner work was limited. The field season normally lasted from 6 to 8 weeks and continued 7 days a week without interruption. The field season was always planned for the winter months, from mid-January through mid-March, with occasional shifts 2 or 3 weeks either way. This is often the best time to be in the desert, although occasional winter storms bring high winds and freezing or near-freezing temperatures. Most days are warm and plesant.

The research program varied from year to year, although it was always directed toward our larger goal of understanding the changes in the Quaternary environment of the Western Desert and the human adaptations to those changes. During the first season (1972), when we went into the area without any knowledge of specific sites to be worked, and with only a limited idea of our long-range goals, we made extensive but brief trips into several different areas, partly to find out what kinds of occupations were present, and partly to familiarize ourselves with the desert and how best to work there. We made the unexpected discovery that the Western Desert contains a surprisingly rich and varied complex of archaeological remains. We also learned that although traces of occupation are widespread, erosion and deflation have destroyed much of the evidence, and relatively intact sites occur in only a few, very restricted situations.

Subsequent seasons have generally followed a similar investigative pattern. Initial efforts are directed at a site or sites found during a previous season. These sites are selected because they seem to hold promise of contributing data on one or more specific problems that serve as a focus for that season, such as intrasite settlement patterns in the Saharan Mousterian (1973), tool kits and butchery techniques in the Aterian (1974), or comparisons of Terminal Paleolithic and Neolithic economic strategies (1975, 1977). Meanwhile, each year additional detailed surveys are conducted in the same general area. These surveys are usually limited to 2 hours' travel each way from camp, and are concentrated in those geomorphic situations (such as sand pans and basins) where preservation of the archaeological materials and associated faunal remains is most likely to occur. This usually results in the identification of additional sites, and the selection of some of these for excavation later that season. There is a certain opportunistic aspect to the surveys, for they occasionally check those areas not thought

to be promising, and these checks sometimes result in the discovery of important new sites that do not relate to the field topic of that season but are worthy of later investigation. In addition, surveys are conducted each season to at least one more distant area, to gain further knowledge of the desert and to provide data on which to plan future projects in those areas. When sites are discovered no collections are taken; any surface material examined is carefully replaced in its original position so as not to distort any subsequent study of the pattern of artifact arrangement. Those sites selected for intensive study are always collected within a standard grid, with each piece recorded by type on the site map or "scatterpattern."

Excavations are conducted by small crews, usually six to nine men and one or sometimes two supervisors. The laborers are drawn from a single Bedouin band, and over the years they have gained considerable experience and expertise. The same group has been used since 1962, and today our crews are composed mostly of the sons of those who began with us. All field notes are made in duplicate and completed each night. The copies are separated; one is turned in to the director of the expedition and is eventually placed on file at Southern Methodist University in Dallas; the other remains with the archaeologist until the excavation is completed, and is ultimately filed at the Institute for the History of Material Culture in Warsaw.

Laboratory analyses are always carefully coordinated with the excavated schedule to be certain that the analysis of all lithic materials can be completed before the end of the field season. Once the collections reach Cairo, they are usually divided by the Department of Antiquities; part remain at the Museum in Egypt and the rest may be shipped abroad. It is obviously necessary to complete our analyses before this division occurs.

The laboratory analyses are organized so that each artifact—except for small chips and similar debris, which are only counted and identified as to raw material—from every studied site is first recorded individually on coding forms. These descriptions follow a format established for each class of artifact and include dimensions, raw material, technological features, and other attributes expected in that artifact class. A preliminary manuscript describing all tools individually is also prepared, and those items selected for illustration are keyed to that manuscript and then stored separately. Finally, for each site a brief report is written describing the general area and the site's appearance before excavation, the stratigraphic situation, and methods of collection and excavation. The report includes a brief summary of all features and artifacts, and any comments or conclusions evident at that time. Site reports and other laboratory data are prepared in duplicate. Maps and stratigraphic profiles are not duplicated in the field, but immediately on arrival in Cairo, they are delivered to the draftsman who prepares the final ink drawings and makes three blueprint copies. One copy goes to Dallas, the second goes to Warsaw, and the third remains in Cairo. The final inked drawings are all carried to Dallas by hand.

METHODS OF PRESENTATION
AND DESCRIPTION OF STONE ARTIFACTS

The presentation and description of the archaeological lithic material recovered during several field seasons in the Western Desert follow the system already used in several technical reports and studies published by the authors and others associated with the Combined Prehistoric Expedition. The only significant difference results from the fact that this presentation is a rather general summary, whereas the monographs and technical reports are much more detailed and include basic data such as measurable attributes, results of significance tests, and so forth.

It is now widely recognized that the analysis of lithic artifacts may serve several purposes, of which the simple description and comparison of assemblages is not the most important; typological and technological analyses are just as frequently used in generating and testing alternative hypotheses. As in earlier, technical reports, two types of analysis, technological and typological, are used in the present study. These two types serve different purposes but are not entirely independent, and it is believed that both are necessary for more complete understanding of the material.

TECHNOLOGY

The study of technology follows the practice already applied elsewhere (Schild 1969; Schild and Wendorf 1977b; Wendorf and Schild 1974). The aims of the study are a total reconstruction of all technological procedures performed at a site and their quantitative evaluation. This is done by means of a list of all the recognized categories of artifacts that result from core and tool preparation, exploitation, and reshaping. The frequencies of the artifact types, clustered into several technological classes, define the General Structure of the assemblage, and this reflects certain technological, functional, and economic emphases of the human group that made the assemblage.

Certain limiting factors govern the construction of technological lists. One of the most important of these factors is that each list is created for, and is therefore applicable to, only one chronological and technological unit. It has therefore been necessary to prepare technological, taxonomic lists for each of the units recognized in the Western Desert.

The first such list defines the structures of the Acheulian assemblages. This list, which has been published and discussed elsewhere (Schild and Wendorf 1975, 1977b), contains 34 categories grouped into larger classes as follows:

    I. Initial or Primary Flaking
    II. Levallois Technology
    III. Regular Flake Production
    IV. Regular Blade Production
    V. Chips
    VI. Retouched Tools and Characteristic Tool-Production Waste (Schild and Wendorf 1977b: 17)

The list of types falling within particular groups may be found on the captions accompanying quantitative bar graphs elsewhere in this volume. Most of the types are widely known (such as the various Levallois pieces, simple and change-of-orientation cores, naturally backed knives, retouched tools, and primary flakes) and the others have been defined by Schild and Wendorf (1977b: 19–22).

Despite the existing definitions and conventional understanding of particular types, problems may arise in the consistency of classification. The classification used here is dynamic and is concerned with technological processes rather than static and morphologically identical forms. Thus the procedure is heavily dependent on the analyst's experience and understanding of stoneworking. The most difficult area is the proper classification of forms such as flakes from particular types of cores, notch spalls, resharpening spalls, biface trimming flakes, and chips. The margin of error will vary according to experience, but it can never be entirely eliminated.

The General Structure of an inventory may be presented as *large* and as *restricted*. The restricted count, used here, excludes such categories as undetermined fragments of cores for flakes, undetermined flakes, simple chips, and crushed chips, since it is felt that a preponderance of these taxa may distort the proportions of other groups.

Beside the classification of all of the debitage, three technological indices are used. Two of them, the Levallois (IL) and Blade (Ilam) indices were formulated by Bordes and Bourgon. The third one, the General Levallois Index (IGL) (Schild and Wendorf 1977b), is computed as follows:

$$\frac{\text{Categories 4–9 of structure count} + \text{retouched Levallois pieces} \times 100}{\text{All categories of restricted technological structure}}$$

This index groups all elements associated with Levallois technology and, by including the categories appearing during Levallois core preparation and exploitation, may detect the presence of Levallois technology even when other characteristic Levallois pieces are absent.

A second list, revealing the General Structure of Middle Paleolithic assemblages, has been constructed for the Mousterian and Aterian occurrences of Bir Sahara and Bir Tarfawi (Schild and Wendorf 1975). The list contains 39 categories clustered into 9 groups as follows:

    I. Initial
    II. Levallois
    III. Flake
    IV. Blade
    V. Core Rejuvenation and Early Removal from Precores
    VI. Chip
    VII. Tools and Tool-Production Waste

VIII. Hammerstone
IX. Undetermined

Again, detailed lists of all types may be found in the captions of the appropriate figures.

The dynamic technological list for the Middle Paleolithic inventories of the Western Desert may be used in both restricted and unrestricted (large) forms. The restricted list omits types 28, 29, 37, 38, and 39—that is, all chips, chunks, and undetermined artifacts. The three technological indices used in the description and comparison of Middle Paleolithic materials are the same as those used for the Acheulian.

The third list, designed for both the Terminal Paleolithic and Neolithic assemblages, has been little used in this volume. It is replaced by general characterization of the technology and an evaluation of the core group in each assemblage. The limited use of the list reflects the incomplete status of the study of these materials.

TOOL AND CORE MORPHOLOGY

The classification of Acheulian bifaces from the Western Desert largely follows the biface taxonomy proposed by Bordes (1961). The classification of bifaces is highly complex, somewhat controversial, and never entirely satisfactory. Despite existing type lists, some of which are designed specifically for African material (see, e.g., Kleindienst 1962), the classification of bifaces is a problem that needs extended and carefully designed study if it is to serve more important purposes than local, crude comparisons of general styles.

Despite these reservations, preliminary field analyses of the rich Acheulian sites of Dakhla revealed that the taxonomic system proposed by Bordes (1961) harmonized relatively well with the morphological variability of the specimens found. Such agreement may be partly subjective, a function of our previous experience in classification. It is obvious that Bordes' system is not a panacea, and there are several flaws in it, mainly the omission or near-omission of some of the more important classes. On the other hand, Bordes' classification was intended to be a set of guidelines along which individual taxonomies might be developed.

Work on the taxonomy of bifaces from the Western Desert of Egypt resulted in a list of categories constructed specifically for the recovered sample (see Schild and Wendorf 1977b). The system combines statistical and morphological descriptions, so the taxa should be considered not as types in the Platonic sense but rather as constellations of individuals, each unique in its total form but all associated by variable series of common attributes. For this reason, only statistical descriptions of the classes can give an adequate picture of their distinct features, particularly since the categories may overlap or grade smoothly into one another (compare tables of measured attributes and descriptions in Schild and Wendorf 1977b).

The creation of the list of the bifaces was greatly simplified by the use of the indices proposed by Bordes (1961). The most important of these are as follows:

$$\frac{m}{e} = \text{Index of Proportional Thickness}$$
$$\frac{L}{a} = \text{Index of Height of Maximal Width}$$
$$\frac{L}{m} = \text{Index of Proportions}$$
$$\frac{n}{m} \times 100 = \text{Index of Midwidth}$$

where L = maximal length, m = maximal width, e = maximal thickness, a = height of maximal width, and n = width at midlength.

The rather high frequency of backed bifaces in the material from Dakhla necessitated the adoption of the Central European method of dealing with these pieces. Although backed bifaces are present in the sub-Saharan Acheulian, their classification has always been very sketchy and never satisfactory (see, e.g., Clark and Kleindienst 1974; Howell and Clark 1963; Kleindienst 1961, 1962). Unfortunately, the Central European classifications also are far from ideal in that they usually emphasize either unrelated attributes or the very individual treatments of taxonomic problems preferred by particular scholars (compare the classifications of Bosinski 1969; Chmielewski 1969; Kowalski 1967a, b, 1969; Kozlowski 1972; Krukowski 1939; Wetzel and Bosinsky 1969).

The result of our taxonomic work on the bifaces from the Western Desert of Egypt is a list containing 39 categories clustered in nine groups as follows:

   I. Subtriangulars
  II. Cordiforms
 III. Ovals
  IV. Thick Elongates
   V. Amygdaloids
  VI. Diverse, Thick Bifaces
 VII. Backed Bifaces
VIII. Double-Backed Bifaces
  IX. Other

The classification and presentation of tools other than bifaces (handaxes) associated with the Acheulian, Mousterian, and Aterian sites of the Western desert again largely follows the scheme introduced by Bordes and Bourgon (Bordes 1953, 1954, 1961; Bourgon 1957). Thus, categories 1–61 and 63 are those of Bordes; category 62, *varia*, has been broken down into a number of subcategories. The subcategories in the Acheulian are the following:

62a. Bifacial edge piece (for definition see Wendorf and Schild 1974: 141)
62b. Atypical sidescraper
62c. Bifacially worked pebble
62d. Spheroidal piece (hammerstone?)
62e. Undetermined and fragments

The tool classes added to the Mousterian–Aterian complex include the following:

62a. Undetermined sidescraper
62b. Bifacial triangular point
62c. Bifacial edge piece
62d. Spheroidal piece
62e. Regular hammerstone
62f. Undetermined and fragments (compare Schild and Wendorf 1975).

Bordes' taxonomic list for the Lower and Middle Paleolithic (1961) is too well established in the literature to warrant repeating here. Perhaps only the indices introduced by Bordes and Bourgon, employed widely throughout this work in both their restricted and unrestricted (large) forms, need be mentioned.

ILty (Typological Levallois Index) =
$$\frac{\text{categories } 1–4 \times 100}{\text{categories } 1–63}$$

IR (Sidescraper Index) =
$$\frac{\text{categories } 9–29 \times 100}{\text{categories } 1–63}$$

IC (Charentian Index) =
$$\frac{\text{categories } 8 + 10 + 22 – 24 \times 100}{\text{categories } 1–63}$$

IAt (Total Acheulean Index) =
$$\frac{\text{categories } 36 + 37 + \text{bifaces} \times 100}{\text{categories } 1–63 + \text{bifaces}}$$

IAu (Backed Knife Index) =
$$\frac{\text{categories } 36 + 37 \times 100}{\text{categories } 1–63}$$

IBif (Biface Index) =
$$\frac{\text{bifaces} \times 100}{\text{categories } 1–63 + \text{bifaces}}$$

Group I (Index of Levallois Group) =
$$\frac{\text{categories } 1–4 \times 100}{\text{categories } 1–63}$$

Group II (Index of Mousterian Group) =
$$\frac{\text{categories } 5–29 \times 100}{\text{categories } 1–63}$$

Group III (Index of Upper Paleolithic Group) =
$$\frac{\text{categories } 30–37 \times 100}{\text{categories } 1–63}$$

Group IV (Index of Denticulate Group) =
$$\frac{\text{categories } 43 \times 100}{\text{categories } 1–63}$$

The present authors usually add converging denticulates or Tayac points (category 51) to the last group.

A final group (VI) has been added to these indices (Wendorf and Schild 1976a) to establish the proportion of Aterian elements present in the assemblages:

Group VI (Index of Aterian Group) =
$$\frac{\text{Aterian pedunculated} + \text{biface foliate pieces} \times 100}{\text{categories } 1–63}$$

N. Chavaillon (1971, 1973) prefers to number this group as V; however, the latter number should be reserved for the Index of European Biface Foliate Elements.

Bordes' taxonomic list has provoked enormous controversies, some of which rather naively are believed to have established new paradigms in archaeology. The basic discussion has concentrated on functional versus cultural meanings of the taxa and of the resulting taxonomic groupings of assemblages (L. R. Binford 1973; L. R. and S. R. Binford 1966; S. R. Binford 1972; Bordes 1973; Bordes and de Sonneville-Bordes 1970; Mellars 1970—to name only the most widely known contributions).

To those who are familiar with Middle Paleolithic materials located beyond the geographical limit of Bordes' interest and beyond the basis of his taxonomy, it has long been apparent that there are large groups of Middle Paleolithic assemblages that cannot be properly classified by means of this taxonomy. Thus a majority of the retouched tools of the so-called post-Micoquian complex of Central Europe simply do not fit into the typology; and, despite similarities in many of the common forms, the typology had to be greatly modified to allow comparison of Middle Stone Age material from sub-Saharan Africa with that of Europe (Wendorf and Schild 1974).

Today, archaeologists familiar with a wide geographical range of Middle Paleolithic assemblages seem to share the view (although not published) that there is some value in the arguments of both sides of the "Bordian controversy." Bordes' taxonomy contains both functional and stylistic elements. The selection of types is, however, uneven; as well as elements common in almost all Middle Paleolithic entities, such as simple sidescrapers, it also includes types that may conceal hundreds of potential stylistic possibilities, such as bifacial foliates (see also comments in Lubin 1965).

In reality, the situation may be very complex. If the inapplicability of Bordes' taxonomy to certain areas should have a general stylistic (that is, cultural) significance, then the regions in which it can be applied may correspond to a very large "cultural area" throughout which some flow of information must have existed. Within this area, the taxonomy seems for the most part to measure certain functional emphases, such as an orientation toward denticulates, although some stylistic tendencies may occasionally also be observed, as in the Aterian of North Africa or the Musielievo type of assemblages from the Balkans.

In summary, it is very difficult to establish detailed groupings of stylistic elements by means of Bordes' taxonomy, which would indicate a very intensive and geographically limited flow of information within Middle Paleolithic societies. The effort needs more attribute-oriented, stylistic, and statistical analyses. Nevertheless, Bordes' taxonomy must, for the moment, be used, as being both the only one existing and also a good starting point for further research.

The core taxonomy for both the Lower and Middle Paleolithic of the Western Desert is conventional and well established in the literature. Additional explanation will therefore not be given.

The considerable technological and typological unity of Terminal Paleolithic assemblages across North Africa and the Sahara has allowed the use of Tixier's taxonomy (1963, 1967) in the Western Desert; its use has already become common in the Nile Valley. The use of this typology should not, however, be taken to indicate that all the artifact classes found in the Terminal Paleolithic and Neolithic assemblages of the Western Desert are identical to those of the Maghreb. There are several morphological variations, such as between the group of Bou Saada and Ounan/Harif points of the Western Desert. Complete counts of the Terminal Paleolithic and Neolithic assemblages from the Western Desert are also given in the form of cumulative graphs drafted on forms kindly furnished by Tixier.

This volume includes a stylistic study of certain tool attributes of the Neolithic and Terminal Paleolithic assemblages. This study, prepared by Close, follows the method she developed and yields important new information on the stylistic clustering of assemblages.

The description of cores for the Neolithic and Terminal Paleolithic again follows the lines developed during earlier work along the Nile Valley and in the Western Desert. The taxonomy is functional and based on the study of core technology, preparation, exploitation, and remodeling.

THE MODERN ENVIRONMENT

TOPOGRAPHY

The region studied in these investigations occupies the southwestern quarter of Egypt. It is known as the Southern Libyan Desert and comprises an area of more than 300,000 km² (Figure 1.8). There are two prominent geomorphic features that serve as boundaries for the Southern Libyan Desert (Simons 1973: 501–502). Along the northern and eastern sides is the high escarpment (over 400 m near Dakhla) separating the low-lying Southern Libyan Desert from the uplands of the Eocene plateau. These uplands, known as the Northern Libyan Desert, form a vast, gray, gloomy landscape. Numerous solution basins dot its surface, and it is strewn with countless gray limestone cobbles and pebbles. The Northern Libyan Desert is shaped much like a giant frying pan, with all of the north half of Egypt west of the Nile Valley as the basin of the pan, and with the handle as a relatively narrow peninsula projecting southward from the pan paralleling the Nile almost to the Sudan. Some of the largest springs in Egypt, the oases of Kharga, Dakhla, and Farafra, occur along the foot of the Eocene plateau. The western edge of the pan is bordered by the Sand Sea, a massive pile of eolian sand that extends southward from the Qattara Depression and along the Egyptian–Libyan frontier to beyond the southern edge of the Eocene plateau at Farafra.

On the west, the Southern Libyan Desert ends abruptly against a second plateau, the Gilf el Kebir, an enormous block of Nubian sandstone rising abruptly some 300 m above the adjacent floor of the desert. The Gilf el Kebir is neither as extensive nor as high as the Eocene plateau, which frames the northern and eastern sides, but in many respects it is even more dramatic. The eastern edge of the Gilf is cut by numerous steep-sided canyons that extend for long distances back into the plateau and end abruptly with vertical cliff faces. Little or no rubble occurs at the foot of the Gilf or within the incised canyons, but a complex net of huge alluvial fans is spread out at canyon mouths. Several of the canyons have been closed by falling dunes. No surface water or springs are known anywhere in the Gilf el Kebir. The Gilf is over 200 km long and 50 km wide and extends from near the southwest corner of Egypt northward until it disappears under the Sand Sea.

Below the scarps of the Eocene plateau and the Gilf el Kebir stretch the seemingly endless flatlands of the Southern Libyan Desert, only occasionally interrupted by gebels or isolated strings of dunes, the latter light tan in color and contrasting sharply with the prevailing warm browns of the remaining landscape. To the south the desert extends into the Sudan without break.

The popular impression of the Sahara as a vast expanse of sand is not correct, at least not for the Southern Libyan Desert. Except in a few rather restricted areas, sand dunes are rare. Far more common are broad, flat peneplains mantled with small pebbles, all of about the same size and equidistant from each other, a result of countless eons of wind abrasion, deflation, and sorting. In some areas this flat, monotonous landscape is broken by numerous flat-topped and steep-sided gebels, the sides and bases of which are covered with blocks of rubble. There are also occasional low-domed outcrops of basement rocks, and the surfaces here are strewn with rounded cobbles. Radiating and result-

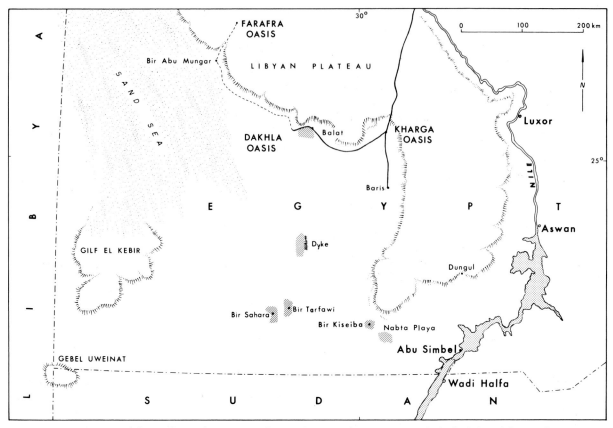

FIGURE 1.8. *Map of the Southern Libyan Desert, showing location of major areas studied (shaded) and discussed in text.*

ing from these basement upthrusts are long lines of hog-backs, some more than 50 km in length, with hardened cores of metamorphosed rocks. In a few areas, there are steep-sided and deeply incised wadis, which bear witness to a more moist climate in the past but now are often choked with sand. The colors are warm browns and tans, and the landscape is vast, barren, empty, and almost moonlike.

CLIMATE

The southwestern portion of Egypt is an almost totally rainless desert (less than 1 mm per year), with very low relative humidity, extremely high maximum summer temperatures with average daily maxima over 40°C, and mild to cold winters with temperatures frequently around or below 0°C. It is the driest part of the Sahara, lying midway between the southernmost reach of the winter rainfall belt along the Mediterranean and the northernmost occurrence of the summer tropical rainfall belt of central Africa (Figure

1.9). Although neither of these climatic systems contributes moisture to the area, each influences the seasonal changes in the climate.

In winter (December to February) numerous depressions pass from west to east along the Mediterranean and are the main influence upon the weather. When the depressions approach the eastern Mediterranean, strong southwesterly winds blow across Egypt, sometimes accompanied by sandstorms. As the depressions move farther east, the winds shift to the northwest, bringing rain to the coast and to inland areas, sometimes as far south as Cairo. In southern Egypt, however, the effects are limited to cold northerly winds, occasionally accompanied by sparse sleet, but almost never associated with any measurable precipitation. Most of the time, a high pressure cell covers the Western Desert of Egypt. The average daily maximum temperature varies between 20 and 22.5°C. The average daily minimum temperature is between 5 and 7.5°C. Some winter rains do occur in southern Egypt to the east, in the Red Sea Hills and along the Red Sea Coast, due to the convergence there of

FIGURE 1.9. *Climatic map of Egypt and adjacent portions of Sudan and Libya. Note the rainless, hyperarid zone (lightly shaded) that lies between the southern (summer rainfall belt) and the northern (winter rainfall belt) zones. Heavy shading indicates areas over 1000 m above sea level. Data from* World Weather Records, 1951–1960, World Weather Records, 1967, *and* World Climatic Data, 1972. *(Graphics after Simons 1973: 461.)*

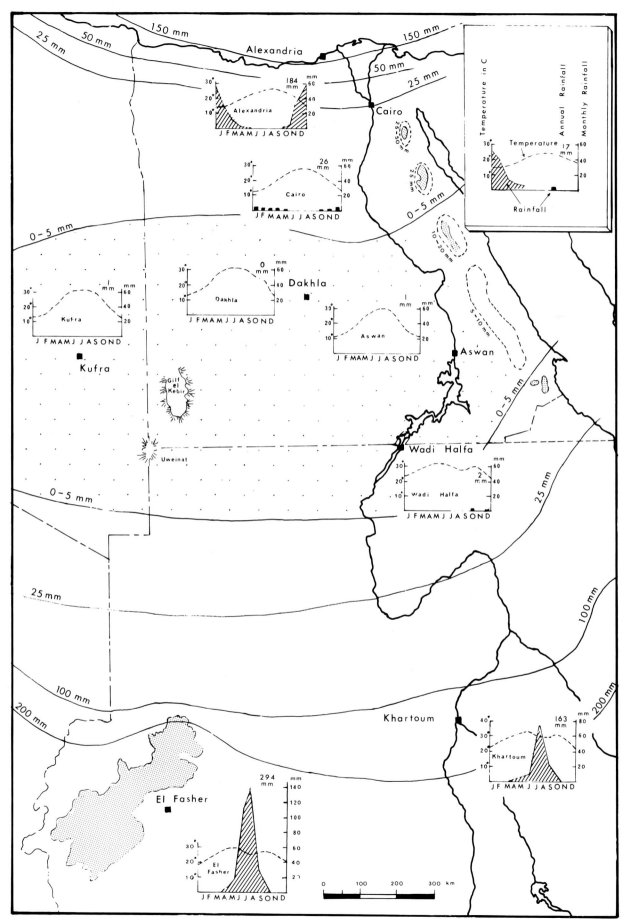

FIGURE 1.9.

the southeast (Indian) and the northwest (Atlantic) air masses. These rains, however, never pass west beyond the mountain peaks of the Red Sea Hills.

Spring (March to May) is a transitional season, the main features of which are the southward shift of the track of depressions and a northward movement of the Sudan trough. Two to six depressions per month move rapidly across Egypt, and are usually preceded by hot, dry, dust-laden southerly winds that sometimes cause severe sand storms, known as *hamsiin*. Moderate to severe heat waves also occur when the Sudan trough moves northward, bringing hot, dry air and low relative humidity. Rains, insofar as they fall at all, are most frequent during this period, when they are associated with upper level cold fronts moving overland. It should be emphasized, however, that there is no true rainy season, and 10 years or more may lapse between rains of any extent. Rainfall averages are, therefore, meaningless.

The warmest month in southern Egypt is usually June, but the entire summer (June to September) is hot and very dry. The prevailing winds are from the northwest, and are part of the circulation around the huge, Asiatic summer low centered over northwestern India. Average daily maximum temperatures in July range between 40 and 42.5°C, and average daily minimum temperatures between 22.5 and 25°C.

The autumn climate (October and November) is, like the spring, transitional. It is characterized by a pronounced drop in temperature, by occasional high winds, accompanying depressions moving from west to east, and by rare rains, the latter representing the very end of the unstable summer system of the Sudan.

Although the absence of rainfall and the high summer temperatures are the most obvious features of the climate, this is also a region with rare cloud cover and thus almost continuous sunshine (the annual mean is more than 11 hours per day), and high values for global radiation and therefore extreme diurnal temperature variations. The relative humidity is low throughout the year, but there is some seasonal and daily variation. At sunrise in January the relative humidity may range between 50 and 60%, but by midday it has fallen to between 20 and 30%. In July at sunrise the average relative humidity is less than 30%, and by noon it will vary from 10 to 20% (Thompson 1965). Evaporation is also high, with a mean of 5 m per year (14 mm per day) recorded for Aswan.

VEGETATION

The impression on first seeing the Western Desert is that it is completely devoid of any type of plant life: that there are no grasses, shrubs, or trees but only a vast sea of barren rock and sand. To a large extent this impression is true, yet there is some vegetation, although limited to the immediate vicinity of the occasional wells and springs where the underlying structure has brought water close to the surface, or

FIGURE 1.10 *View of Bir Sheb, Egypt, showing typical vegetation near wells.*

as occasional small patches of vegetation in the lower parts of the larger wadis.

In a survey of plant life in the eastern Sahara, Kassas (1971) has noted that over much of this rainless desert, where precipitation is not a recurring phenomenon, vegetation tends to be "accidental"; that is, it occurs only in a few, specially favored localities where runoff water accumulates after such rains as do fall. The plants in these accidental communities are mostly ephemerals or potential ephemerals, but they may also include a few perennials that subsist for more than a year on the stored water. Typically, however, the plant growth will last for only a short season, then dry back to a long dormancy that may extend for several consecutive years. The more characteristic plants in this accidental group are prickly clover (*Fagonia parviflora*), *Zygophyllum coccineum,* halfa grass (*Demostachya bipinnata*), *Tribulus mollis,* and triple-awned grass (*Aristida plumosa*).

A few trees and bushes occur in the vicinity of the major springs and wells (Figure 1.10). The most prominent plants in these areas where water is available near the surface are date palm (*Phoenix dactylifera*), dom palm (*Hyphaene thebaica*), tamarisk (*Tamarix amplexicaulis* and *T. nilotica*), and two varieties of acacia (*Acacia raddiana* and *A. flaua*). The only known examples of the ancient Pharaonic palm (*Medemia argun*) also have been found here (Boulos 1968). In the marshy areas surrounding the water holes occur reeds, such as *Phragmites communis* and *Typha australis*. Slightly farther from the water grow rushes (*Juncus arabicus*), and sticker legumes, such as halfa grass (*Desmostachya bipinnata* or *Imperata cylindrica*) and camel thorn (*Alhagi maurorum*), form open carpets in disturbed or open areas near the wells.

FAUNA

The general scarcity of plant life in the Western Desert is paralleled by a paucity of fauna. The impression of lifelessness is misleading, however, for the careful observer will find several kinds of beetles and rodents present in all but the driest areas. The most common of the rodents are four varieties of jumping or kangaroo mice (*Gerbillus gerbillus, G. campestris, Acomys cahirinus,* and *Jaculus jaculus*). One occasionally sees a few gazelle (*Gazella dorcas*), particularly near the *abyar* or wells, and a rare fox (*Vulpes rüppelli*). Barbary sheep occur in the Gilf el Kebir, but are unknown elsewhere. Lizards, particularly geckos, are pre-sent almost everywhere, but snakes are rarely seen, and the few observed are either horned vipers (*Cerastes cerastes*) or Egyptian cobras; they usually occur near the better watered oases. Scorpions also are sometimes seen in or near these better watered localities, but they are rare in the desert itself. Birds are surprisingly common; flocks of migrant ducks, geese, and cranes occasionally fly over the area, and there are usually several small birds in the vicinity of any location where vegetation is found.

2
The Bir Sahara—
Bir Tarfawi Area

The basins of Bir Tarfawi and Bir Sahara were first seen by us in April 1972, during the course of a brief reconnaissance southward from Dakhla. We were guided there by Bahay Issawi, geologist with the Geological Survey of Egypt, who had seen exposures of lacustrine sediments when he passed by the previous year on a trip to the Gilf el Kebir. Our inspection disclosed several clusters of Middle Paleolithic artifacts eroding from these sediments and also exposed on the deflated floors of both basins. We immediately decided to make this area the center of our efforts during the next season.

And so it was, in late January 1973, we arrived at our camp, which already had been placed on the north edge of the Bir Sahara basin by the Geological Survey. There were 30 tents in all, arranged in three groups. The largest group, about half the total camp, was made up of the tents for the scientists, a dining tent, a cook tent, and servants' quarters. The second group consisted of the tents for the drivers and mechanics, and the third tent group was for the workers. A well had been dug in the lowest part of the basin, adjacent to a small grove of tarfa trees. The water was near the surface here, and the well was only 1.5 m deep. We were 350 km from our nearest supply base, Kharga Oasis, and

all fuel and food had to be brought with us—no great hardship, but requiring careful planning.

One of our major problems was fresh meat. Refrigeration was at a premium, and never dependable. Goats and sheep, although hardy animals that might withstand the rigors of desert travel, were rejected because they require fodder not available in the Tarfawi area; the closest supply would be at Kharga. Chickens and turkeys are much too fragile; they quickly sicken and die when carried long distances over rough terrain. We decided on ducks, 120 of them that season, as the perfect "meat on the hoof" for the desert. They seemed to thrive on desert travel. Once they reached camp the ducks were kept in an old tent each night, but they were allowed out each day to feed (see Figure 1.7).

The ducks were a noisy lot, and always made a terrible din at night when they heard a strange noise. We noted, however, that the cook, who slept near the duck tent, effectively solved that problem. Each day, two of the ducks would be killed, dressed, and served for dinner that evening. The cook carefully selected the birds that were making the most noise. Evidently, either the ducks began to notice too, or he simply got rid of all the noisy ones, because the duck tent was deathly quiet for the last month.

GENERAL GEOLOGY AND GEOMORPHOLOGY

Near the center of the Nubian Desert, around 350 km west and slightly north of Abu Simbel, and 50 km north of the Sudanese border, is an extensive sandy plain in which three small deflational basins occur (Figure 2.1). The plain occupies an irregular and ill-defined area between 28° and

29° W and 22°25′ and 23°25′ N. Except for the depressions, the landscape of this area is almost flat. The exact size and shape of the sandy plain are still unknown because of the lack of detailed air photographs and adequate maps. The sharpest boundary is on the east side, where a large field of

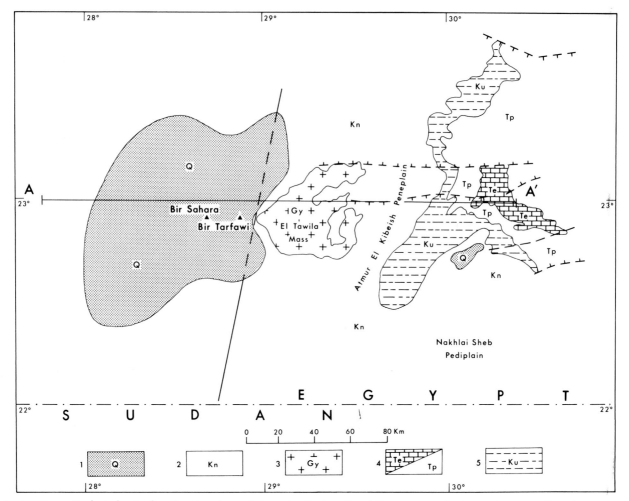

FIGURE 2.1. *Geological map of southwestern desert of Egypt showing location of Quaternary sandy plain and major geological rock units and faults. A–A' indicates line of general cross section, Figure 2.5. Key: 1, Quarternary deposits; 2, Nubia Formation; 3, Precambrian granite; 4, Eocene and Paleocene limestones; 5, Upper Cretaceous shales. Prepared by B. Issawi.*

basement rocks, the so-called El Tawila Mass, borders the area. On the south and southwest, extending far into northern Sudan, sand sheets with occasional rock saddles, ridges, and dunes surround the plain. On the west, another smaller outcrop of basement rock known as the Black Hill can be seen on the horizon halfway to the Gilf el Kebir plateau. Some 70 km to the north, dark sandstone masses occur and the first buttes break the monotony of this seemingly endless sand sheet (Issawi 1973b). A discontinuous surficial cover of sandy carbonate concretions serves as the best definition of the true extent of the Bir Sahara–Bir Tarfawi sandy plain.

The general elevation of the area is around 250 m above sea level, with the exception of the three shallow deflational depressions, some 10 m lower. The eastern basin is known as Bir Tarfawi; 22 km to the northwest is a much smaller and unnamed basin; and 14 km west of Bir Tarfawi is a depression that was mistakenly identified by us as Bir Sahara (Figures 2.2 and 2.3). In fact, the "true" Bir Sahara is a well about 30 km southwest of Bir Tarfawi that was dug by Beadnell (1931: 248) in 1927, but it was not located by our

group until the 1979 season. We have continued to refer to the third large basin as Bir Sahara, although we recognize that the true well of that name is a short distance away.

Both the Bir Sahara and Bir Tarfawi basins have irregular, elongated outlines, about 8 km and 15 km in maximum length, and are oriented north-northeast to southwest. Their outlines are capricious, with numerous "bays," "peninsulas," and buttes. The central parts contain modern dunes, extensive patches of limestone and marl at several elevations, and numerous truncated spring conduits on the floors (Figure 2.4) and around the margins. Remnants of the predeflational surface appear here and there overlooking the floors of the basins. Very shallow, flat, inconspicuous wadis can be observed entering the depressions and disappearing on the plain after a few hundred meters. Patches of salt crust dot the floor near modern wells or at abandoned, sanded-up water holes. The water occurs about 2 m below the floor of the depressions at 238 m above sea level; the discharge was extensive, estimated at 440 gallons per day at Bir Sahara (Issawi 1973b).

A carefully collected sample of this water was dated by

FIGURE 2.2. *View across the depression of Bir Sahara looking west. Note recent phytogenic dunes in upper left.*

FIGURE 2.3. *View of the northern portion of the Bir Sahara basin, looking northwest. Foreground shows plateau remnant southeast of Sites BS-11, BS-12, and BS-1 with crumbly carbonates on slightly deflated surface. Line of backdirt piles from trenches in right background is located at Sites BS-12 and BS-1. Site BS-11 is near the center, across deflated area covered by sand sheet separating it from Sites BS-12 and BS-1.*

FIGURE 2.4.   *A circular spring conduit exposed by deflation on the floor of the Bir Sahara basin. Note modern phytogenic dunes and camp on skyline.*

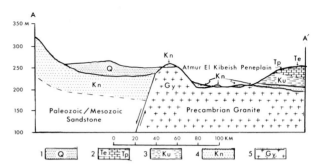

FIGURE 2.5.   *General west–east cross section of the southern part of the southwestern desert of Egypt, showing the relationship of the Quaternary sediments of the sandy plain to faulting and pre-Quaternary rock units. Prepared by B. Issawi. See Figure 2.1 for identification of units.*

radiocarbon at 290 years BP ± 70 (SMU-433), indicating that it is mostly of local origin and is not fossil water derived from upland areas to the west, as some have believed (Beadnell 1931).

A discontinuous, narrow stretch of date palm, dom palm, acacia, and tamarisk trees along the dunes and in the interdunal lows marks the axis of Bir Tarfawi. At Bir Sahara the central chain of recent dunes is covered by low tamarisk bushes; the only trees, also tamarisks, are adjacent to the well.

The general stratigraphic situation of the sandy plain at the Bir Sahara–Bir Tarfawi area indicates, according to Issawi (1973b), that the deposition of these sediments took place in a faulted syncline of the Nubia sandstone underlain by late Paleozoic–early Miocene sandstones that emerge farther west at the Gilf El Kebir plateau (Figure 2.5). To the east, the upthrown igneous mass of the Precambrian granite of El Tawila domes the synclinal basin in which the Quaternary sediments were blocked. This reconstruction is solely based on the surface geology and can be confirmed only by extensive deep drilling.

Basing his assumptions on the study of the Darb el Arbain area, Issawi (1973a) believes that the last transgression of Tethys occurred during the early Eocene, and that since then the area has generally been dry land on which the weathering processes have been at least partly responsible for the peneplanation. The occasional relief results from igneous activity and structural deformations.

QUATERNARY LITHOSTRATIGRAPHIC SEQUENCE

The Bir Sahara–Bir Tarfawi area provides the basic sequence for the early upper Pleistocene of the Western Desert (Figure 2.6). The sequence consists of a series of alternating lacustrine and eolian events associated with human occupations as well as rich vertebrate and invertebrate faunas. It is perhaps the best such sequence known for the entire Sahara. Several distinct lithostratigraphic units form the framework for the sequence (Figures 2.7 and 2.8).

PLATEAU CARBONATES AND UNDERLYING SANDS

On the surface of almost the entire plain is a nearly continuous sheet of carbonate crust in the form of flakes, plates, and large rectangular to hexagonal structures, or a litter of small spongy nodules of sand and carbonate. The carbonate is gray, cemented, rarely porous to cavernous. At some places a friable gray clay containing similar carbonate nodules and quartz grains was observed by Issawi (1973b) to underlie the carbonate-covered surface. In most places, however, the carbonate crust or nodules rest immediately on a sand unit whose upper portion is sometimes made up of two different sands. The lower, which certainly constitutes the lowest recognized unit in the area, is a white, friable, medium-grained, well-sorted sand. The Nubia sandstone, supposedly underlying this unit, has never been reached, even though a bore hole reaching down to about 235 m above sea level was cut into the floor of the Bir Sahara depression. This was some 15 m below the surface of the carbonate crust and/or nodule-littered surface. The upper unit, rarely present, is made up of a very coarse, gritty sand containing very small quartz gravels and is friable, poorly to moderately sorted with subrounded to subangular feldspars. Its thickness only slightly exceeds 20 cm (Issawi 1973b).

Toward the west from Bir Sahara several very low, inconspicuous mounds dot the carbonate-littered surface,

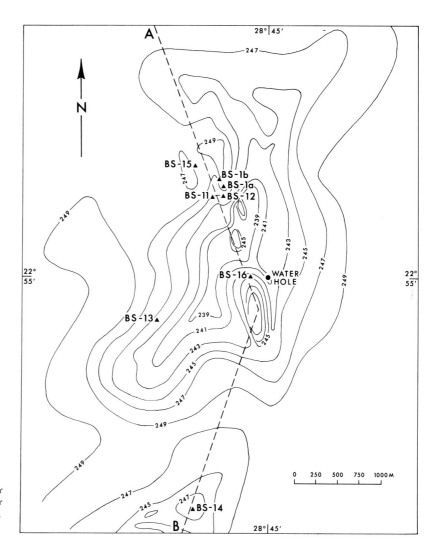

FIGURE 2.6. *Topographic contour map of the Bir Sahara basin showing the location of the general cross section (Figure 2.8). Map by B. Issawi, February 1973.*

suggesting their association with fossil springs; however, none of these mounds appearing on the plateau was tested.

Numerous Acheulian sites were observed on the surface of the carbonate plateau. Most of these are clearly in lag situation dropped from a higher surface, although some offer slight suggestion that a portion of the material may be almost *in situ*. These are characterized by less abraded tools, some of which have their "groundward" faces almost completely fresh. Because of their secondary position, only a few grab samples were collected. The stratigraphic relationship between the Acheulian sites and the flaky carbonate crust is not clear, for both are certainly lowered.

UPPER ACHEULIAN PONDS

At the southwest edge of Bir Tarfawi, a series of irregular oval remnants of very hard, dense freshwater limestone, some of them more than 100 m long, was observed. Only

slightly below the level of the adjacent carbonate-covered plain, the limestone was homogeneous, thin (maximum about 30 cm), and displayed networks of desiccation cracks that penetrated to the sand below. These limestone beds now stand 2 to 3 m above the surrounding dune surface, presenting a typical reversed topography resulting from the deflation of the less resistant sands surrounding the limestone (Figure 2.9). This unit was not observed elsewhere.

On the deflated sand surface surrounding the limestone remnants are several loose clusters of Upper Acheulian artifacts, mostly bifaces, all heavily abraded. Within the limestone several similar bifaces were found *in situ*, apparently representing artifacts that were worked or thrown in from the adjacent, now deflated, Acheulian campsites (Figure 2.10). No associated fauna was observed.

These localities were discovered while we were en route to the Gilf el Kebir after the work at Bir Sahara and Bir Tarfawi was completed, so they have not yet been studied. The chronological relationship between Upper Acheulian

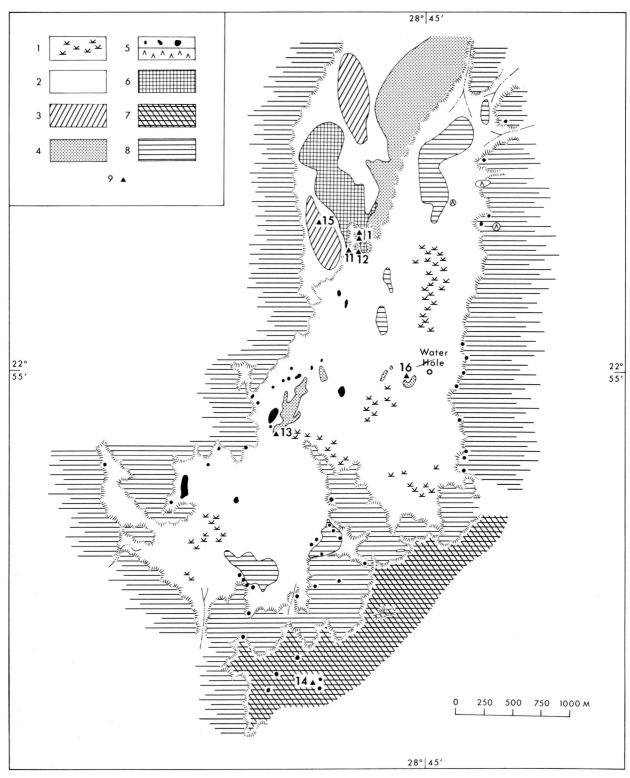

FIGURE 2.7. *Geological map of the Bir Sahara depression showing major sedimentary units and locations of archaeological and geological sites. Key: 1, vegetation; 2, recent eolian sand and/or exposed basal sand or older Mousterian dune; 3, upper lacustrine silts; 4, older silt/calcareous units; 5, spring and ferrocrete mounds; 6, upper dune unit with top carbonates; 7, Acheulian spring and deflated basal sand unit; 8, plateau carbonate; 9, archaeological and geological sites. Map by B. Issawi, February 1973.*

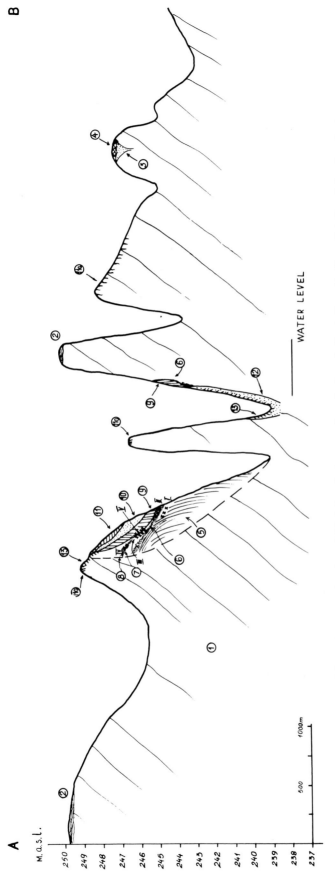

FIGURE 2.8. *Schematic cross section through Bir Sahara basin approximately along the line indicated in Figure 2.6. Key: 1, basal sand unit; 2, plateau carbonates; 3, Acheulian spring conduit; 4, Acheulian spring evaporites; 5, older Mousterian dune; 6, black layer grading upslope into lower vegetation horizon; 7, beach mottled sands; 8, silts, marls, and evaporites of older lacustrine series; 10, upper dune; 11, upper lacustrine series; 11a, sandy evaporites; 12, recent eolian sands; 13, recent reddish yellow soil. Cultural horizons indicated by Roman numerals (I–V) and crosses.*

23

FIGURE 2.9. *View of freshwater limestone lacustrine deposits at south end of Bir Tarfawi.*

FIGURE 2.10. *Biface in situ in freshwater limestone lacustrine deposits at south end of Bir Tarfawi.*

ponds and the Upper Acheulian resting on the surface of the plateau carbonate is unknown. They could, however, be contemporaneous.

FINAL ACHEULIAN SPRINGS

At the southern rim of the depression of Bir Sahara were several pronounced mounds of fossil springs. Many of these had occasional Acheulian bifaces on their slopes; the largest mound, standing slightly more than 3 m above the sur-

rounding wind-scoured oldest sands, had numerous Acheulian bifaces arranged in a typical radiating slide pattern on its carbonate, cemented surface and sandy slopes. The locality was designated as Site BS-14 (E99C14).

The central part of the flat-topped hill was highly cemented by a solid mass of carbonates of unknown thickness. This limestone cap was so hard it could not be penetrated with heavy picks or other equipment available, but a small trench was dug along the east rim and this yielded some data on the contents of the spring (Figure 2.11). The lowest sediment, archaeologically sterile, is the basal sand unit, which here is loose to slightly consolidated, white (10YR 8/2), coarse to medium grained. The upper part of this sand is clearly truncated. Over the truncation is deposited a very coarse, well-sorted sand with Acheulian artifacts, fossil remains, and rootlike carbonized sand rods (Figure 2.12). Its thickness varies from 70 to 90 cm, but the base slopes gently toward the center of the hill. This is covered by a 30-cm-thick unit of medium blocky evaporites, made up of carbonate cemented sand (with more than 70% carbonate), thickening toward the center. Its upper part contains more-rounded and smaller concretions of carbonates. The whole carbonate unit wedges out at the rim of the spring hill. A thin, coarse-grained, reddish yellow (7.5YR 7/6) sand overlies the external part of the evaporite rim.

The data suggest that the trench is located at the rim of a spring pool containing archaeological remains mostly deposited during the period of its major activity. The bed made up of evaporites indicates a somewhat lesser discharge, a dying source, marked by the decayed vegetation that eventually covered the spring eye.

The limited faunal remains that were recovered from the spring sand bed included tooth enamel fragments of a medium-sized or large ruminant, and a few pieces of ostrich eggshell. A few other bones were collected while eroding from the supposedly basal part of the carbonate seal: One upper molariform tooth and an acetabulum of an equid, probably *Equus asinus;* and a jaw fragment with adjacent tooth belonging to a warthog (*Phacochoerus aethiopicus*) were identified (Gautier, this volume).

The isolated situation of the fossil spring at Site BS-14 and the very limited excavations do not suffice to establish a precise relationship of the site to the previously mentioned units, either the plateau carbonates or the Upper Acheulian ponds at Tarfawi. However, some suggestions may be offered. The top of the mound, located at about 247 m above sea level, is slightly more than 2 m below the surface of the plateau. This observation could indicate that a period of deflation took place before the formation of the spring and after the plateau carbonates had been deposited.

OLDER MOUSTERIAN DUNE

After the death of the spring at the Final Acheulian site of BS-14, a signficant period of eolian erosion followed during

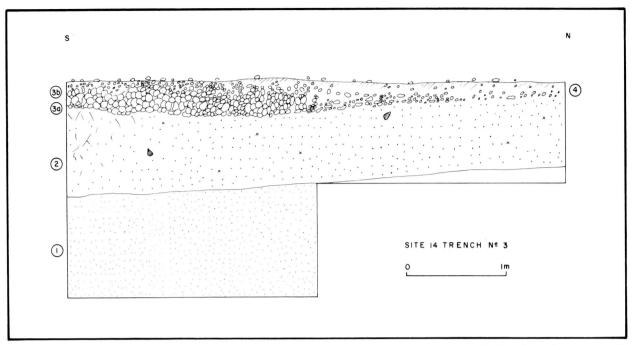

FIGURE 2.11. *Site BS-14. Cross section of northern edge of the spring pool showing stratigraphy. Key: 1, basal sand unit; 2, coarse, sorted sand with Acheulian artifacts and carbonized sand rods–spring sands; 3a, lower part of blocky evaporites with rare Acheulian artifacts at base; 3b, upper part of blocky evaporites; 4, recent eolian sand with weak red soil.*

FIGURE 2.12. *Site BS-14 trench, showing basal sands at bottom of trench, coarse spring-pool sand unit, and cap of blocky evaporites.*

which the depression was excavated for the first time down to at least 242 m above sea level, thus more than 8 m below the surrounding plateau. The depression may well have been considerably deeper, since a core, located near Trench 1 at Site BS-12 (E99C12) in the older Mousterian dune went down to about 235 m, about 5 m below the floor of the depression, without any reported change in sediments. After the basin was excavated, possibly down to the level of the water table at that time, this hole of unknown size was filled with sand dunes, exposed today over a large portion of the floor in the northwestern part of the depression. A

long section pertaining to this event was exposed by a series of trenches in Bir Sahara at archaeological sites BS-1 (E99C1) and BS-12 (Figure 2.13).

Here, the foreset and topset dune beds extend laterally for more than 200 m (Figure 2.13:1), assuming a thickness of at least 5 m with their topmost section at or just below 245 m above sea level. At Site BS-12 the topset beds contained numerous but heavily sandblasted Mousterian artifacts, with denticulates and notches the only recovered tools. The presence of these tools indicates that an occupation occurred during the formation of the dunes, and this in turn suggests that some water must have been available at that time. The dunes, therefore, could have been of phytogenic origin. This sand unit is today consolidated to cemented, medium to coarse grained, white (2.5Y 8/0), with iron enrichment or reduction stains and destroyed lamination in its upper part.

OLDER LACUSTRINE SERIES

An intricate series of lacustrine, shore, and inblown sediments follows after the deposition of the dune. It starts with a horizon informally referred to as the "black layer" (Figure 2.13:2b), a black to grayish brown (10YR 5/2) sand heavily stained with concentrated manganese. The unit is uniformly deposited at similar elevations in several places at the margin of the basin, indicating a primarily continuous bed. At the lowest point, at Site BS-16 (E99C16), its base is 243.8 m above sea level, whereas at Site BS-1 it

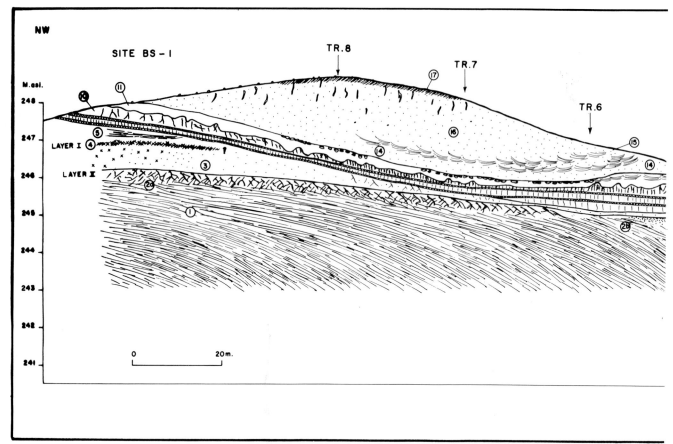

FIGURE 2.13. *Cross section at Sites BS-1 and BS-12. Key: 1, older Mousterian dune; 2a, lower vegetation horizon passing down into black layer, 2b; 3, iron-stained, mottled beach sand; 4, upper vegetation layer at Site BS-1; 5, iron-stained mottled sand with inconspicuous traces of lamination in places; 6, 8, 10, silt layers; 7 and 9, burnt layers; 11, white marl; 12, sag structures; 13, white marl with lenses of silt and*

reaches 245.1 m, gradually disappearing upward from this point on. Laterally, the black layer slopes very gently toward the center of the basin, becoming more intense and thick while descending. Upward, it passes gradually into a vegetation layer at Sites BS-1 and BS-11 (Figures 2.13:2a and 2.14), marked by a thick mat of carbonized root casts (lower vegetation layer at Site BS-1), and a slight rise in the $CaCO_3$ content (Figure 2.18); its texture is not significantly different from that of the underlying and overlying sands.

The black sand seems to grade down very gently, but at some places it shows a clear erosional contact with the underlying dune, as at Site BS-13 (E99C13). Here it fills numerous small channels excavated in the dune. The deeper parts of these channels are usually a more intense black.

At Site BS-16, where the black layer assumes its lowest elevation above sea level, it grades up into a powdered, mineralized, slightly laminated peatlike sediment. Repeated analyses of this peatlike sediment failed to yield any pollen.

Samples of the peatlike sediment were given various pretreatments and submitted for radiocarbon dating. The extracted humates gave a date of 37,740 BP ± 1980 years (SMU-95), whereas the residue yielded a date of 28,000 BP ± 1250 years (SMU-108). A second sample from the same

locality, treated only with acid (and thus combining the humates and residue), gave a date of 33,080 BP ± 1120 years (SMU-218). These dates are younger than others obtained on shell from overlying beds, and the spread between

FIGURE 2.14. *View of Site BS-11 showing black layer grading up into lower vegetation horizon where figure is pointing; mottled sands and marl occur above the black layer. Occupation at this site is just below and within black layer.*

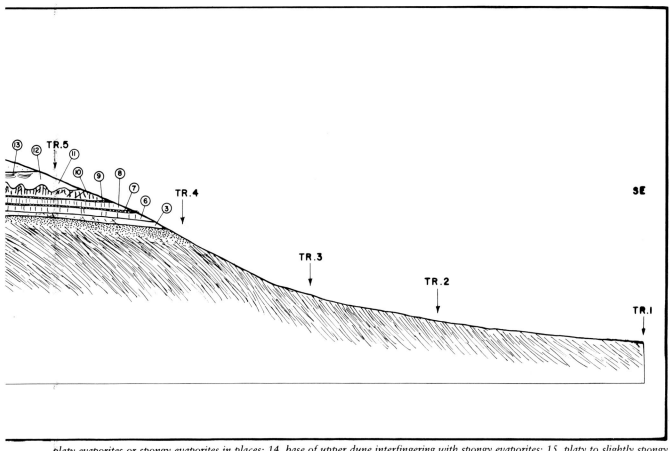

platy evaporites or spongy evaporites in places; 14, base of upper dune interfingering with spongy evaporites; 15, platy to slightly spongy evaporites; 16, main body of upper dune with carbonate cemented root casts in top part; 17, reddish yellow soil.

the dates on the humate and residue fractions indicates that some secondary organic circulation occurred and that neither date can be accepted with confidence.

The thickness of the black layer usually fluctuates between 20 and 40 cm with maximal values of about 70 cm in the erosional channels at Site BS-13.

Several extensive Mousterian occurrences are stratigraphically associated with the black layer. Those located closer to the center of the depression, at an elevation between 244.5 m and 245.0 m above sea level (Site BS-12, upper level; Site BS-13, lower level), are embedded in the black layer; those located slightly higher, at an elevation between 245.0 m and 245.5 m above sea level (Site BS-11), are just below the black layer and in its lower portion. Still farther up the slope of the depression some traces of occupation were recorded at Site BS-1 in the lower vegetation horizon and the upslope stratigraphic continuation of the black layer. It is highly possible that these slight differences in the absolute elevations and lateral placement of the settlements reflect minor fluctuations of the shore. The fauna from the blacker layer and just below it consists of the following: wild ass (*Equus asinus*), white rhinoceros (*Ceratotherium sinum*), warthog (*Phacochoerus aethiopicus?*), ex-

tinct camel? (*Camelus thomasi*), buffalo (*Homoioceras antiquus?*), and an unidentified large antelope. All are represented by only one or two bones (Gautier, this volume).

The exact environmental conditions in which this manganese-rich horizon was deposited are not well understood. The channeling at Site BS-13 and the lateral differentiation suggest a near-shore environment, a conclusion that is reinforced by the occurrences of the *in situ* Mousterian settlements embedded in the layer. The manganese is obviously a feature that occurred secondary to the deposition of the sand, and it may represent a manganese-enriched horizon forming under shallow water in a relatively warm environment.

The top of the black layer is slightly truncated at places and, in turn, covered by a bed of iron-stained gray sand (5Y 6/1) sloping gently toward the center of the basin (Figure 2.13). At some places (BS-13) its lower portion is conformably laminated over minuscule swales excavated in the surface of the black layer. The thickness of the gray sand unit varies according to its lateral position in the basin, and toward the edges of the basin it thickens upward considerably. In the downslope sections of the bed there is a thick mat of well-formed and carbonate-cemented root casts

FIGURE 2.15. *Older Lacustrine series as seen downslope from Site BS-1. Eroded black layer at base covered by mottled sands with rootlet casts, and, in turn, by silts overlain by white marls; burnt layer seen as a horizontal fissure within silts; platy and spongy evaporites just above white marl.*

(Figure 2.15). At Site BS-1 this sand thickens to more than 1.5 m (Figure 2.13:3–5), and here numerous brown to bluish iron enrichment and reduction streaks mark the whole bed, most probably reflecting the presence of a pseudogley hydromorphic soil. Its upper portion contains a clear vegetation zone (upper vegetation layer, Figure 2.16). It is again an extremely thick mat of carbonate-cemented microrootlet casts that appear as spongy structures tightly knotted together. This horizon is also marked by a slightly higher $CaCO_3$ content and considerably finer texture (Figure 2.18). The vegetation is, in turn, covered by inconspicuously laminated sands, identical to those in the level below.

FIGURE 2.16. *Site BS-1: two vegetation horizons separated by mottled, pseudogley sands. Person indicates upper vegetation horizon with main cultural layer in it and below. Lower vegetation horizon seen in lower-right portion of picture, just above base of trench.*

At Site BS-13, at the base of the sand, was an extensive, partially destroyed Mousterian settlement. The cultural horizon yielded metapodial fragments of the white rhinoceros (*Ceratotherium sinum*) (Gautier, this volume).

At Site BS-1 the upper vegetation horizon, located near the top of the sand level, contained another Mousterian settlement. The artifacts had been vertically displaced, undoubtedly by the roots from the near-shore vegetation; therefore it is reasonable to assume that this upper vegetation horizon developed after the settlement. Unfortunately, the bones in the cultural horizons had been almost totally destroyed, presumably because of the chemical environment of the soil (hydromorphic pseudogley), and the remaining small abraded bone fragments were unidentifiable.

The environmental interpretation of the gray, mottled sand is that of a shore and near-shore sandy sediment reflecting minor pulsations, with the shore sometimes emerging and then covered by water. The time pattern for these pulsations is unknown, but they could well be seasonal. The sandy beach was fed either by inblown eolian sands or by reworking of the older Mousterian dune. The latter seems to be more likely in the context of the climatic reconstruction.

The gray sand is conformably overlain by a series of alternating light gray to brown (5Y 7/2 to 2.5Y 7/2) thin layers of silt, less than 1 m thick (Figure 2.13:6,8,10 and Figure 2.16). Near the base of these silts are two to three reddish brown (2.5 YR 5/4) or pink (5YR 8/3) burnt layers interbedded between the silts (Figure 2.13:7, 9). In the section between Site BS-1 and Site BS-12 (Trench 5) an oval pit, about 80 cm in diameter and 50 cm deep, was dug through the lowest burnt layer, the underlying silt, and into the sand of the black layer. The pit was filled with blocky silt of the second silt layer, and was covered by the second burnt layer. There were no artifacts associated; however, the feature is obviously artificial, and most probably of human origin. It seems likely to have been a small water hole dug during a dry season, immediately after the burning of the near-shore aquatic vegetation. The interpretation of the burnt layers suggests that all of them represent fires that swept the dried near-shore and aquatic vegetation. Similar rhythmic phenomena were observed along the shores of prehistoric lakes in the Fayum (Wendorf and Schild 1976b). It is highly likely that they were started by man. Samples of the two lowest burnt layers were collected for paleomagnetic and thermoluminescent dating, and submitted to the Research Laboratory for Archaeology and the History of Art, Oxford; the results are not yet available.

A bed of light gray (2.5Y 7/2) to white marl (Figure 2.13:11 and Figure 2.15) with medium to coarse blocky structure overlies the alternating silt beds (Figure 2.13:6, 8, 10). The contact, however, is erosional at places (BS-13) and/or displays very pronounced slump structures (Figure 2.13:12). The upper part of the marl grades up into platy evaporites with thin streaks of silt (Figure 2.13:13), and still higher, into a cemented bed of spongy evaporites. In the deeper portion of the basin this lacustrine series is reduced to one bed of whitish marl (Site BS-11 and geological locality BS-16). The thickness of the whole bed rarely exceeds 1 m. A sample of this marl at BS-16 from just above the black peaty layer gave a radiocarbon date of 34,600 BP ± 970 years (SMU-215) on carbonates. This provides a minimum age for the sediment.

At Site BS-13 the very base of the marl contains numerous washed-down animal bones seemingly redeposited from an adjacent shore now completely removed. Among the recovered bones were the wild ass (*Equus asinus*), white rhinoceros (*Ceratotherium sinum*, the most common), extinct camel (*Camelus thomasi*), and buffalo (*Homoioceras antiquus?*) (Gautier, this volume).

Slightly farther down the sloping bed of the marl unit near Site BS-13, and nearer the axis of the depression, a collection of molluscs from the snail-laden upper portion of this bed gave the following identification: *Melanoides tuberculata, Lymnaea natalensis, Gyraulus costulatus* (all frequent), and *Biomphalaria alexandrina, Bulinus truncatus,* and *Hydrobia* sp. (less abundant). At geological locality BS-16 another molluscan sample collected from the base of the same white marl unit contained very frequent *Melanoides tuberculata, Lymnaea natalensis,* and *Gyraulus costulatus; Biomphalaria alexandrina, Bulinus truncatus,* and *B. forskalii* are also present (Gautier, this volume).

A sample of *Melanoides* shells collected from the surface of this marl unit near Site BS-13 yielded a date of 32,780 BP ± 900 years (SMU-80), and another molluscan sample of large and carefully cleaned *Melanoides* shells from the same unit at geological locality BS-16 gave a radiocarbon date of >41,450 BP (SMU-81). A sample of smaller and thus not as well cleaned *Melanoides* shells from the same place gave a date of 40,710 BP ± 3270 years (SMU-82). The two absolute dates are younger than dates from an overlying unit and are therefore regarded as contaminated by more recent carbonates.

Both the gray silts and marl units clearly represent lacustrine sediments of an expanding lake that certainly exceeded 248 m above sea level (the highest recorded elevation). Despite a persistent search for the beach facies of this lake, nothing resembling a near-shore or shore environment was found; it obviously was destroyed by subsequent erosion. The alternating homogeneous layers of silts in the basal part of the unit, burnt plant growth layers, traces of erosion between the lower and upper unit, as well as the slump structures all point to the fact that the level of the lake had never been stable, but had undergone considerable and possibly rapid changes. Some of these changes may be associated with a seasonal rhythm. Near the top of the upper unit a shrinkage of the lake is marked by the appearance of rich evaporite layers obviously formed at the near-beach environment and often displaying excellent plant casts. No archaeological remains were found associated with either of these units.

UPPER DUNE

An invading dune is recorded at Sites BS-1 and BS-12 interfingering at the base with spongy evaporites (Figure 2.13:14). The dune is friable, medium grained, and pale yellow (2.5Y 8/4). Several thin layers of platy to slightly spongy carbonate-cemented sand structures occur in the lower part of the dune (Figure 2.13:15). Near the top, numerous carbonate-cemented root casts and patches of lime were observed. A thin reddish yellow (5YR 7/6) soil with fine crumbly structure tops the dune at Site BS-1 (Figure 2.13:17). The formation of the soil clearly postdates the development of carbonate-cemented root-drip structures, as is shown by their broken sections, which display discolored sand grains. The whole thickness of the preserved dune slightly exceeds 3 m in its thickest portion.

The sections at Site BS-11 and geological locality BS-15 reveal a large (about 400 m long and almost 2 m thick) lens of consolidated to cemented light gray (2.5Y 7/2) upper dune sand, which overlies the truncated marl of the lower lacustrine series (Figure 2.17:7) and, in turn, is covered by a unit of later silts (Figure 2.17:8).

UPPER LACUSTRINE SERIES

New units of silts unconformably overlie the dune (Figure 2.17:8). Only two moderately extensive patches of these sediments are at Bir Sahara, both in the northern portion of the basin and at elevations close to 247.5 m above sea level. At geological locality BS-15 a thin (about 30 cm) gray (10YR 7/1) sandy silt displaying irregular blocky structure contains numerous snails and clams. It rests on the upper dune. The molluscan assemblage includes four frequent lacustrine species: *Melanoides tuberculata, Biomphalaria alexandrina, Gyraulus costulatus,* and *Bulinus forskalii.* Also present are *Lymnaea natalensis, Bulinus truncatus, Corbicula consobrina,* plus a terrestrial snail, *Pupoides coenopictus* (Gautier, this volume). There are two radiocarbon dates that refer to this unit. A sample of selected large *Melanoides* shells gave a radiocarbon date of > 44,700 BP (SMU-79), and clamshells, some of which were collected from the surface, dated 30,870 BP ± 1000 years (SMU-75). The second date is likely to have been contaminated by younger carbonates from the surface.

The basal silt grades up into a darker, loose to slightly consolidated horizon of brown (10YR 5/3), thin (about 30 cm) sandy silt displaying fine crumbly structure and carbonate nodules, resulting from pedogenetic alterations subsequent to deposition (Figure 2.18:9). Again it contains rich molluscan fauna. The assemblage here includes frequent land snails of *Zootecus insularis* as well as a few *Pupoides coenopictus.* Three lacustrine snails are also still frequent—*Melanoides tuberculata, Biomphalaria alexandrina,* and *Gyraulus costulatus*—and *Lymnaea natalensis, Bulinus truncatus,* and *B. forskalii* are present but not

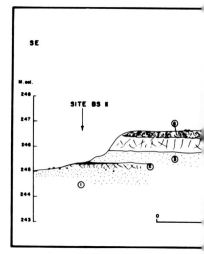

FIGURE 2.17. *Cross section between Sites BS-11 and BS-15 (geological locality). Key: 1, older Mousterian dune; 2, black layer passing upslope into vegetation layer; 3, mottled sands; 4, silts; 5, platy evaporites; 6, spongy evaporites; 7, upper dune; 8, upper lacustrine series, basal marl; 9, upper lacustrine series, brown upper marl; 10, reddish soil.*

common (Gautier, this volume). The top of the upper silt is slightly truncated.

The upper lacustrine series certainly marks a new aggradation at Bir Sahara. The highest recorded elevation of the already truncated silts is 247.5 m above sea level, but the beaches are not preserved. The presence in the upper lake of *Corbicula consobrina*, a variety that prefers larger bodies of water, as well as the absence of this bivalve in the lower lake, may indicate that the upper lake was the larger (Gautier, this volume). Because of the high stand of this lake, it is quite possible that the carbonate-cemented root casts that are observed in upper portions of the younger dune, at an elevation slightly over 248 m above sea level, were formed during this phase of the lake. Similarly, the rodlike carbonates occurring on the plateau remnants (Figure 2.3) in the basin as well as in the northern part of the rim could have been formed during this time. These are identified in Figure 2.7 as "upper dune unit with top carbonates" (Issawi 1973b), and seem to form a single mantle when followed on the surface. The upper lacustrine unit is archaeologically sterile at Bir Sahara.

All the lacustrine units at Bir Sahara were personally sampled by P. J. Mehringer, a palynologist with considerable experience with arid sediments. These samples were subjected to a variety of pretreatment and flotation techniques; however, none of them yielded pollen.

The upper lacustrine sequence is much better developed in the depression at Bir Tarfawi. For reasons not clearly understood, the lower lacustrine sequence is not represented there; following the Upper Acheulian ponds the next recorded event at Tarfawi is the excavation of an extensive elongated depression and the filling of this depression by dunes, believed to be contemporaneous with the upper dune at Bir Sahara. It is presumed that the indurated Acheulian lake sediments served as a protective armor and prevented the pronounced deflation that preceded the Mousterian occupation at Bir Sahara. It is not possible to make a direct lithostratigraphic connection between the

two depressions; however, there are strong indications favoring this interpretation. First, Bir Tarfawi contains only one post-Acheulian lake; second, the archaeology associated with this lake is different from that at Bir Sahara, although both are of Middle Paleolithic character. All the sites associated with the Bir Tarfawi lakes contain Aterian elements that elsewhere in North Africa are known to post-date those Middle Paleolithic assemblages that lack these elements, that is, the Mousterian.

The investigations of the archaeology and geology associated with the upper lacustrine series were concentrated in the northern portion of the Tarfawi depression, where a large area of indurated lake silts and associated archaeological sites was discovered (Figure 2.19).

The landscape in this area has a rolling topography with flat to slightly concave patches of indurated lacustrine sediments preserved at differing elevations, varying as much as 10 m. Large sand areas surround the patches, always at lower elevations. Here, numerous Aterian sites occur in a lag position often very close to the preserved lake sediments.

A few small spring mounds dot the area, particularly on the northeast side. Two of these have a few Acheulian handaxes scattered on their slopes, thus suggesting their association with the springs; however, none was found *in situ* in the vents, and none of the springs was excavated. Other nearby spring vents either lacked any evidence for adjacent archaeological remains, or seemed to be associated with later Aterian occupations (Figure 2.20). Two modern large phytogenic dunes covered by tamarisks stood along the eastern margin of the area. This section of the depression could be considered an excellent example of an inverted topography caused by eolian deflation, which lowered the dunes that once stood around interdunal ponds and left the indurated lacustrine sediments at higher elevations.

In the center of this area was the largest pond, preserved today as an elongated L-shaped flat remnant (Figures 2.21

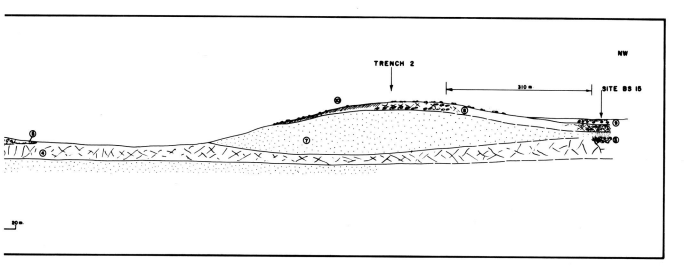

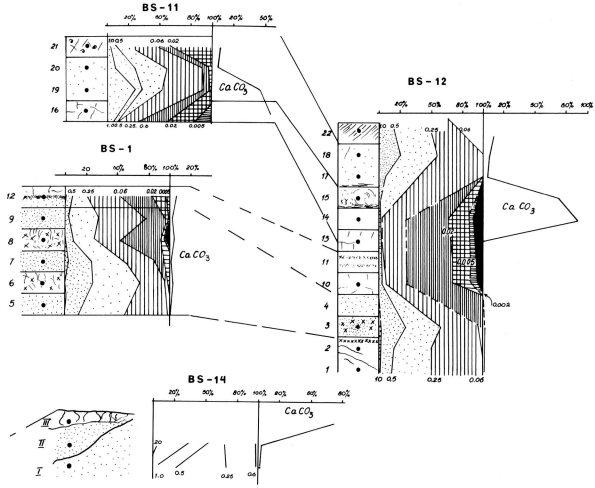

FIGURE 2.18. *Grain size and* CaCO₃ *curves of sediments from Bir Sahara basin. Key: 1, foreset beds of lower Mousterian dune; 2, topset beds of lower Mousterian dune; 3, black layer; 4, iron-stained patchy sand; 5, iron-stained patchy sand below lower vegetation layer; 6, lower vegetation layer; 7, patchy sand between two vegetation layers; 8, upper vegetation layer; 9, patchy sand above upper vegetation layer; 10, basal silt; 11, silt with burnt layers; 12, sandy silt with burnt layer; 13, silt above burnt layers; 14, white, highly calcareous silt; 15, spongy evaporates; 16, sandy silt truncated at top; 17, base of younger Mousterian dune; 18, upper part of younger Mousterian dune; 19 and 20, younger Mousterian dune; 21, lower portion of younger lacustrine silt; 22, reddish yellow recent soil. Crosses indicate presence of human occupation. No scale. Analyses by J. Kossakowska-Such and T. Wesolowska.*

FIGURE 2.19. *View of northern portion of Bir Tarfawi, looking east. Note modern phytogenic dunes in far distance.*

cality revealed a complex lithostratigraphic sequence consisting of eolian and lacustrine deposits (Figures 2.20, 2.21, and 2.23).

The Dune

Here the sequence starts with the deposition of a thick dune of which the foreset and topset bedding was exposed. The dune sand was white (10YR 8/1) and cemented to consolidated (Figures 2.24:1 and 2.25:1). The near top section of the dune contained a few heavily wind-blasted artifacts, possibly flakes, of an undeterminable technology, but supposedly of Aterian origin (Figure 2.24:1a). A bore hole cut 6.5 m below the bottom of Trench 9 was in sand throughout and did not reach bedrock.

The Lake

The lowest lacustrine sediment is a silty sand, grayish brown (25YR 5/2) to dark reddish brown (5YR 3/2), unconformably overlying the dune (Figures 2.24:2 and 2.25:2). In some localities it also contains medium-sized, rounded, carbonaceous concretions, an undoubtedly postdepositional feature. A sample of these concretions from

and 2.22). The northern part of this remnant contained a mass of animal bones eroding from the lacustrine silts as well as concentrations of lithic artifacts, some still within the sediment and others on the surface of the adjacent lowered sands. Extensive excavations and trenching at this lo-

FIGURE 2.20. *Site BT-14, looking east. Note line of trenches in Areas A, B, and C. Figures in left center at Area N. Phytogenic dunes in middle distance, and two spring mounds near left center. Plateau surface seen on skyline.*

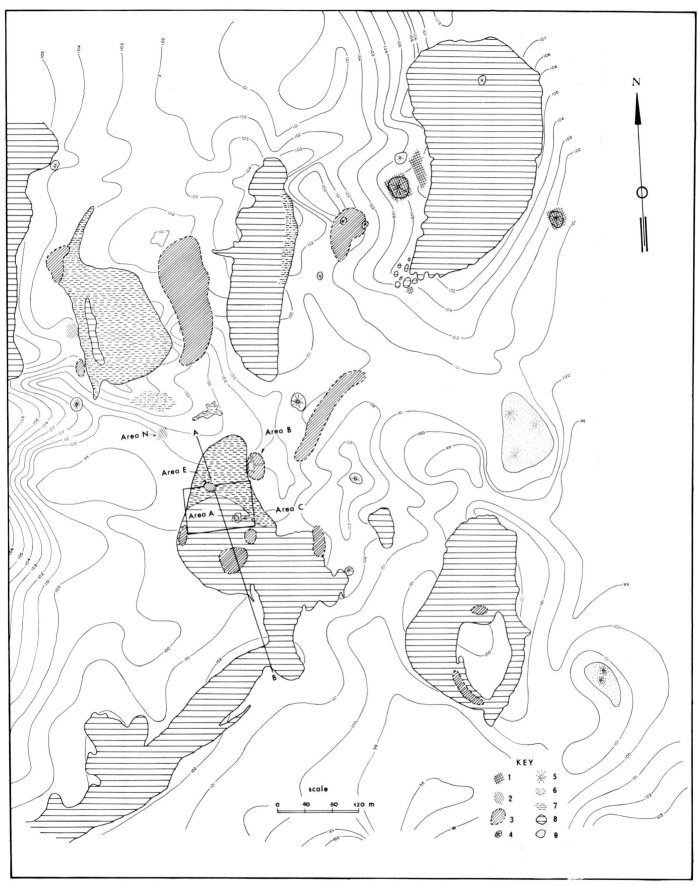

FIGURE 2.21. *Map of Site BT-14 showing rock units and topography. Key: 1, Acheulian occurrences; 2, Neolithic–Early Kingdom occurrences; 3, Aterian concentrations; 4, fossil spring mounds; 5, phytogenic dunes; 6, basal brown silty sand; 7, olive silt; 8, gray calcareous lower silts and/or evaporites; 9, eolian sand, mostly pre-lake dune. Datum assumed. Map by M. Tawakol, February 1974.*

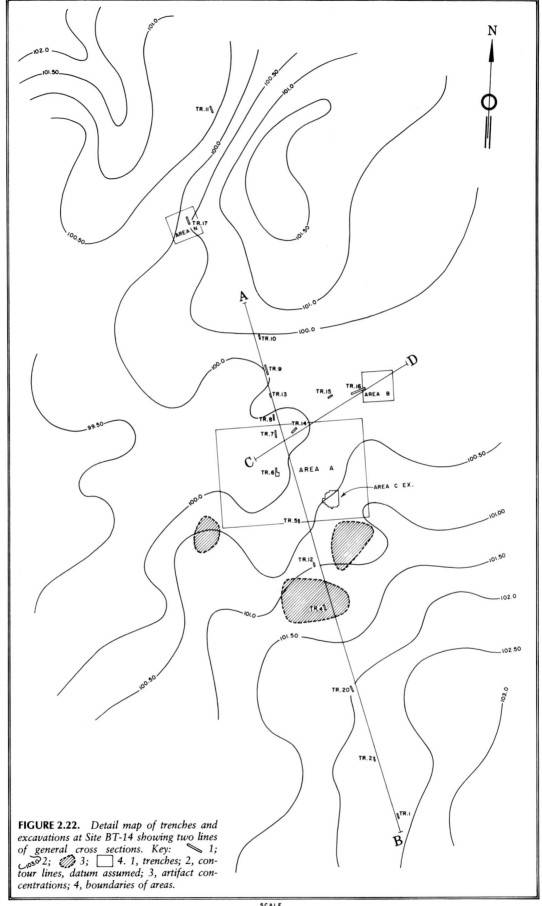

FIGURE 2.22. *Detail map of trenches and excavations at Site BT-14 showing two lines of general cross sections. Key:* 1; 2; 3; 4. *1, trenches; 2, contour lines, datum assumed; 3, artifact concentrations; 4, boundaries of areas.*

SCALE

0   20   40   60   80m

FIGURE 2.23. *View at Site BT-14, from the vicinity of Trenches 9 and 10, looking southeast; line of trenches seen in the middle; excavations at Area C in left center; phytogenic dunes on horizon.*

Site BT-14 (E99D14), near Area N, gave a radiocarbon date of 26,530 BP ± 470 years (SMU-205), which is considered a minimum date since the carbonates are, in most cases, a postdepositional feature and are likely to be contaminated by still later carbonates. The dark layer is draped over the undulating dune topography, but it is more strongly developed in the deeper portions of the basin. The dark layer contains rare Aterian artifacts that cannot be tied in with a specific concentration in the area; presumably, the settlement from which they came was destroyed by subsequent erosion. Mammalian fauna occurs commonly, and among those present are frequent bones of *Gazella rufifrons*, followed by an unidentified large antelope, buffalo (*Homoioceras antiquus*), and white rhinoceros (*Ceratotherium sinum*). There was also a single example of a medium-sized antelope. Numerous fish bones are also present, including several fragments of a clariid skull, *Lates* vertebrae, plus fine spines and a vertebrae of a clichid, possible *Sarotherodon* sp. A fragment of crocodile tooth, relatively numerous fragments of turtle, a single fragment of ostrich eggshell, and unidentified bird and rodent remains complete the collection. The aquatic fauna is identical to that of the present day in the Nile (G. Howes, *in litteris*). The gastropods are also numerous but they are limited to three species. Among them the most common is *Hydrobia* sp., followed by *Biomphalaria alexandrina* and *Gyraulus costulatus*. A sample of this dark horizon was collected for radiocarbon dating, and the organic matter in the sample dates 21,950 BP ± 490 years (SMU-214). This date must also be viewed as minimal since it was not possible to give the sample adequate pretreatment. The dark color in this sediment is apparently due to the presence of organic particles. The exact environment that produced the layer is not understood. It has a superficial resemblance to sandy peat; however, the presence of fish would suggest a standing body of permanent water.

Immediately above the dark layer is a thick, light gray (10YR 4/2), highly carbonaceous silt containing numerous calcium carbonate nodules and cavernous concretions (Figures 2.24:3 and 2.25:3). The silt is very rich in snails, especially numerous in the top of the unit where they formed a breccia. Four species occurred frequently: *Melanoides tuberculata, Lymnaea natalensis, Gyraulus costulatus,* and *Hydrobia* sp. Present but less numerous are *Biomphalaria alexandrina, Bulinus truncatus,* and *B. forskalii.*

A specially collected sample of large *Melanoides* shells from the breccia in Trench 6 gave a radiocarbon date of 44,190 BP ± 1380 years (SMU-177). The sample is regarded as possibly contaminated by minute fragments of younger carbonates that could not be removed from the insides of the shells, and the real age for this sediment is believed to be beyond the reach of the laboratory's capability. It is, therefore, not seen as conflicting with the date of greater than 44,700 BP (SMU-79) from the upper lacustrine series at Bir Sahara. These data also clearly indicate that the two dates previously given from the dark layer are much too young, indicating once again the potential hazards of random dating of old lacustrine sediments.

Laterally to the north and eastern edges of the lake, the light gray silt unit grades into laminated sandy silts or silty sands of a beach (Figures 2.24:3b and 2.25:3b). Here the molluscan fauna includes three frequent forms: *Melanoides tuberculata, Gyraulus costulatus,* and *Hydrobia* sp. Also present are *Lymnaea natalensis, Biomphalaria alexandrina,* and *Bulinus truncatus.* The land snail *Pupoides coenopictus* also occurs here. The beach yielded numerous Aterian artifacts, derived from a settlement totally destroyed by the expanding beach, suggesting that the lake was still aggrading. Toward the south edge of the basin the light gray silt grades into cavernous evaporites (Figure 2.24:3a). The location of the sandy beaches with worked-in materials along the northern and eastern edges of the lake as well as the formation of shallow water bioevaporites in the southern section indicate that the prevailing winds were from the southwest.

The light gray silt unit contains throughout its depth occasional scattered bones from large vertebrates. *Gazella dama* is the most common, followed by extinct camel (*Camelus thomasi*), jackal (*Canis [aureus] lupaster?*), and fox (*Vulpes rüppeli*). There is also one possible turtle. The beach facies of this unit yielded fewer remains, but these included *Gazella dama* and *G. rufifrons.*

Conformably above the lower light gray unit is a layer of carbonaceous silt, also light gray (10YR 7/2), consolidated to cemented, with large blocky structure. This layer contained numerous carbonate concretions throughout (Figures 2.24:4 and 2.25:4). In the center of the basin this unit grades up into a very carbonaceous white silt (10YR 8/2), overloaded with concretions of calcium carbonate (Figure 2:24:5). These concretions could be of pedogenetic origin. Laterally to the northeast there is a small section of a beach facies similar to that associated with the unit below, but much more weakly developed (Figure 2.25:4b). Elsewhere this beach has been removed. Throughout the carbona-

NW

A

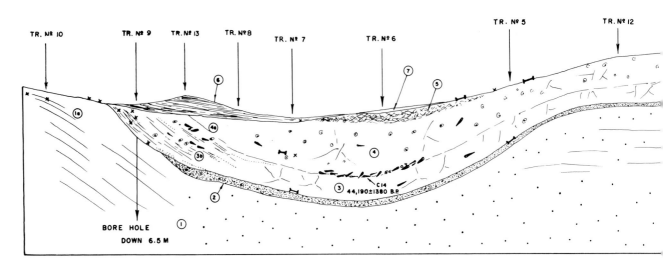

FIGURE 2.24. *Site BT-14, general cross section along A–B line. Key for symbols: 1, gastropods; 2, artifacts; 3, bones. Key for sediments: 1, dune sand; 1a, dune sand, topset beds with heavily eolized artifacts; 2, grayish brown silty sand; 3, light gray carbonaceous silt; 3a,*

ceous silt there are numerous snail shells of species similar to those recovered from the underlying horizon. Scattered Aterian artifacts and very frequent animal bones occur in the unit. Thousands of bones, some in clustered masses, together with rare artifacts, both fresh and heavily eolized, were found on the deflated surface of this layer. The most numerous are bones of white rhinoceros (*Ceratotherium*

sinum) and *Gazella dama*, followed by buffalo (*Homo-ioceras antiquus*), extinct camel (*Camelus thomasi*), and an unidentified medium-sized antelope. A few bones of a large antelope and a jackal (*Canis [aureus] lupaster?*) were also present.

Along the southeastern margin of the basin, just below the deflated surface and within this carbonaceous silt unit,

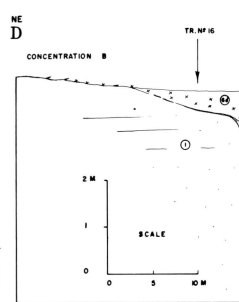

FIGURE 2.25. *Site BT-14, general cross section along C–D line. Key: 1, dune sand; 2, grayish brown silty sand; 3, light gray carbonaceous silt; 3b, silt and sands of beach with numerous Aterian artifacts; 4, light gray carbonaceous silt; 4b, inconspicuous beach facies; 5a, pocket of reworked silt; 6, olive silt; 6a, finely laminated olive silt; 6b, similar to 6a, with numerous Melanoides shells; 6c, similar to 6a, with small carbonate concentrations; 6d, beach sands with numerous Aterian artifacts.*

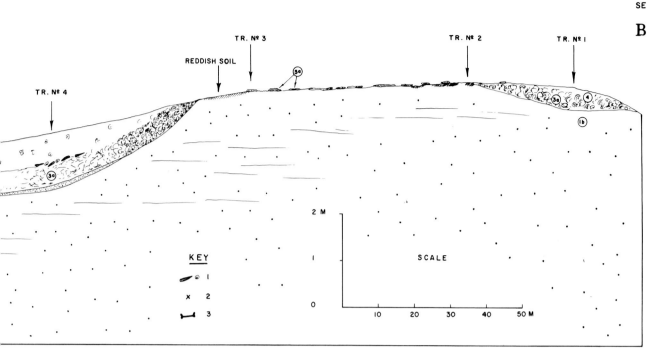

cavernous evaporites; 3b, silts and sands of beach with numerous Aterian artifacts, lacustrine and terrestrial gastropods; 4, light gray carbonaceous silt; 4a, inconspicuous beach facies; 5, white silt; 5a, evaporites on surface; 6, olive silt; 7, modern eolian sand.

was an Aterian living floor composed of a single concentration. The cultural horizon was about 15 cm thick. It contained a few scraps of bone of which three were identified as white rhinoceros (*Ceratotherium sinum*) and gazelle (*G. rufifrons* and *G. dama*) (Gautier, this volume).

The carbonaceous silt layer is in turn unconformably overlain by a usually thin unit of loose olive yellow (2.5Y 6/6) silt (Figures 2.24:6 and 2.25:6). In some places, olive yellow silt truncates the underlying beach features, whereas in others it passes into a beach contemporaneous with the early phase of this new period of sedimentation (Figure 2.25:6a–6d). At the latter beach, the sandy silts contain Aterian artifacts washed down from the immediately adjacent and deflated settlement of Site BT-14, Area B.

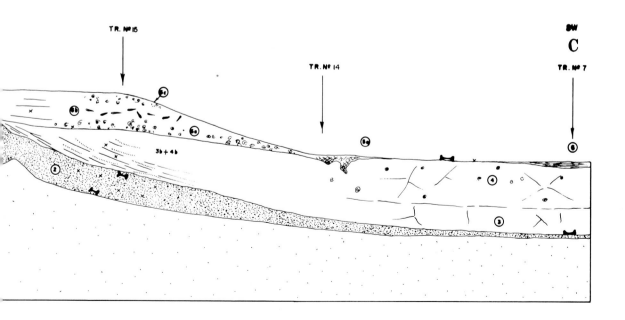

The olive yellow silts contain a molluscan fauna with *Melanoides tuberculata* as the most numerous species, and rare animal bones, among which were two bones of fossil camel (*Camelus thomasi*) and two of gazelle (*G. dama*). The sample is too small for reliable comparisons; however, the lack of rhinoceros and bovid may have some significance. Two unfinished Aterian bifacial foliates, broken during manufacture, and a "knocker pile" of chipping debris occurred at the base of the unit near the northern portion of Area A. This testifies to a fluctuation in lake level between the carbonaceous silt layer and the olive yellow silt unit. The olive yellow silts are the latest lacustrine deposits recorded within the upper lake episode in the Bir Tarfawi area.

It is highly probable that there was another fluctuation in the lake level during an earlier phase of the lake. This lowered lake may be reflected by the formation of numerous calcareous, spongy concretions, possibly of pedogenetic origin, in the top part of the upper gray silt unit. The concentration of the animal bones in the topmost level of this unit as well as the presence of a living settlement within it prove that this surface was occasionally dried and/or covered by shallow water, which attracted the animals and facilitated hunting during the time of obvious scarcity of water.

The next phase in the development of the lake is marked by the appearance of the olive silt, much less indurated and now eroded in most places. A clear unconformity separates the olive silt from the underlying gray silt unit. This unconformity is best displayed in the northern and eastern sections where the older beaches are cut and the truncations are covered by olive silt. The physical phenomena responsible for the truncation are unknown, although deflation is highly likely since there are *in situ* undisturbed knocker piles at the contact of gray and olive silt units, thus proving that the lowermost portion of the lake went dry before the olive silt began to accumulate. It is impossible to evaluate the span of time represented in this erosional phase as Aterian occupation occurred both before and after it, but it could have been relatively short.

It has been impossible to establish the maximal high water stand in the later lake, but it must have reached 4 m higher than its early beach facies at Area B, as indicated by the deposition of the olive silt in a remnant 200 m to the northwest (Figure 2.21).

The next episode at both Bir Sahara and Bir Tarfawi is a pronounced deflation that cut through the accumulated lacustrine and preceding eolian sediments to a level that could have been very close to or even below the modern water table. There is no record of younger Pleistocene sediments in either depression. It is believed that the general morphology of the area was developed during this time. This assumption is indicated by the presence of several lithic sites of Early Kingdom Age, located close to the modern wells, only a few meters above the present water level. These sites are only partially *in situ*, but they clearly display preserved occupational patterning. The tools are fresh to semifresh, which shows that these sites were only recently exposed. Ostrich eggshells from one of these sites (BT-20) gave a radiocarbon date of 4510 BP ± 70 years (SMU-74). There is no trace of Terminal Paleolithic in either depression, or in the entire area. Neolithic settlements, so frequent in many other sections of the Western Desert, are also absent, unless some of the sites near Bir Sahara and Bir Tarfawi, containing lithics similar to those recovered at a Neolithic site at Wadi Bakht in the Gilf el Kebir, are of this age. None of these localities contained ceramics, but the sites were all deflated, and therefore the pottery would have been destroyed. Unfortunately, our information on Early Kingdom lithics in the Sahara is not adequate for a distinction from those obtained at later Neolithic sites in the Western Desert.

Still more recent sand dunes partially fill the depressions. They contain traces of occupations of Later Historic age with wheel-made pottery, a handmade pottery with design motifs resembling that of Early Khartoum wares, occasional pieces of iron and bronze, scraps of faience, together with camel and human bones.

ASSOCIATED ARCHAEOLOGY

LATE ACHEULIAN

Localities of the Late Acheulian period on the carbonate plateau are dispersed, and the artifacts are never seen in the tight concentrations that would suggest an almost *in situ* occurrence. Because of this, none of the sites was investigated in detail. Occasional observations suggest that the scattered bifaces, rather large in size, were mostly of amygdaloid variety, with a few cordiform and lanceolate pieces. A few cleavers were noted, but only in one cluster southwest of Bir Sahara. Chipping debris, cores, and other tools were almost absent. These rather strange, thin accumula-

tions of bifaces occur most frequently near small remnants of deflated tufa, suggesting fossil springs.

The clusters of Acheulian bifaces near the early ponds at the south end of Bir Tarfawi are all in lag position on sandy slopes of the reversed topography. Here too the settlements are destroyed, deflated, and dispersed. The scattered bifaces are mostly of the amygdaloid and cordiform variety (Figure 2.26), and seem to be smaller than those found with some of the assemblages on the carbonate plateau; cleavers were absent. It is very likely that these Acheulian occupations occurring on various geomorphic features represent considerable time depth; however, this assumption cannot be

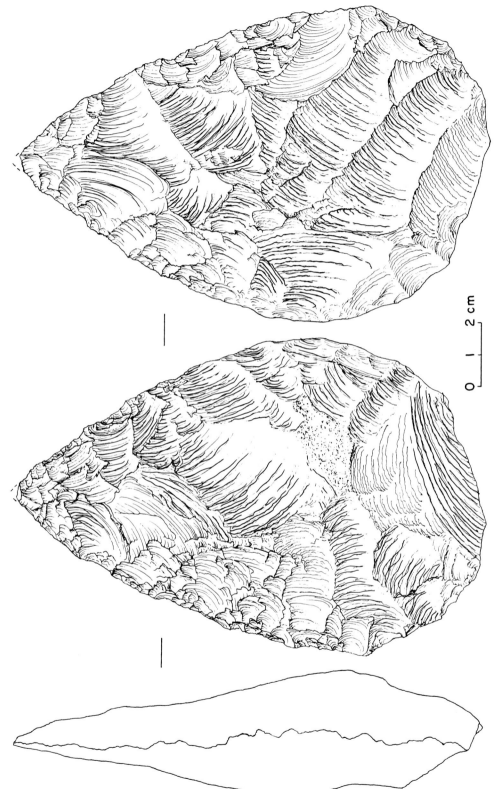

0 1 2 cm

FIGURE 2.26. *Slightly elongated, subcordiform biface with thinned oblique base found in situ in hard freshwater limestone pond sediment at south end of Bir Tarfawi.*

39

firmly based on either lithostratigraphic or taxonomic grounds.

FINAL ACHEULIAN

The only site that was both archaeologically promising and also important from the geological point of view was that of BS-14 (E99C14). It yielded a considerable surface collection, and a much more restricted collection of *in situ* material recovered from limited excavations at the edge of the spring pool.

The spatial distribution of artifacts demonstrates a typical slide pattern, with most of the handaxes concentrated on the eroded slopes of the spring cone, and a few resting on the edges of its carbonaceous seal.

The raw material is almost exclusively quartzitic sandstones, with rare quartz pieces. Debitage is poorly represented, undoubtedly a result of the surface environment as shown by the clearly different quantitative proportions in the small assemblage recovered from the trench; the latter yielded a few bifaces and over 100 biface trimming flakes. In the surface collection the strongest debitage group is still biface trimming flakes, although their number is significantly smaller than the minimal values required to shape the bifaces found at the site (see Chapter 7). The few recovered cores include two semidiscoidal ones, one single platform for flakes, one globular of the change-of-orientation group, and two Levallois specimens.

The bifaces form the strongest tool group (IBif: 88.28) totaling 113 specimens. Their quantitative and qualitative distributions show pronounced stress on two major groups, subtriangular (Group I) and cordiform (Group II), which account for 40.4% and 35.3%, respectively. The two groups are made up mainly of fine, elongated ogivo-triangular and pelecyform bifaces with thinned butts, both slightly tending to cordiforms, and cordiforms and subcordiforms with thinned butts, of which several have distinctly oblique bases (Figures 2.27 and 2.28). The amygdaloids, which are the third strongest group (Group V), account for 11.1%, and are much rarer than the first two groups. The group of discoidal, oval, and limandes is relatively strong, attaining slightly over 8%. This group is dominated by discoidal bifaces (eight specimens). Among other forms, a few fine lanceolates (three specimens) deserve mention.

The other tools include five spheroids, four inverse sidescrapers (Figure 2.29a), two other sidescrapers including one bifacial, and single specimens of bifacial edge piece, chopping tool, denticulate (Figure 2.29b), and an undetermined tool fragment.

MOUSTERIAN

One of the most striking scenes awaiting an unwarned traveler coming to the depression of Bir Sahara is the large dark portions of the deflated floor virtually carpeted with Mousterian artifacts. The impression of the presence of dozens of sites concentrated in this relatively miniscule basin is exceptionally strong. It must have been the same impression that was shared by K. S. Sandford (1933) when he had reached the Laqiya Depression in the Southern Libyan Desert and saw enormously rich concentrations of "late middle Paleolithic implements."

Unfortunately, almost all of the concentrations in the Bir Sahara area are entirely destroyed by deflation, which has exposed many once buried sites. Nevertheless, the reconstructed sequence of Mousterian sites in the area is certainly one of the richest in the whole of North Africa. Five consecutive Mousterian horizons were recognized as follows, all associated with the lower lacustrine series:

1. Traces of Mousterian occupation contemporaneous with the sedimentation of the lower dune (Site BS-12, lower level).
2. Extensive Mousterian settlements embedded in the so-called black layer formed at the very beginning of the older lacustrine series. The settlements are included either in the thick black layer, low and close to the center of its occurrence, between 244.5 m and 245.0 m above sea level (Site BS-12, upper level; Site BS-13, lower level); or just below the black layer and in its lower portion at places slightly higher, at 245.0 m to 245.5 m above sea level (Site BS-11). Still farther up the slope some traces of occupation were recorded at Site BS-1 in the lower vegetation horizon, an upslope stratigraphic continuation of the black layer. It is highly possible that these slight differences in the absolute elevations and lateral placement of the settlements reflect minor fluctuations of the shore.
3. An extensive Mousterian settlement in gray mottled sands just above the slightly truncated black layer at Site BS-13 (middle level).
4. Two large adjoining concentrations in the upper vegetation horizon shortly before maximal aggradation of the lower lacustrine series (Site BS-1, upper level).
5. A redeposited bone horizon, possibly associated with a Mousterian settlement, located on the shore of the maximal aggradation of the lower lacustrine series (Site BS-13, upper level).

Site BS-12 (E99C12)

Site BS-12 is at the northwest rim of the depression at the foot of a projecting peninsula-like erosional remnant of indurated lake sediments and older dune. When first discovered there were numerous artifacts scattered over the exposed surface of the older dune. Five trenches were excavated, mainly for stratigraphic purposes. These showed that most of the site had been destroyed by wind deflation, and the remaining portion did not offer sufficient promise to warrant more extensive excavations. Bone was poorly preserved.

The top of the lower dune sand at this site yielded 86

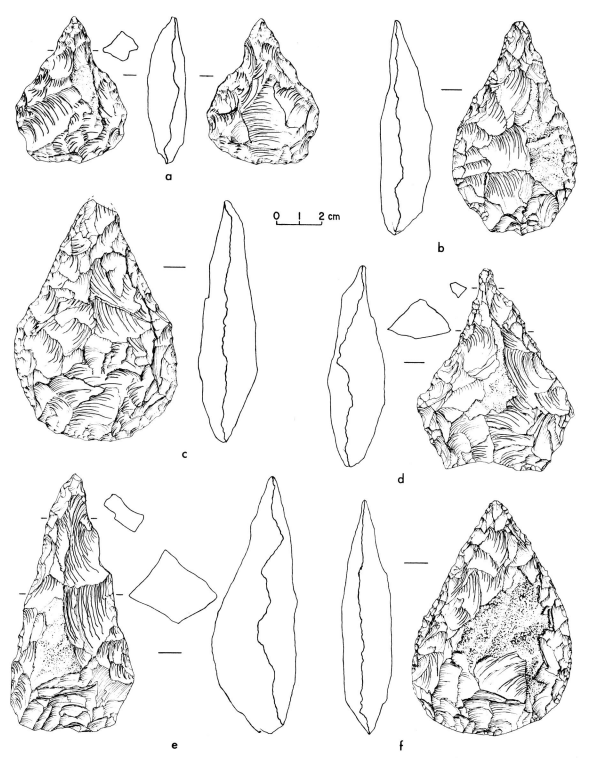

FIGURE 2.27. *Tools from Site BS-14, surface: (a–c), pelecyform bifaces; (d) subtriangular, irregular biface; (e) ficron, quadrilateral, pick-like biface; (f) cordiform biface with oblique base.*

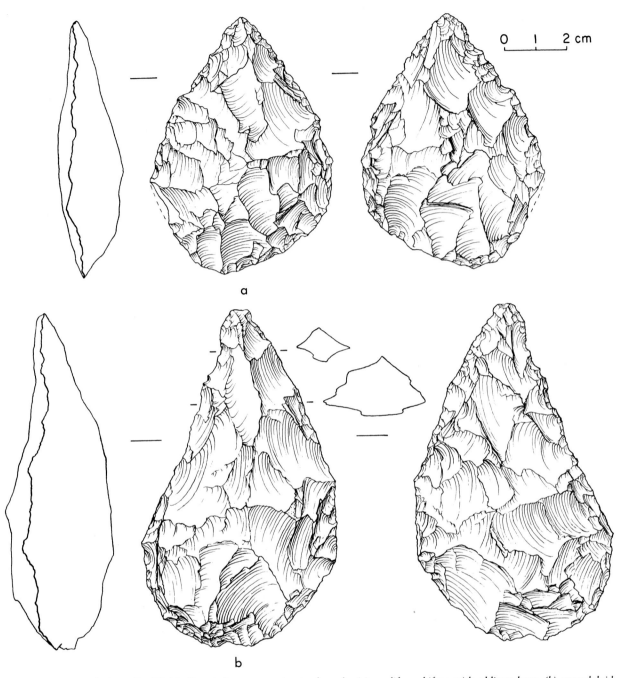

FIGURE 2.28.   *Tools from Site BS-14, Trench 3, coarse spring-pool sands: (a) cordiform biface with oblique base; (b) amygdaloid, asymmetric, reniform biface.*

highly wind-abraded artifacts. Because of the abrasion some of the tools cannot be properly classified, but among those recognized are a Levallois core for flakes, a discoidal core, and a globular core. There were also a few denticulates and a notched flake.

The upper occupation level at this site is in the black layer. The collection from this horizon is largely limited to material recorded from the surface; the test trenches yielded only 30 artifacts, and the entire collection, including the surface material, contains only 32 tools and Levallois pieces. Of these, the most numerous are denticulates (12), notches (4), and Levallois flakes and points, some of which are atypical (10). Other tools include a retouched flake (1), a bec (1), and a chopping tool (1). The few identifiable cores are mainly Levallois (2); the others are either unidentified (3) or initially struck (1). The raw material is identical

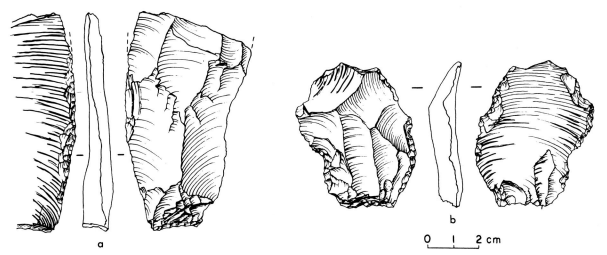

FIGURE 2.29. *Tools from Site BS-14, Trench 3, coarse spring-pool sands: (a) inverse convex sidescraper on broken Levallois blade; (b) bilateral denticulate on flake with thinned base.*

to that used at Sites BS-11 and BS-13, to be described later. Considering the size of the assemblage, the structure of this collection is not significantly different from that recovered at Site BS-11.

Site BS-11 (E99C11)

Across a flat concavity from Site BS-12 is a low flattish remnant of lacustrine sediments. At the southeast tip of this remnant is a small deflational concavity, open on the east and west sides, and bounded elsewhere by a low scarp capped by silt and evaporite. The southern portion of the depression was covered by modern dune sand. The floor of this small concavity was littered with numerous artifacts, some deflated but others eroding from the top of the underlying sediment. An area approximately 10 by 24 m was collected and scraped (Figure 2.30). This represented almost all of the exposed remaining portion of a larger settlement. A trench 2 by 10 m was cut into the northwest face of the low escarpment and yielded a number of *in situ* artifacts associated with an occupation floor just below the black layer or in its lower portion. The opening of a larger surface under the scarp was not possible with the available equipment because of the concrete-like capping of the remnant.

The horizonal distribution of artifacts indicates that the recovered portion is in fact a fragment of a much larger settlement, obviously destroyed by erosion (Figure 2.30). The slightly concave shape of the floor and the relative paucity of surface artifacts along the northern scarp suggest some sliding toward the central and southern portion of the concavity. This suggestion is reinforced by the fact that the artifacts recovered from the trench do not indicate any significant thinning in this area. However, it is believed that the spatial distribution of the artifacts generally reflects the

original distribution of a settlement characterized by a more or less even spread of debris with only a few suggestions of subclusters. The density is low, as indicated by a mean of 19 artifacts per square meter, of which 1.3 are tools.

The bulk of the recovered assemblage was made of gray and brown quartzitic sandstone of the Nubia Formation. The outcrops for these sandstones are observed along the rim of the sandy plain, the nearest of which occur just east and northeast of Bir Tarfawi, some 20 km from the site. Other outcrops of this material are found 30 to 40 km to the south and southwest. A few pieces made of Eocene chert were also used, and the nearest recorded sources of this material are along the southwestern tip of the Libyan plateau, just east of the Atmur el Kibeish peneplain, more than 150 km distant.

The General Structure of the lithic assemblage suggests a raw-material economy in which the blocks of stone were carried to the settlement and shaped there into cores (see Chapter 7). This is indicated by the occurrence of significant frequencies of Levallois preparation flakes (IGL:22.1). Only a few Levallois cores were found. This fact, together with the high values for Levallois preparation debris, indicates that many of the cores were taken elsewhere after they were shaped. This may suggest some emphasis on lithic-workshop-type activities for this settlement.

The main type of core is unpatterned change of orientation, both flat and globular varieties. Next in number are single-platform cores for flakes. Discoidal, opposed-platform, and Levallois cores (Figure 2.31f) are very rare. The general quantitative structure is characterized by the low Levallois Index (IL:1.4). The Blade Index is extremely low (Ilam: 2.7), which may indicate that, though some of the recovered blades are from blade cores (Figure 2.31d), others are more accidental than intentionally obtained. The hard hammer technique was employed.

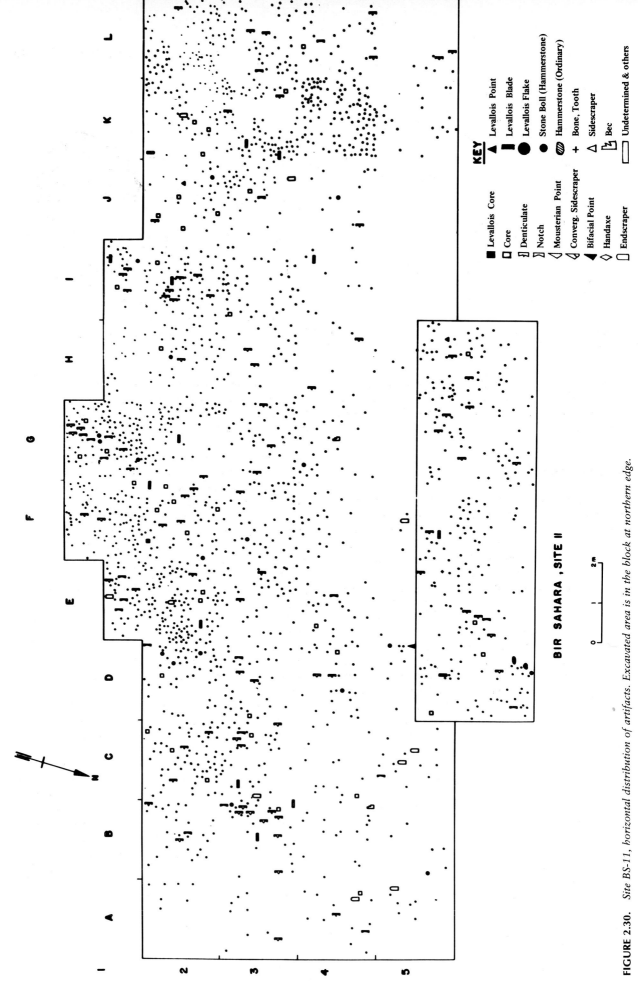

KEY

▲ Levallois Point	◼ Levallois Core	▬ Levallois Blade	▢ Core
● Levallois Flake	◨ Denticulate	● Stone Boll (Hammerstone)	◿ Notch
▨ Hammerstone (Ordinary)	◺ Mousterian Point	+ Bone, Tooth	◿ Converg. Sidescraper
△ Sidescraper	◆ Bifacial Point	◰ Bec	◇ Handaxe
▢ Undetermined & others	▱ Endscraper		

BIR SAHARA, SITE II

2m

FIGURE 2.30. Site BS-11, *horizontal distribution of artifacts. Excavated area is in the block at northern edge.*

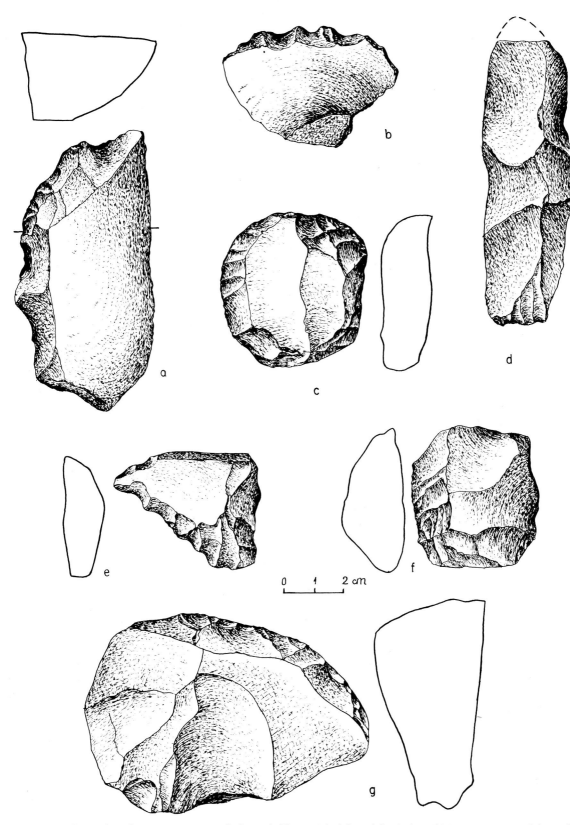

FIGURE 2.31. *Lithic artifacts from Site BS-11: (a) thick, single-blow notched, lateral denticulate; (b) inverse, transversal denticulate; (c) endscraper on retouched flake; (d) Levallois blade; (e) bilateral denticulate passing into triangular; (f) small Levallois flake core; (g) semi-Quina transversal scraper.*

The recovered tool assemblage totals 157 pieces, including Levallois flakes (Figures 2.31, 2.32, and 2.33), and the overwhelming category is that of denticulates, reaching 68.5% (restricted, Group IV, plus No. 51). The denticulate group is composed of a large variety of forms, of which the most common are the bilateral (Figure 2.31e), transversal (Figure 2.31b), simple lateral (Figure 2.31a), triangular, and converging denticulates made on flakes or elongated bladelike flakes. Notches (Figure 2.32a, d), the next most common group, constitute almost 20% of all tools, whereas sidescrapers are rare (Figure 2.31g), with a fre-

quency of just over 7%. The Typological Levallois Index is 7, and the Upper Paleolithic Group is very rare. The collection also includes 10 very regular spheroids produced by pecking.

Site BS-13 (E99C13)

At about the same elevation as Site BS-11, in the southwest portion of the basin, is a small oval remnant, measuring about 20 by 25 m, rising slightly above the evenly sloping sides of the depression. Wind erosion has carved a

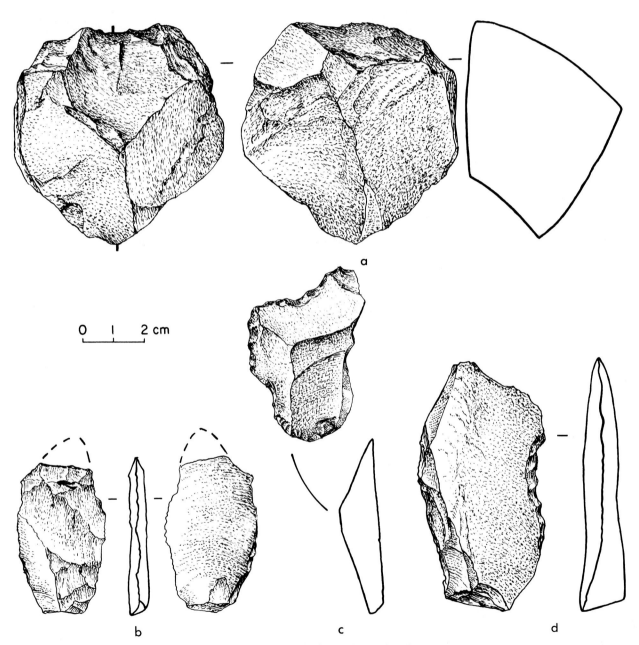

0   1   2 cm

FIGURE 2.32.   *Tools and core from Site BS-11: (1) globular core for flakes; (b) Levallois flake; (c) multiple notched flake; (d) notched flake.*

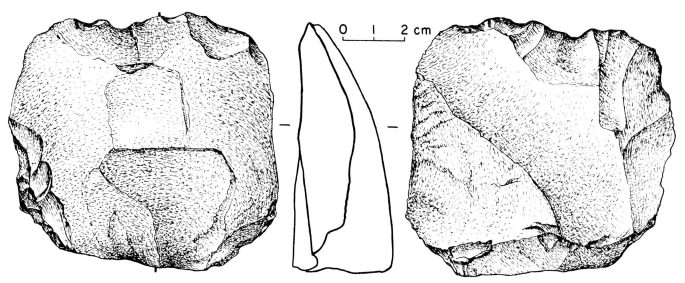

FIGURE 2.33. *Artifacts from Site BS-11: bifacial edge piece with partially thinned butt, on flake.*

notch into the western face of the depression, exposing a litter of artifacts along the flattish floor of the remnant. A scarp, standing slightly more than 1 m in height, forms the east face of the eroded notch. Beyond the scarp the marl-capped lacustrine sediments gently slope down toward the axis of the basin. Three cultural levels occur at this locality. The lowest is represented by only one artifact, and the upper cultural layer is inferred from a cluster of faunal remains without artifacts. The major occupation is the middle cultural layer.

The exposed artifacts, representing the occupation of the middle cultural level, formed an elongated, thin concentration, measuring about 18 by 7 m (Figure 2.34). Some of the artifacts were clearly eroding from the sediments at the very foot of the scarp. The artifacts on the surface were scatter-patterned and collected, and a block covering 46 m² was

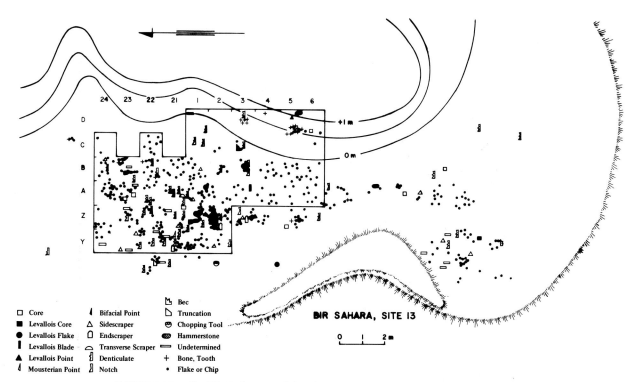

Legend			
□ Core	⌇ Bifacial Point	↳ Truncation	⌣ Bec
■ Levallois Core	△ Sidescraper	⌣ Chopping Tool	
● Levallois Flake	⌀ Endscraper	⬭ Hammerstone	
▮ Levallois Blade	⌒ Transverse Scraper	⚊ Undetermined	
▲ Levallois Point	⌇ Denticulate	+ Bone, Tooth	
⌇ Mousterian Point	⌇ Notch	• Flake or Chip	

BIR SAHARA, SITE 13

0   1   2 m

FIGURE 2.34. *Site BS-13, horizontal distribution of artifacts, both surface and excavated.*

excavated into the area where the artifacts were the most dense. Another 12 m² were cut into the foot of the adjacent scarp face.

The distribution of the artifacts seems to show a relatively small cluster, the main body of which measures about 6 by 7 m, with an obvious thinning toward the south. The excavation also indicated a thinning toward the east, and the northern and western portions, which were deflated to a level below the cultural layer, had only a few artifacts, indicating the end of the concentration. The total area occupied by the concentration measures about 18 by 7 m, with a mean density of 22 artifacts, of which 1.9 are tools, per square meter. On squares Y to Z/1–3 a cluster of 14 tools seems to record a special activity area. Here, on a surface measuring slightly more than 2 m², were three Levallois points, three converging sidescrapers, a Mousterian point, a partially bifacial Mousterian point, a notched flake, and two denticulates. This cluster stands out from the heavily denticulate-dominated remainder of the concentration (Figure 2.35).

The living floor occurs in the lower portion of the mottled beach sands containing occasional silt lenses. The base of this unit displays conspicuous lamination. Immediately above these laminations is the middle cultural level, a zone about 10–15 cm thick. One or two artifacts occurred slightly higher in the mottled sand, about 20 cm above the living floor. In the underlying black sand unit, in a swale just above the truncated lower dune, was a distal portion of a tibia from the extinct camel (*Camelus thomasi*) and a single artifact, a discoidal flattish chopping tool, bidirectionally worked over most of its perimeter, displaying clear evidence of battering on the edges. This artifact and the camel bone are the only evidence for the lower cultural level at this site.

At this locality two silt units overlie the mottled sand, and in the basal portion of the upper calcareous one, an equivalent to the marl horizon, were numerous animal bones, apparently derived from a settlement on an adjacent beach that is now destroyed. No artifacts occurred with the bones; however this presumably man-made accumulation is considered to be the upper cultural level.

The preferred raw material in the middle cultural level was gray and brown sandstone, basically the same as at Site BS-11. The structure of the assemblage clearly displays a

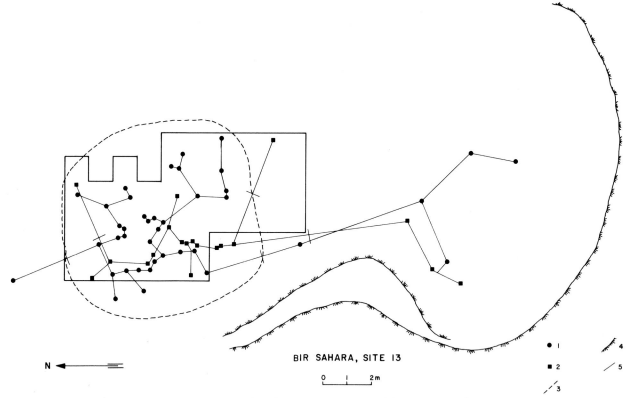

BIR SAHARA, SITE 13

0   1   2m

FIGURE 2.35. *Dendrogram for Site BS-13, main level, surface and excavated. Simplified Wroclaw dendrite spread over denticulates (thin lines) and sidescrapers plus points (thick line). Key: 1, denticulates; 2, sidescrapers and points; 3, limit of main tool concentration; 4, limit of remnant; 5, cutoff branches of the dendrites. Right-angled block in the center shows the excavated and just-eroded portion of the site. The basic statistics for the nearest distance values of the typical Mousterian dendrite (sidescrapers and points) are as follows: N = 14; Σ = 1000; Σ² = 99,950; x̄ = 76.9; S² = 1773. The randomly generated dendrite is characterized by the following data: N = 14; Σ = 1910; Σ² = 286,250; x̄ = 136.4; S² = 1978.9. The mean nearest distance values of the two samples are significantly different at the 2% level of p, and the mean nearest distance of the Mousterian cluster is significantly smaller than that of the randomly generated one, thus suggesting a possibility of nonrandom patterning of the first one (for method, see Florek et al. 1951; Golachowski et al. 1974; and Perkal 1961).*

lesser stress on the whole Initial Group, including primary and Levallois core-preparation flakes (see Chapter 7; IGL:23.8). The Levallois pieces also are more numerous here than at Site BS-11 (IL:14.3). The basic structure and the scarcity of cores imply a raw-material economy in which most of the Levallois flakes and cores, as well as some other blanks, were made elsewhere and brought to the site in a finished form. This explanation is well supported with a high index of Group VII (Tools and Tool-Production Waste). Because of more numerous classic Levallois pieces, the Levallois Technological Index (IL) is higher than at Site BS-11, although the value of the whole Levallois Group (IGL) is not basically different from that at Site BS-11 and BS-12, a result of low frequency of the Levallois preparation flakes. The core types are identical to those at Site BS-11, although the Blade Index is higher (Ilam:5.7).

The middle cultural layer yielded 115 tools (Figures 2.36, 2.37, and 2.38). The tool kit is dominated by various denticulates (55.1% restricted, Group IV + No. 51), especially when the tools from the supposed activity cluster are excluded. The range of variation within the tool group is closely similar to that at Site BS-11, and the sites differ primarily in that sidescrapers are almost twice as numerous at Site BS-13. Also, in contrast to Site BS-11, spheroids are absent. The so-called Upper Paleolithic elements, consisting of endscrapers and borers, are low. A few heavy hammerstones complete the collection.

Site BS-1 (E99C1)

On the same peninsula-like erosional remnant at which Site BS-12 was located, but 60 m north and slightly to the west, is the first of two other concentrations identified as Sites BS-1A and BS-1B. At both concentrations, the artifacts occur on the steep erosional slope of the remnant, weathering out of beach sands of the lower lake. The first of the two concentrations (BS-1A) has been more destroyed by erosion, and artifacts occur on the surface for some 23 m along the scarp. The second concentration (BS-1B) is immediately adjacent on the north, and here the artifacts occur on the slope for only about 15 m. A trench 5 by 10 m was cut into the remnant slope in the center of the first concentration, and this disclosed a relatively thick cultural horizon, beginning in the upper vegetation layer and descending 60 cm, almost to the lower vegetation layer, an upslope equivalent of the black layer. The sand unit here is mottled, displaying ferruginous enrichment and reduction streaks, a hydromorphic pseudogley soil. It is obvious that the artifacts were vertically displaced by root action. It is likely, however, that the horizontal displacement would have been minimal. Vertical displacement of the artifacts did not permit us to determine whether multiple or only a single occupation is represented in this thick cultural horizon.

The spatial distribution of the artifacts in the excavated area displays a pattern quite different from that at either

BS-11 or BS-13. Here the density is high (230 artifacts, of which 4.3 are tools, per square meter), and the scatter of the artifacts is almost even, without any concentration of tools and/or debris (Figure 2.39). It is obvious that the excavated area is entirely confined within a much larger occupation cluster.

The raw material at Site BS-1A is almost entirely a brownish quartzitic grit sandstone, different in color and texture from that utilized at Sites BS-11, BS-12, and BS-13, and obviously quarried or collected from different outcrops. The number of other rocks used at this site is insignificant. This homogeneity is striking, particularly since the quality of the raw material here seems to be lower than at the other sites.

The assemblage also differs from that at the other Mousterian sites in its General Structure (see Chapter 7). Here the Initial Group, containing primary and early-stage preparation flakes, is low; however, the Levallois core-preparation flakes form over half of the total restricted count. It is striking that the high index of the Levallois preparation flakes is not reflected in the numbers of Levallois cores recovered or in the value of the Technological Levallois Index, both of which are rather insignificant. The explanation of this peculiar General Structure calls for a model in which (a) the initial lithic preparation took place elsewhere, (b) the final preparation of the Levallois cores was at this site, and (c) many of the cores were then taken to a third locality. The IGL (66.9) group is primarily composed of Levallois preparation flakes (465 pieces) and regular Levallois flakes (IL:14.3). The Blade Index (Ilam:6.3) is similar to that at Site BS-13.

The cores are practically nonexistent, accounting for only eight pieces, of which one was Levallois, one semidiscoidal, one change of orientation globular, and one single platform for flakes. The others were small, undetermined fragments. The recovered tool inventory forms the richest tool collection at Bir Sahara (215 pieces, including Levallois) (Figures 2.40 and 2.41). As with previously described assemblages, it is dominated by denticulates, which attain a level of around 60% (restricted). All of the recognized types of denticulates are present. The Upper Paleolithic Group is at almost the same level as before, and sidescrapers are low. The major structural difference observed at this site is a much higher Typological Levallois Index (ILty:36+), which is almost three times larger than at BS-13 and five times larger than at BS-11.

Among the differences that separate this site from the older ones are some stylistic characteristics. The most pronounced of these is the size of the tools and blanks, noticeably smaller than before. Another stylistic peculiarity is a poorly executed and not too clear peduncle at the base of a Levallois point.

ATERIAN

The northern section of the largest remnant of indurated lake deposit at Bir Tarfawi was designated as Site BT-14.

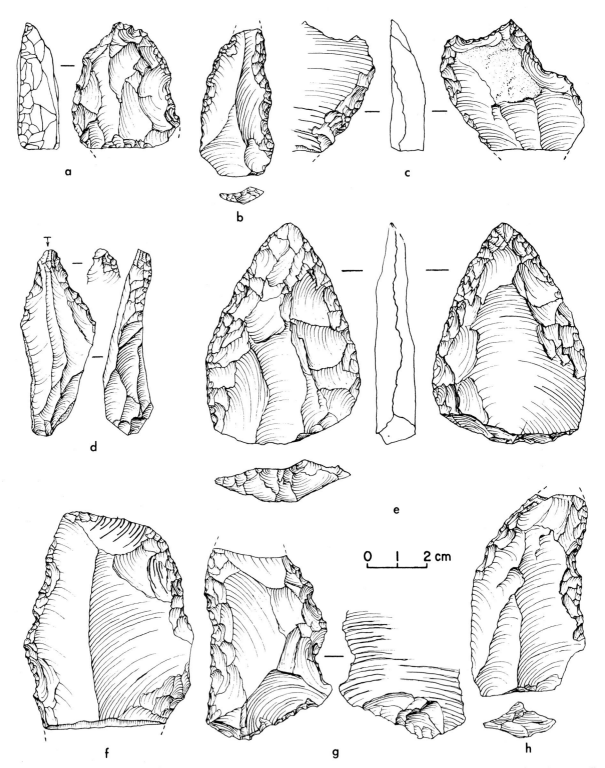

FIGURE 2.36. *Site BS-13, lithic artifacts: (a) converging sidescrapers; (b, g) converging denticulates with simple direct retouch on Levallois point (?) and Levallois flake; (c) bec; (d) borer; (e) Mousterian point, partially bifacial; (f) bilateral denticulate on Levallois flake; (h) converging sidescraper, slightly denticulated, on Levallois flake. All except c and d (excavated) were surface finds.*

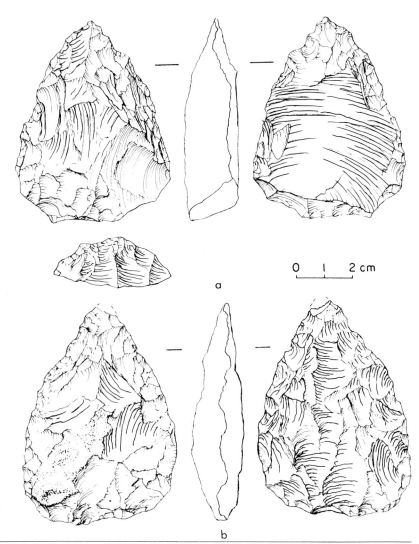

FIGURE 2.37. Tools from Site BS-13, surface: (a) Mousterian point; (b) bifacial point.

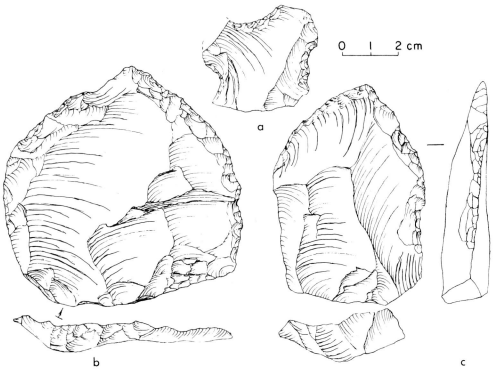

FIGURE 2.38. Tools from Site BS-13, surface: (a) Multiple notch piece; (b, c) converging sidescrapers.

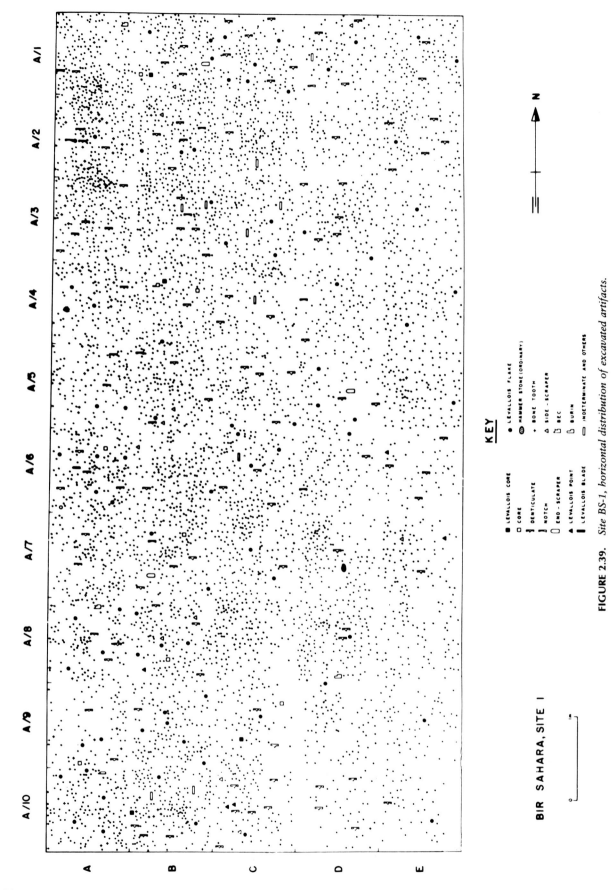

FIGURE 2.39. *Site BS-1, horizontal distribution of excavated artifacts.*

BIR SAHARA, SITE I

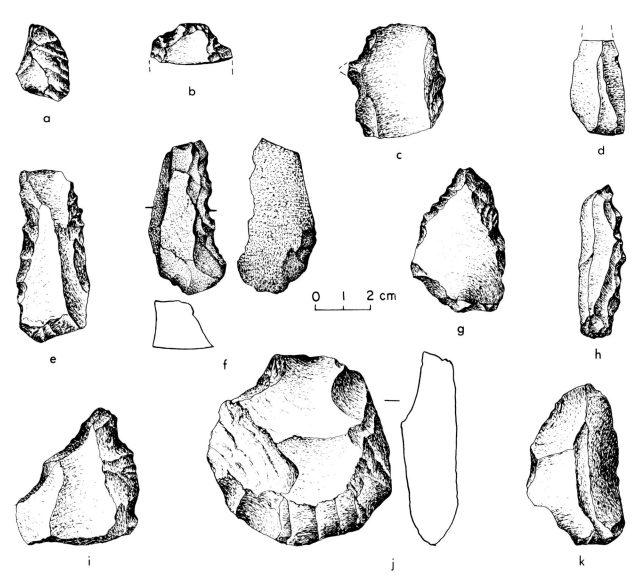

FIGURE 2.40. *Lithic artifacts from Site BS-1, excavated: (a) convex microsidescraper; (b) nosed endscraper; (c) side bec and lateral denticulate; (d) broken Levallois point; (e) lateral denticulate; (f) bilateral denticulate; (g) lateral bec on retouched flake; (h) inverse converging denticulate; (i) asymmetric converging denticulate; (j) Levallois flake core; (k) Levallois flake.*

This was the only area where a mass of animal bones occurred on the surface, some windblasted, some fresh and semifresh, and many just weathering out of the calcareous silt unit. With the bones were scattered Aterian artifacts, some of which were undoubtedly dropped from a higher level, and some of which were fresh or semifresh. Other concentrations of Aterian artifacts occurred either on the calcareous lake sediments or on the lowered dune surfaces usually immediately adjacent to the lake sediments. Some of these clusters are of enormous size, representing a continuous litter of dropped artifacts, the largest of which covered an area of 180 m in length by 50 m in width. Presumably, almost all of them could represent many reoccupations of suitable places near lakes.

Site BT-14 (E99D14)

Several distinct areas were selected for further work at this locality and were designated Areas A, B, C, D, E, F, and N. A grid measuring 65 by 100 m was laid over the cluster of bones in the north section of the remnant of lake sediment, and within this area the artifacts were scatterpatterned and collected by the archaeologists. The collecting, cleaning, and on-the-spot identifying of bones was done by paleontologist A. Gautier (see Figure 2.42), who also drew the map showing contours reflecting the density of bone occurrences (Figure 2.43), and all of the least destroyed clusters.

When the site was first seen, it was obvious that the

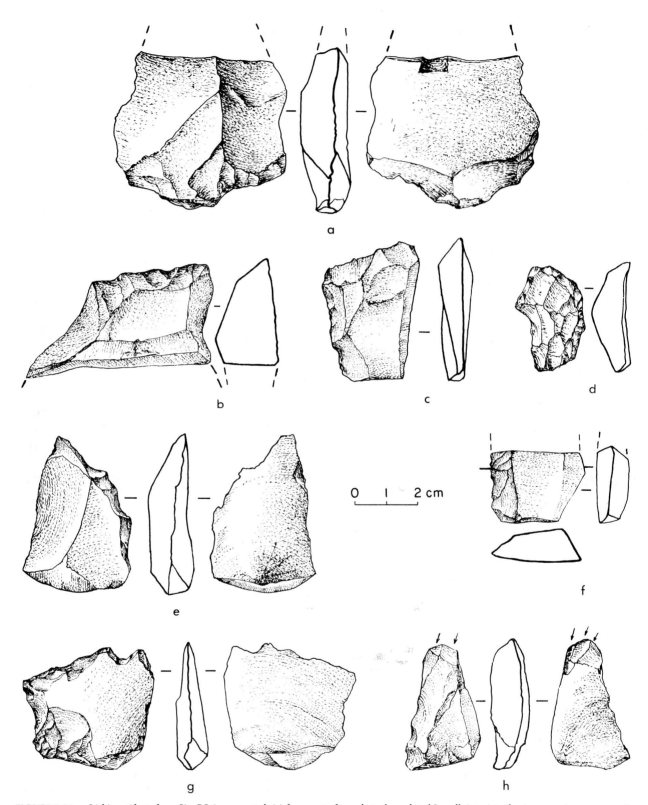

FIGURE 2.41.   *Lithic artifacts from Site BS-1, excavated: (a) fragment of poorly pedunculated Levallois point; (b, e) converging asymmetric denticulate; (c) lateral denticulate; (d) convex sidescraper; (f) lateral sidescraper; (g) transverse denticulate and bec; (h) atypical burin.*

FIGURE 2.42. *Site BT-14, Area A. Paleontologist A. Gautier cleaning one of the bone concentrations.*

bones were grouped in concentrations ranging from over 250 pieces of usually highly weathered bone (Figure 2.44) to dispersed, vague agglomerations containing less than 10 pieces of bone per 25 m² (Figure 2.43). Except for one large and not very dense cluster on the green silt, all of the others were on the surface or just subsurface of the upper gray silt unit. The clusters represent dispersed bones of single or several animals. The latter were usually of different species, thus indicating overlapping occurrences. All of the clusters are characterized by the presence of fragments of skull, including jaws, thoracic elements, and lower limb bones, in most cases poorly preserved and/or very damaged by deflation. The upper limb bones, shoulder, and pelvis areas were all missing, suggesting a systematic butchering pattern that would remove those bones around which the most meat occurred (Gautier, this volume, and on-the-spot identification).

Several areas were distinguished within the grid on the basis of stratigraphy and evident clustering of artifacts. The large surface of exposed gray calcareous silt was called Area A; a concentration on its surface in the southeast corner of the grid was labeled Area C; a small concentration on the surface of the olive silt in the north-central section received the name of Area E; and an unpatterned scatter of artifacts on a large olive silt remnant in the northeast section was designated Area D. Five other clear, large clusters were seen on the adjacent surface of either lake sediments or lowered dunes. One of these, Area B, on the dune surface was partially collected over an area measuring 89 m² (Figure 2.45). Another, Area N, located 140 m northwest of Area A, on the highly deflated surface of the lowest lake unit, the grayish brown silty sand, was also collected and scatterpatterned. The collected area here measured 200 m². This was a Neolithic/Early Kingdom occupation with a few highly wind-abraded Aterian artifacts.

Fragments of eolized ostrich eggshell occurred on the surface throughout the gridded area (113 pieces were collected), and a few were found fresh and *in situ* in the stratigraphic trenches. The surface eggshell pieces might have been sufficient for a radiocarbon date; however, their original association could not be established and there was some possibility that a few pieces could have originated with the nearby later occupation. None of them was dated. Three pieces of red ocher, one of which showed signs of use striations, were also found within the gridded area, and almost certainly come from the Aterian occupation.

The remaining nearby concentrations were all on the surface; two were immediately to the south of Area A in lag position and the third, near the southwest corner of Area A, was partially *in situ*. None of these was collected, except for the very edge of the closest one to the south, where it impinged slightly into the southeast corner of the large grid. In the center of the cluster designated as Area C several artifacts were noted eroding from the top of the gray silt units. It seemed obvious that the concentration here was largely still *in situ*, and an area measuring 118 m² was excavated, which completely exposed a buried Aterian living floor.

At all localities the lithic artifacts were made exclusively from quartzitic Nubia sandstone, unusually fine grained, light gray, mottled to reddish in color, or from a coarser-grained brownish quartzitic sandstone. The outcrops of this sandstone occur about 6 km to the northeast.

Area A. Most of the fauna but relatively few artifacts were found in Area A. Some of these surface artifacts were wind abraded, and obviously dropped from a higher elevation; others were fresh or almost fresh, with unabraded groundward faces. The scatterpattern distinguished between those that were fresh and the more eolized specimens (Figure 2.46). The two groups of artifacts, however, share general structural similarities, and the abraded group is assumed to have been originally deposited in shallow water or in a seasonally dry lake. The two groups probably represent the same kind of association of fauna and artifacts as those still in the process of exposure. The fauna that must have been in the higher lake sediments had been destroyed, but the associated artifacts, more resistant, survived, although suffering considerable wind abrasion.

The lithic collection from Area A is characterized by an unusually high proportion of retouched tools, over 26% (restricted), not including Levallois pieces (see Chapter 7). The General Levallois Index (IGL:24.9) is much lower than at the other localities. The Technological Levallois Index (IL:8.0) is also low, but is not significantly different from that in the other areas. The Typological Levallois Index here, however, is much lower (ILty: ±15.0), and cores and core-preparation debitage are generally rare. The Group of Flake Exploitation forms just over 50% of the total collection. Blades are almost nonexistent, and the Blade Index (Ilam) is only 2.7; these blades are almost exclusively produced from Levallois cores and the few non-Levallois blades could be accidental. A total of 48 cores was recovered, of which Levallois cores for flakes form 47.2% of all identifiable pieces. The next in number

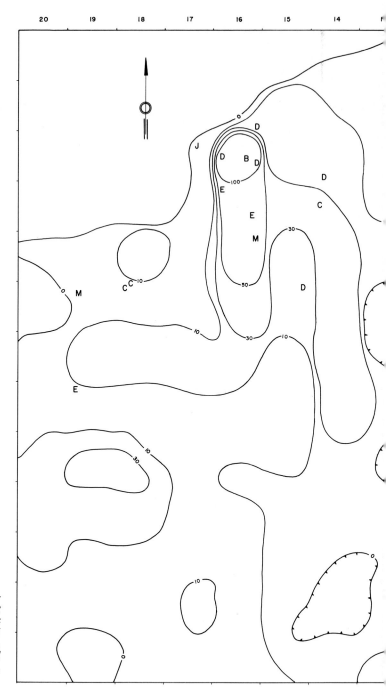

FIGURE 2.43. *Iso-osteologic map of large gridded area showing density of bone. Key: 1, iso-osteologic contours enclosing areas with bone fragment density per 25 m²; 2, iso-osteologic contour enclosing areas of less than 10 bone fragments per 25 m²; B, big bovid; C, camel; D, Gazella dama; E, equid; G, red-fronted gazelle; J, jackal; L, large antelope; M, medium-sized antelope; R, rhinoceros. Prepared by A. Gautier in the field, February 1974 (see Appendix 4, this volume).*

are globular and flat, change-of-orientation cores for flakes, representing 38.9%. Single-platform cores for flakes were not numerous (8.3%), and opposed-platform cores for flakes and discoidal cores occurred as single specimens only (2.8% each).

The tool kit contains 399 pieces, including Levallois, and is dominated by denticulates (44.4%, restricted), of which the majority are made on flakes. The simple group includes convex, bilateral, concave, transversal, as well as circular varieties (Figure 2.47). Denticulates on blades are rare. Converging denticulates are quite numerous, and include both symmetrical and asymmetrical forms (Figure 2.48). The next most important tool class is that of sidescrapers, representing 18.5% (restricted). Simple convex sidescrapers are the most numerous, followed by convergent and transversal varieties; significantly lower values are found for the remainder (Figure 2.49). Semi-Quina retouch is very rare, but present. Mousterian points are well represented (Figure

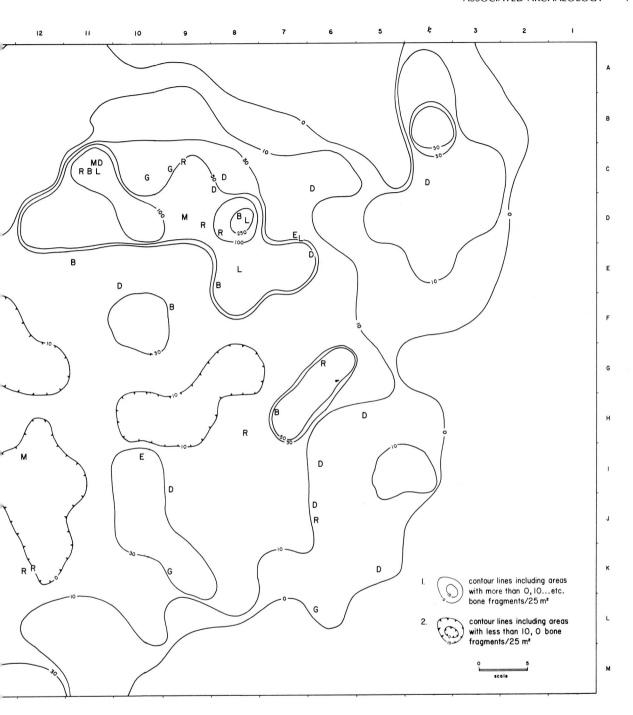

I. contour lines including areas with more than 0, 10...etc. bone fragments/25 m²

2. contour lines including areas with less than 10, 0 bone fragments/25 m²

scale

2.50), forming almost 7% of the total restricted count, so the Mousterian Group is rather high (25.9%, restricted). The value for tools in the Upper Paleolithic Group is low (3.5%, restricted). This group includes a few endscrapers, borers, and two burins. The Aterian tools are rare (4.4%, restricted), but the following varieties of pedunculates were recognized: Levallois points, Levallois blades, endscrapers, Levallois flakes, bifacial edge pieces, perforators, and simple flakes. Bifacial foliates are even less numerous (Figure 2.51 a,c), slightly less than 2% (restricted).

The collection from Area A includes 83 fresh tools (not including Levallois) that are assumed to have been just eroded from the gray silt unit. The proportions of main tool groups within the "fresh" assemblage show almost no differences from the eolized collection, except for slightly higher percentages for sidescrapers and Mousterian points.

FIGURE 2.44. *Dense cluster of gazelle bone weathering out of gray silt unit at Site BT-14, Area A.*

FIGURE 2.45. *Site BT-14, Area B, looking west. Collection in process. Trenches seen in middle distance on profile line A–B. Phytogenic dune on horizon.*

Only in limited instances was it possible to establish a direct association between the tools and identifiable fauna. These few cases are where fresh artifacts occurred within the scatter of identifiable animal bones. The artifact groups form an interesting pattern, the most striking feature of which is their relative scarcity. Indeed, a large cluster of animal bones consisting of at least one rhinoceros, one bovid, one large and one middle-sized antelope, and a gazelle (*G. dama*) was associated with only 10 tools including 5 denticulates, 2 sidescrapers, 1 Mousterian point, 1 Levallois flake, and 1 endscraper. There is one example of a small cluster of *G. dama* bones associated with more tools than usual. This cluster included 4 denticulates, 3 cores, 1 notch, 1 converging sidescraper, and 1 Mousterian point (Table 2.1). Some bone clusters had only one tool, and others none. There were also fresh tools weathering from the surface that were not clearly associated with any bone cluster, although they occurred within the general area of a

thin scatter of bone scraps. It is possible that some of these may represent partially deflated living floors like that at Area C, to be described later.

The overall picture that emerges from these observations is that at the center of the area there are clusters of animal bones clearly associated with a limited number of tools, mostly restricted to only a few categories. Of these, the dominant kinds are various denticulates, some of them very large, followed by sidescrapers and Mousterian points. All remaining tools appear in negligible quantities.

Although none of the other surface tools could be convincingly related to a specific bone cluster, they display the same general characteristics as those that appear to occur in association with animal remains. It seems likely, therefore, that this very unusual association of bones and lithics, striking in both the overall scarcity and limited variation of the artifacts, and the clearly selected anatomical remains, is of a very special character. The tools apparently served to butcher the animals, and the most productive portions of the animals were taken elsewhere. The repetitive nature of these occurrences suggests that this lake, when shallow, was a favorite kill locality for Aterian men over a long period of time. The newly eroding bone and lithic material represent only a limited and possibly short time span within this interval; however, the extremely rare tools and bones recovered from the trenches, as well as the structure of the more eolized lithic assemblage on the surface, indicate a similar pattern throughout the time when the lake was shallow.

The associations of fresh tools and bones, however, are too rare for testing of the significance of specific cooccurrence. Also, the possibility that some of the artifacts found on the surface were originally associated with settlement activities cannot be excluded, since there was a living floor at the edge of the lake sediment. Only large-scale excavations in the basin can resolve this question and provide reliable material for testing the possible association of specific tools with particular animals.

Area C (Excavated). In the southwest corner of the gridded area there seemed to be a conspicuous cluster of artifacts, some of which were fresh, on the surface. This surface concentration was designated Area C and collected separately. In the section where the fresh artifacts occurred a test pit was dug, disclosing a cultural layer about 15 cm thick buried just under the surface in the upper gray silt unit. The pit was expanded to clear an area of 118 m², sufficient to expose the total *in situ* concentration. The placement of this concentration showed that most of the surface material in Area C has been dropped from a higher level and almost certainly did not form a part of the *in situ* living floor. The limits of the *in situ* living floor did not coincide with the extent of the lag material, but instead lay farther to the west and north; therefore, it could be assumed that only a few fresh pieces in the west portion of the surface collection could have been originally associated with the *in situ* living floor.

The horizontal distribution of *in situ* artifacts (Figure

2.52) indicates a conspicuous, large (but not dense), circular concentration 9 by 11 m in size. The artifact density, including chips, is low, about 36.24 per square meter. The central portion is denser, and the perimeter of the excavated block contains only isolated artifacts. Small scraps of bone are numerous, although only three animal species were identified: rhinoceros, red-fronted gazelle, and *Gazella dama*. Large bone clusters, as observed at Area A, were not present. The distribution of artifacts and bones at Area C (excavated) gives an impression totally different from that at Area A or at any of the other worked areas.

The raw material utilized in Area C (excavated) was also quartzitic sandstone, but a high proportion of it was of a fine-grained gray variety. The main lines of the General Structure show relatively high percentages for the Initial Group, pertaining to the early stages of core preparation (see Chapter 7). The waste flakes resulting from the shaping of Levallois cores form the highest percentage (42.7%) of all recognized categories. This is also reflected in the unusually high value for the IGL (71.5); however, despite this high IGL, the Technological Levallois Index is rather low: 8.9%. Blades are rare (Ilam:1.7). All identified cores from Area C (excavated) were Levallois for flakes (14). This group included a single specimen of an opposed-platform Levallois core for flakes made on a flake.

The tool assemblage is comparatively poor, containing only 127 pieces, including Levallois; however, the percentages of the recovered tools form a very interesting structure. The Typological Levallois Index is very high, 44.1; the Mousterian Group is still higher, 56.3; the Sidescraper Index is 38.0, and the Denticulate Group is much lower than elsewhere (14.1). The Aterian Group is low (2.8) and similar to that seen in the other areas at the site, whereas the Upper Paleolithic Group is nonexistent. Among the retouched tools, Mousterian points (Figure 2.53) and convergent sidescrapers (Figure 2.54) are the most numerous. Aterian pieces consist of only two tip fragments of foliated objects broken during manufacture.

The concentration clearly was left at a time when the lake had shrunk, thus permitting a small Aterian group to settle on the exposed lacustrine sediments. It was not determined whether this concentration was an isolated occurrence, or if there were others, but it must have been a short-lived camp, and after the occupation the living floor was covered by the expanding lake. The observed fluctuations in lake level could have had a seasonal character, or they may have resulted from a period of unusually low precipitation.

As a living site it clearly differs from the approximately contemporary assemblages associated with the kills and embedded in the same lake unit. The differences are reflected not only in the distribution of artifacts, their densities, and their associations, but also by its dramatically distinct General Structure and the proportions of tool classes.

Area C (surface). The collection from the area designated Area C (surface) is surely not a homogeneous assemblage. It is believed that some of the artifacts may have been primarily associated with the very top of the occupation horizon of Area C (excavated), whereas others were dropped from a higher level. The olive silt borders the eastern edge of the surface concentration, and some of the artifacts may originally have occurred in this unit.

The raw material utilized was quartzitic sandstone. The collection from the area contains only 630 pieces, including chips. The General Structure of the inventory indicates that the Flake Group forms over 85% of the total assemblage, and although tools are relatively numerous (accounting for almost 20%), the artifacts associated with core preparation slightly exceed 20%. These indices are clearly different from those at Area C (excavated). The collection includes 14 cores, of which the most numerous are Levallois (57.1%), followed by the change of orientation for flakes variety (28.6%), and single platform for flakes (14.3%). All the Levallois cores are for flakes, but two have opposed striking platforms and one has semi-Nubian preparation (Guichard and Guichard 1965).

The General Levallois Index (IGL:42.9) is half that seen in the collection from the excavated section, and the IL (6.7) and Ilam (.8) are similar. The tools are not numerous (81 pieces, including Levallois). The ILty (19.75) is about half of that at Area C (excavated) and the Sidescraper Index (18.5, restricted), Charentian Index (10.8, restricted), and Group II (27.7, restricted) values are also much smaller. On the other hand, the denticulates are three times more frequent (53.8, restricted); the Upper Paleolithic Group (.15, restricted) and the Aterian Group (4.6, restricted) are both generally similar. In general, the indices are much closer to those from the surface collection from Area A than they are to those from Area C (excavated).

Area B. About 10 m northeast from the central gridded area, immediately adjacent to the lake sediments and on a dune beach lowered by deflation, is an elongated, dense Aterian lithic concentration. When first seen it was 30 m long and over 10 m wide. The concentration is heavily masked by a recent eolian sand sheet of varying thickness. It is quite possible that the concentration continues toward the northeast and may link up with an enormous elongated patch of deflated Aterian artifacts 70 m away. A block of 89 m² was collected and scatterpatterned at the southwestern edge of this concentration. All the artifacts were eolized, although some were almost fresh, indicating that they had been exposed only recently.

The scatterpattern shows the western edge of a concentration whose limits could also be seen on the northern and southern peripheries (Figure 2.55). A test block 6 m long was excavated under the covering sand sheet; however, it failed to determine the edge of the concentration in that direction. Furthermore, spot checks farther to the east and northeast disclosed artifacts under the sand cover throughout this area. It could not be determined whether several distinct clusters occur within this huge litter of artifacts, but this seems likely.

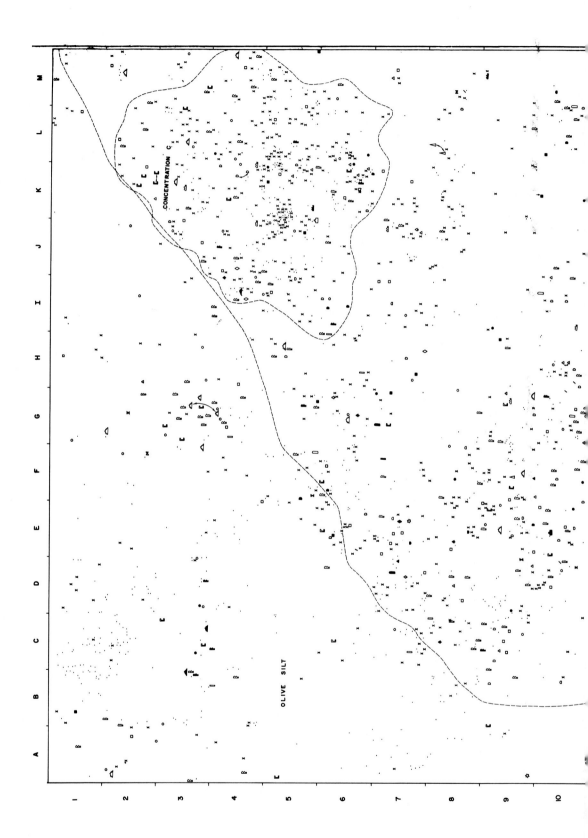

CONCENTRATION C

OLIVE SILT

60

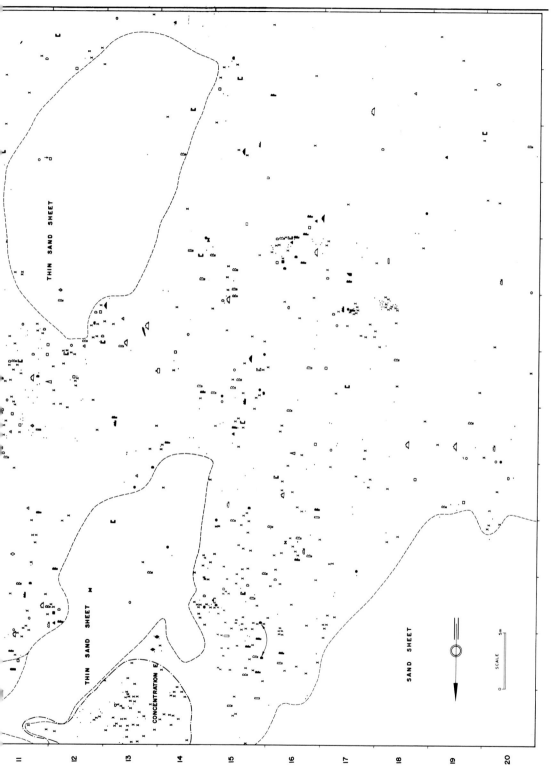

FIGURE 2.46. *Scatterpattern of surface artifacts from Site BT-14, Areas A, C, D, and E. Includes both eolized and fresh specimens (blackened).* · *Chip;* × *Flake;* ′ *Blade;* □ *Levallois flake;* ○ *Core;* △ *Mousterian point;* △ *Levallois point;* △ *Foliated piece;* ▯ *Levallois blade;* ◁ *Retouched piece;* ≃ *Chopper;* × *Bifacial edge piece;* ▯ *Endscraper;* ▨ *Denticulate;* ▷ *Sidescraper;* ▫ *Transverse sidescraper;* ∝ *Converging sidescraper;* ▫ *Notch;* ⧠ *Bec;* ⟡ *Pedunculate;* ⟡ *Bec;* ⬦ *Pedunculate;* ↑ *Burin;* ◁ *Converging denticulate;* ⧪ *Disc;* ◁ *Truncation.*

61

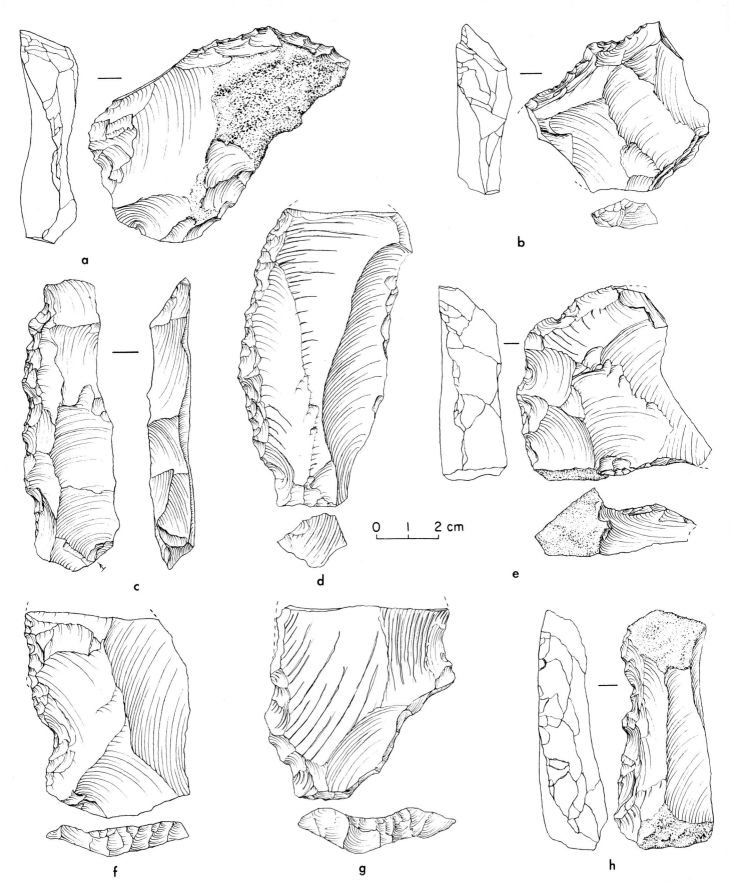

FIGURE 2.47. *Denticulates from Site BT-14 Area A (a–f); Area C, surface (h); and Area D (g): (a, b) transverse denticulates; (c, d) convex side denticulates on blades; (e–g) convex on flakes (f, g, on Levallois flakes); (h) concave denticulate.*

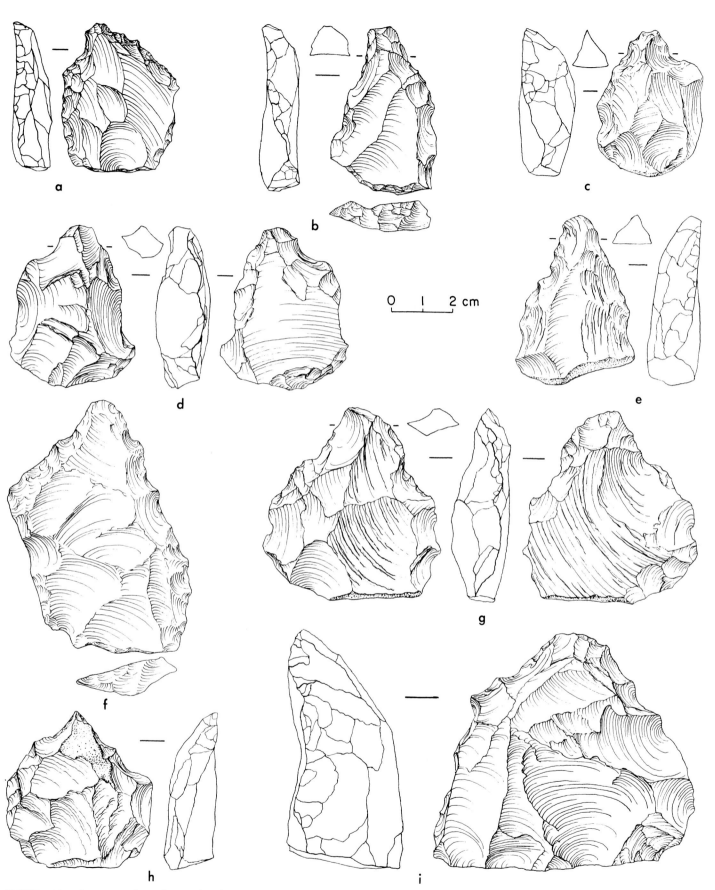

FIGURE 2.48. *Converging denticulates and perforator from Site BT-14, Area A (b–d, g, i); Area C, surface (a, e); and Area D (f, h): (a) perforator; (b, c, e, h) converging denticulates passing into perforators; (d, f, g, i) converging denticulates.*

63

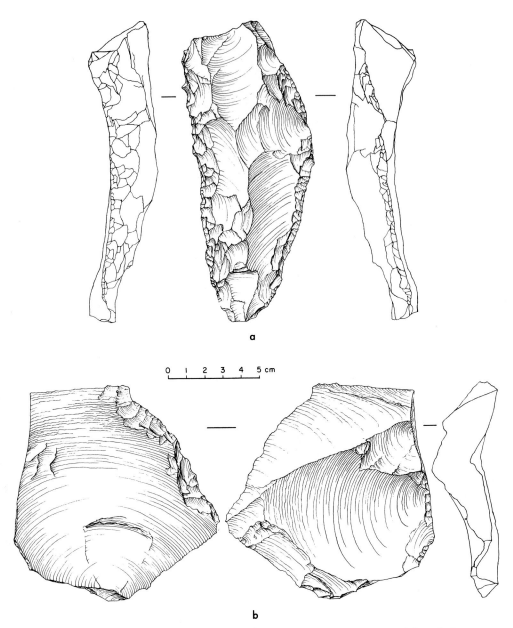

FIGURE 2.49. *Large, slightly denticulated sidescrapers from Site BT-14, Area A: (a) bilateral; (b) inverse.*

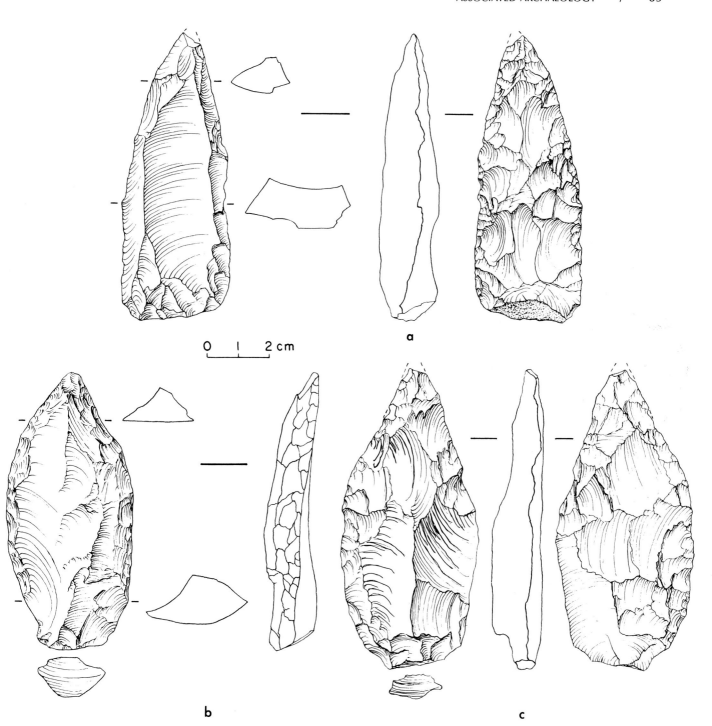

0 1 2 cm

FIGURE 2.50. *Tools from Site BT-14, Area A (c); Area C, surface (b); and Area D (a): (a) atypical Quinson point; (b) elongated Mousterian point on flake; (c) elongated bifacial Mousterian point.*

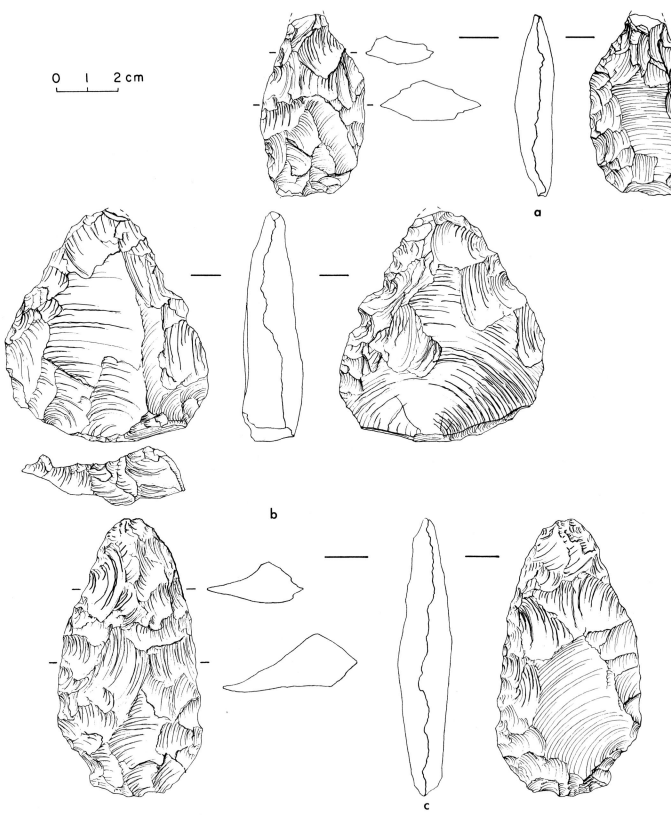

0 1 2 cm

FIGURE 2.51. *Tools from Site BT-14, Areas A (a, c) and C, surface (b): (a) bifacial foliate on flake; (b) bifacial Mousterian point, wide, on Levallois flake; (c) bifacial foliate.*

Table 2.1
Occurrence of Tools and Fauna in Site BT-14, Area A

Animal occurrence	Tool present
Gazella dama	Pedunculate, denticulate
Gazella dama	Cores (2), bec
Gazella dama	Denticulates (2), transverse denticulate, converging denticulate, notch, converging sidescraper, Mousterian point, cores (3)
Gazella rufifrons	Burin, Levallois flake, sidescraper, core
Medium-sized antelope	Core
Medium-sized antelope	Core, bifacial edge piece
Medium-sized antelope	Converging denticulate, notch, transverse sidescraper
Medium-sized antelope	Converging denticulate, transverse sidescraper, notch
Bovid	Denticulate
Bovid	Denticulate
Bovid	Mousterian point, notch, sidescraper
Bovid	Levallois flakes (2), core
Rhinoceros	Pedunculate, endscraper, denticulate, Levallois flake
Equid, medium-sized antelope	Denticulates (2), sidescraper, notch
Gazella dama, bovid	Denticulates (4), sidescrapers (2), core
Large bovid, large antelope	Converging sidescraper, pedunculate, core
Gazella dama, equid, large antelope	Bifacial foliate, endscraper, Mousterian point, converging sidescraper
Rhinoceros, bovid, medium-sized antelope, *Gazella dama*, large antelope	Denticulates (4), Mousterian point, converging sidescraper, sidescraper, transverse denticulate Levallois flake, endscraper

A series of three trenches excavated toward the adjacent basin provides the basic stratigraphic setting for this locality. It clearly demonstrates that the surface artifacts at Area B pass into the sandy beach facies and, farther down, into a snail-rich olive silt unit, the youngest lake sediment exposed in the sequence. No fauna was found at Area B in the olive silt; however, in the adjacent main block (Area D), which may be tied to Area B, this silt contained rare bones, among which two occurrences of *Gazella dama* were recognized. Slightly farther, about 30 m to the northwest, were a few scattered remains of extinct camel (*C. thomasi*) also buried in the olive silt (Figure 2.56).

The raw material utilized at Area B was exclusively quartzitic sandstone, not significantly different from that in Area A. Here, in contrast to the collection from Area A, the General Structure of the assemblage is characterized by a rather low proportion of retouched tools (10.3%), and significantly higher values for the Initial Group (initial core preparation), at about 16%. Levallois core preparation flakes are very numerous, reaching almost 30% of all recovered artifacts (excluding chips); the Flake Group attains slightly over 32%.

Here in Area B, as in the previously described Aterian collections, Levallois cores form the most important class among the 54 identified specimens. All the Levallois cores are for flakes and they represent 66.7% of the total core number. A few have opposed striking platforms; two are made on flakes. Five are prepared and unstruck. Single-platform cores for flakes are the next most important group (14.8%), followed by globular and flattish change-of-

orientation (9.2%) and subdiscoidal (7.4%) cores. There is a single example of an opposed-platform core for flakes.

The General Levallois Index is high (IGL:59.0); however, the Technological Levallois Index (IL) is 10.9%, not very different from that at Area A. The Blade Index (Ilam) is very low. The tool assemblage totals 401 pieces, including Levallois. The Typological Levallois Index (ILty) is very high, over 40%. The Sidescraper Index is low, 18% (restricted), and similar to that at Area A. The Mousterian Group is slightly lower than at Area A, 20.7% (restricted), and the Upper Paleolithic Group, at 4.6%, is nearly the same as at Area A. The Denticulate Group is 62.9% and therefore the highest recorded at Site BT-14, yet less than seen in some Mousterian assemblages at Bir Sahara. The Aterian Group is only slightly higher than in Area A, reaching 5.9%, the highest recorded at Bir Tarfawi (Figure 2.57). Among the denticulates the most numerous are simple and converging specimens on flakes. Two varieties of sidescrapers are most frequent—simple convex and convergent convex (Figure 2.58). Pedunculate tools are very rare. Only four are present, and these include a Levallois flake, a convergent sidescraper (partially bifacial), and two stem fragments. Bifacial foliates are more numerous, with 10 specimens in the collection, including the unfinished examples (Figure 2.59).

The collection at Area B is generally similar to that from Area A, except for the core-preparation and core-exploitation elements, differences that suggest varying approaches to the raw-material economy. At Area B the blocks of quartzitic sandstone had been brought from the

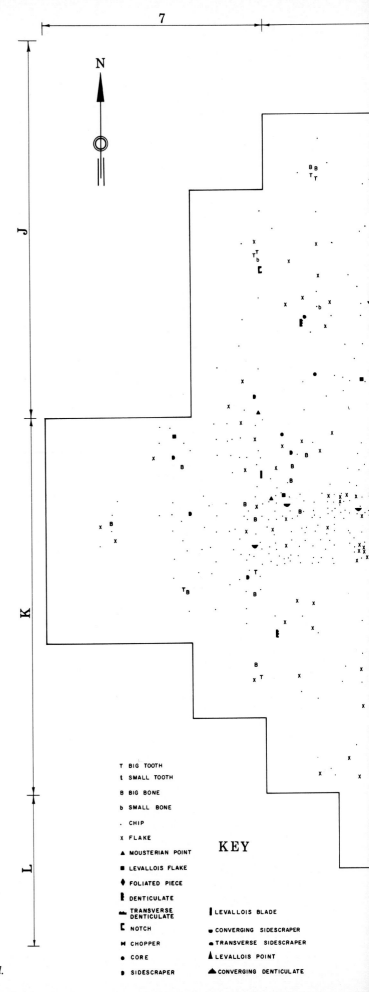

FIGURE 2.52. *Scatterpattern of Site BT-14, Area C, excavated.*

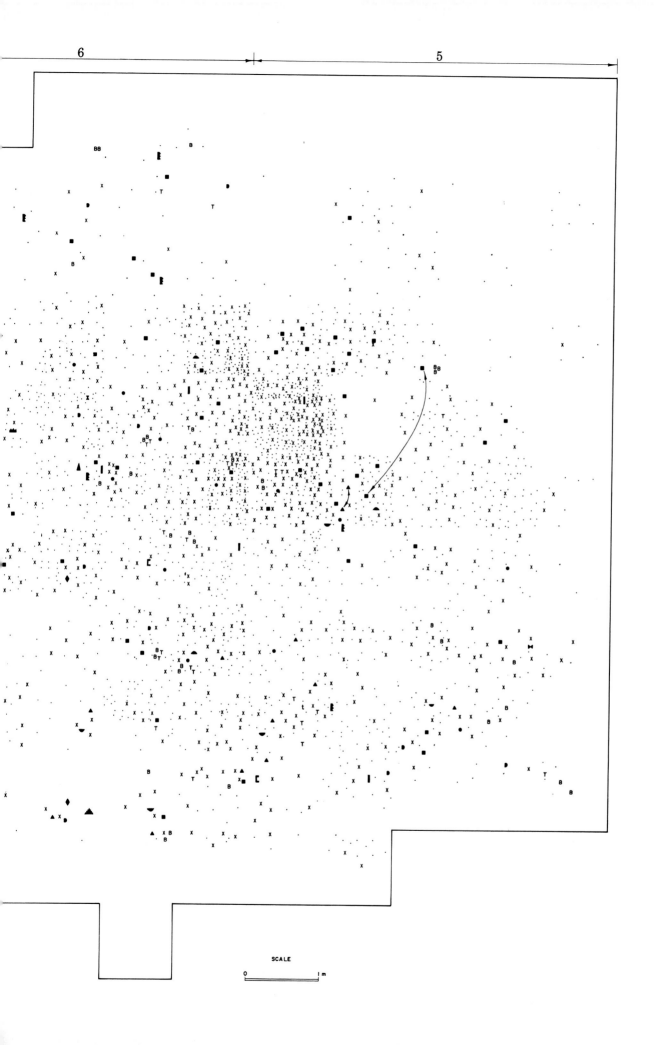

SCALE

0   1 m

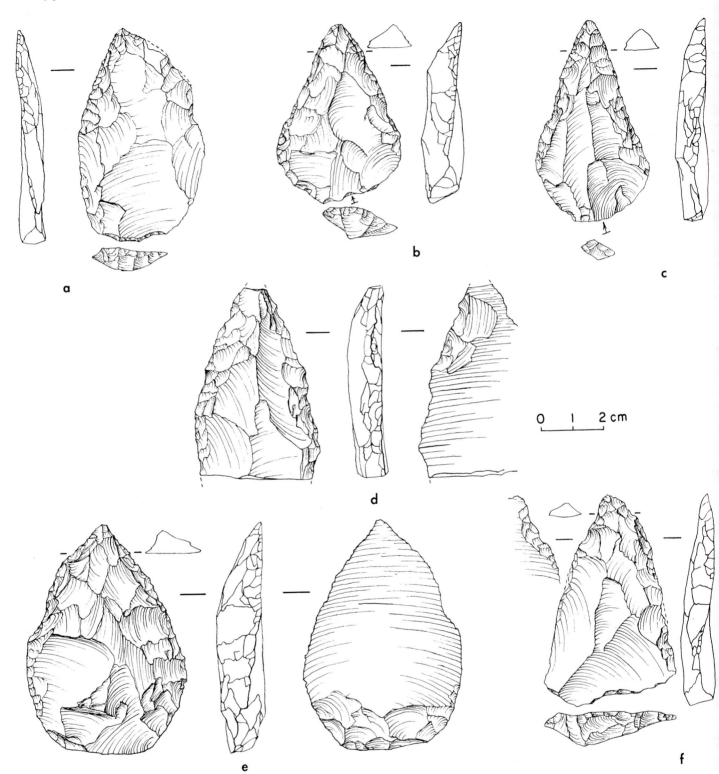

FIGURE 2.53. *Mousterian points from Site BT-14, Area C, excavated: (c) elongated; (d) elongated on Levallois blade (?) and partially bifacial; (e) with inversely thinned base.*

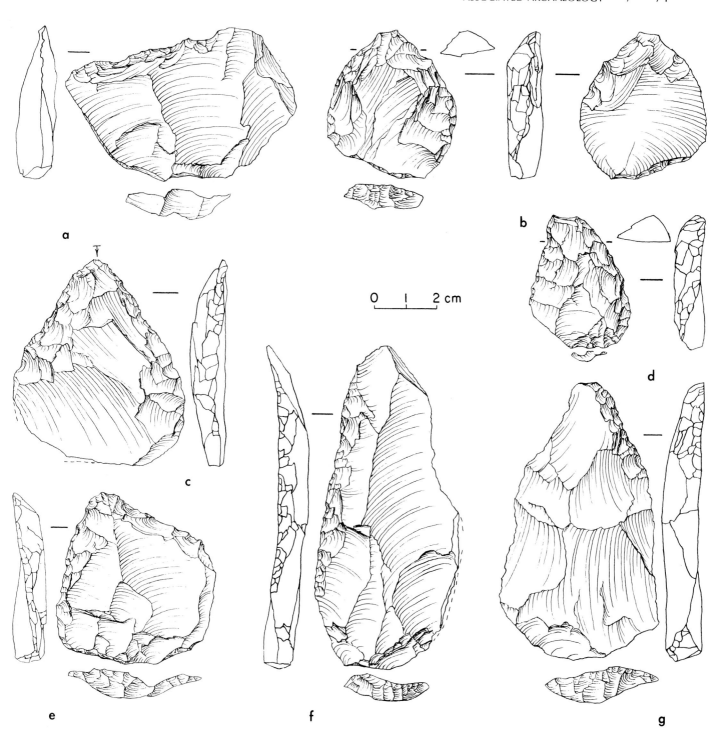

FIGURE 2.54. *Sidescrapers from Site BT-14, Area C, excavated: (a) transverse; (b) converging, partially bifacial; (c) converging, on Levallois flake; (d, e) asymmetric; (f) simple, convex, on Levallois blade; (g) simple convex, on Levallois point (?).*

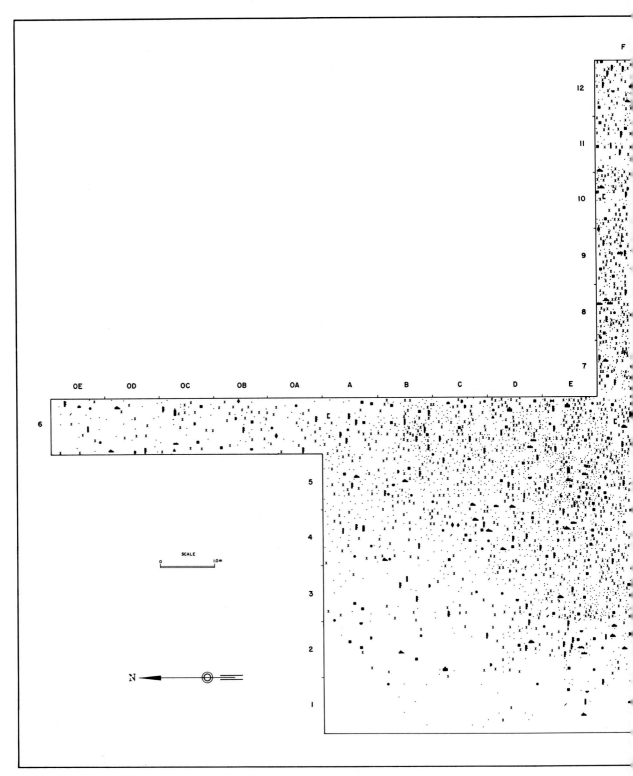

FIGURE 2.55. *Scatterpattern for Site BT-14, Area B.*

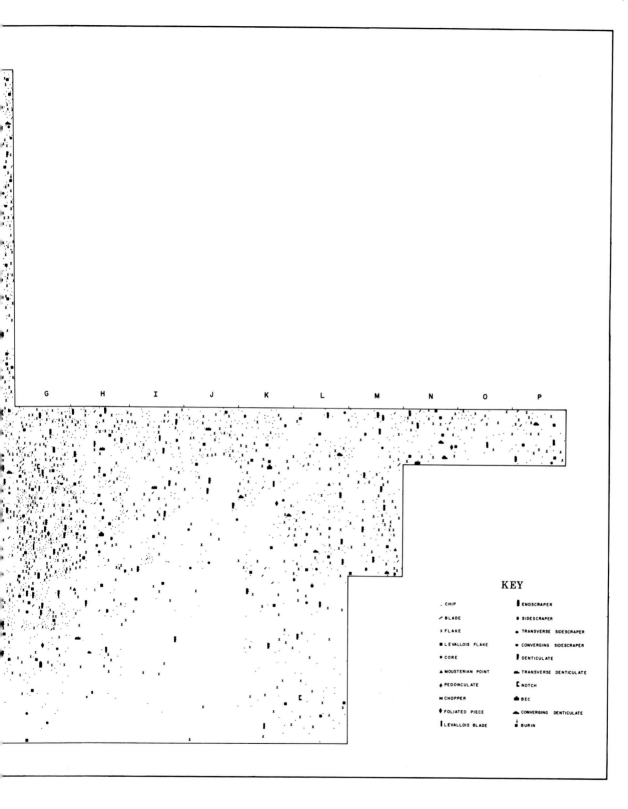

KEY

. CHIP	▌ ENDSCRAPER
⁄ BLADE	▐ SIDESCRAPER
x FLAKE	▬ TRANSVERSE SIDESCRAPER
■ LEVALLOIS FLAKE	▼ CONVERGING SIDESCRAPER
● CORE	▌ DENTICULATE
▲ MOUSTERIAN POINT	▬ TRANSVERSE DENTICULATE
♦ PEDONCULATE	⌐ NOTCH
⋈ CHOPPER	▄ BEC
◆ FOLIATED PIECE	▲ CONVERGING DENTICULATE
▌ LEVALLOIS BLADE	▟ BURIN

FIGURE 2.56. *Fragmentary long bone of* Camelus thomasi, *Site BT-14, surface, olive silt unit.*

Levallois Index. These differences may not indicate the presence of major cultural divisions; rather, they may simply reflect the various activities related to the settlements.

Area D. The separation of Area D from Areas A and C is based entirely on lithostratigraphic grounds. Artifacts assigned to Area D were those collected in the northeast corner of the gridded area exposed on the olive silt unit. The artifacts did not form conspicuous concentrations, although there was a suggestion of a slight cluster of tools, almost exclusively denticulates, in Squares 3–4/G–H. In another section, Squares 3–4/C–D, several very fresh artifacts occurred on the surface. Scraping of the silt in this vicinity failed to reveal additional buried material. On lithostratigraphic grounds, the artifacts from Area D should be largely contemporaneous with those from Area B, as shown by the sediment sequence in the trenches.

The collection from Area D is one of the smallest at Site BT-14. It numbers only 501 pieces, including chips. The Flake Group is the most numerous, slightly over 50%; the core-preparation elements are low, below 10%. There are six identifiable cores in the collections, including two Levallois, both unstruck, one for points, the other for flakes. A globular and a flattish change-of-orientation core for flakes, and two single-platform cores for flakes complete the group. The tools, of which there were only 61, including Levallois, are dominated by denticulate pieces (66%, restricted). Next in importance are Levallois flakes and blades (the Typological Levallois Index, ILty, is 18.0). The remaining tools are unique occurrences. The presence of a Quinson point is to be noted (Figure 2.50a). The collection is too limited for meaningful comparisons; however, it demonstrates the same characteristic high denticulate orientation found in

outcrop and fully processed at the site, whereas at Area A this initial step was done somewhere else. Both Area B and Area C had high values for core-preparation elements, especially in Levallois at Area C. These assemblages from Area B and Area C also differ strikingly in some indices, such as the Sidescraper, Charentian, and the Mousterian groups, which are much higher at Area C; the denticulates are only one-fourth as frequent. The assemblages share similar technological indices as well as the Typological

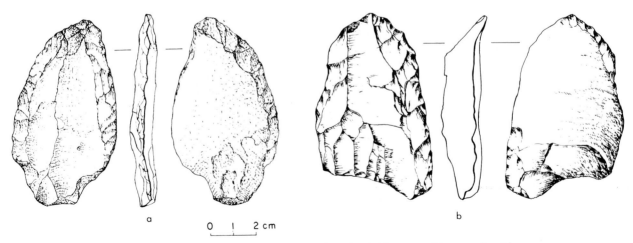

a

0 1 2 cm

b

FIGURE 2.57. *Tools from Site BT-14, Area B: (a) pedunculated sidescraper; (b) converging sidescraper.*

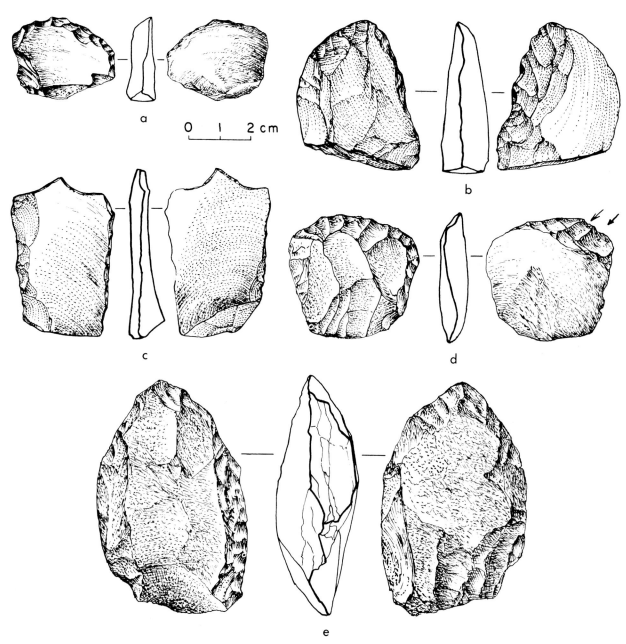

FIGURE 2.58. *Tools from Site BT-14, Area B: (a) transverse sidescraper; (b, e) bifacial sidescrapers; (c) bilateral sidescraper; (d) flat burin on endscraper.*

all the other Aterian assemblages at Site BT-14, except that at Area C (excavated).

Area E. Along the north edge of the gridded area, in Squares A–B/12–14, was a small patch of olive silt, and the artifacts found on the surface of this silt were collected separately and designated as Area E. Immediately adjacent, on the south edge of Area E (Squares B/13–14), was a very tight knocker pile consisting of 2 very fresh, bifacial

foliates, which were broken during manufacture and unfinished (Figure 2.60), and 101 biface trimming flakes and chips, many *in situ.* Some of the flakes and chips were made of material identical to that used on the bifacial foliates; others were of a different color, indicating that other bifaces had been prepared at this place and taken away. This assemblage was in the very base of the olive silt, possibly on the contact between that unit and the underlying gray silt. The knocker pile was so tightly clustered that it

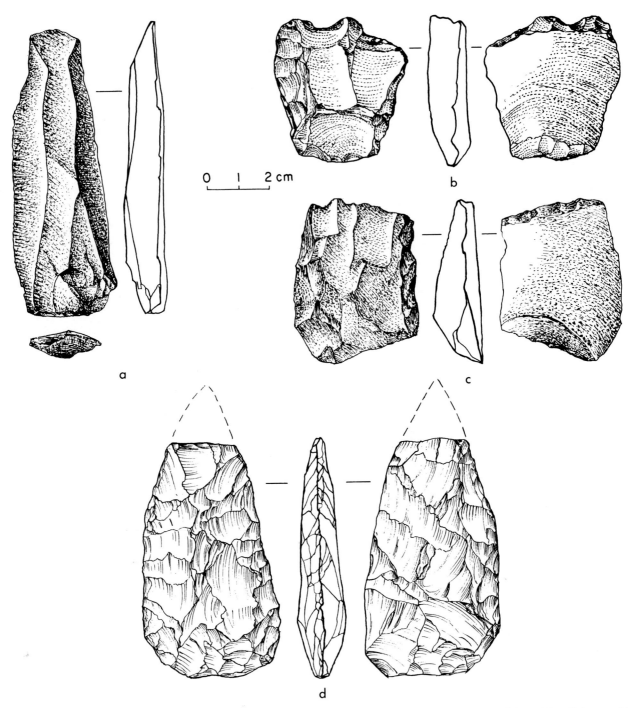

FIGURE 2.59. *Tools from Site BT-14, Area B: (a) Levallois blade; (b) opposed-platform Levallois core on flake; (c) Levallois core; (d) bifacial foliate.*

could not be shown on the small-scale scatterpattern, except for the two bifaces.

The remaining artifacts from Area E are too few for meaningful characterization; only 70 pieces were found, one of which was a convergent, convex sidescraper.

Area F. The collection found on the surface of Square 2-M, consisting of eight pieces, was believed to be associated with a larger surface concentration exposed just to the south of the main gridded area. No further work was done at this concentration.

FIGURE 2.60. *Site BT-14, just south of Area E. Knocker pile and two bifacial foliates broken during manufacture. (Trowel points to one of them; the other is slightly subsurface.) On contact between upper gray silt and olive silt units.*

Area N. A partially dispersed cluster of artifacts and fire-cracked rocks, located 140 m northwest of the gridded area, was designated as Area N. The artifacts rested on top of the slightly deflated, brown, basal, sandy silt unit, which here contained freshwater and terrestrial fauna. The collection found on the surface included nine heavily eolized recognizable Aterian artifacts. Also, there were two conspicuous concentrations of fire-cracked rocks situated immediately southeast of the artifact concentration. Isolated rocks, obvious manuports as well as burned pieces of sandstone, were also scattered here and there. The artifact concentration is not very dense, and seems to be composed of at least one subconcentration just west of the main group. The limited network of articulating pieces demonstrates, however, that this subconcentration is an integral part of the settlement.

A grid measuring 20 by 20 m was laid out over the concentration and the artifacts were scatterpatterned (Figure 2.61). The collection contains 897 pieces, including chips. There were 69 retouched tools, 2 lower grinding stones, 2 upper grinders, and 1 hammerstone. The raw material is basically of local quartzitic sandstone; however, there are 2 cores made of imported Eocene flint, as well as

several flakes and about 30 chips of the same material. Another material used is quartz, probably from the nearby basement outcrops of the El Tawila Mass. Quartz is represented by 29 pieces, of which one is an upper grinder and another is a hammerstone.

The small collection of recovered tools is very monotonous, and it consists mainly of various denticulates (47.8%) of which over one-third were on large blades and three were convergent. The next important group is retouched pieces, representing 27.5%, followed by becs (7.2%) and notches (2.9%). A single saw on a blade and unidentified fragments complete the lithic inventory.

Most of the cores are for flakes, either single-platform or globular change-of-orientation variety. There are also six semidiscoidal cores, and one single-platform core for microblades made of Eocene flint. The surface collection also yielded a fragment of a shell bracelet, but neither pottery nor bone was present.

The brown silt, which forms the base of the Aterian lacustrine sequence here, was excavated and screened in the area below the surface concentration. No artifacts were found associated with the silt.

An assessment of the collection from Area N is extremely

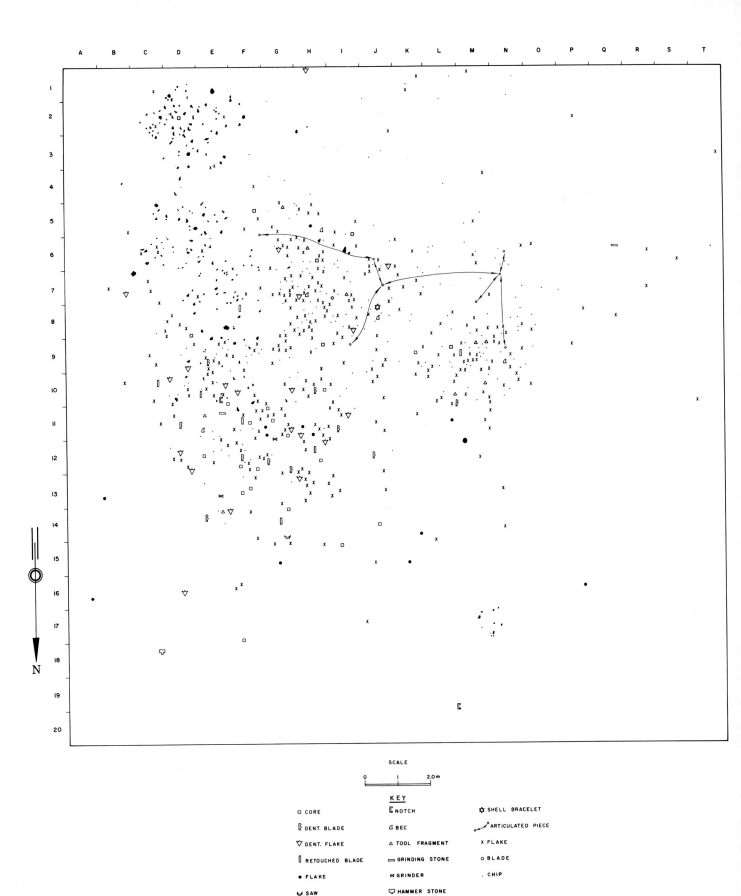

FIGURE 2.61. *Scatterpattern of Site BT-14, Area N, surface. Burned stones indicated by irregular black patches.*

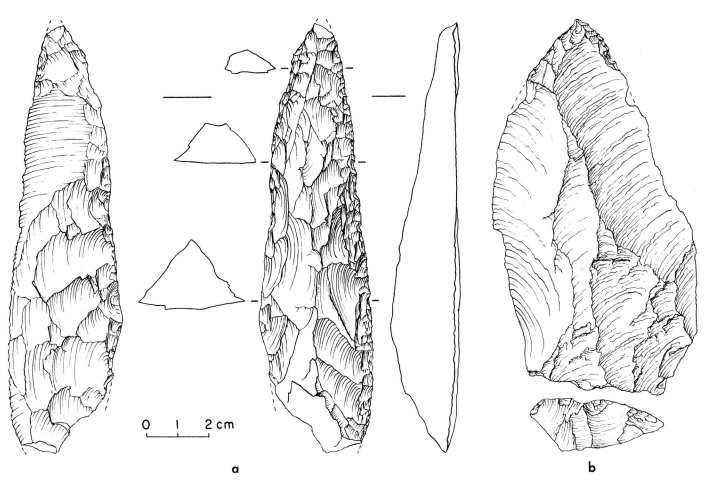

FIGURE 2.62. *Tools from trenches at Site BT-14: (a) elongated bifacial foliate on blade, Trench 7, lower gray silt unit; (b) retouched Levallois point, Trench 16, olive silt beach unit.*

difficult. It is clearly not Aterian, but it shares many resemblances, particularly in the emphasis given to denticulates made on long blades, with a group of sites studied at Bir Tarfawi and Bir Sahara in 1973 and vaguely dated between Neolithic and Early Kingdom (Hays n.d.). Locality N differs from these other later sites in the absence of worked ostrich eggshell and perforators and, except for two of them (Sites BT-23 and BT-24), by a lower frequency of Eocene flint, and a greater emphasis on denticulates. This occupation at Area N, however, may have belonged to the same entity, but may display a different activity emphasis. Only one of these other sites, BT-20, has been dated, and this was on the ostrich eggshell that dated 4510 BP ±70 years (SMU-74). The absence of pottery and bone in all of these sites prohibits a closer determination of age.

Trenches. Several of the trenches excavated mainly for stratigraphic purposes yielded occasional artifacts, but never in sufficient quantities to merit frequency analysis and never representing living floors. The oldest lacustrine unit, the brown silty sand, yielded several artifacts in Trenches 15 and 16. They appeared to be washed down from a higher beach; however, the primary source from which they were derived was not established. Among the artifacts in these trenches were 4 denticulates, 1 concave sidescraper, 1 chopping tool, 2 atypical Levallois flakes, and 2 undetermined tool fragments, together with 59 flakes and chips, and 1 unworked fragment of ostrich eggshell.

The lower gray silt unit, near the center of the basin in Trench 7, yielded a large, elongated, bifacial foliate (Figure 2.62a), and in Trench 8 it contained an asymmetric convergent denticulate, partially bifacial, and a flake. No artifacts were found in the upper gray silt unit in the trenches, but the shallow-water facies of the two gray silt units, which could not be distinguished here, contained in Trench 15 and 16 2 denticulates, 1 bilateral sidescraper, 1 bec (?), 2 Levallois flakes, 173 flakes and chips, and 2 unworked fragments of ostrich eggshell. In Trench 9 the same unit had 2 convergent sidescrapers, 2 Levallois flakes, 1 unidentified tool fragment, 1 Levallois core, and 427 flakes and chips. Still farther toward the beach in Trench 9 the collection from this unit was even larger. It contained 2 denticulates, 5 Levallois flakes, 5 unidentified tool fragments, 1 Levallois core for flakes, 1 undetermined core, and 1108 flakes and chips. These artifacts, redeposited in near-beach sediments, surely indicate an intense occupation of the lake margins. Judging from the present morphology of the area, the levels to which the beach logically extended were destroyed by both subsequent lake aggradation and by still later deflation.

The olive silt unit in Trench 9 contained 1 unfinished bifacial foliate, 2 Levallois flakes, and 226 chips and flakes. The near-beach facies of this unit in Trench 16, in the easternmost portion closest to Area B, yielded 5 denticualtes, 2 retouched flakes, 1 Levallois flake, 2 Levallois cores for flakes, a fragment of a Levallois core, and 84 chips and flakes. Farther from the beach to the west, this same trench and olive unit had 4 denticulates, 1 retouched Levallois point (Figure 2.62b), 2 Levallois flakes, 1 unidentified tool fragment, and 31 chips and flakes.

The collection of tools from the latest recognized near-beach sediments indicates a strong resemblance to the collection from Area B. It is, in fact, a lakeward continuation of that cultural layer, partially reworked.

The artifacts associated with the near-shore sediments of the lower lake units in the northern section of the beach basin (Trench 9) are unusually numerous. They may represent a near-beach settlement reworked into the shore sediments by an expanding early lake. Tests were dug on either side of Trench 9 and between Trench 9 and Trench 10, in hopes of finding the remnant of the settlement from which they were derived. No such remnant was found.

3
Gebel Nabta and Vicinity

Like most archaeological discoveries, the Nabta sites were found accidentally during one of our not-too-frequent rest stops while traveling between Bir Tarfawi and Abu Simbel. We found it as we were leaving the field at the end of the 1973 season, and decided to test what later became known as E-75-6 the following year.

Even this brief first inspection indicated that the Nabta area contained numerous Neolithic and Terminal Paleolithic remains associated with extensive playa and eolian deposits. However, the work at Bir Tarfawi had not been completed, and most important, the extensive butchery site there had not been excavated. We decided, therefore, to divide our team and try to work both areas simultaneously. As it turned out, this was a mistake. We put part of our crew, including several geologists from the Geological Survey, at Nabta to begin mapping the early Holocene playa sediments there. This required a complete camp, and most of the expedition's vehicles, because water had to be hauled from Abu Simbel, 125 km away. Water was available at Bir Tarfawi, and the rest of our crew was to set up a complete camp there. The maintenance of two camps placed a considerable strain on the resources of the Geological Survey, leaving us with some vehicles that had seen better days and, in fact, were not suitable for desert service.

All went well at Nabta, which was set up first and became a base for the second camp at Bir Tarfawi. The departure to Tarfawi began early one morning with a convoy of 10 vehicles, including a large lorry that carried most of the camp gear and food, a gasoline tanker, several small trucks, and two jeeps. We expected to arrive at Bir Tarfawi late that evening, but we had moved only 20 km when the first "event" occurred—the big lorry broke an axle. This took the rest of the day and a night to repair. It was late January, and the night was cold, near freezing, and no one was very comfortable, but we did have our bedrolls. The next event was near Bir Dibis, about noon the following day, when the jeep we were riding in threw a rod. It had to be abandoned there to be picked up later.

At this point the trucks were still traveling as a group, but, as evening came on, the convoy began to scatter as the faster vehicles reached the sand sheet 150 km south of Bir Tarfawi. The going that day had been unexpectedly hard. Many of the vehicles overheated, and much of the drinking water had been used to refill the radiators. One of the trucks left behind was the gasoline tanker, which ran on diesel fuel, of course. As night approached, everyone began to worry about the tanker. It was then that we discovered that the diesel fuel for the tanker was packed on the large lorry. The tanker was somewhere behind us and out of fuel, but none of the vehicles had enough gasoline to return to the tanker. The last reserve jerry cans had long before been emptied into the vehicles. Only by draining the gas from several trucks and combining the fuel into one could that vehicle go back with diesel fuel for the tanker. Yet another night had to be spent without shelter on the desert, and this time there was no drinking water.

The next day saw the final push to Bir Tarfawi, and the first vehicles arrived shortly before noon, only to find the well contaminated with decayed vegetation and filled with sand. On this occasion even the camp manager took his turn with the shovel and bucket in the effort to clean the well. He had to, because otherwise he would have been last in line for water.

GENERAL GEOLOGY AND GEOMORPHOLOGY

About 100 km west and slightly north of Abu Simbel and 60 km north of the Sudan border (22° 32′ 30″ N; 30° 38′ 15″ E) is a prominent hill known as Gebel Nabta (Figure 3.1), a Kurkur limestone–capped remnant of Nubia sandstone (Figure 3.2). A second and even larger Nubia remnant with Kurkur limestone capping is Birket el Sheb, located about 32 km southwest of Gebel Nabta. The area around these landmarks was investigated by the Combined Prehistoric Expedition during three seasons: 1974, 1975, and 1977. The data recovered provide the next major segment of the later Quaternary history for the Nubian Desert.

The landscape in the vicinity of Gebel Nabta is broken by granite domes, small sandstone conical remnants, elongated strings and groups of dunes, or isolated barchans and numerous sand-choked shallow wadis. Here and there are extensive flat areas, some with clay, silt, or fine sand sediments, remnants of alluvial and lacustrine deposition in enclosed basins. Other flat areas, sometimes slightly inclined, are covered by thin veneers of rounded pebbles and gravels and represent stony desert pavements (serir), possibly of several ages. Some of the gebels and higher remnants show gravelly sediments of alluvial origin, at different ele-

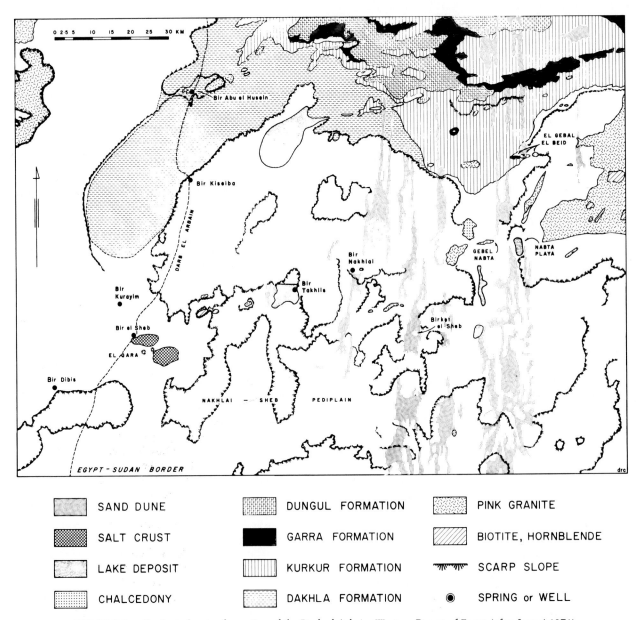

	SAND DUNE		DUNGUL FORMATION		PINK GRANITE
	SALT CRUST		GARRA FORMATION		BIOTITE, HORNBLENDE
	LAKE DEPOSIT		KURKUR FORMATION		SCARP SLOPE
	CHALCEDONY		DAKHLA FORMATION		SPRING or WELL

FIGURE 3.1. *Geological map of a section of the Darb el Arbain, Western Desert of Egypt (after Issawi 1971).*

FIGURE 3.2. *View of Gebel Nabta, looking west across Site E-75-7 in middle distance.*

FIGURE 3.4. *The Darb el Arbain as seen west of Gebel Nabta. Bones of dead camel in foreground. Note the numerous paths formed by camels.*

vations, impoverished deflated and inverted remnants of past wadi channels. The average elevation of the area is about 240 m above sea level.

Several desert wells occur in this portion of the Western Desert. The nearest to Gebel Nabta is Bir Nakhlai, about 35 km to the west and slightly south. A little farther, about 15 km southwest of Nakhlai, is Bir Takhlis. Still farther, about 45 km southwest of Bir Takhlis, is Bir el Sheb; beyond that, about 120 km from Gebel Nabta, is Bir Dibis. About 70 km northwest of Gebel Nabta is Bir Kiseiba, at the foot of the Kiseiba scarp (Figure 3.3).

There are no roads in this area except for a desert track coming southwest from Aswan, via Bir Nakhlai to Bir el Sheb, where it joins the famous caravan trail of Darb el Arbain, linking the Darfur province in Sudan with Kharga and Upper Egypt. The Darb el Arbain passes 75 km west of Gebel Nabta. In this portion, the trail goes in a general northeast–southwest direction, and is marked by a wide band of camel tracks stamped by the thousands of animals that have passed this way over the years (Figure 3.4). Northwest of Gebel Nabta, near Bir Kiseiba, the trail as-

FIGURE 3.3. *View of the currently used well at Bir Kiseiba. The scarp is visible in the background.*

cends the pronounced Kiseiba scarp and then, some 200 km to the north, it descends into the basin of Kharga.

The whole area forms an enormous plain known as the Nakhlai–Sheb pediplain (Issawi 1971). This pediplain, which slopes gently to the north, extends to the south into Sudan and west into the great Sahara. On the north it is bordered by the Kiseiba scarp, some 90 m high. Toward the east, the Kiseiba scarp becomes a part of a series of scarps and clusters of high remnants that mark the southern edge of the high Eocene plateau of the Western Desert. In the northwest it is flanked by the Atmur pediplain, which extends around the El Tawila Mass. The prevailing rock unit in the area is the Cretaceous Nubia Formation, consisting of shales and sandstones, some of which are highly ferruginous. The beds of the ferruginous sandstone often cap the smaller conical gebels and protect them from more rapid erosion. The footslopes of these gebels are covered by a ferruginous sandstone shingle in a sand matrix. This shingle reached its present position by sliding down the slopes of the gebels after the underlying softer sediments had been eroded. This cover now inhibits further erosion at the foot of the gebels and results in their characteristic conical shapes.

The extended escarpment of the Eocene plateau is made up of several conspicuous steps. The lowest one, the Kiseiba scarp, which borders the Nakhlai–Sheb pediplain on the northwest, projects out from the plateau to the southwest as an elongated peninsula, and is covered by sediments of the Dakhla Formation, a northern facies of the upper

Nubia sandstone. The next higher step is the Paleocene Kurkur Formation, composed of limestones intercalating with shales or sandstones. Above this, unconformably overlying the Kurkur beds are limestones, chalky limestones, and calcareous clays of the Garra Formation of lower Eocene or upper Paleocene age. This unit forms the highest part of the scarp in the area immediately north of Gebel Nabta. Behind the scarp the landscape descends gradually and then rises again toward extensive areas made up of limestones, shales, and marls of the Eocene age Dungul Formation. The lower part of the Dungul beds contains flint nodules, which were extensively exploited by Paleolithic man. The exposure of the Dungul Formation nearest to Gebel Nabta is about 40 km to the north.

Numerous faults, generally aligned in an east–west direction, cut the surface of the Nakhlai–Sheb pediplain and the Eocene plateau. Several basalt outcrops, usually the higher landmarks, dot the southeastern part of the pediplain; rolling hills of upthrown masses of basement granite occur in the eastern section. The largest of these masses has its western edge some 10 km northeast of Gebel Nabta, and extends from there to Aswan on the Nile. Smaller granite outcrops are observed even nearer to Gebel Nabta, to the west, north, and northeast.

The surface of the Nakhlai–Sheb pediplain presents some areas of hard Nubia sandstone; other sections are soft and powdery badlands of disintegrated shale. These soft areas are sometimes extremely difficult to cross with vehicles. Other impediments to travel in the area are the large dunes, sometimes over 30 km long, which extend in a north–south direction across the Eocene plateau and the pediplain.

Numerous internally drained, enclosed basins occur in the Nakhlai–Sheb pediplain. These are present along the foot of the scarp where the northward-sloping Nubia sandstone plunges below the cliffs; on the surface of the northward-sloping Kurkur Formation adjacent to the Garra step in the Eocene scarp; and on the pediplain as extensive fault-controlled basins in the Nubia sandstone.

The margins of the basins are frequently concealed by their veneers of colluvial and/or alluvial sediments, as well as the extensive postdepositional deflations. The peripheral drainages entering these basins are inconspicuous and usually appear as shallow and short wadis, with rare and unobvious deltaic fans.

In a few areas extensive flat surfaces armored by chalcedony nodules and pebbles form pronounced geomorphic features that seem to be deflationary residues of older Quaternary clastic sediments. On some of the deflational surfaces are scattered and extremely eolized Acheulian handaxes and other lithic artifacts, including numerous Levallois elements. The latter are most probably Mousterian and/or Aterian in age, and obviously have been dropped from much higher elevations. Sediments that could have been contemporaneous with these artifacts were totally destroyed long ago in all the studied areas. Some of the Mousterian or Aterian artifacts were often reused by Neolithic groups; however, when collected by the Neolithic people, these Middle Paleolithic pieces were already heavily wind abraded and appeared much like those found today.

Possibly the only place where the older Quaternary lake sediments were removed recently is the small, shallow basin surrounding Bir Dibis, an isolated desert well located at the western margin of the Nakhlai–Sheb pediplain. There, a small cluster of Late Acheulian handaxes, mostly amygdaloids, was found on the surface of gravels at the sloping edge of the basin. Small remnants of whitish lacustrine marl or silts occur within the basin, thus suggesting the presence of the sediments laid down by an older lake of unknown age, but presumably earlier than Neolithic.

QUATERNARY SEQUENCE

The basis for our reconstruction of the late Quaternary lithostratigraphic sequence is derived from the work at three Holocene basins filled by clays, silts, and sands, given the names Nabta Playa, located 10 km southeast of Gebel Nabta; El Kortein Playa, some 20 km north of Gebel Nabta; and El Gebal El Beid Playa, 10 km north of El Kortein. Most of the work was done at Nabta Playa, where five sites were excavated during three field seasons, 1974, 1975, and 1977.

Nabta Playa

The Nabta Playa depression is a kidney-shaped basin almost 10 km long and 7 km wide. The margins of the playa are covered by gravelly colluvium, alluvium, and slope deposits gently dipping toward the center of the basin. Three granite outcrops are found on the northern and northeastern periphery, and large exposed areas of Nubia sandstone flank the basin on the west. Small outcrops of the sandstone protrude through the floor of the playa near its center (Figure 3.5). The fill of the basin is made up of clays, silts and eolian sediments, the latter both fossil and modern. Here and there in the lowest portions of the basin are seen a few clumps of *kharit* bush and very thin layers of modern playa silts lying unconformably over the deflated surface of older playa sediments. Several barchan dunes have invaded the playa along its western margins, trapped by small outcrops of Nubia sandstone. Extensive fields of fossil dunes, whose formation preceded the sedimentation of the playa clays, occupy the center of the basin. They appear as low, rounded knolls littered with artifacts of various ages. Apparently similar old dune fields are exposed along the eastern margin of the playa.

Two of the excavated sites, E-75-6 (E101K1) and E-75-9 (E101K4), were near the center of the basin along the western edge of the central fossil dune field (Figures 3.5 and 3.6); the other three sites, E-75-7 (E101K2), E-75-8 (E101K3), and E-77-4 (E101K5), were all within the western field.

The early part of the stratigraphic sequence at Nabta Playa has been exposed at the sites in the central part of the basin. The sequence begins with the deposition of a field of

NABTA PLAYA AREA

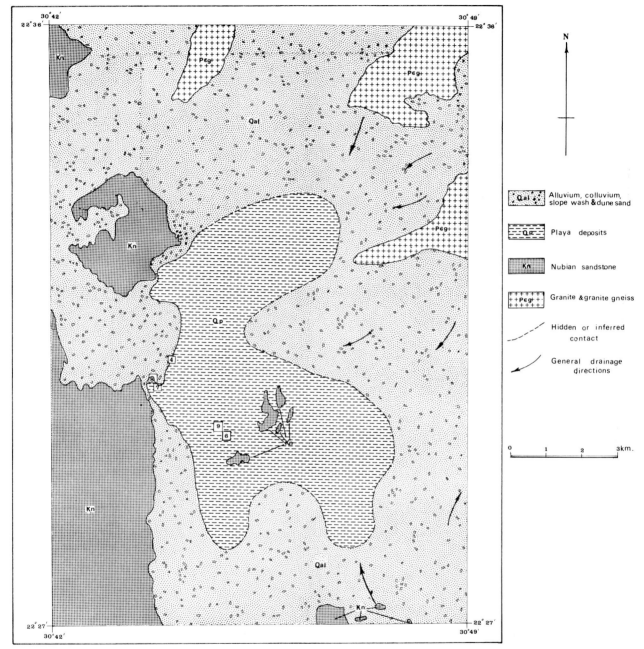

FIGURE 3.5. *Map of Nabta Playa and vicinity. Prepared by C. Vance Haynes, 1977.*

dunes (Figures 3.7:1, 3.8, and 3.9:1) in the basin over the weathered surface of shales belonging to the Nubia Formation. The dune sand is loose, when exposed, to cemented when covered by playa. It is yellow in color (10YR 7/6 to 8/6), often manganese and iron stained in the deeper swales. Calcium carbonate cemented root casts are visible at the top of the dune, often forming extensive mats exposed by differential deflation. The earliest human occupation, of Terminal Paleolithic aspect, occurs at several sites (E-75-6,

E-75-7, and E-75-9) embedded in the upper part of this dune, sometimes in dug pits down to 40 cm deep, but mostly at the very top (Figure 3.7:2, 3 and Figure 3.8:1, top). Ostrich eggshell from this cultural layer in the top of the dune at Site E-75-6 gave a date of 8290 BP ± 80 years (SMU-257). Because the cultural strata at Site E-75-6 are very compact, with a total thickness of 20 cm in places, and contain more than one occupation, this sample may be contaminated by some admixture of the later, Neolithic ostrich

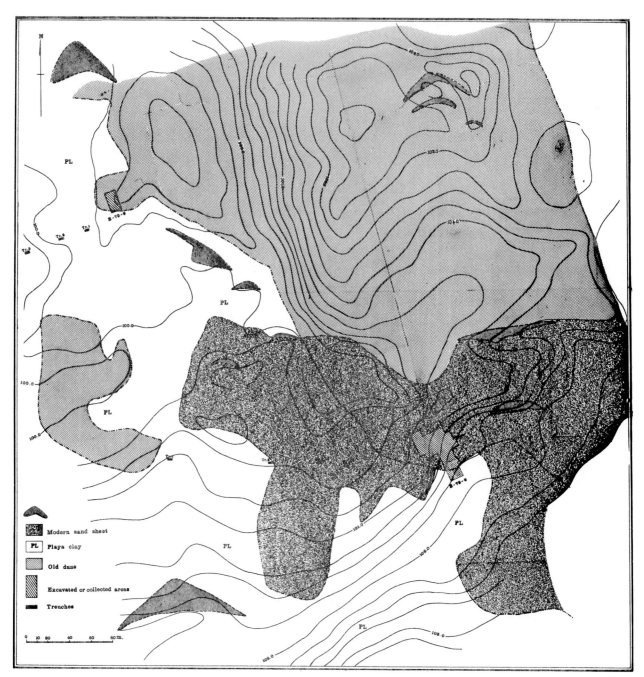

FIGURE 3.6.   *Map of area in vicinity of Sites E-75-6 and E-75-9. Datum assumed.*

eggshells. Even so, the date is one of the two oldest from this site.

The top dune sand is truncated and over this surface of erosion a thin bed of sand with minute streaks of silt was deposited. It contains shells of *Bulinus truncatus* and *Zootecus insularis* as well as cultural material of Terminal Paleolithic age, the latter probably derived from the underlying cultural horizon (Figures 3.7:4 and 3.8:2b). This thin bed, which contains freshwater molluscs and land snails, may have been formed as a beach and shallow-water sedi-

ment in an expanding lake. The fine-grained deep-water facies contemporaneous with this episode has not been found.

The Terminal Paleolithic occupation in the top of the underlying dune and the reworked portion of this settlement in the beach deposit yielded numerous faunal remains. The most common was a small gazelle (*Gazella rufifrons*), followed by a larger gazelle, possibly *G. dama*, and hare (*Lepus capensis*). Birds, as yet not identified, were also present, as was one bone of a large bovid (domestic

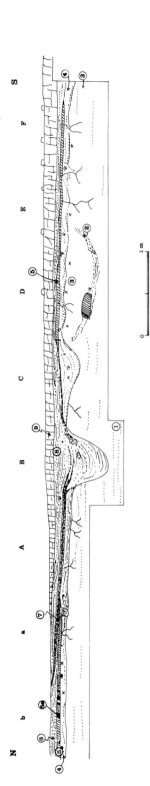

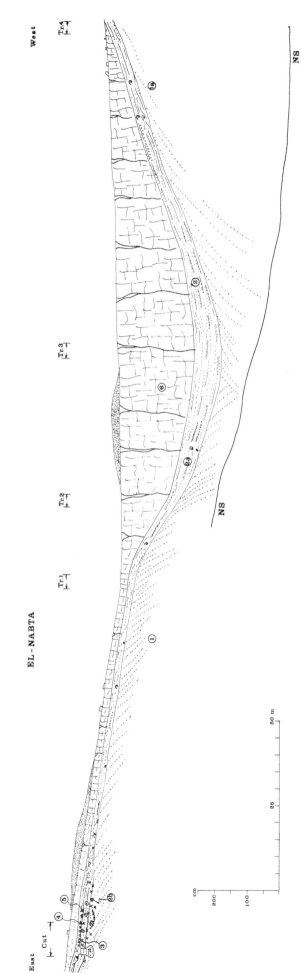

FIGURE 3.7. *Cross section of Site E-75-6 along east wall, Squares b–F. Key: 1, laminated dune sand; 2, fireplace pit in Terminal Paleolithic horizon; 3, Terminal Paleolithic cultural layer; 4, lacustrine sands with snails and redeposited Terminal Paleolithic artifacts; 5, cemented sandy silt with numerous root casts; 5a, burned stones; 6, laminated sand; 7, Neolithic cultural layer; 8, laminated lacustrine sand; 9, playa clays.*

EL-NABTA

FIGURE 3.8. *General cross section through Site E-75-6 and nearby playa sub-basin. Key: NS, Nubia sandstone; 1 and 1a, dune sand; 2 and 2a, lacustrine sands with snails, of both Terminal Paleolithic and Neolithic age, undifferentiated; 2b, Terminal Paleolithic cultural layer; 3, cemented sandy silt; 4, Neolithic layer; 5, lacustrine sand; 6, playa clay.*

EL-NABTA

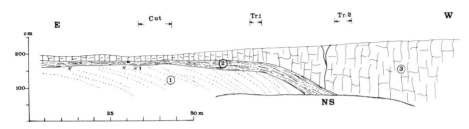

FIGURE 3.9. *General cross section through Site E-75-9. Key: NS, Nubia sandstone; 1, dune sand with Terminal Paleolithic cultural layer in top; 2, lacustrine sands and silts with traces of Neolithic in top; 3, playa clay.*

Bos?). The last was initially thought to have been somehow derived from the overlying Neolithic occupation, but since domestic cattle (?) also are present at several other Terminal Paleolithic sites in this area (see subsequent discussion), it is now regarded as of Terminal Paleolithic age. Over the thin laminated lacustrine sand is a very thin (5–10 cm thick) layer of consolidated to cemented silty sand, brown in color (7.5YR 3/4), displaying a horizontal network of numerous rootlets (Figure 3.7:5). This layer contains burned stones, some charcoal, as well as a few artifacts, possibly of Terminal Paleolithic age (Figure 3.7:5a). The exact assignment of the artifacts found in the horizon is confused because of the similarities in some lithic elements in both the Terminal Paleolithic and Neolithic assemblages. It should be noted, however, that all the uncovered Neolithic pits had been cut through this horizon.

A unit of inconspicuous, loose to friable laminated sand, about 10 cm thick, covers the cemented silty sand (Figure 3.7:6). This sand is preserved only in places, and there are no artifacts associated with it.

Immediately above the sand where it occurs, or on the cemented silty sand elsewhere, is the Neolithic cultural layer (Figure 3.7:7). It is a dark, loose, grayish brown (10YR 5/2) ashy sand with charcoal flecks and powder, sometimes in lenses. Numerous large bell-shaped and smaller cylindrical pits were dug from this layer into the basal dune. A large well was excavated down to 2m below the surface of the cultural layer, thus indicating the level of the water table during occupation. The cultural layer contains chipped stone artifacts, grinding stones, pottery, bone tools, and abundant animal remains. The animal bones were mostly those of a small gazelle (*Gazella rufifrons?*) followed by hare (*Lepus capensis*). In contrast to the fauna from the Terminal Paleolithic layer, the large gazelle (*G. dama?*) was represented by only three identified examples. Among other fauna were a small unidentified carnivore, two bones of cattle or large bovid (?), turtle, and birds. There were also bones of small rodents and two fragments of *Unio* shells.

In most of the sites, particularly the ones excavated during the 1974 and 1975 seasons, the Terminal Paleolithic occupation is almost immediately (less than 10 cm) below the Neolithic cultural layer, and all of the Neolithic pits had cut through it. Because of this stratigraphic situation, and the occasional admixtures of diagnostic Terminal

Paleolithic artifacts (Ounan–Harif points), there were some faunal collections that could not be securely separated into the two major occupation periods. From these possibly mixed collections, there were identifications of additional species: six bones of hedgehog (*Erinaceidae* sp.), two bones of mongoose (*Herpetes ichneumon*), one bone from a wild cat (*Felis libyca*), and two fish vertebrae (possibly of *Lates* sp.).

The identified plant remains from the Neolithic cultural layer (Hadidi, this volume) include numerous charcoal fragments of *Acacia ehrenbergiana, Tamarix* sp., and *Salsola baryosma,* pericarps from dom palm (*Hyphaene*), numerous fibers and roots of palm, some of which may be from date palm (*Phoenix*), the weeds *Calendula* and *Medicago* (both of which today occur primarily with winter crops), an unidentified grass, two grains of six-row barley (*Hordeum vulgare*), and one glume tentatively identified as barley (*Hordeum?*). These seem to represent three vegetational provinces: Mediterranean (*Hordeum* and *Calendula*), Saharo-sindian (*Salsola*), and Sudano-decanian (*Acacia*). The plant remains, as well as the fauna, suggest a generally dry savanna landscape with more luxuriant woodland vegetation around the playa margins.

A large series of radiocarbon dates has been obtained from the Neolithic layer on both charcoal and ostrich eggshells, as follows:

SMU No.	Location	Material	Date
208	Feature 132	Charcoal	7930 BP ± 40
240	Pit 1, below wash	Charcoal	8070 BP ± 70
203	Burned area	Charcoal	8010 BP ± 80
249	Pit 2, below wash	Charcoal	8040 BP ± 90
253	Humates from SMU-249	Humates	8070 BP ± 90
252	Pit 1, below wash	Charcoal	8080 BP ± 90
219	Humates from SMU-208	Humates	8120 BP ± 80
199	Feature 117, same location as SMU-191, surface	Charcoal	8120 BP ± 100
255	Pit 3, below wash	Charcoal	8130 BP ± 60
200	Trench NW of Feature 100 (1974)	Charcoal	8360 BP ± 70
191	Surface	Eggshell	7680 BP ± 70
189	Surface concentration, 10 m east of Feature 131	Eggshell	8200 BP ± 100
202	Same as SMU-189	Eggshell	8330 BP ± 110

Except for the date from sample SMU-200, which appears to be too old, even older than the date from the Terminal Paleolithic occupation, all of the dates form a tight cluster, almost within one standard deviation of 8100 BP (6150 BC). This would suggest that the time span for the Neolithic occupation at this site was short, no matter how many repeated resettlements may have been represented. This observation is reinforced by the lithostratigraphic dynamics.

Immediately above the Neolithic occupation is another thin lacustrine horizon composed of light yellowish-brown (10YR 6/2) sand, cemented to friable, with silt streaks and molluscan fauna (*Bulinus truncatus* and *Zootecus insularis*). When preserved this layer is from 10 to 15 cm thick on the flat surface, and thicker in the fill of the pits and the walk-in well. The majority of the fill in almost all the pits is the result of human activity and is composed of anthropogenic sediments and debris, which came into the pits through the dynamics of natural infilling after abandonment. The upper portion of almost all pits, however, showed the presence of the laminated lacustrine sand with molluscs and rare washed-in artifacts. This clearly indicates that the pits were not entirely filled before the aggradation of the basin began. It was quite likely that the rising lake was the reason for the abandonment of the site.

As can be seen from the transect (Figure 3.8:5), downslope from the site toward the bottom of the nearest basin, the lacustrine sand above the Neolithic layer seems to merge into the lacustrine sand unit deposited just above the dune (Figure 3.8:2b). These two lacustrine sands could not be separated in the basin (Figure 3.8:2 and 2a). The lithology and stratigraphy of these beds indicate very similar depositional regimens for both the post–Terminal Paleolithic and post–early Neolithic transgressions. The corresponding deep-water deposits were not found but they are assumed to be somewhere farther west in the basin, where the subsequent playa beds seem to exceed 5 m in thickness.

Conformably over the lacustrine sand, but without any gradations, is a unit of playa clay (Figures 3.7:9 and 3.8:6) whose upper surface is strongly wind truncated. The clay is brown (10YR 5/3), displays medium to large angular blocky structure, slickensides, and large desiccation cracks forming clear polygons and cutting the bed down to its base. The maximum measured thickness of the playa clay unit in the nearest sub-basin is 2.35 m. This clay also forms the final fill in the pits and in the well. Some pits are completely filled with clay, and presumably these had been covered by perishable organic tops that disintegrated after the clay began to accumulate. The playa clays at Site E-75-6 and E-75-9 are culturally sterile. The next recorded event in this area is the recent truncation of the playa and older sand dunes (Figure 3.9). There are no data available on the ultimate thickness of the playa bed in this area before the truncation occurred. Today, there are thin modern sand sheets over the playa in the immediate vicinity of the sites.

The dynamic interpretation of the sections at Sites E-75-6

and E-75-9 suggests two clear lacustrine pulsations separated by a local decline of the water table of at least 2 m. The first aggradation is marked by the lacustrine sands over the Terminal Paleolithic occupation; the subsequent Neolithic settlement and the well dug down to 2 m below the living floor indicate a recession of at least 2 m, but possibly even more in the interval separating the two occupations. The second aggradation, almost certainly responsible for the abandonment of the site by the Neolithic settlers, comes immediately after that occupation. The post–early Neolithic aggradation is certainly of a major character as indicated by the accumulating body of playa clays. The immediate deposition of playa clay just over the near-beach or shallow-water sandy facies indicates a rapid enlargement of the lake and the deposition of fine-grained particles in deeper water derived from the surrounding catchment area, which was supposedly covered by vegetation. From this time on the playa forms a continuous water body, presumably seasonally fluctuating and depositing silts and clays in the Nabta basin.

On the western margin of Nabta Playa is another area that was investigated in detail, and has contributed additional data toward the understanding of the history of the basin. Two of the three sites excavated in this area provided important data (Sites E-75-7 and E-75-8; see Figures 3.10–3.13).

Site E-75-7 is about 6 m higher than Sites E-75-6 and E-75-9. Here the Terminal Paleolithic occupation is embedded in the top of a laminated sand unit that rests on Nubia sandstone (Figure 3.14:1). The sand is yellow to brownish yellow (10YR 7/6 to 7/8 and 6/6), cemented and mottled, showing enrichment and reduction of iron, a pseudogley development. The bed consists of evenly laminated sand with intercalating layers of clay, light yellowish-brown (10YR 6/4) to very pale brown (10YR 7/3), displaying small jointing. The clay layers are up to 15 cm thick (Figure 3.14:1a). The dip of the bed is toward the northwest, and possibly reflects the relief of the buried Nubia sandstone. The laminated sand–clay unit is interpreted as resulting from the redeposition of eolian sands due to surface wash; however, a participation of eolian action in the building of this unit cannot be excluded. The degree of the velocity of this wash seems to be reflected in the sediment itself as either sand or clay layers, with the clay layers representing deposition of suspended particles in a body of water or low-velocity surface runoffs. This unit seems to be represented on the west side of Site E-75-8 as the oldest Quaternary sediment (Figure 3.16:2).

The next unit at Site E-75-7 is laminated lacustrine sand with silt streaks and lenses as well as reworked artifacts lying uncomfortably over the sand–clay unit (Figure 3.14:2). The lacustrine sand bed here is similar to appearance to the near-shore sand units recognized at Site E-75-6.

Conformably above the lacustrine sand is a thick body of brown (10YR 5/3) clays with medium to large blocky structure, slickensides, and polygonal desiccation cracks descending to the base of the sediment.

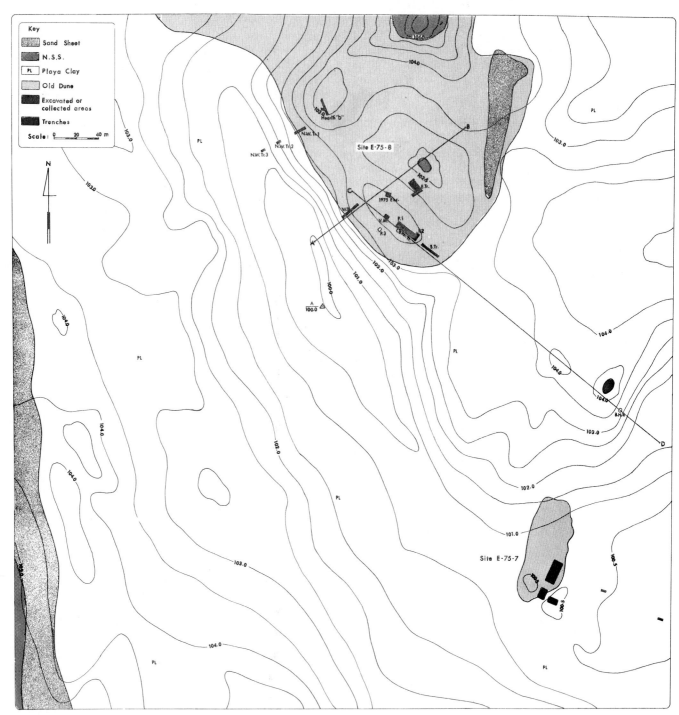

FIGURE 3.10. *Map of the western section of Nabta Playa showing location of Sites E-75-7 and E-75-8, major rock units and excavated areas. General cross sections A–B and C–D indicated by letters.*

Near the eastern edge of Site E-75-7 the clay had been recently removed by deflation and the Terminal Paleolithic occupation was exposed on the surface, as were several Neolithic artifacts, the latter all heavily windblasted. Several rounded clay-capped features were also exposed on this deflated sand surface. The subsequent excavations in-dicated that all these features were wells, sunk down to 2.5 m below the surface (Figures 3.14:4 and 3.15). An analysis of the dynamics of the sediments that fill these wells pro-vides further data for the understanding of the hydrological history of the Nabta basin.

The first phase of filling of the wells, possibly occurring

FIGURE 3.11. *View of Site E-75-7, looking southeast across site. The dark surface in middle background is playa clay. A modern barchan dune is visible on the distant horizon.*

FIGURE 3.13. *View of Site E-75-8. Figure standing on beachlike feature, contact between playa clay and dune.*

FIGURE 3.12. *Site E-75-8, looking southwest. Note mantle of fire-cracked rocks and concentrations of stones marking partially deflated hearths.*

during the use of the wells, consists of laminated sand with occasional lenses of clays, isolated burned stones, and Early Khartoum pottery. It also contains semivertical to inclined iron reduction streaks, sometimes conformable with the stratification. It is very pale brown (10YR 7/4) to yellow (10YR 7/6) in color (Figure 3.15:6).

The second phase of filling was clearly formed after the abandonment of the wells and consisted of the sediments that had been previously excavated when the wells were dug and left as backdirt around them. It consists of mixed layers of sand, blocks of indurated sands, and rolled clay chunks and blocks, all of which indicate that the wells had been dug through a layer of already deposited and indurated playa clays. The final part of the second filling in the wells displays laminated sands and lenses of microchunks of rolled clay, all possibly blown in or washed.

The third and last phase of filling in the wells is a unit of brown (10YR 5/3) playa silt and clays deposited in the shallow pans in the top of the partially filled wells (Figure 3.15:12). It showed typical blocky structure and has no laminations.

The dynamics of the infilling of the excavated wells suggest the following sequence of events: The wells were dug after the Terminal Paleolithic occupation and after the deposition and induration of playa sediment of an unknown thickness. The use of the wells demonstrates a considerable drop in the water table, which also resulted in the immediately preceding induration of the clays and sands. A second episode of rising playa covered the wells.

The sequence at Site E-75-7 is probably not the same as that found at Site E-75-6. The difference in the elevations and the presence of the relatively thick basal sands at Site

FIGURE 3.14. *General cross section of Site E-75-7. Key: 1, yellow laminated sand; 1a, playa layers; 2, lacustrine sand with reworked Terminal Paleolithic artifacts; 3, playa clay; 4, Neolithic well.*

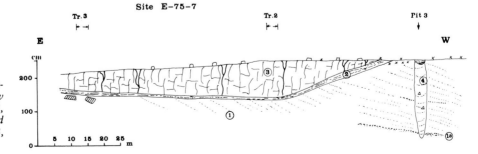

Pit 3

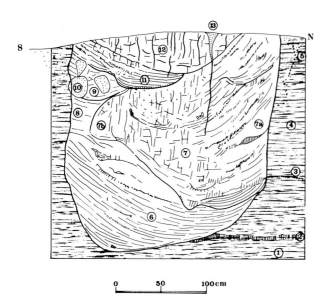

FIGURE 3.15. *Profile through Pit 3, Neolithic walk-in well. Key: 1, yellow laminated sand; 2 and 3, clay streaks; 4 and 5, yellow laminated sand, mottled, pseudogley; 6, first phase of filling, laminated sand with occasional playa lenses and burned stones; 7, second phase of filling, laminated sands and clays (7a); 7b, cemented sand; 8, laminated sand pocket with chunks of rolled clay; 9, inconspicuously laminated sand between cemented sand blocks (10); 11, third phase of filling, laminated sand and lenses of rolled clay pellets; 12, homogeneous clay; 13, desiccation crack filled with sand.*

E-75-7 indicate that the deposition of the sand–clay unit could be contemporary with the early lacustrine aggradation covering the Terminal Paleolithic cultural layers at Sites E-75-6 and E-75-9. On the other hand, the next lacustrine event at Site E-75-6, in part early Neolithic, could have been generally contemporaneous with, although slightly earlier than, that represented by the first playa clays and the preceding lacustrine sands at Site E-75-7. If so, then it indicates that at that moment the maximal seasonal stands of the water in the basin represented by the playa silts covering Site E-75-6 were at least 6 m higher than at Site E-75-6.

The wells dug through the playa clays obviously indicate a general recession of groundwater to at least 2 m below the surface at Site E-75-7, which was temporary, but not seasonal. The next rising of the water is indicated by the playa clay plugs in the tops of the almost entirely filled wells. This last sequence of recession and aggradation is well represented in the nearby site of E-75-8.

Some 300 m northwest of Site E-75-7 is an elongated sandy hill, standing 6 m above Site E-75-7 and formed around outcrops of Nubia sandstone (Figure 3.10). The whole deflated top of the hill and the adjacent playa surface are littered with fire-cracked rocks and other cultural debris. It is an enormous area of occupations, the full extent of which was not accurately determined, but a surface more than 500 m long and 300 m wide is indicated. It doubtless represents numerous occupations over a long period of time.

When first seen, the surface of the hill was dotted by many partially or totally deflated hearths composed of fire-cracked sandstone rocks. A beachlike feature, marked by a line or concentration of fire-cracked rocks, was evident along the southwest and western margins of the hill, a de-

flated contact between the playa clays and the sandy knoll.

The site (E-75-8) was tested during the 1975 season and further excavated in 1977. These excavations, consisting of a series of trenches, pits, and bore holes, provide the basic data for the next part of the Nabta Playa history. Two general sections (Figures 3.10, 3.16, and 3.17), record the geological past of this locality. In the topographic lows of the rolling surface of Nubia sandstone is a more or less horizontally laminated sand with streaks of clay, identical to that at Site E-75-7 (Figures 3.16:2 and 3.17:2). Here it is culturally sterile; however, the unit was exposed in only a few trenches.

Conformably above the sand is a playa clay bed of 3 m maximum thickness. The clay displays coarse, blocky structure and slickensides, and it is deeply desiccated (Figures 3.16:3 and 3.17:3). Its upper surface is truncated by both early Holocene and modern deflation. It also is culturally sterile.

A dune is deposited over the deflational basin, deeply cut into the playa clay, on the top of the hill and against the rising Nubia sandstone in the southeastern portion of the knoll (Figures 3.16:4 and 3.17:4). The dune fills the wide and deep desiccation cracks opened in the underlying playa clays, and shows foreset and topset bedding. The formation of this dune was preceded by a sand sheet laid down over the deflated playa clay surface. The dune is cemented to consolidated, yellow (ranging from 7.5YR 6/6 to 6/8 and 10YR 7/6), and culturally sterile.

Over the dune is a complex of cultural sandy strata, much destroyed in the northwest section of the site but well preserved in the southernmost tip. The lowest of these (Figure 3.17:5) is a thick (up to 1 m) layer of sand with charcoal flecks and powder, artifacts, fire-cracked stones, Early Khartoum pottery, and several superimposed concave

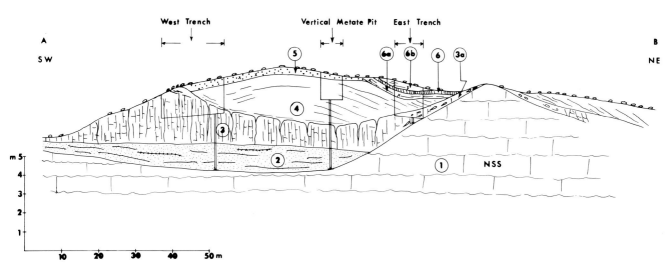

EL NABTA, SITE E-75-8

GENERAL CROSS-SECTION

FIGURE 3.16. *General cross section through Site E-75-8 along A–B line (see Figure 3.10). Key: 1, Nubia sandstone; 2, yellow sands with clay lenses; 3, truncated playa clays with deep desiccation polygons; 3a, washed Nubia sandstone rubble in playa silt matrix; 4, dune sand; 5, lower cultural layer, grading into silt and clay; 6, silty sand; 6a and b, laminated reworked dune sand with washed-in artifacts.*

rock-lined and rock-filled hearths (Figure 3.18). The layer is brown to light brownish-gray (ranging from 10YR 5/2–5/3 to 10YR 6/2–6/4) and black in the infillings of the hearth basins. It is exposed on the surface on the southern and central part of this settlement; there, however, the lower cultural layer is partially deflated and much thinner. The lower cultural layer is consolidated to loose when on the surface and has no bedding except for the lines of hearths, which occur in at least five sequential settings (Figure 3.19:2a–2d). Down the slope, toward the southeast, this layer grades into brown (10YR 5/3) silty sand, which farther down becomes typical playa clay (Figure 3.20:2e). In the lower southern portion this layer is overlapped by a bed of silt that is mottled, showing iron reduction stains, medium blocky structure, and vertical jointings (Figures 3.17:6 and 3.20:2f). It becomes more sandy upslope and grades into the previously described playa clay downslope. There are occasional hearths at the contact between the playa and the underlying sand (Figure 3.19:2c). In the eastern section of the site this layer is destroyed by beach sands, which show inconspicuous lamination and more washed-in artifacts and land snails (*Zootecus insularis*) (Figures 3.16:6a and 3.21:3). Just above this beach sand is the silty sand with traces of lamination, consolidated, containing numerous washed-in land snails (Figures 3.16:6 and 3.21:3). The snail shells from this layer yielded a radiocarbon date of 9240 BP ± 80 years (SMU-472), a date some 2000 years earlier than that for charcoal from corresponding layers in the Connecting Trench. A second series of beach sand overlies the silty sand. This sand is loose to

consolidated, laminated with root casts, rare land snails, and isolated hearths, and contains some artifacts (Figures 3.16:6b and 3.21:5). It is obvious that the beach sequence at the eastern section of the site is equivalent to the playa clays at the lower, southern part of the site.

The fauna associated with this first Neolithic horizon at Site E-75-8 includes caprovid (sheep/goat) as a minor element initially, but becoming most numerous at the top of the unit, followed by the small gazelle (*G. rufifrons*), hare (*Lepus capensis*), and a large gazelle (*G. dama?*). Other forms present include cattle(?) (26 specimens), hedgehog (Erinaceidae), porcupine (*Hystrix cristata*), unidentified birds, reptiles, and small rodents. The decline in the frequency of hare in Site E-75-8, when compared with the Neolithic level at Site E-75-6, may indicate more arid conditions (Gautier, this volume), or perhaps a change in hunting strategy.

Plant remains from the upper part of the lower cultural horizon include roots of palm, a pericarp of dom palm, several grains of six-row barley (*Hordeum vulgare*), one of emmer wheat (*Triticum dicoccum*), numerous unidentified grass and tubular roots, and a wild date palm seed, probably *Phoenix reclinata* Jacq., a small tropical African palm with edible fruits known from Darfur, Gebel Marra, and southern Sudan. Charred wood was present but has not yet been identified.

Several radiocarbon dates were obtained from this layer. From slightly above the base in Pit 3, charcoal dated 6960 BP ± 150 years (SMU-421); two samples from hearths in the middle of the horizon dated 6690 BP ± 80 years

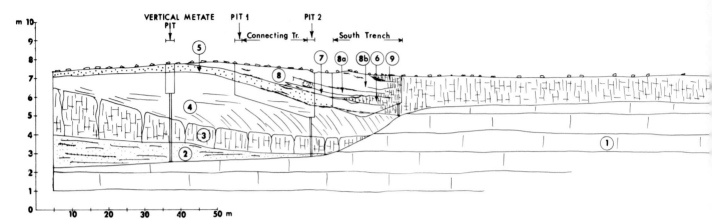

FIGURE 3.17. *General cross section through Site E-75-8 along C–D line (see Figure 3.10). Key: 1–5 as in Figure 3.16; 6, playa silts; 7, middle cultural layer; 8, sand with undifferentiated cultural material; 8a, lower portion of upper cultural layer, shows numerous vegetation*

FIGURE 3.18. *View of Connecting Trench and Pit 2, Site E-75-8, during excavation.*

(SMU-424) and 6570 BP ± 70 years (SMU-452). A sample from somewhere in the lower part of the unit (in Vertical Metate Pit) gave a date of 7120 BP ± 150 years (SMU-242), and charcoal from a deflated hearth at the north end of the site (but undoubtedlfy associated with this horizon) dated 6700 BP ± 50 years (SMU-261). A hearth at the very base of the overlying horizon dated 6500 BP ± 80 years (SMU-435). These six dates indicate a time range for the lower Early Khartoum cultural horizon at Site E-75-8 from around 7000 BP to 6600 BP (5050–4650 BC) or about 1000 years later than the Early Khartoum occupation at Site E-75-6.

The layers above the lowest Neolithic horizon are pre-served only in the southern portion of the site and in the adjacent silts and clays between this site and E-75-7.

The playa clastic sediments (Figure 3.20:2f) that cover the lowest Neolithic layer mark a temporary positive pulsa-tion. This temporary aggradation of playa silts is followed by a small recession reflected in the deposition of light yellowish-brown (10YR 6/4), consolidated to loose eolian sand (Figures 3.17:7 and 3.20:3) over the silt downslope and over the earliest Neolithic horizon slightly upslope. The bed of sand is thin (20–30 cm) and contains numerous rounded small sand nodules cemented by calcium carbon-ate. Farther upslope, it merges with an 80-cm-thick layer of very pale brown (10YR 7/4) sand, without any evident bedding and in total obviously contemporaneous with sev-eral succeeding events of deposition in the playa–dune bor-der zone. The yellowish brown sand bed (Figures 3.17:8 and 3.20:5) contains a middle cultural layer with Early Khartoum pottery, stone tools, and several rock-lined fire-places (Figure 3.20:3a), some of them in shallow basins cut into the underlying playa silts. A few fireplaces and a shal-low pit (Square 5–6) excavated farther upslope, at the base of the pale brown sand, may be associated with this occu-pational horizon. Plant remains from this layer include the fragments of three weeds today commonly associated with cultivation (*Calendula, Tribulus longipetalus,* and *Sol-anum*), palm roots, and several as yet unidentified frag-ments of wood, tubulars, grasses, and a cereal. The only date available for this horizon is that of 6500 BP ± 80 years (SMU-435) from the contact with the underlying lowest cultural layer.

A pale brown (10YR 6/3) to light yellowish-brown (10YR 6/4) consolidated to almost loose eolian sand covers

SITE E-75-8

CTION

casts and grades into lacustrine silts; 8b, higher portion of upper cultural layer, grades into lacustrine silts; 9, uppermost playa clays. Bore holes indicated by vertical columns.

the middle cultural layer (Figures 3.17:8a and 3.20:4). Downslope the sand grades into sandy silt (Figure 3.20:4a), and even farther downslope into silt (Figure 3.20:4a). Upslope this unite disappears into the very pale brown unstratified sand. The middle section of this sand shows vegetation casts in a distinctive mat. It also contains small calcium carbonate nodules. In the downslope section at the

playa–dune border zone, this layer is clearly stratified into two horizons. The first merges into slightly areally expanding silts (Figure 3.20:4a); and the second overlaps the playa silts (Figure 3.20:4c, 4d). The archaeological materials embedded in the pale brown sand bed and the contemporaneous silts and clays in the dune–playa border zone form the lower part of the upper cultural horizon at the site.

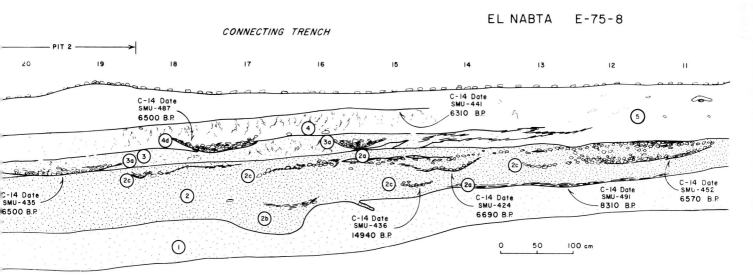

FIGURE 3.19. *Profile of Connecting Trench and Pit 2, Site E-75-8. Key: 1, dune sand; 2, lower cultural layer; 2a, lens of charcoal at base of lower cultural layer; 2b, pit; 2c, stone-lined hearths; 2d, lens of eolian (?) sand; 2e, silty sand; 2f, playa silt; 3, middle cultural layer; 3a, stone-lined hearths; 4, lower portion of upper cultural layer showing numerous vegetation casts; 4a, silty sand grading into silt; 4c, charcoal-enriched upper portion of unit; 4d, stone-lined hearths; 5, upper cultural layer, undifferentiated in northern portion; 5a, charcoal lenses; 5b, silty sand; 5d, laminated sand; 5e, stone-lined hearth; 5f, cultural pit filled with playa silt; 6, playa clay; 6a, stone-lined hearth at base of unit.*

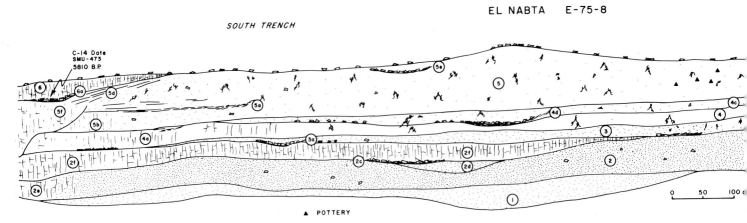

FIGURE 3.20. *Profile of portion of South Trench, Site E-75-8. Key as in Figure 3.19.*

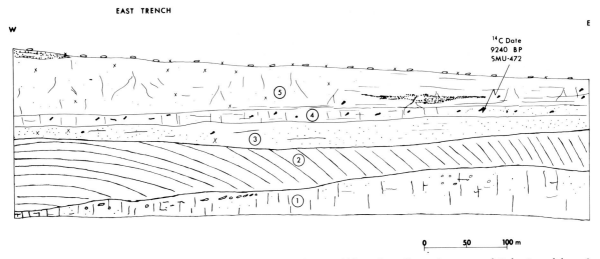

FIGURE 3.21. *Profile of East Trench, Site E-75-8. Key: 1, Nubia sandstone rubble in playa silt matrix, truncated; 2, laminated dune; 3 and 5, reworked sand with inconspicuous lamination and washed-in cultural layer, contains rare land snails; 4, silty sand with numerous land snails.*

The cultural materials here are clearly less intense than in the lower horizons; however, there are a few rock-lined, basin-shaped hearths, mostly at the base and in the lower part of this sand. The archaeological content of the lower section of the upper cultural horizon also reflects a major change in ceramics and stone tools, both chipped and ground. Charcoal from a hearth in the top of this horizon in the upslope section gave a radiocarbon date of 6310 BP ± 80 years (SMU-441), only some 200 years later than the youngest dates from the underlying Khartoum horizon at this site.

A thick, although deflated, bed up to 1 m thick, of slightly consolidated to loose eolian sand, overlies the pale brown sand and forms the upper section of the upper cul-

tural layer. This top sand (Figures 3.17:8b and 3.20:5) is very pale brown in color (10YR 7/4), mottled with pseudogley iron enrichment and reduction stains, and contains rare root casts. Upslope this unit forms a uniform sand bed together with the two previously described horizons. Downslope, however, it grades into silty sand and later into playa silt (Figure 3.20:5b, 5d). There are occasional rock-lined hearths and charcoal lenses (Figure 3.20:5a) within the horizon. Charcoal from one of these hearths, near the top of the unit, dated 5810 BP ± years (SMU-473). The deflated surface of this sand is armored with dropped hearthstones, which now serve to prevent further deflation. A dug pit, filled with later playa (Figure 3.20:5f), was excavated from the top of this layer to a depth of 90 cm into the underlying units. The cultural material from the uppermost strata at Site E-75-8 is similar to that in the immediately underlying sand, and the archaeological content of the two units has been described as the upper cultural horizon.

A bed of playa clay (Figure 3.20:6) overlaps conformably the uppermost sand unit in the downslope sector. It is typical playa clay, brown (10YR 5/3), with blocky structure and iron reduction stained areas. A rock-lined hearth (Figure 3.20:6a) occurs at the very base of the clay bed. Numerous fire-cracked rocks also cover the deflated surface of the playa clays; however, there are very few artifacts among the surface debris in this area. The topmost playa clays represent a small positive pulsation and the last Holocene sediments recorded at Site E-75-8.

El Kortein Playa

About 20 km north of Nabta Playa is another and much smaller basin, one of several, situated at the south side of the middle mountain of an unnamed three-mountain group that forms an east–west line of outliers in front of the Eocene ecscarpment. We gave these three light-colored mountains the informal name of Gebal El Beid (White Mountains). A steplike ascent toward the mountains forms the north edge of this playa. The main drainage into the basin evident in the morphology comes from the north as a short but wide wadi, choked with sand dunes and gravels. Several sandstone hills, some of which are at least 50 m high, border the playa on the northeast and northwest sides. Veneers of alluvial gravel cover the flat surfaces of some of the bordering sandstone hills, and a few very rolled flakes occurred within the top of the gravel cover. These alluvial gravels, undoubtedly Quaternary in age, indicate the magnitude of erosion that has taken place during the late Pleistocene.

The terrain to the south of the playa gently slopes toward the north, following the dip of the underlying Nubia Formation. The landscape in that area is totally controlled by deflation with exposed Nubia Formation sediments on the surface—shales, weathered and powdered, as well as sandstone, the latter usually occurring in the form of low ridges or hills. A thin bed of desert pavement and/or wash covers the sandstone and shale beds in the low basin-like, wind-scoured depressions. There are also a few very small closed drainage basins in this area with very thin plates of intercalating sand sheets and modern playa silts showing—in some cases, several alternating layers. A few dry *kharit* bushes find their place in the midst of these small basins, indicating occasional, recent weak rains (Figure 3.22).

The studied basin, slightly more than 1 km in diameter (Figure 3.23), was given the name of El Kortein Playa ("the ball playa") because of the concentration of large naturally formed balls, concretions of silicified limestone derived from the Garra Formation and found in a shallow wadi entering the basin from the northeast.

The central portion of the El Kortein basin is deeply

FIGURE 3.22. *View of Site E-77-3, El Kortein Playa, looking west.*

deflated, exposing underlying sands and eroded clays, and numerous artifacts in lag position and/or eroding from the desiccated lower sediments. The margins of the playa are covered by a thin veneer of gravel and alluvial wash masking the exact extent of the playa sediments. Trenching and boring in the north side, however, demonstrated that the playa silts extend up to the foot of the bordering Nubia sandstone hills. In the very center of the basin, over the exposed oldest sands, is a small area of laminated recent playa silts and sand sheets formed in a shallow depression around a few *kharit* bushes. Modern sand dunes enter the basin from the north along a line of small sandstone hills, and falling dunes form just at the foot of the bordering hills on the northeast side.

Three sites, two of Terminal Paleolithic and one of Neolithic age, were excavated and trenched here. In addition, four bore holes were sunk to the bottom of the basin. These provide the data that permit the reconstruction of the lithostratigraphic sequence.

The lowest Quaternary unit is a bed of sand resting directly on Nubia sandstone (Figure 3.24:2). It is laminated, yellow (7.5YR 6/6 to 10YR 6/6), cemented in the upper portion to consolidated farther down. The sand is covered by a thin unit of brownish yellow (10YR 6/6) silty sands, deposited over the truncated surface (Figure 3.24:2b). The exposed top is mottled, showing pseudogley iron enrichment and reduction areas as well as numerous root casts forming nets and/or mesh (Figure 3.24:2a). The surface of the sand is not leveled, but is slightly rolling, indicating that eolian action could have played a role in the deposition of the lower sand bed. The sand appears to have formed a low topographic rise near the bottom of the basin. Although the main sand body appears to be basically of eolian origin, its upper portion is lacustrine.

Several concentrations of Terminal Paleolithic artifacts were recorded eroding from the top of the thin silty sand bed and/or lying on the surface. One of the best of these, Site E-77-3 (E101G1), was collected and excavated. Here

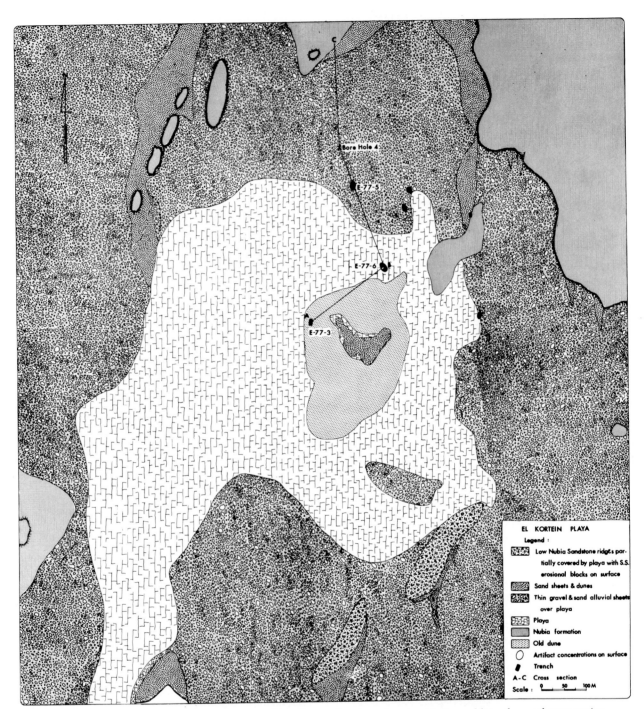

FIGURE 3.23. *Geological sketch of El Kortein Playa, showing location of excavated sites and line of general cross section.*

the cultural layer is at the very top of the silty yellow sand. The surface collection contains a few highly eolized artifacts, apparent Neolithic admixtures, but basically the collection is homogeneous and of Terminal Paleolithic age. Faunal preservation was poor but included the following species: red-fronted gazelle (*G. rufifrons*); a small, unidentified gazelle; hare (*Lepus capensis*); porcupine (*Hystrix*

cristata); and a large bovid, believed to be domestic cattle. A sample of charcoal from two *in situ* hearths (Figure 3.24:2c) gave a radiocarbon date of 8840 BP ± 90 years (SMU-416).

The next event in the history of the El Kortein basin is the deposition of playa clays over the yellow silty sand (Figure 3.24:3). The clays are light yellowish-brown (10YR 6/4),

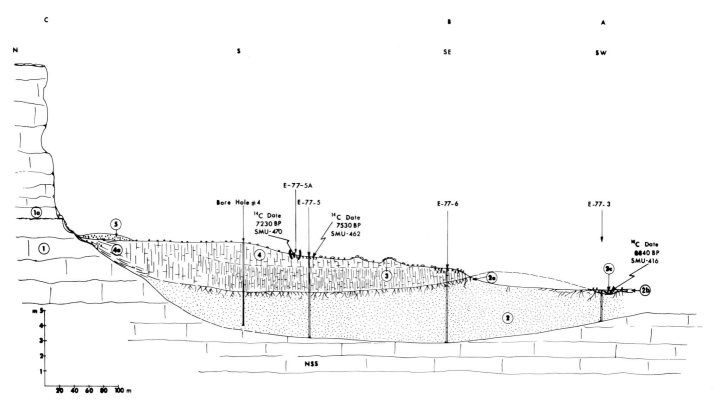

FIGURE 3.24. *General cross section of El Kortein Playa. Key: 1, Nubia sandstone; 2, dune sand; 2a, mat of vegetation casts; 2b, silty sand with Terminal Paleolithic cultural layer at top; 2c, hearth basins filled with sandy silt; 3, lower playa clay unit with Terminal Paleolithic cultural layer at top; 4, upper playa silt unit with embedded Neolithic sites; 4a, beach zone; 5, modern wash.*

and show medium angular blocky structures and numerous slickensides. The upper portion of the bed contains a large Terminal Paleolithic site, E-77-6 (E101G3), the cultural layer of which is about 30 cm thick and is clearly churned up by contracting playa clays. The associated bones and charcoal flecks are ground and highly fragmented, and the flint artifacts show typical silt polish resulting from the churning process. Many of the artifacts were found in an upright position. The upper portion of these clays resembles vertisols, now highly cemented. The site could not be radiocarbon dated because of the destruction of the charcoal, nor was there any identifiable fauna.

Above the vertisol-like, churned-up lower playa clays is a bed of playa silts, consolidated to loose at places, without evident bedding or angular structure (Figure 3.24:4). It is light yellowish-brown (10YR 6/4) and contains fine casts of vegetation mesh, particularly in the area around Site E-77-5 (E101G2). The character of the contact of this unit with the underlying clays is not clear; however, the drastic change of sedimentation and the environment indicated by the churning of the lower clays and the difference in texture is indicative of two varying regimens.

At the foot of the surrounding sandstone hills on the north, a beach facies marks the limits of the basin in this vicinity. The beach is made up of laminated silty sands and sands with partially rolled, and some almost angular, ferruginous sandstone pebbles and gravels over a sandstone "terrace." The laminated sands and silts grade downslope into the main body of playa clays and silts.

The surface of the upper silt in the northeast section of the basin is littered with artifacts. An oval concentration of these, partially *in situ*, was excavated and designated as Site E-77-5. It is a Neolithic settlement containing Early Khartoum style pottery. The associated fauna is rare and consists of the following species: red-fronted gazelle (*G. rufifrons*), hare (*Lepus capensis*), a small unidentified rodent, and a large bovid, believed to be domestic cattle. A small sample of charcoal from a hearth in the near center of the oval concentration gave a radiocarbon date of 7530 BP ± 180 years (SMU-462).

Nearby were two stone-walled structures embedded in the upper silt at the same general elevation as the oval concentration. These were designated as Site E-77-5A, and one of the structures was excavated. It contained some Early Khartoum pottery, a few lithic artifacts, and a hearth on the floor adjacent to the east wall. Charcoal from this hearth dated 7230 BP ± 100 years (SMU-470). The deflation at Site E-77-5 and 5A and the thickening of the playa silts to the north indicate that at least 1 m of silts formed after the occupation of these two localities.

El Gebal El Beid Playa

Some 10 km north of El Kortein Playa, on the other side of the range of three mountains, is another and much larger basin, which we named El Gebal El Beid Playa (Figure 3.25). It is a huge basin, extending for several kilometers, and it has not been mapped in detail. El Gebal El Beid Playa seems to occupy the area between the northern footslopes of the range of three mountains and the next Nubia sandstone step before the Eocene scarp. There are isolated sandstone ridges and small hills within the basin, as well as low irregular sandstone and/or shale rises separating the playa into several usually small sub-basins (Figure 3.26). One of these contained a few small concentrations of artifacts, both Neolithic and Terminal Paleolithic in age. The Neolithic ones were highly wind-worn and seen only on the surface. One of the Terminal Paleolithic concentrations, designated as Site E-77-7 (E101G4), was selected for collection and excavation because it contained obviously fresh material just eroded from the deflated surface of playa sediments in the floor of the basin. The excavations in this basin were limited to the tests at this concentration and to two bore holes. These provide the basic data for the lithostratigraphy of one of the sub-basins.

A thick bed of fine- to medium-grained dune sand fills the central portion of the sub-basin (Figure 3.27:2). The sand is yellow (10YR 7/8, 7/6), and the bed contains several thin horizons of sandy playa silts, often laminated, pale brown (10YR 6/4, 6/3), ranging in thickness from 1 to 3 cm (Figure 3.27:2a). Toward the edge of the basin these sands and silts grade into or interfinger with powdered silty sand mixed with small gravel, fragments of shale and/or sandstone, which are rounded to slightly rounded, and streaks of laminated playa, also containing slightly rolled fragments of ferruginous sandstone. It is an obvious near-beach feature of the temporary basin, with several genera-

FIGURE 3.25. *View across the basins where El Gebal El Beid Playa is located, looking northeast from near the base of the central hill of the three-hill group. Note scarp in foreground, which forms southern edges of the enclosed basin system.*

tions of wash present (Figure 3.27:3). Upward, the lateral wash–beach bed grades into slightly sandy playa silts and clays, light yellowish-brown (10YR 6/4), consolidated to cemented (Figure 3.27:4) with rare blocky structure. The bed contains rare lenses of unsorted sand (Figure 3.27:4a).

Still higher is a bed of finely laminated sandy silts showing mats of root casts throughout the bed. Its surface is deflated, but several remnants standing up to 2 m above the truncated surface witness a once much thicker bed of these laminated silts and fine sands.

Within the truncated top of the laminated silts and sands is the cultural horizon of Site E-77-7. The faunal remains are scarce; however, they include red-fronted gazelle (*G. rufifrons*), a small unidentified gazelle, and a large bovid, believed to be domestic cattle.

At the foot of the elongated Nubia sandstone hill bordering the investigated sub-basin on the west is a bed of powdered shale and sandstone rubble that seemingly grades down into the lateral playa wash–beach facies (Figure 3.27:6). Sandstone slabs, obviously fallen from the top of the adjacent knoll, cover the rubble and shale bed.

BRIEF SUMMARY OF EVENTS IN THE NABTA AREA

The Quaternary sequence in the basins below the Eocene and Kiseiba scarps begins everywhere with a long period of pronounced deflation that destroyed most of the older sediments, leaving them as deflated, unconnected remnants. This period of deflation is responsible for the extensive lowering of the desert, excavation of basins, and the total stratigraphic break between the older Pleistocene sediments and the most recent series. Although the age of this pronounced superarid phase has not been established, it is certain that it must be placed somewhere between the Aterian and about 9500 BP, as indicated by the radiocarbon date obtained at El Gebal El Beid Playa.

A forerunner of a considerable change in the sedimentation pattern is the deposition of eolian sands in the bottom of the deflated basins, sometimes in the form of seemingly phytogenic dunes, surface washes composed of reworked dune sands, and thin silt and/or clay beds. It appears to be a period of scattered but heavy rainfalls within a still basically arid climate, probably not very different from that of today. This change occurred before 9000 BP.

The gradual increase in precipitation and the appearance of vegetational cover eventually led to the formation of playa lakes depositing silts and clays in the lower portions of the basins (Playa I). It should be noted, however, that the forming of silt and/or clay was also dependent on the rock characteristics of the catchment area and the presence of the exposure of shale outcrops within the drainage basin. Local, individual, geomorphic, rock, and vegetational characteristics, as well as the size of the catchment areas, should account for the presence of silts and clays earlier in some of the basins (e.g., El Gebal El Beid Playa) than in

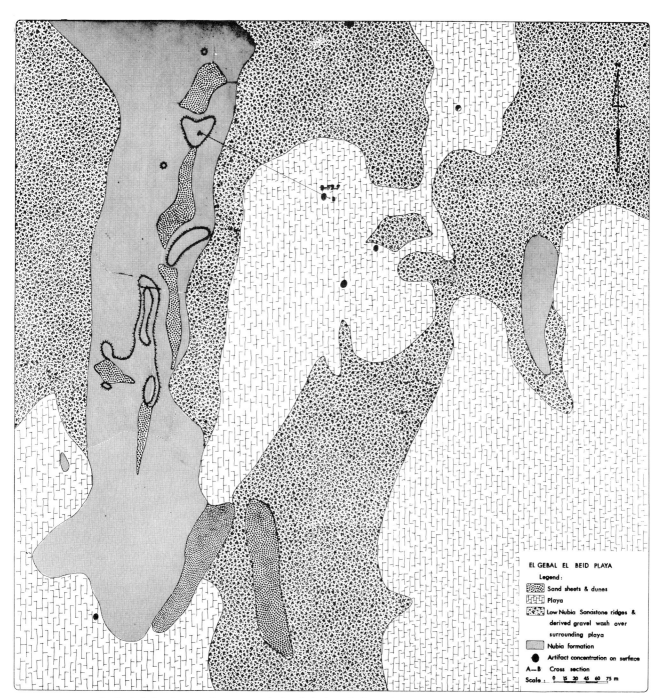

FIGURE 3.26. *Geological sketch map of a portion of El Gebal El Beid Playa, showing artifact concentrations and line of general cross section (A–B).*

others (e.g., El Kortein). Despite these differences it is certain that the playas were established by 9000 BP and possibly slightly earlier.

There is no doubt that the seasonal expansion and shrinkage of playa lakes were responses to the local precipitation pattern—however, some more pronounced pulsations in this pattern are suggested in this early part of the sequence.

Examples of a positive phase of such a pulsation are the near-shore and beach sediments deposited over the Terminal Paleolithic settlement at Site E-75-6 and the lower clay unit over Site E-77-3 in the sequence of El Kortein. This expansion of the lake (Playa I) seems to have occurred after 8900 BP, and possibly after 8600 BP, if the date from the Terminal Paleolithic occupation at Site E-75-6 is correct.

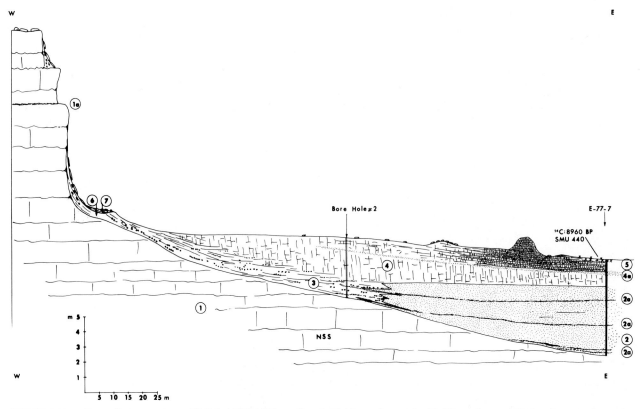

FIGURE 3.27. *General cross section at El Gebal El Beid Playa. Key: 1, Nubia sandstone; 1a, Nubia sandstone deflational terrace; 2, sand; 2a, silt and/or clay lenses; 3, silty sand with gravels and sandstone rolled fragments, beach facies; 4, playa clays; 4a, sand lenses; 5, laminated playa silts with numerous root casts and exposed Terminal Paleolithic cultural layer; 6, powdered shale and sandstone grading into beach; 7, modern dune sand.*

An obvious negative pulsation is recorded at Site E-75-6 in the water-table drop of more than 2 m, which must have preceded the earliest Neolithic occupation at that site. This drier phase, of unknown time span, also seems to be documented at Site E-77-6 in El Kortein Playa, where a very extensive Terminal Paleolithic settlement was established on the playa clays and churned up by contracting clays instead of being covered by accumulating lacustrine sediments of this phase. This drying trend must have begun before 8100 BP, and almost certainly was reversed immediately after that date, as indicated by the combined cultural and sedimentary evidence of playa clays being deposited over partially filled Neolithic pits at Site E-75-6.

The expanding playa clays (Playa II) over the early Neolithic settlement at E-75-6 are believed to be the same as those that underlie the dune at Site E-75-8 and the clays through which the Neolithic wells at E-75-7 were dug. The volume of the sediment accumulation of this playa lake is documented at Site E-75-8, where the clays attained a thickness of at least 3 m.

Playa II is followed by a major episode of aridity, which is well documented at Site E-75-8 following the deposition of the middle playa sediments. Here the Playa II clays that were previously accumulated and then cut by deep desiccation polygons are deflated and covered by a dune.

The next expansion of playa and increase in precipitation are shown by a series of clays and silts abutting the dune at Site E-75-8 (Playa III). The oldest date for the beginning of this event at Site E-75-8 is around 7000 BP.

The events associated with the upper section of the sequence at El Kortein Playa were slightly different from those at Nabta. According to the radiocarbon dates from Sites E-77-5 and 5A, the accumulation of the upper series of lacustrine silts in this basin must have begun slightly before 7000 BP, a date in general agreement with the chronology of the events at Site E-75-8 in Nabta Playa.

In short, the building up of Playa III continues from at least slightly before 7000 BP, until 5820 BP, with several minor pulsations as shown in the southern section at Site E-75-8 where sandy, eolian, and anthropogenic layers at times encroach on the playa silts and at other times are covered by them. These fluctuations, however, are regarded as of a minor nature within a period of a well-established pattern of precipitation.

ASSOCIATED ARCHAEOLOGY

There are two major archaeological entities associated with the Holocene playa sediments in the Nabta area. The older of these, embedded in the tops of dunes, in runoff-eolian sediments, and in silts of Playa I, is of Terminal Paleolithic character. The second entity is a Neolithic with pottery and apparently domesticated cereals. Both the Terminal Paleolithic and the Neolithic are associated with domestic (?) cattle (Gautier, this volume).

Numerous sites of these two entities occur in every basin between the Nile Valley and the Kiseiba scarp, including a huge playa that parallels that scarp east of Bir Kiseiba. The number of sites or occupation units cannot be estimated, because in most instances they are deflated, secondarily dispersed, and mixed. A typical example is at the very foot of Gebel Nabta, adjacent to another large but unmapped playa where there is a very extensive area, perhaps a kilometer or more in length, that is littered with lithic artifacts, mostly Neolithic. Only a few pieces of pottery were evident, the remainder having been destroyed by thermal and deflational action. One small area here was tested (Site E-77-1), but it was abandoned when the extent of the deflation became evident. The sites selected for intensive excavation were limited to those that seemed to offer the greatest potential. The major emphasis was in Nabta Playa, where all the identified *in situ* sites were excavated.

TERMINAL PALEOLITHIC

There appear to be four distinct taxonomic units represented in the Terminal Paleolithic assemblages of the Nabta area. Six of the best sites known, each containing at least some *in situ* material, were studied in detail. All except one site have traces of later Neolithic occupations in the same locality, and two of them had major Neolithic settlements in stratigraphically higher positions. The geomorphic situations that were selected for both the Terminal Paleolithic and Neolithic occupations were basically the same—that is, on dunes surrounded by playa (Sites E-75-6, E-75-9, and E-77-3), on dunes or higher sandy areas along playa margins (Site E-75-7), and on seasonally dry playa surfaces (Sites E-77-6 and E-77-7). The coincidence of Neolithic and Terminal Paleolithic occupations in the same localities suggests that little or no basic geomorphic changes occurred between the two major periods of occupation.

Site E-77-7 (E101G4)

The oldest of the four Terminal Paleolithic taxonomic units is represented by a small assemblage recovered from Site E-77-7 at El Gebal El Beid Playa and dated at 8960 BP ± 110 years (SMU-440). It was a thin but well-marked concentration, oval in outline, measuring 8 by 10 m (Figure 3.28). Excavation and the semifresh condition of the artifacts indicated that almost all of the concentration had been recently deflated and exposed on the surface. Only the base of a fireplace, which yielded the charcoal from which the radiocarbon date was obtained, and a very few lithic artifacts and bones were preserved within the sediment. The position of the fireplace within the bedded playa silts indicates that the occupation took place during a seasonal, dry interval. The finds consist of stone artifacts, numerous fragments of ostrich eggshell, and a few eggshell beads. The horizontal distribution of artifacts is not even. There is a small subconcentration of eggshell fragments and stone along the east side, another eggshell-fragment cluster in the center, and a very small knocker pile near the northwest corner. Despite these subconcentrations, however, the few articulations between artifacts extend across the total site area, suggesting only a single occupational unit.

The lithic assemblage is numerically small and is made on brown Eocene chert. The cores are either the single- or opposed-platform varieties for blades, usually well prepared with preshaped flaking surfaces and backs, mostly wedge-like (Figure 3.29). There is only one core classified as change of orientation for flakes. The blades are narrow and elegant, showing in several instances traces of core preparation on their dorsal surfaces.

The tool assemblage contains only 90 pieces, but its structure is quite clear (Figure 3.37). The most important element, accounting for almost 50% of the assemblage, are backed bladelets, mostly composed of the straight-backed and pointed variety, with the arch-backed and pointed specimens second in number (Figure 3.30). Worked bases are rare in both varieties. Other backed bladelets include a few La Mouillah points (or backed bladelets with microburin scars), shouldered, and gibbous examples. The next important tool class is that of notches and denticulates (around 14%) (Figure 3.31), followed by truncations (10%), mostly on bladelets. The microburin technique is mostly represented by Krukowski microburins and bladelets with microburin scars. The Krukowski microburins are obviously associated with the shaping of the tips of pointed backed bladelets. Burins are rare, but present, and there are also a few perforators, almost all double backed. There were only two endscrapers recovered, and there were no geometrics.

The assemblage from Site E-77-7, although small, stands apart from all other Western Desert Terminal Paleolithic collections known. Some of its characteristics, like the emphasis on straight-backed and pointed-backed bladelets and the absence or rarity of geometrics, recall the Shamarkian and Qarunian assemblages from along the Nile and in the Fayum Depression, although the core technology seems to be different.

The next group, only about 200 years later, is represented by the assemblages recovered at Sites E-77-3 and E-75-6 (lower layer). Also possibly of this group are parts of the surface collections at the mixed Terminal Paleolithic and Neolithic localities of E-75-7 and E-77-4.

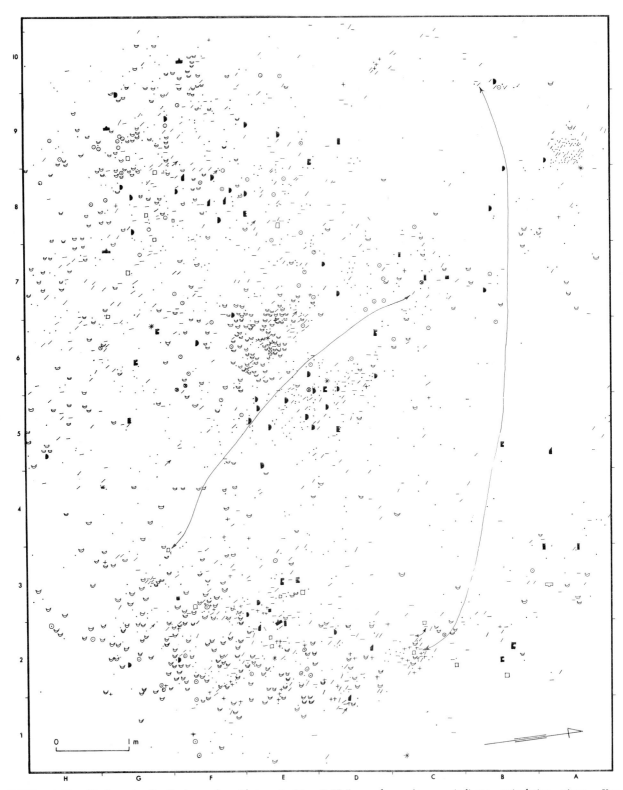

FIGURE 3.28. *Horizontal distribution of artifacts at Site E-77-7, surface. Arrows indicate articulating pieces. Key: · Chip; ∕ Blade; – Flake; ∗ Retouched piece; ▽ Burin spall; ◀ Truncation; ⊗ Misc. piece; ◖ Lunate; ✹ Stemmed point; ▲ Perforator; ⊔ Hammer stone; ▮ Denticulate; ∕ Microburin; + Bone; ▫ Potsherd; ◡ Ostrich eggshell; ⊠ Bifacial piece; ● Ogival base; □ Core; ▲ Triangle; ▮ Notch; ▮ Burin; ˢ Scaled piece; ▲ Endscraper; ▲ Trapeze; ▶ Backed blade; ⊕ Grinding stone; ⊙ Bead; ▼ Point; ▪ Scraper; ▲ Bifacial arrowhead; ▮ Strangulated pc.; □ Ochre; ˢ Shell; ᶜ Charcoal; ◕ Burned clay; ◇ Polished rock; ◠ Stones.*

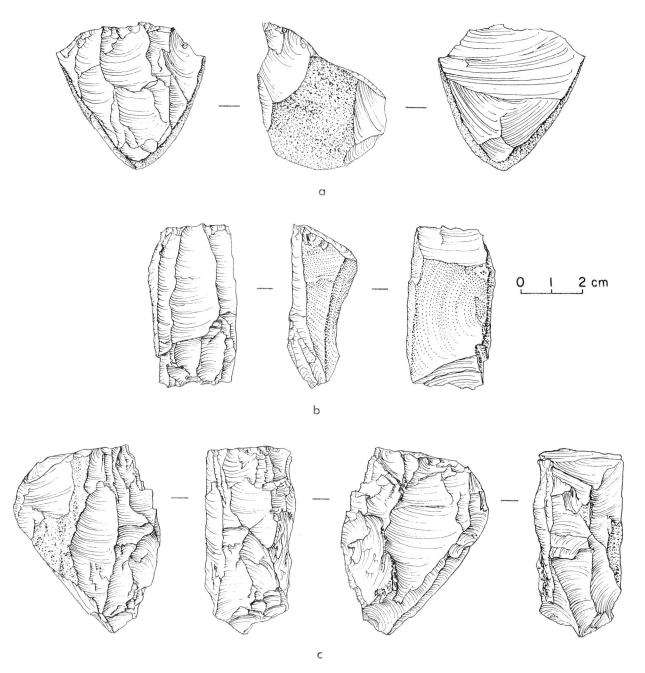

FIGURE 3.29. *Cores from Site E-77-7: (a) Single platform; (b, c) opposed platform.*

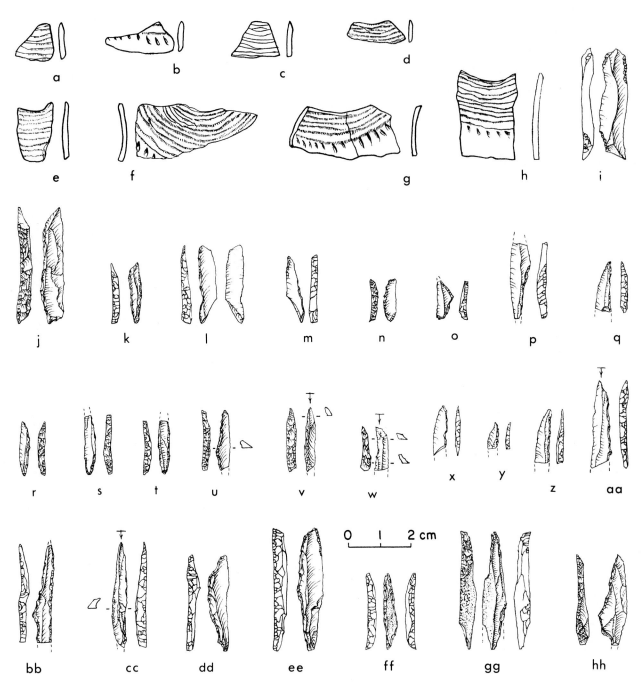

FIGURE 3.30. *Tools from Site E-77-7: (a–h) decorated ostrich eggshells; (i) piquant-trièdre; (j, k) La Mouillah point; (l, m) Krukowski microburins; (n) arch-backed bladelet with rounded base; (o, p) shouldered pieces; (q–cc) straight-backed bladelets; (dd, ee) arch-backed and pointed bladelets; (ff, gg) perforators; (hh) gibbous backed bladelet.*

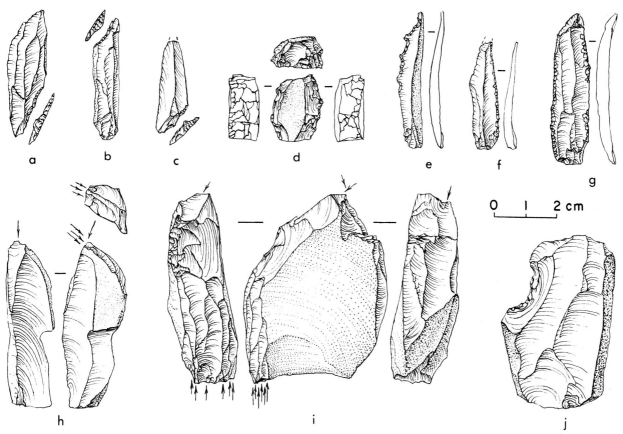

FIGURE 3.31. *Tools from Site E-77-7: (a) straight oblique proximal truncation with traces of microburin scar; (b) concave oblique distal truncation; (c) convex oblique basal truncation; (d) endscraper; (e) denticulate; (f, g) retouched blades; (h) dihedral burin; (i) multiple mixed burin on old flake; (j) notched flake.*

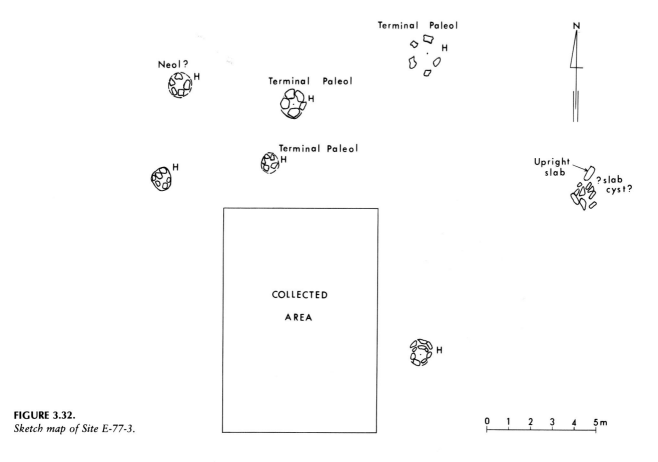

FIGURE 3.32.
Sketch map of Site E-77-3.

Site E-77-3 (E101G1)

This site is near the center of El Kortein Playa, on the exposed surface of the yellow silty sand. It appeared as a moderately large scatter without any clear-cut concentrations. Although most of this extensive scatter is evidently of Terminal Paleolithic age, there are occasional Neolithic tools, usually more wind abraded, on the surface. Numerous clusters of fire-cracked rocks also occur on the surface and others are slightly embedded in the very top of the yellow sand (Figure 3.32), and a slab-lined structure with a few upright standing rocks deeply embedded in the yellow sand was found about 10 m northeast of the collected area (Figures 3.33 and 3.34).

Because evident occupational units were lacking in this locality, a more or less arbitrary area within the large scatter was selected for study. This area, measuring 7 by 10 m, was scatterpatterned (Figure 3.35). Three rounded basins, filled with subsequent sand and silt lacustrine sediments, were visible within the gridded area, but the scatterpattern of artifacts shows a more or less even distribution throughout. A small trench, 2 by 3.75 m, was excavated across two of the circular basins. It showed that the basins were shallow with concave floors and were sunk into indurated silty sand. Portions of their walls were fire reddened, and their fill, composed of unstratified sands and sandy silts with small angular blocky structure, contained charcoal, burned rocks, and 36 Terminal Paleolithic artifacts, slightly silt polished (Figure 3.36). It is obvious that these basins are fireplaces. The radiocarbon date of 8840 BP ± 90 years (SMU-416) was determined on charcoal collected from both of the basins. Beyond the basins there were a few artifacts *in situ* in the very top of the silty sand, but most of the artifacts were on the surface.

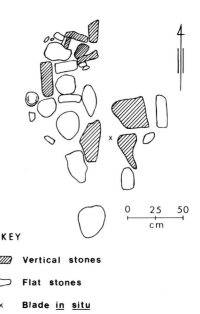

KEY

▨ **Vertical stones**

▱ **Flat stones**

× **Blade in situ**

FIGURE 3.34. *Plan of slab-lined feature at Site E-77-3, of probable Terminal Paleolithic age.*

The spread of artifacts and the presence of several fireplaces, some of which are undoubtedly Terminal Paleolithic in age, suggest that the remains here record more than one occupational unit. Therefore, the collection must be viewed as a sample that may include elements from more than one Terminal Paleolithic camp.

The raw material utilized at Site E-77-3 is predominantly gray chert, with occasional pieces of chalcedony, quartz, jasper, and petrified wood. The cores are predominantly for flake production and are represented by two main groups:

FIGURE 3.33. *View of slab-lined feature at Site E-77-3 before excavation.*

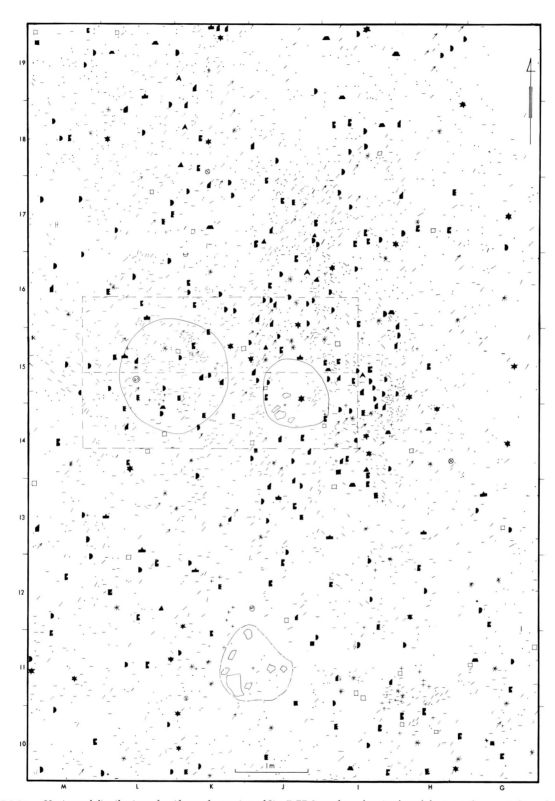

FIGURE 3.35. *Horizontal distribution of artifacts of a portion of Site E-77-3, surface, showing hearth basins and excavated trench (broken line). For key, see Figure 3.28.*

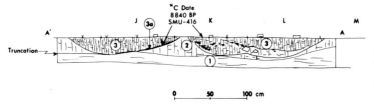

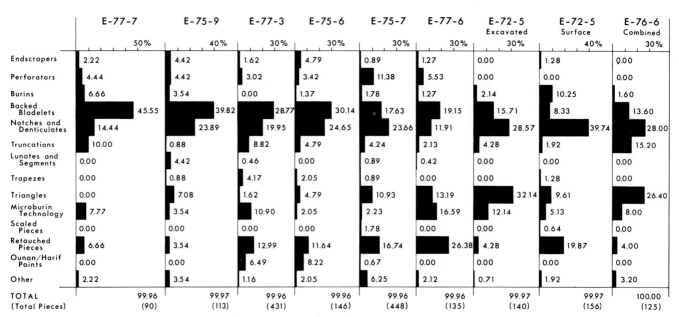

FIGURE 3.36. *Cross section through two adjacent hearth basins at Site E-77-3. Key: 1, laminated eolian sand; 2, silty sand; 3, silty sand with charcoal flecks, artifacts, bones, burned stones, and ocher, lacustrine fill with washed-in artifacts; 3a, lens of charcoal and burned silty sand.*

single platform, unprepared, for flakes; and change of orientation, unpatterned, for flakes. Both groups are equally common. Cores for blades are very rare and are represented by only a few specimens of the single-platform, opposed-platform, and change-of-orientation groups.

The tool collection is quite large, numbering about 500 pieces, among which there are only a few obvious Neolithic admixtures, such as three bifacial points. The structure of the tool assemblage (Figure 3.37) is characterized by the emphasis on backed bladelets (28.8%) (Figure 3.38) and notches and denticulates (19.9%). Among the backed bladelets the most numerous are arch-backed pointed and straight-backed pointed varieties, followed closely by shouldered specimens. La Mouillah points (Figure 3.39) also occur and are about half as frequent as each of the other three types. Microburin technology is well represented (Figure 3.40), accounting for 10.9%, and is mainly composed of simple and Krukowski microburins. Truncated bladelets and small flakes account for 8.8%; stemmed points represent 6.5%, and geometrics are almost equally frequent (6.3%). Among the geometrics the trapezes are the most numerous (4.2%); triangles (elongated scalenes with small short sides, and equilateral varieties) comprise 1.6%, and segments are rare (6%). Perforators (3.0%) and endscrapers (1.6%) are rare, and burins are absent.

The stemmed points, formally called Ounan points, Type

107 on the type list, require further comment. The range of variation present at this site, and at other sites within this group, is larger than that described by Tixier (1963:149–150, 1967:799). Made either on bladelets or on small flakes, few of these points exceed 30 mm in length. The stems are usually symmetrical and straight, rarely bent in the typical Ounan fashion, and are either well shouldered or poorly defined and convergent. The retouch may be direct or alternating and either of these may be combined with flat, invasive, diagonal retouch on the ventral face. The distal end is either left unworked, or truncated, or backed. The backs and truncations vary from convex to straight to slightly concave. In comparison with stemmed Ounan points found in Algeria (Tixier 1955:98) or in the central Sahara (Clark *et al.,* 1973:270) the points in the Western Desert are much shorter and broader, and their distal ends seem to be more frequently modified. Although many of the specimens have exact counterparts among the classic Ounan points, as a group these tend to resemble the Harif points of the Negev and Sinai, dated just before 8000 BC (Bar Yosef and Phillips 1977; Marks 1973; Marks and Scott 1976).

The collection from Site E-77-3 also contains several grinding stones, both the lower and upper pieces. Four of these were *in situ* in the hearth basins. They include a relatively small sandstone lower grinder with two opposed, small, oval, grinding concavities (Figure 3.40:k), two hand-

	E-77-7	E-75-9	E-77-3	E-75-6	E-75-7	E-77-6	E-72-5 Excavated	E-72-5 Surface	E-76-6 Combined
	50%	40%	30%	30%	30%	30%	30%	40%	30%
Endscrapers	2.22	4.42	1.62	4.79	0.89	1.27	0.00	1.28	0.00
Perforators	4.44	4.42	3.02	3.42	11.38	5.53	0.00	0.00	0.00
Burins	6.66	3.54	0.00	1.37	1.78	1.27	2.14	10.25	1.60
Backed Bladelets	45.55	39.82	28.77	30.14	17.63	19.15	15.71	8.33	13.60
Notches and Denticulates	14.44	23.89	19.95	24.65	23.66	11.91	28.57	39.74	28.00
Truncations	10.00	0.88	8.82	4.79	4.24	2.13	4.28	1.92	15.20
Lunates and Segments	0.00	4.42	0.46	0.00	0.89	0.42	0.00	0.00	0.00
Trapezes	0.00	0.88	4.17	2.05	0.89	0.00	0.00	1.28	0.00
Triangles	0.00	7.08	1.62	4.79	10.93	13.19	32.14	9.61	26.40
Microburin Technology	7.77	3.54	10.90	2.05	2.23	16.59	12.14	5.13	8.00
Scaled Pieces	0.00	0.00	0.00	0.00	1.78	0.00	0.00	0.64	0.00
Retouched Pieces	6.66	3.54	12.99	11.64	16.74	26.38	4.28	19.87	4.00
Ounan/Harif Points	0.00	0.00	6.49	8.22	0.67	0.00	0.00	0.00	0.00
Other	2.22	3.54	1.16	2.05	6.25	2.12	0.71	1.92	3.20
TOTAL	99.96	99.97	99.96	99.96	99.96	99.96	99.97	99.97	100.00
(Total Pieces)	(90)	(113)	(431)	(146)	(448)	(135)	(140)	(156)	(125)

FIGURE 3.37. *Bar diagram of main tool indices from nine Terminal Paleolithic assemblages from the Nabta, Dyke and Kharga areas.*

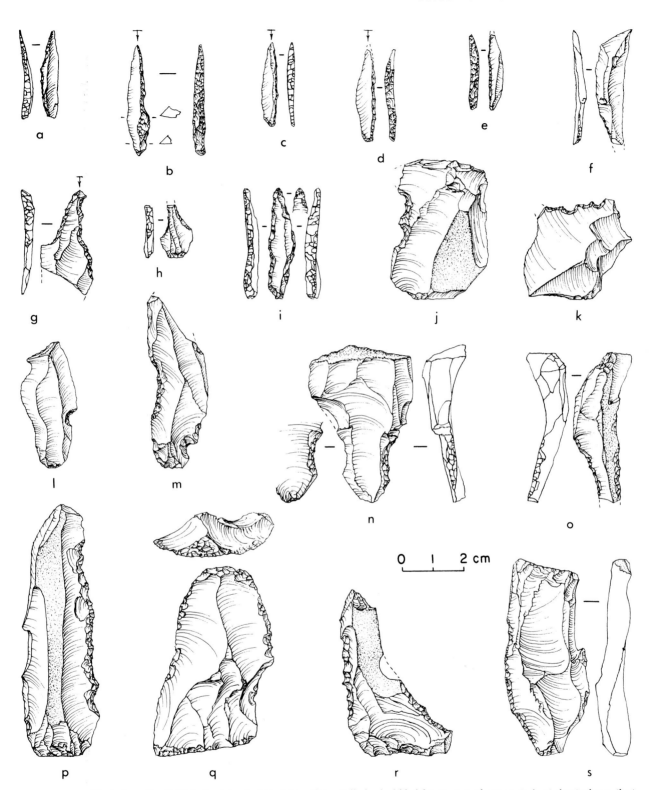

FIGURE 3.38. *Tools from Site E-77-3: (a–e) backed bladelets; (f) partially backed bladelet; (g–i) perforators; (j, k, p) denticulates; (l–n) notched pieces; (o, r, s) continuously retouched pieces; (q) endscraper.*

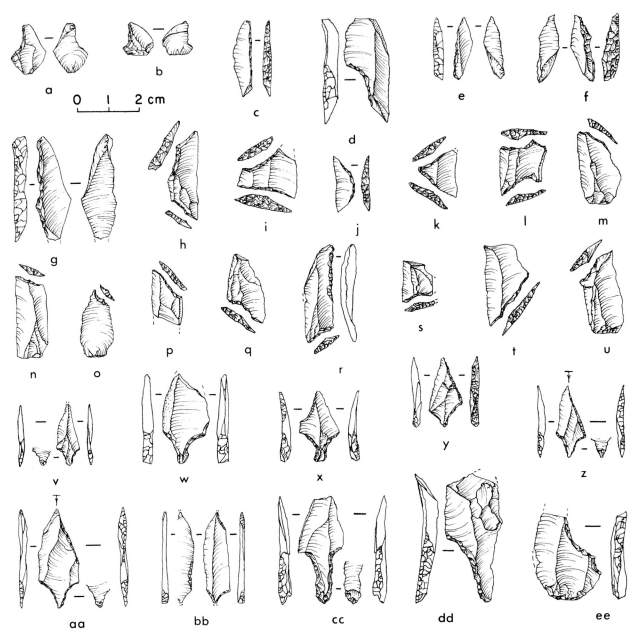

FIGURE 3.39. *Tools from Site E-77-3: (a, b) microburins; (c) La Mouillah point; (d) piquant-trièdre; (e–g) Krukowski microburins; (h, i) trapezes; (j) lunate; (k) triangle; (l–u) truncated pieces; (v–cc) stemmed points; (dd, ee) shouldered bladelets.*

stones, one of which fits the lower grinder, and a fragment of another milling stone. The surface collection includes three other handstones and several fragments of sandstone with ground surfaces.

Of four ostrich-eggshell beads recovered, three were from the trench. Undoubtedly, others had been present, but were removed or destroyed by wind during the deflation of the sites.

Site E-75-6 (E101K1)

Another assemblage within the same Terminal Paleo-

lithic group is from the lower level at Site E-75-6 (Figure 3.41). This occupation is concentrated in the eastern portion of the excavated area (Figure 3.42). The extent of this Terminal Paleolithic occupation is not known, except toward the north where it was truncated by the immediately subsequent lacustrine sediments. The exposed Terminal Paleolithic area measures 8 by 10 m (Figure 3.43). It is in part destroyed by later Neolithic pits and subsequent erosion in the eastern portion. There seem to be three denser, overlapping clusters, two of which are associated with shallow basin-shaped pits, about 1.5 m in idameter, containing large fire-cracked rocks, and similar to those found

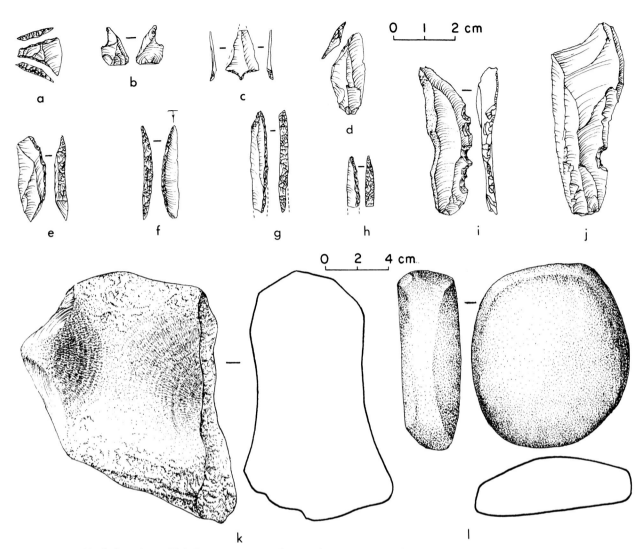

FIGURE 3.40. *Tools from Site E-77-3, Pit 1: (a) trapeze; (b) microburin; (c) stemmed point; (d) truncation; (e) La Mouillah point; (f–h) backed bladelets; (i) denticulate; (j) notched piece; (k) milling-stone fragment; (l) handstone.*

FIGURE 3.41. *View of Site E-75-6 looking east, showing stratigraphy. Left hand of figure is on stone at base of Terminal Paleolithic hearth basin; right hand indicates Neolithic layer.*

FIGURE 3.42. *View of Site E-75-6 during the excavation of Terminal Paleolithic layer, looking southwest. Vehicle is standing on playa clay surface.*

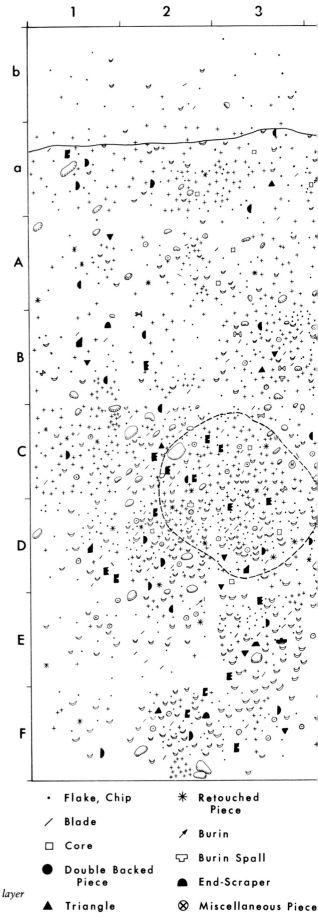

FIGURE 3.43. *Horizontal distribution of artifacts from Terminal Paleolithic layer at Site E-75-6.*

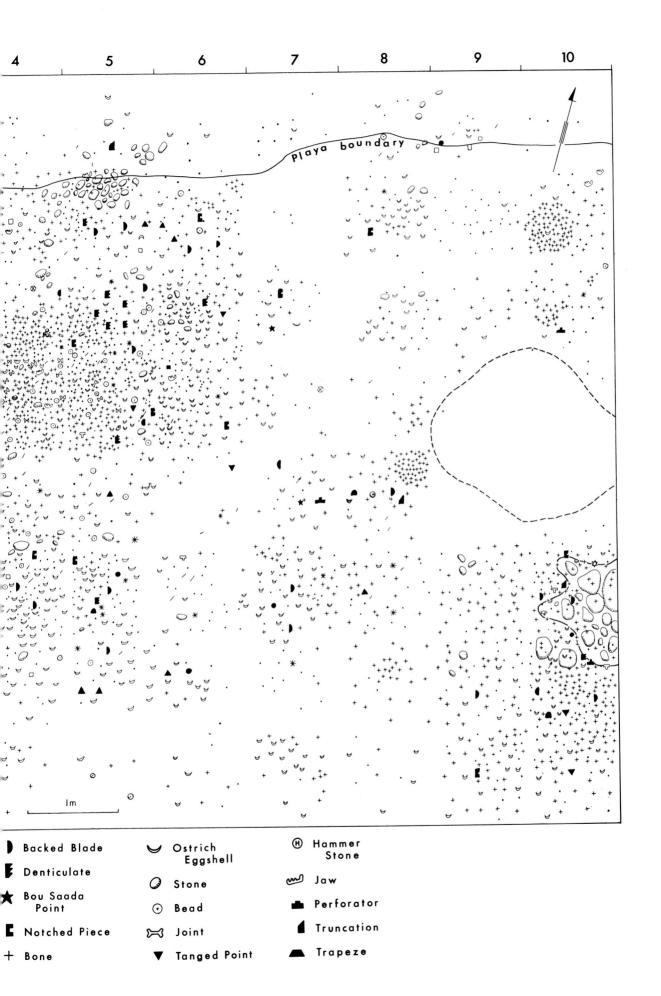

Playa boundary

▌ Backed Blade	⌣ Ostrich Eggshell	Ⓗ Hammer Stone
Ɛ Denticulate	⌔ Stone	ᨬ Jaw
★ Bou Saada Point	⊙ Bead	⬗ Perforator
ⴹ Notched Piece	⋈ Joint	◀ Truncation
+ Bone	▼ Tanged Point	◣ Trapeze

1m

at Site E-77-3. The Terminal Paleolithic occupation here also represents more than one instance of settlement, as indicated by the overlapping concentrations and separate hearth basins. The accompanying fauna seems to suggest an economic emphasis on the hunting of large gazelle (*G. dorcas*) and hare (*Lepus capensis*).

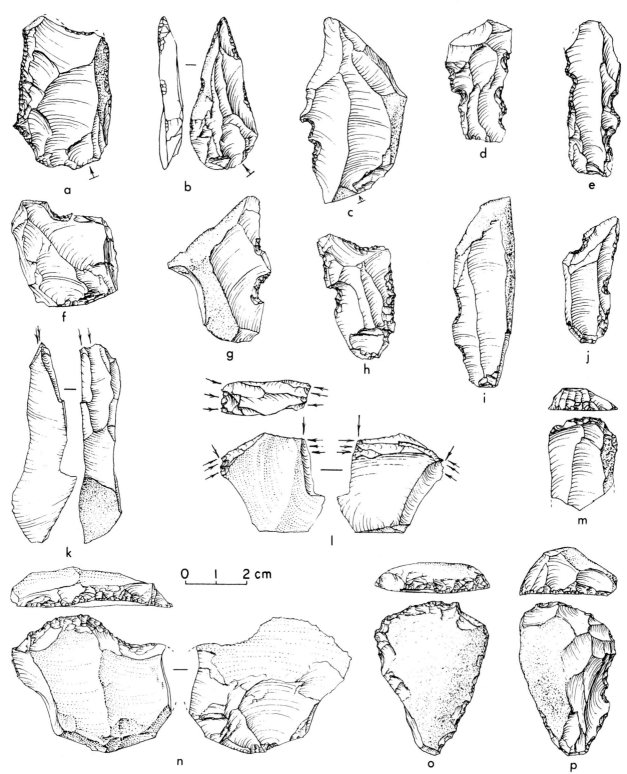

FIGURE 3.44. *Tools from Site E-75-6, Terminal Paleolithic: (a) retouched flake; (b) perforators; (c–e) denticulates; (f–j) notched pieces; (k) single-blow burin; (l) multiple dihedral burin; (m–p) endscrapers.*

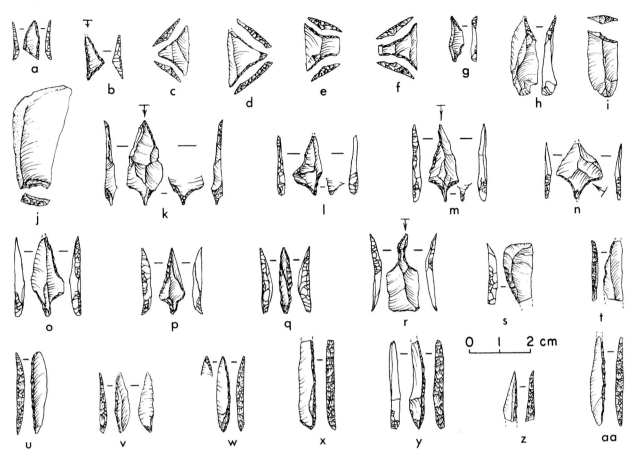

FIGURE 3.45. *Tools from Site E-75-6, Terminal Paleolithic. (a–d) triangles; (e, f) trapezes; (g–j) truncations; (k–p) Ounan points; (q, r) perforators; (s) partially backed bladelet; (t) arch-backed bladelet; (u–aa) straight-backed bladelets.*

The total lithic assemblage contains over 300 tools (Figures 3.44 and 3.45). The raw material used and the cores are exactly the same as those from Site E-77-3, and the structure of the tool kit is also very similar, although here the endscrapers are slightly more numerous and burins are present. Within the geometrics, triangles replace trapezes as the most numerous group (Figure 3.37). Truncated bladelets and small flakes (4.8%) are about half as frequent as at Site E-77-3. Other differences are evident in the microburin technique, which is less frequent, and the stemmed points, which are slightly more common.

A total of 18 grinding stones, mostly fragments, come from this occupation, as well as numerous ostrich-eggshell fragments and beads, and a few small fragments of bone points with rounded cross section (Figure 3.46). The radiocarbon date on ostrich eggshell of 8290 BP ± 80 years (SMU-257) provides a chronological setting for this layer. Although this date is 500 years later than that from Site E-77-3, and there is some possibility of contamination by later shells, it may, nevertheless, be correct.

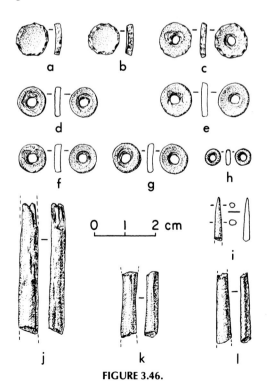

FIGURE 3.46. *Bone and shell artifacts from Site E-75-6, Terminal Paleolithic: (a, b) unfinished eggshell bead blanks; (c) unfinished eggshell bead blank, perforated; (d–h) completed eggshell beads; (i–l) bone point fragments.*

FIGURE 3.46.

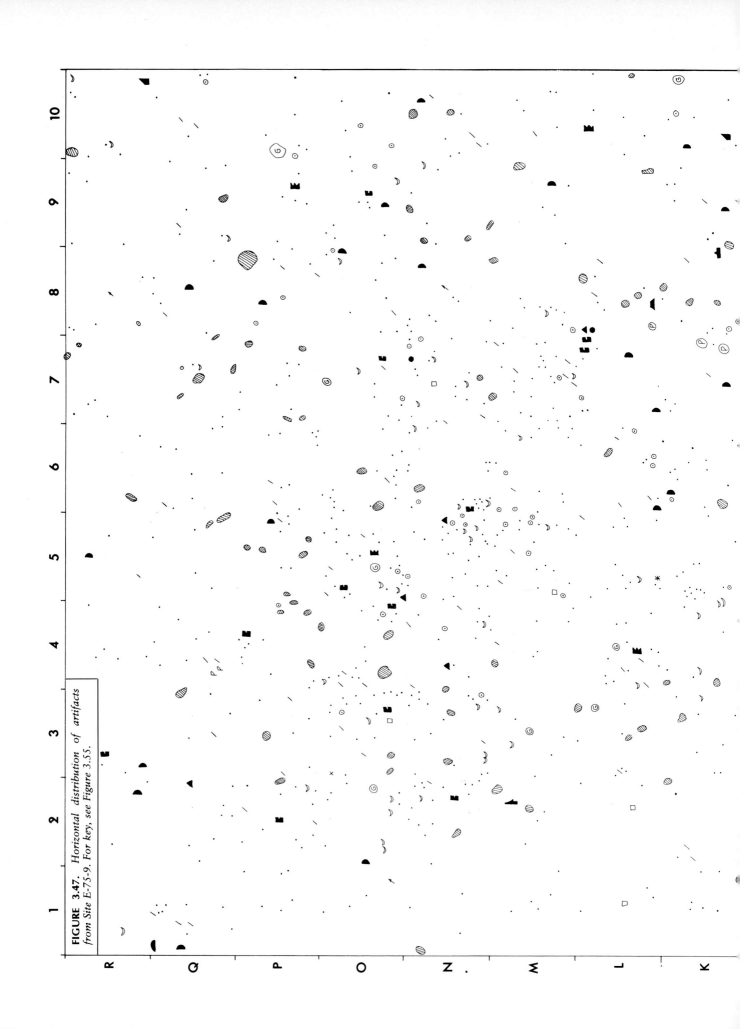

FIGURE 3.47. Horizontal distribution of artifacts from Site E-75-9. For key, see Figure 3.55.

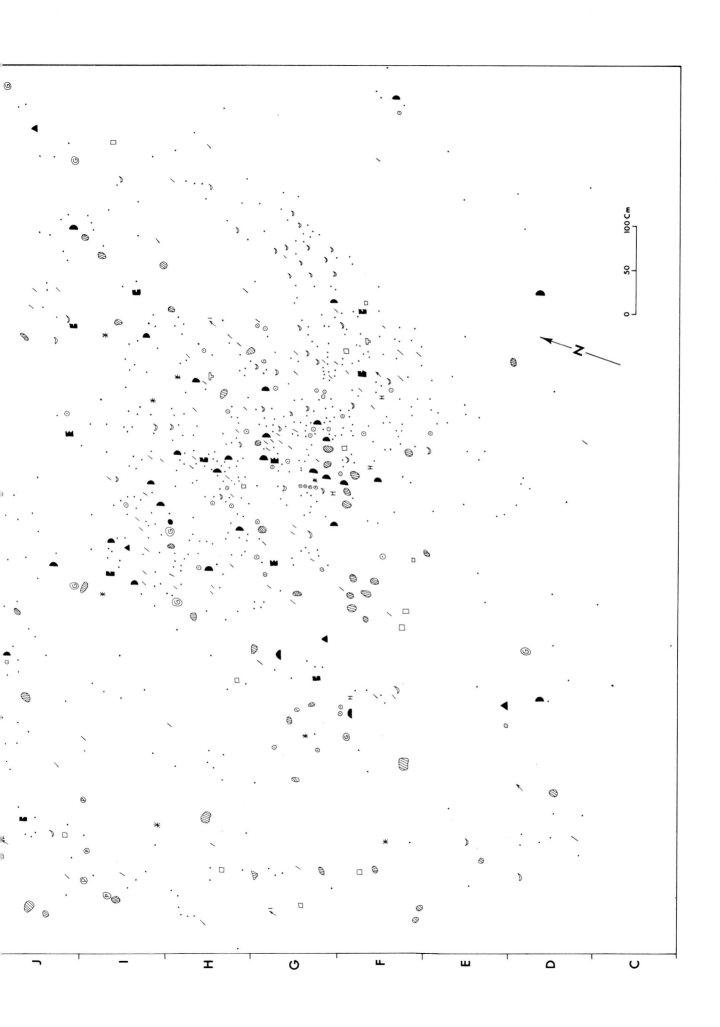

Site E-75-9 (E101K4)

The third variety of Terminal Paleolithic in the Nabta area is that from Site E-75-9, located some 360 m northwest of Site E-75-6, and occurring in the same stratigraphic position in the top of the basal sand unit. The site is located in an area of extensive deflation, adjacent to the area of contact between the central dune field and the overlapping remnant of playa. The exposed occupational debris occurred in a small "window" surrounded on three sides by playa clays. A few small, circular Neolithic pits with playa seals were also exposed in the immediate vicinity, suggesting a possibility of Neolithic contamination of the assemblage, as confirmed by the occurrence of a few pieces of Early Khartoum pottery in the western and central sections. The artifacts were scattered in a large (13 by 10 m), thin concentration, the limits of which did not exceed the collected area (Figure 3.47). The stratigraphic trench (Figure 3.10), cut just beyond the edge of the site, disclosed only a few artifacts still *in situ*. Within the scatter of surface artifacts, a small subcluster occurred in the southern section. Burned stones were scattered more or less evenly over the surface.

The raw material used at this site is different from that employed in the Terminal Paleolithic assemblages described earlier. Here it is a black or dark gray Eocene chert, of excellent quality, that occurs in large nodules, as indicated by the recovered waste products. Quartz and chalcedony were also present. Most of the cores are classified as change of orientation for flakes. Cores for blades are rare, and are either of the single-platform or of the change-of-orientation variety.

The tool assemblage includes only 112 pieces. It is characterized by a heavy emphasis on the backed bladelet group (39.8%), composed almost entirely of arch-backed pointed bladelets. Geometrics are well represented, at least twice as frequent as in either of the other Terminal Paleolithic groups (Figure 3.48). They are represented by two main elements: triangles (6.2%, including elongated with small short sides, the most common, and isosceles triangles) and segments and lunates (4.4%). Microburin technology is present, stemmed points are absent, and truncations are almost nonexistent (one piece only).

The surface of the site was littered with numerous ostrich-eggshell beads, both finished and unfinished. The collection also includes two hand grinders.

Site E-77-6 (E101G4)

Stratigraphically, the youngest Terminal Paleolithic unit (Group IV) is that from Site E-77-6. Here the oval concentration measured about 20 by 13 m. It was very dense and without any apparent subclusters. Only a small area (5 by 5 m) was collected and scatterpatterned as a sample (Figure 3.49). The occupation floor was nonexistent, destroyed by the churning clay stratigraphically correlated with the upper part of Playa I.

The raw material used is the same dark gray to black chert employed at Site E-75-9. The most numerous cores are the single-platform and change-of-orientation varieties for flakes. Blade cores are well represented, often displaying back, side, and pre-flaking-surface preparation. A significant number of cores for blades are made on large chert flakes or blades and are often exploited on the edge of the pieces. These may grade into nucleiform burins (Figure 3.50).

The tool assemblage (Figures 3.51–3.53) collected from the sampled 25 m² area contained 235 pieces and had a configuration different from that seen in the other Terminal Paleolithic assemblages (Figure 3.37). Although the backed bladelet group, mostly of the straight-backed and shouldered varieties, is still the most numerous (19.1%), its value is considerably below the values seen in the other groups. The geometrics form the next most numerous tool group (13.6%) and are composed almost entirely of elongated scalene triangles with one short side, sometimes concave, and with only one segment. Other tools are notches and denticulates (11.9%), followed by perforators (5.5%), almost all double backed. The value for the microburin technology is the highest in any Nabta group (16.6%), obviously associated with the production of the elongated scalene triangles and also reflected in a relatively high percentage of shouldered-backed bladelets. Burins and endscrapers are rare, both represented by only a few pieces. The value for truncated pieces is low (2.1%). Stemmed points were not present. There were no grinding stones in the collected area, although they were present elsewhere on the site.

Site E-75-7 (E101K2)

An obviously mixed tool assemblage was collected at Site E-75-7, which is located at the foot of a low projecting knoll, with Nubia sandstone core. The knoll is at the eastern edge of an extensively deflated area. The occupational evidence occurred as an unpatterned scatter of artifacts, Neolithic wells (shown as playa-sealed rings), slabs (some still vertical), and grinding stones. Work at the site consisted of gridding and collecting in four arbitrarily designated areas, excavating six wells, and cutting several stratigraphic trenches (Figure 3.54). The trenches failed to disclose occupation floors, but a few Terminal Paleolithic artifacts were found at the very top of the yellow sand unit and in the overlying lacustrine sediment (Area C).

The collection from the main scatterpattern area (Figure 3.55), measuring 200 m², contained many grinding stones, a few sherds of Early Khartoum pottery, and 448 flaked stone tools. The tools are almost entirely made on both light and dark gray Eocene chert. Agate, chalcedony, and quartz were also present. Cores are not numerous, and those present are mostly for flakes, almost all being of the change-of-orientation, globular variety. The tool structure clearly reflects the mixed character of this large surface collection (Figure 3.37). The frequency of backed bladelets

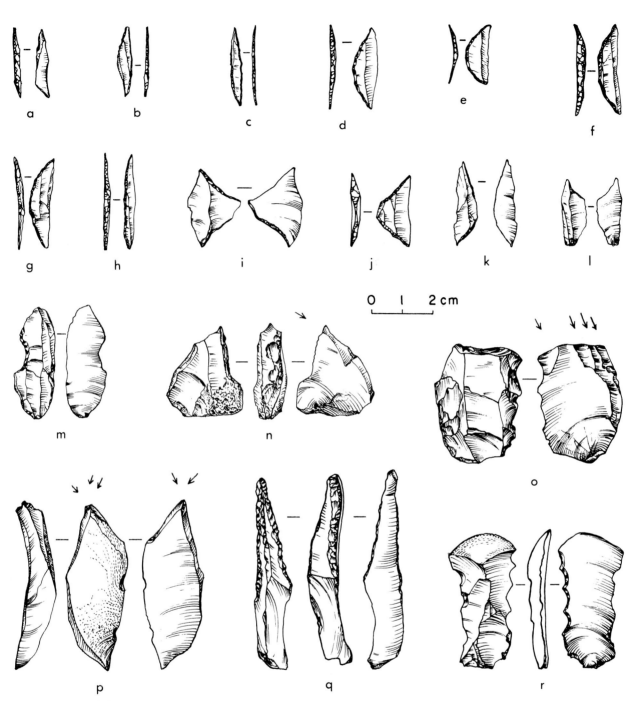

FIGURE 3.48. Tools from Site E-75-9: (a) triangle; (b, c) perforators; (d–g) lunates; (h) backed bladelet; (i, j) trapezes; (k) atypical trapeze; (l) truncated piece; (m) notched piece; (n) burin; (o) multiple burin on truncation with denticulated lateral edge; (p) dihedral burin; (q) perforator; (r) denticulate.

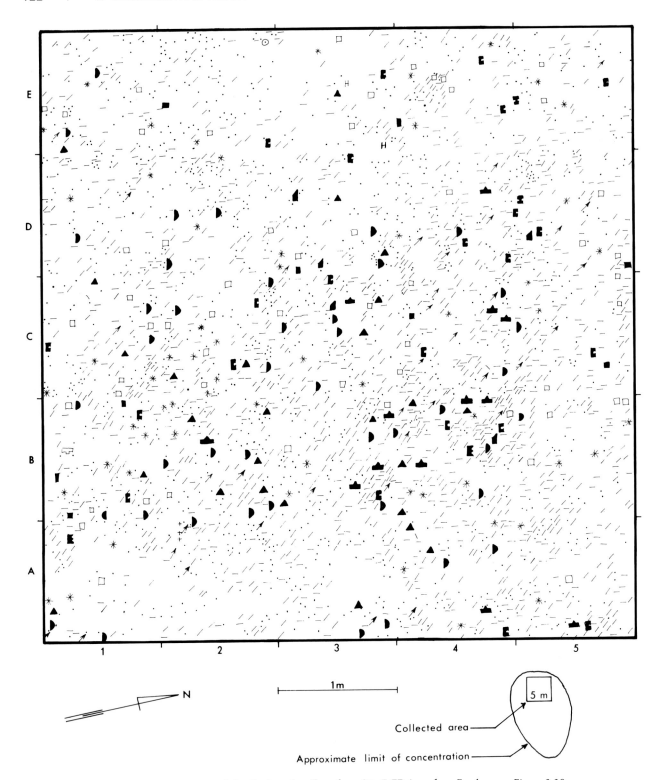

FIGURE 3.49. *Horizontal distribution of artifacts from Site E-77-6, surface. For key, see Figure 3.28.*

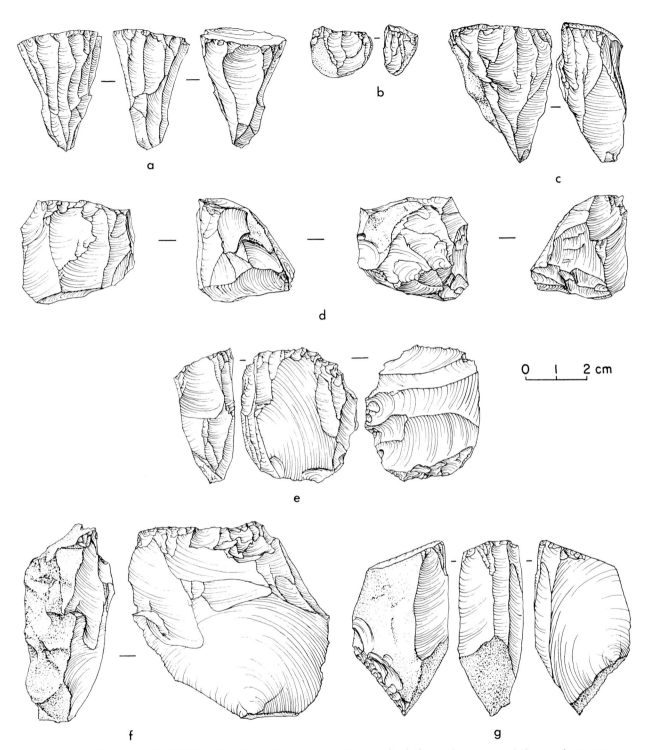

FIGURE 3.50. *Cores from Site E-77-6: (a) single platform, conical; (b, c) single platform; (d) unpatterned change of orientation; (e) ninety-degree; (f, g) single platform, on flake.*

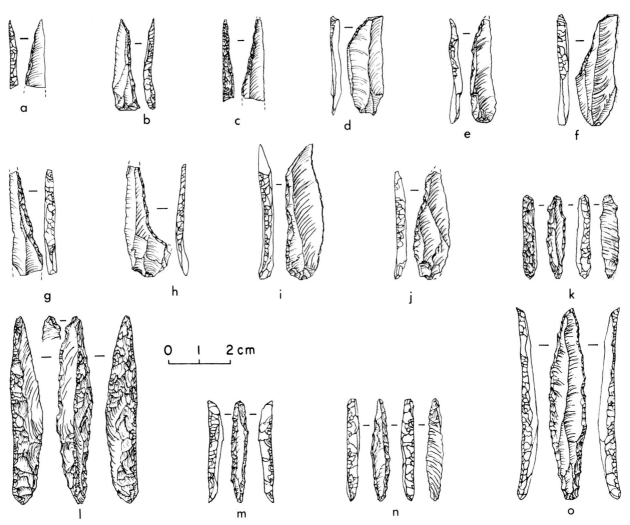

FIGURE 3.51. Tools from Site E-77-6: (a–c) backed bladelets; (d, e) arch-ended bladelets with microburin scar; (f–h) shouldered bladelets; (i, j) La Mouillah points; (k–o) perforators.

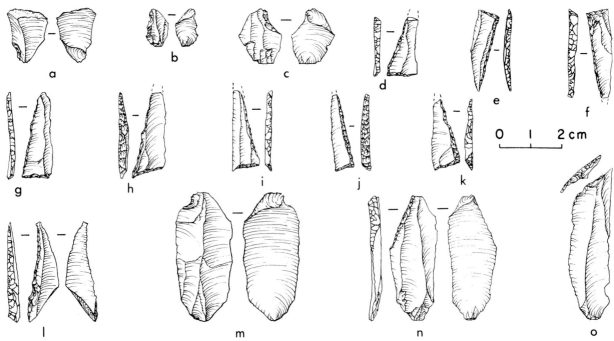

FIGURE 3.52. Tools from Site E-77-6: (a–c, m, n) microburins; (d–k) triangles; (1) Krukowski microburin; (o) truncation.

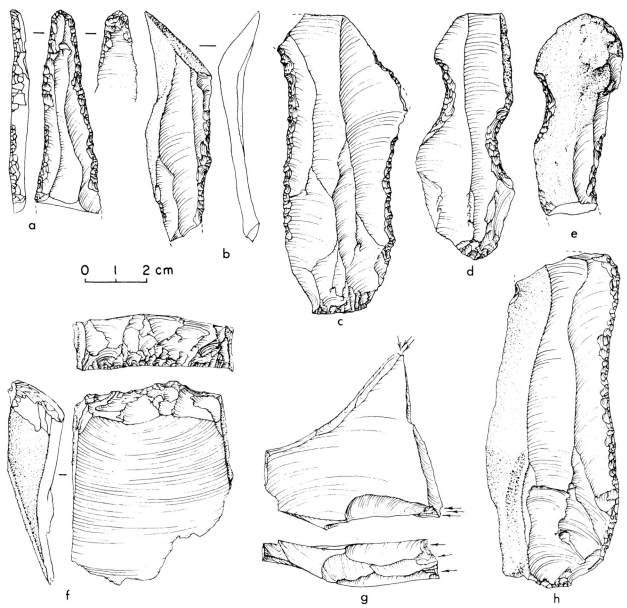

FIGURE 3.53. *Tools from Site E-77-6: (a–c, h) retouched pieces; (d, e) notches; (f) scraper; (g) multiple mixed burin.*

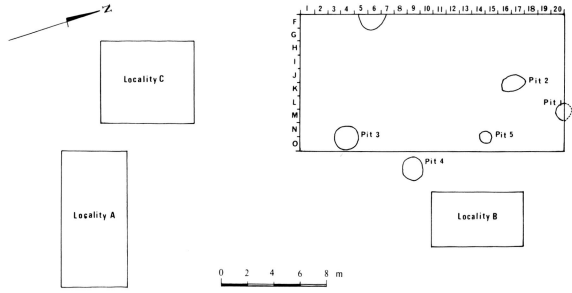

FIGURE 3.54. *Sketch map of collected and excavated areas at Site E-75-7. Note location of wells (pits).*

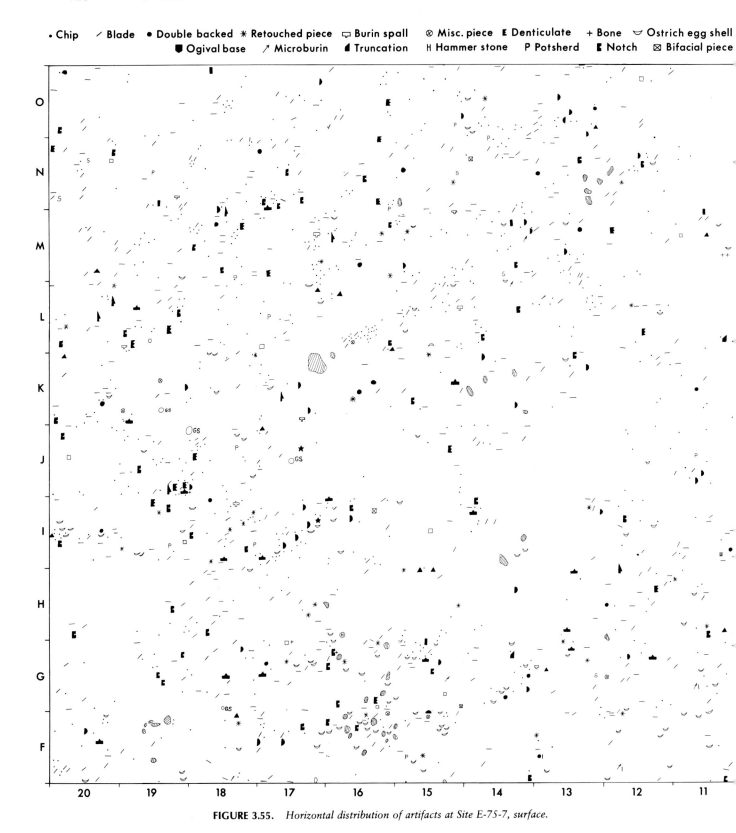

FIGURE 3.55. *Horizontal distribution of artifacts at Site E-75-7, surface.*

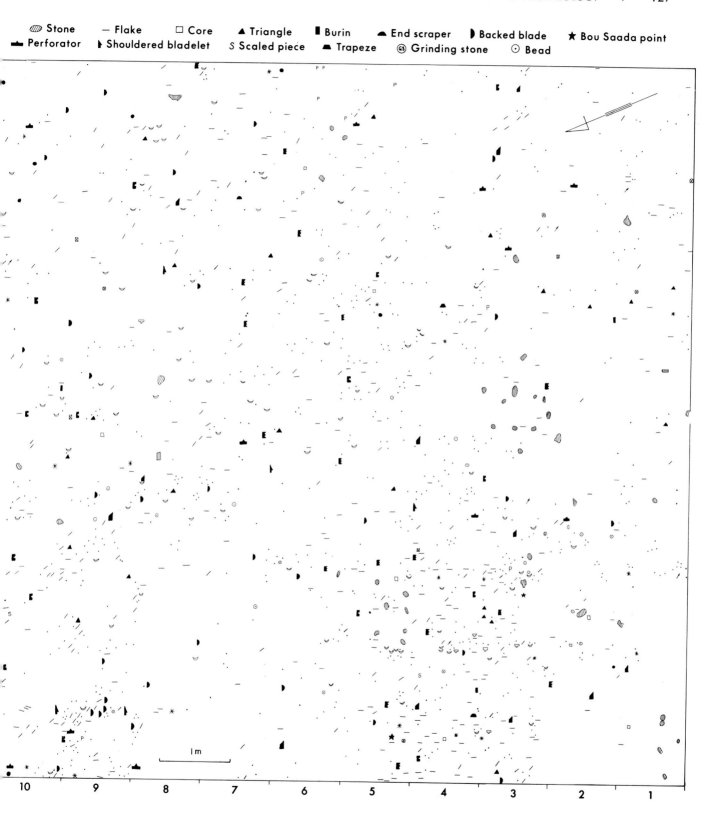

is low (13.8%), with shouldered, arch-backed, and straight-backed bladelets as the dominant varieties. Notches and denticulates are high (23.7%), as are geometrics (12.7%). Perforators of both simple and double-backed varieties have the highest values recorded (accounting for 11.4%). Endscrapers and burins are very low, and microburin technology is at one of the lowest levels (2.2%). A few stemmed points, bifacial arrowheads, and scaled pieces complete the tool inventory (Figures 3.56–3.58).

The very small tool assemblage (37 pieces) recovered in the excavations at Area C in the uppermost portion of the runoff–eolian sand contained several undoubtedly Terminal Paleolithic pieces as follows: a partially backed bladelet, a shouldered bladelet, triangles with small short sides, fragments of backed bladelets, a burin, and a few notches and denticulates. The shouldered bladelet and elongated scalene triangles recall the assemblage from Site E-77-6 assigned to Group IV. Although small, the collection is useful, as it demonstrates the stratigraphic position of the Terminal Paleolithic components.

It is clear that the surface collection from Site E-75-7 reflects some Neolithic characteristics, such as the high val-

ues for perforators, and the presence of scaled pieces and bifacial points. Terminal Paleolithic elements, by contrast, may pertain to more than one taxonomic entity, as indicated by the presence of stemmed points on the one hand (like those in Group II), and numerous elongated triangles with small short sides and shouldered bladelets on the other (Group IV). The scatterpattern did not indicate any evident spatial separation between these possibly distinct entities, except for the small, dispersed concentration at Area C, which might represent a single isolated settlement unit (Figure 3.59).

NEOLITHIC

The basic data on the Neolithic in the Nabta area come from four sites: E-75-6, E-75-7, E-75-8, and E-75-5. These sites disclose three distinct varieties of Neolithic, each occurring in a separate time horizon. The two earlier phases of the Neolithic contain pottery of Early Khartoum style, possibly of two different varieties. The pottery associated with the latest Neolithic is similar to that of the A-Group

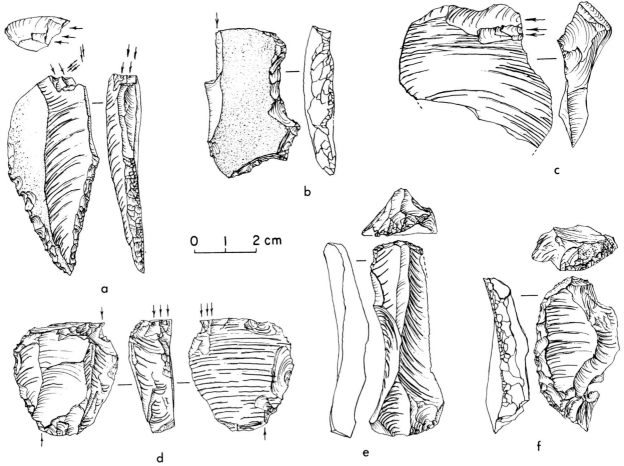

FIGURE 3.56.   *Tools from Site E-75-7: (a) angle burin, déjeté; (b) burin on snap, with multiple retouched notches; (c) transverse burin on notch; (d) multiple burin on snaps; (e) endscraper; (f) endscraper on retouched flake.*

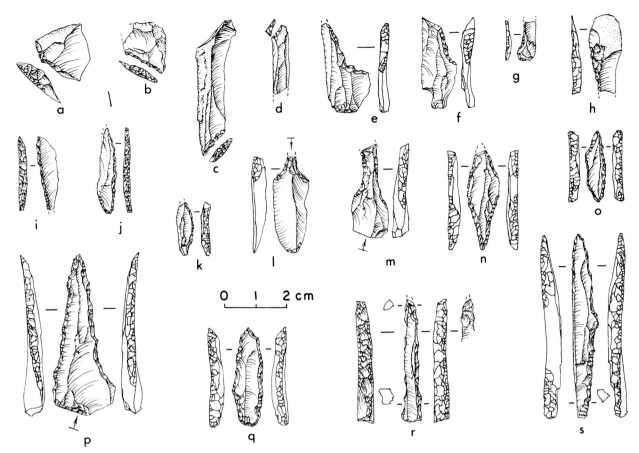

FIGURE 3.57. *Tools from Site E-75-7: (a–d) truncated pieces; (e–h) shouldered bladelets; (i, j) straight-backed bladelets; (k) arch-backed bladelet; (l–s) perforators.*

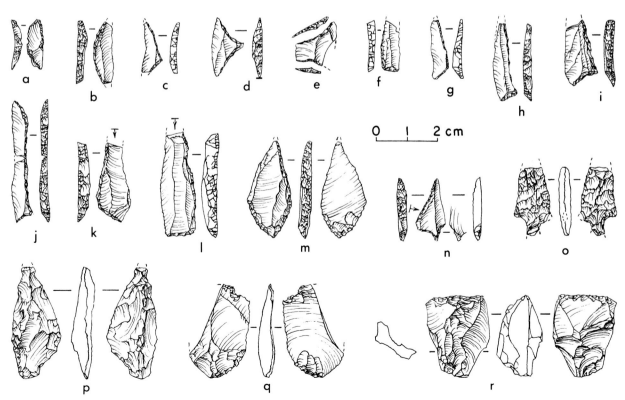

FIGURE 3.58. *Tools from Site E-75-7: (a, b) lunates; (c, d, f–l) triangles; (e) trapeze; (m) point with ogival base; (n) Ounan point; (o, p) bifacial points; (q, r) scaled pieces.*

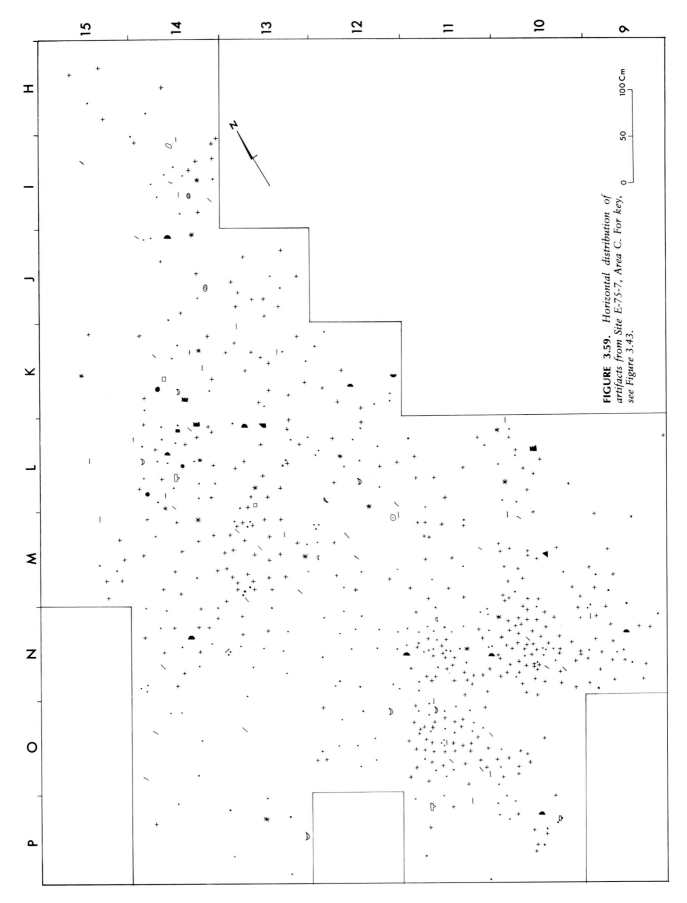

FIGURE 3.59. *Horizontal distribution of artifacts from Site E-75-7, Area C. For key, see Figure 3.43.*

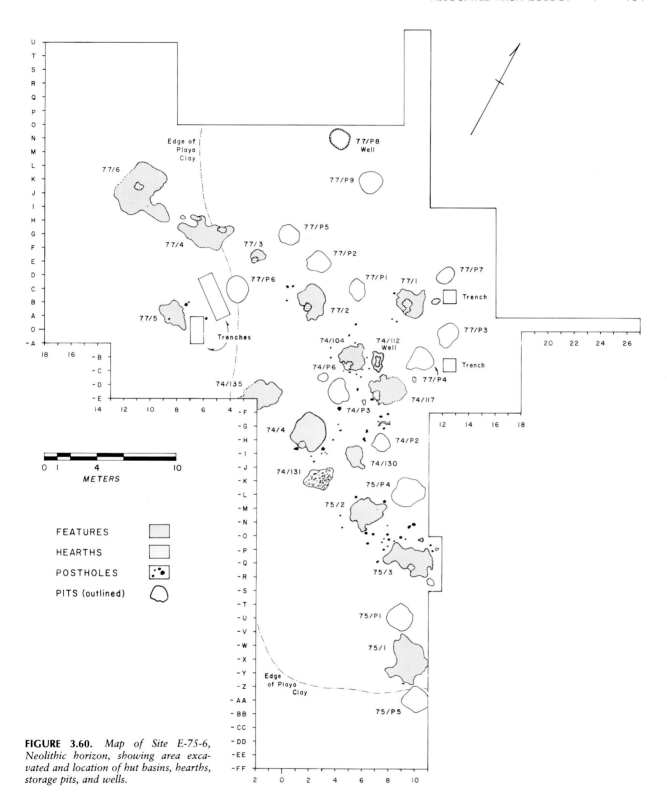

FIGURE 3.60. *Map of Site E-75-6, Neolithic horizon, showing area excavated and location of hut basins, hearths, storage pits, and wells.*

from along the Nile in Nubia. In addition to ceramics, the three varieties of Neolithic can be distinguished by their lithic assemblages.

Site E-75-6 (E101K1)

The earliest Neolithic known from the Nabta area is that at E-75-6, which can be placed stratigraphically at the beginning of Playa II and shortly after the latest Terminal Paleolithic occupation in the same general area. A tight cluster of radiocarbon dates from various features associated with this occupation places the settlement at around 8100 BP.

When first discovered, the surface of the site was covered by a litter of fire-cracked rocks, lithic artifacts, grinding stones, and a very few potsherds. This settlement was one of the most extensively excavated sites in the whole area. During three seasons of work, more than 1000 m² were cleared (Figures 3.60–3.63), and numerous pits, postholes, hearths, burned areas, and a well were discovered and mapped. Even so, the excavations were sufficient to determine the extent of this enormous settlement only on the north, west, and northeast sides. The supposed remainder to the east was buried under thick playa clay.

Because of the erosion accompanying the deposition of the lacustrine sands of the rising lake of Playa II that cover the settlement, the actual cultural layer was preserved only in depressions in the Neolithic living surface. Where preserved, the cultural layer was a mixture of loose gray sand with ash, charcoal powder, charcoal flecks, and small organic remains. The intensity of coloration varied according to depth and location.

There are four distinct kinds of features evident on the cleared surface: (*a*) numerous circular, or almost circular, medium-sized (1.5 m in diameter) bell-shaped or cylindrical pits with sandy lacustrine or clay postoccupational seals (Figures 3.63–3.65 and 3.67); (*b*) a 2-m-deep circular well (Figure 3.66); (*c*) small holes, from 5 to 20 cm in diameter,

FIGURE 3.62. *Site E-75-6. Scraped surface showing top of bell-shaped Neolithic pit before excavation. Note clay playa seal in center.*

FIGURE 3.63. *Site E-75-6. View of trench exposing cross section of a bell-shaped Neolithic pit. Note the lamination in the top center of the fill.*

some (the smaller ones) with pointed bottoms, others with rounded bottoms, filled with either cultural layer or clay, the latter most often in the pointed ones (Figures 3.68 and 3.69); and (*d*) large, irregularly oval, shallow, saucer-shaped remnants of basins, around 3+ m in diameter, filled by an intensive cultural layer and almost always associated with either one or two clear burned areas (Figures 3.70, 3.71, and 3.72). Some of the basins are surrounded by clusters of postholes and seem to occur in two east–west lines, both made up of six separate basins, more or less evenly spaced (Figure 3.60). Two other basins do not appear to be associated with alignments. Most of the bell-shaped or cylindrical pits are also arranged in lines parallel with the basins. The basins and pits that do not form part of the pattern may be parts of other alignments that were either not exposed or were destroyed by subsequent erosion.

One of the circular pits, located at the north edge of the settlement, was identified as a well. It was slightly less than 2 m in diameter, cylindrical in cross section, and 2 m deep.

FIGURE 3.61. *View of Site E-75-6, looking northwest across excavated area during 1975 season.*

EL NABTA/EGYPT, SITE E-75-6 (contin. 1977)

PIT 7/77

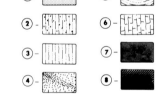

LAYERS IN PITS AND FEATURES

① - ⑤ -
② - ⑥ -
③ - ⑦ -
④ - ⑧ -

FIGURE 3.64. *Plan and cross section of Neolithic bell-shaped Pit 7/77, Site E-75-6. Key: 1, yellow dune sand; 2, gray, loose sand with charcoal powder; 3, sand mixed with cultural debris, reworked backfill; 4, sand with abundant charcoal; 5, laminated lacustrine laid sand; 6, playa clay; 7, burned clay or sand; 8, intensively burned clay or sand. Numbers not in circles indicate various artifacts found in the pits.*

FIGURE 3.65. *View of trench exposing playa-filled storage pit.*

FIGURE 3.66. *Site E-75-6. Excavation of the well.*

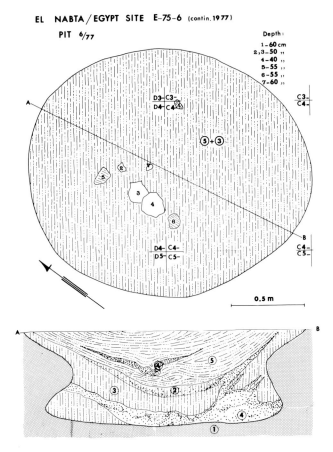

EL NABTA / EGYPT SITE E-75-6 (contin. 1977)

PIT 6/77

Depth:
1 - 60 cm
2,3 - 50 ,,
4 - 40 ,,
5 - 55 ,,
6 - 55 ,,
7 - 60 ,,

0.5 m

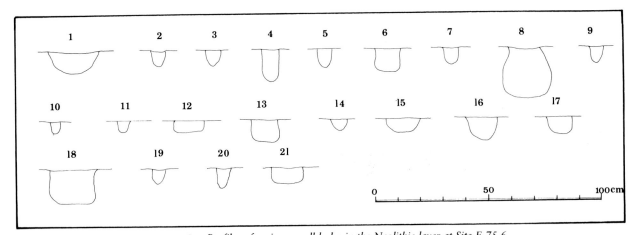

FIGURE 3.67. *Plan and cross section of Pit 6/77. For key see Figure 3.64.*

FIGURE 3.68. *Profiles of various small holes in the Neolithic layer at Site E-75-6.*

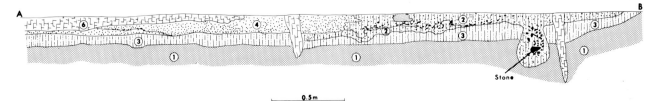

FIGURE 3.69. *Section through portion of Feature 5/77, Site E-75-6. Note pointed postholes filled with clay. See Figure 3.64 for key.*

FIGURE 3.70. *Site E-75-6. Scraped surface showing outline of oval saucer-shaped basin remnant before excavation.*

The fill of the well at the bottom was natural, formed during its use; the upper part contains mixed clay, sand, and reworked cultural debris (Figure 3.73).

It is evident that the alignments indicate an organized multifamily settlement, but it could not be determined if both alignments are part of one very large settlement or if they represent reoccupations of the same general area.

The pits and basins yielded worked stone, ostrich-eggshell fragments and beads, bone points, rare potsherds, numerous faunal remains (mostly hare and small gazelle, with rare cattle), grinders (some of which were deliberately left upside-down in the pits with their handstones below them), and fragments of floral remains, including two grains of six-row barley (Hadidi and Stemler and Falk, this volume). Some of the pits in the southern portion of the settlement cut through the underlying Terminal Paleolithic layer and undoubtedly contain some material from this lower level, such as the stemmed points, which are sometimes slightly polished. One of the small, shallow pits yielded a cache of quartz pebbles, apparently representing storage of raw material (Figure 3.74).

The lithic assemblage recovered from the pits and basins shows quartz and quartz crystal as the most common raw materials, followed by light and dark gray chert similar to that used by the earlier Terminal Paleolithic inhabitants of the site. Chalcedony, agate, and petrified wood were also used, but rarely. Most of the cores and the debitage were of quartz, whereas tools were mostly made from light gray chert. Cores for flakes, including single, opposed, and

EL NABTA / EGYPT, SITE E-75-6 (Contin. 1977)

FEATURE 2/77

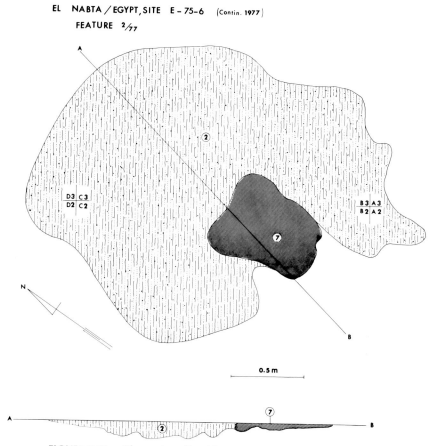

0.5 m

FIGURE 3.71. *Plan and profile of Feature 2/77. For key, see Figure 3.64.*

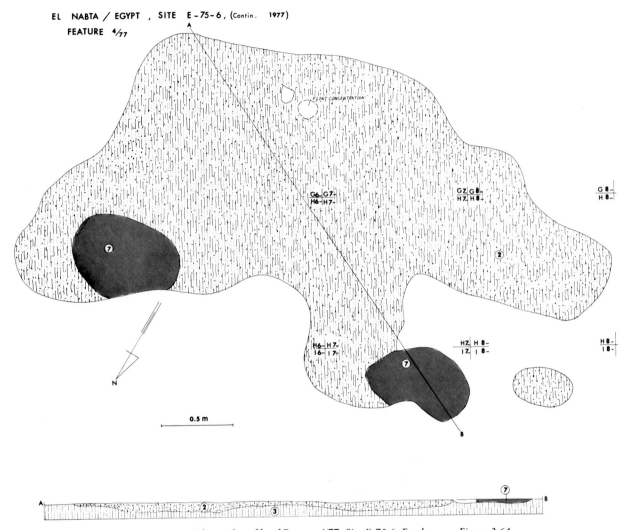

FIGURE 3.72. *Plan and profile of Feature 4/77, Site E-75-6. For key, see Figure 3.64.*

change-of-orientation varieties, are the most numerous. Single-platform cores for bladelets, some made on large flakes, are present but not common.

The recovered tool kit consists of 312 pieces of flaked stone (Figure 3.37). Perforators, mostly double backed, are the most common tools (22.8%) (Figures 3.75–3.77). Backed bladelets represent 17.6%, and of these the arched variety predominates. Notches and denticulates form 9.3% and include characteristic pieces made on large blades and flakes. Geometrics are well represented (8.3%) (Figure 3.78), with triangles the most common (7.3%) including both the short scalene variety and the variety that is elongated with small short sides. Trapezes occur, but they are rare. Burins are not uncommon (6.4%), with most being single-blow on snap and multiple varieties. In contrast with the preceding Terminal Paleolithic, scaled pieces also are quite common (6.4%). Small truncated bladelets and flakes account for 3.5%, and endscrapers are rare (1.3%). Microburin technology is present (1.9%). A few stemmed points (1.3%) are believed to be a Terminal Paleolithic in-

trusion. No bifacial points, ground celts, or axes were found.

The associated grinding stones include several large, oval milling stones, shaped by flaking and picking, with deep, elongated grinding basins. The handstones are circular or oval in outline, shaped by pecking, with opposed grinding faces, and are flat, convex, or plano-convex in profile (Figure 3.76).

Worked bone is represented by seven bone points, all but one of which are fragmentary; all are made on splinters, with elongated tapering points and rounded or oval cross sections (Figure 3.78). The complete example is 7 cm long and 4 mm in diameter, and has a notch at the base.

The pottery is poorly represented, less than 20 sherds, all richly decorated with dense masses of V-shaped incisions, which cover the entire vessel (Figure 3.79). The rims are simple and direct, and only fragments of bowls seem to be represented. They are sand tempered, dark brown, and well fired; the surface is harder than the Early Khartoum pottery in later settlements.

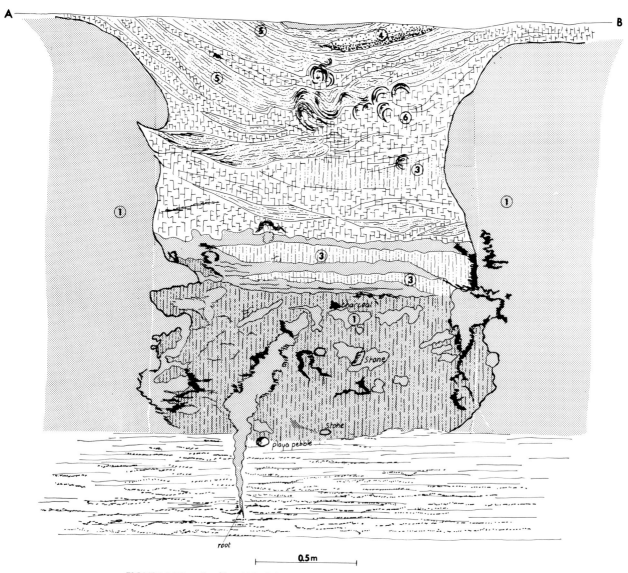

EL NABTA EGYPT, SITE E 75-6 (Contin. 1977)
PROFILE OF PIT № 8 (THE WELL)

A ————————— B

⑤ ④

⑤

⑥

③

①   ①

③

③

charcoal
①
stone

stone
playa pebble

root

|—— 0.5 m ——|

FIGURE 3.73. *Profile of Neolithic well at Site E-75-6. For key, see Figure 3.64.*

FIGURE 3.74. *Small pit containing quartz pebbles in Neolithic layer of Site E-75-6.*

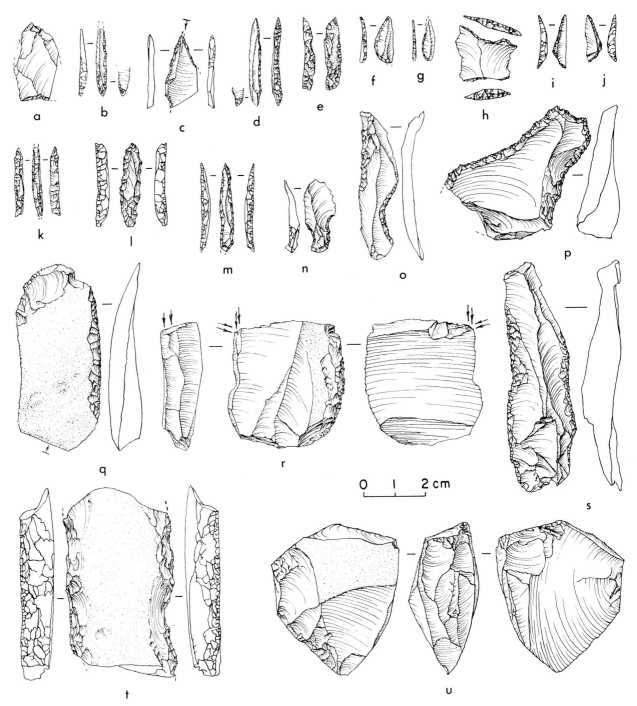

FIGURE 3.75. *Tools and core from Site E-75-6, Neolithic layer: (a) basal truncated piece; (b) elongated point with ogival base; (c) short point, slightly shouldered; (d–g) arch-backed bladelets; (h) trapeze; (i, j) scalene triangles; (k–m) perforators; (n) tanged flake; (o, p) notched and retouched pieces; (q) sidescraper; (r) dihedral burin on sidescraper; (s) retouched blade; (t) bilateral sidescraper; (u) single-platform core on flake.*

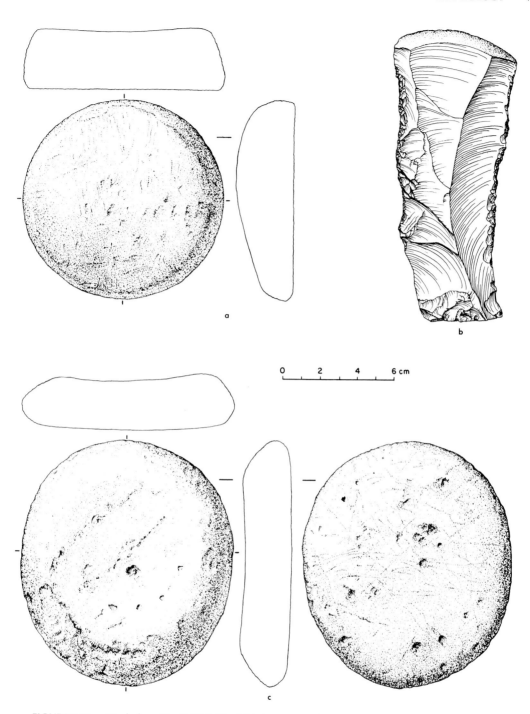

0   2   4   6 cm

FIGURE 3.76.   *Tools from Site E-75-6, Neolithic layer: (a, c) handstones; (b) large retouched flake.*

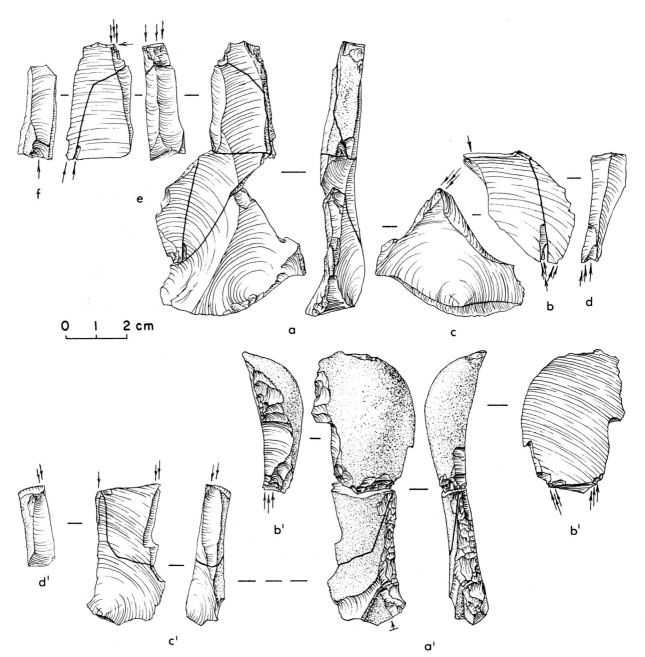

FIGURE 3.77. *Reassembled burins and burin spalls from Neolithic Pit 4 at Site E-75-6.*

Ostrich-eggshell beads are numerous and occur in various stages of completion. The initial step was to form roughly rectangular to almost circular pieces by breaking the edge of the shell. A hole was then drilled from both sides, and the perimeter of the bead was ground and reduced to the desired circular outline and size.

Site E-77-5 (E101G2)

About 20 km north of Nabta Playa, in the smaller basin of El Kortein Playa, is the next Neolithic settlement (Figure 3.80). It is representative of the second phase of the Neolithic with Early Khartoum style pottery. The site is near the center of the basin, slightly northwest of Terminal Paleolithic Site E-77-6. The cultural remains occur on the surface and within the uppermost silts of this playa, tentatively assigned to Playa II. Charcoal from one hearth dated 7530 BP ± 180 years (SMU-462), about 700 years later than the earliest Neolithic in the area at Site E-75-6.

The remains visible on the surface consisted of three separate artifact concentrations, of which the largest and most dense was collected and excavated (Figure 3.81). The

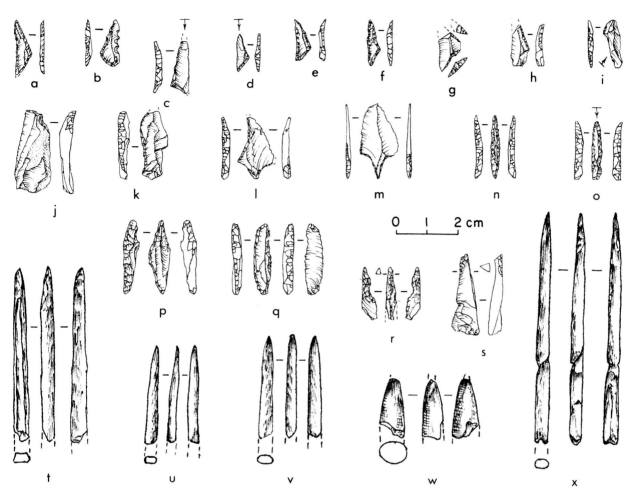

FIGURE 3.78. *Artifacts from Site E-75-6: (a–f) triangles; (g) trapeze; (h) partially backed bladelet; (i) shouldered bladelet; (j) arch-ended bladelet; (k) arch-backed bladelet; (l, m) stemmed point; (n–s) perforators; (t–x) bone points.*

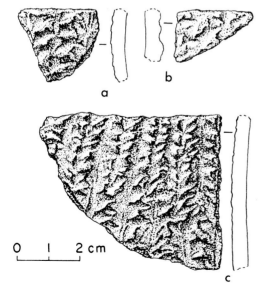

FIGURE 3.79. *Sherds of Early Khartoum pottery from Neolithic layer, Site E-75-6.*

FIGURE 3.80. *View across Site E-77-5 before excavation, looking south. Note slightly raised circle of artifacts in center of picture.*

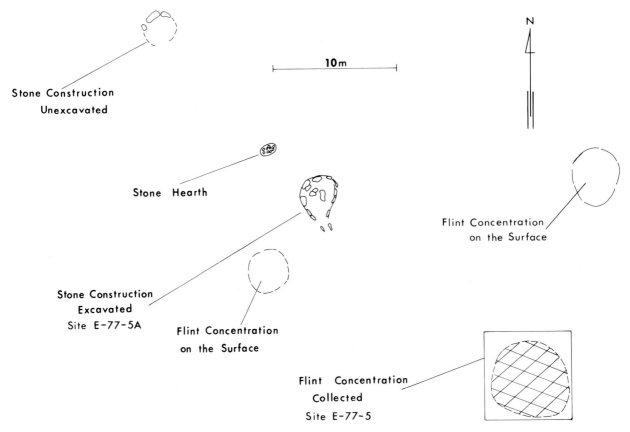

FIGURE 3.81. *General map of Sites E-77-5 and E-77-5A.*

other two were thin. Two vertical slab-lined structures also were evident eroding from the silts, the tops of the slabs standing up to 15 cm above the structure. One of these was more exposed; the second was barely evident on the surface. A cluster of fire-cracked rocks on the surface between the two structures probably represented a partially deflated hearth. Occasional vertical slabs occurred farther upslope toward the northwest where the playa silts were less eroded, thus suggesting the presence of similar structures. The time available did not permit adequate testing and uncovering of a large surface area, thus only one structure, designated as Site E-77-5A, was excavated.

The studied concentration first appeared on the surface as a ring of chipped artifacts, about 6 m in diameter, and almost empty in the center. This area was collected, scatterpatterned, and excavated (Figure 3.82). The excavations showed that the artifact-bearing horizon rests in a very shallow (about 20 cm deep), almost circular basin whose central part (about 3 m in diameter) contains relatively few artifacts (Figure 3.83). The limits of the basin were marked by the dense artifacts on the surface. Almost all the artifacts in the center were buried in the sediment. On the floor of the basin, slightly off-center toward the southwest, was a roughly circular burned area with some charcoal, and it was this charcoal that was dated. A large basin-shaped mil-

ling stone was along the west edge of the clear area, embedded in the sediment. A handstone was found on the opposite side of the empty area.

The scatterpatterned area measures 7 by 8 m, and covers the extent of the concentration. Only a few artifacts occurred beyond the gridded area. The very characteristic pattern of the artifact distribution, the basin-like morphology of the floor, the hearth area inside the basin, and the artifact ring suggest an occupational unit that could have been a circular house, relatively empty in the center and with occupational debris around the periphery. Charcoal from the central hearth gave a radiocarbon date of 7530 BP ± 180 years (SMU-462).

The nearby excavated slab-lined structure (Site E-77-5A) was circular to oval in outline, 2.6 by 3.0 m in diameter (Figure 3.84). The southern portion of the structure still had large, vertical, overlapping slab walls (Figures 3.85 and 3.86), although the slabs in the northern portion were displaced, tilted and diagonal or lying flat on the silt above the floor. On the southeast side were two vertical slabs, and an opening in the wall (on the side away from the prevailing wind) that suggested an entrance. The floor of this construction was at the base of the slabs, 65 cm below the surface. A concentration of charcoal and burnt silt occurred at this level adjacent to the eastern wall, and the slabs here

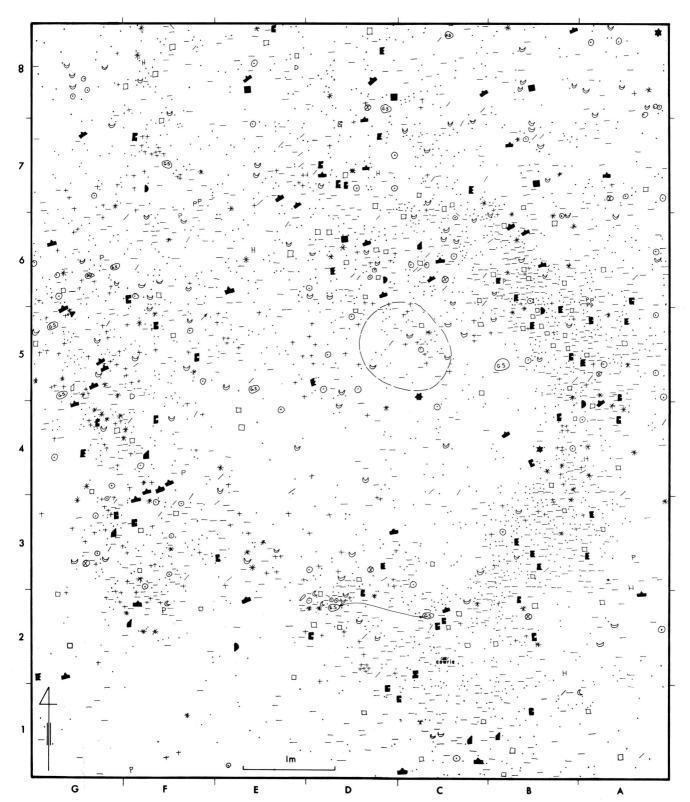

FIGURE 3.82. *Horizontal distribution of artifacts at Site E-77-5, surface and excavated. Note hearth basin in center of collected area. For key, see Figure 3.28.*

SITE E-77-5

CROSS-SECTION OF ROW D, Sq. I-8

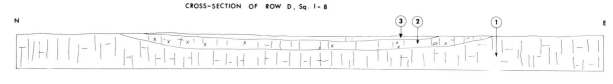

0   50   100 m

FIGURE 3.83. *Cross section through concentration at Site E-77-5. Key: 1, playa silts; 2, silts with cultural debris, cultural layer; 3, silts with occasional cultural remains.*

FIGURE 3.84. *View of exposed slab structure at Site E-77-5A at beginning of excavation. Position of lateral entryway is indicated by shovel.*

were discolored by fire. The charcoal from this hearth dated 7230 BP ± 100 years (SMU-470). Only a few artifacts were found within the structure.

The concentration of Site E-77-5, however, was rich in artifacts, made primarily of quartz and quartz crystal, followed by light gray chert, chalcedony, jasper, and rare dark gray chert. There were 120 cores, almost all of which were for flakes and of the single-platform, change-of-orientation, and opposed-platform varieties. Bladelet cores are rare and all of the single-platform type.

The collection includes 223 tools. Three classes of tools account for over 80% of the assemblage. These include retouched flakes and blades (38.9%), denticulates and/or notches (23.9%), and perforators (22.6%). Perforators were mostly of the double-backed variety. The remaining tool classes never exceed 5% and include truncated small flakes (3.5%), a few arch-backed and fragmentary backed pieces (3.5%), endscrapers (2.2%), a trapeze, a Krukowski microburin, and a scaled piece. There are also three elongated points with long tapering stems, clearly different from those found with the Terminal Paleolithic settlements (Figure 3.87).

Fragments of worked ostrich eggshell, including both finished and unfinished beads, are numerous. The large lower grinding stone found in the circular concentration was roughly oval in outline, shaped by pecking, with a large, well-defined oval grinding face occupying most of the upper surface (Figure 3.88c). The collection also includes 8 hand grinders, all fragmentary, and 15 sherds of Early Khartoum pottery.

The collection from inside the slab-lined structure at Site E-77-5A includes only 23 flakes and chips, 2 retouched pieces (one on a flake, the other on a blade), and 1 side-scraper on a flake. There were also a few scraps of bone, 3 eggshell fragments, and 1 sherd of Early Khartoum pottery.

Site E-75-7 (E101K2)

At the foot of the projecting, silt-covered, Nubia sandstone peninsula on which Site E-75-8 is located, near the western edge of Nabta Playa, is an area littered with burned stones and rare Neolithic artifacts. In the center of this area, on the exposed deflated surface of underlying sand, are the Terminal Paleolithic occupations of Site E-75-7. Neolithic artifacts also occur on this deflated sand surface as well as on the surrounding playa clays (Figure 3.10).

A few upright or diagonal sandstone slabs are clustered along the northwest margin of the artifact-littered area. Several of these slab clusters were tested, but no definable structure or associated occupation was recognized. On the east side of the deflated area, just beyond the edge of the overlapping playa, was a cluster of six pits, clearly visible on the surface because of their playa seals, which contrasted with the surrounding sands. All these pits were excavated or tested, and they proved to be either walk-in or simple wells, ranging in depth from 2.3 to 2.4 m. The wells contained Early Khartoum pottery near the base of their fills, and higher in the fills of all of them were occasional chips and washed-in Terminal Paleolithic artifacts.

In addition to the scatterpatterned areas, a collection was made from the surface of the surrounding playa clay. This collection, some pieces of which were found still embedded in the playa clay, included five strangled blades, a notched blade, two retouched and notched blades, a burin, and two endscrapers (Figures 3.89 and 3.90).

The Neolithic locality at Site E-75-7 seems to have been predominantly related to the extraction of drinking water, possibly available here because of the deep sandy sub-

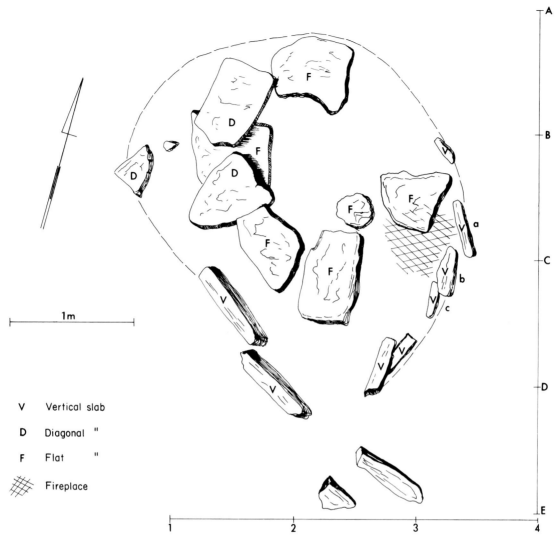

FIGURE 3.85. *Sketch map of slab-lined structure at Site E-77-5A.*

1m

V   Vertical slab

D   Diagonal "

F   Flat   "

⬚⬚⬚   Fireplace

SITE E - 77 - 5A , STONE CONSTRUCTION

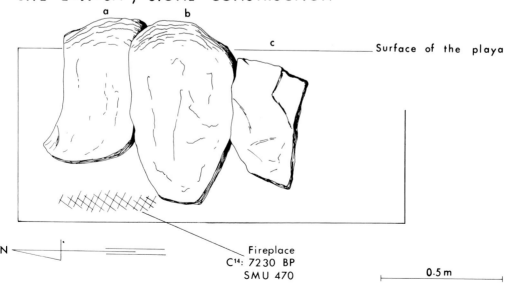

Surface of the playa

N

Fireplace
C¹⁴: 7230 BP
SMU 470

0.5 m

INSIDE VIEW FROM THE WEST TO THE EASTERN WALL

FIGURE 3.86. *Site E-77-5A, lined structure. Detail of overlapping stone slabs of eastern wall.*

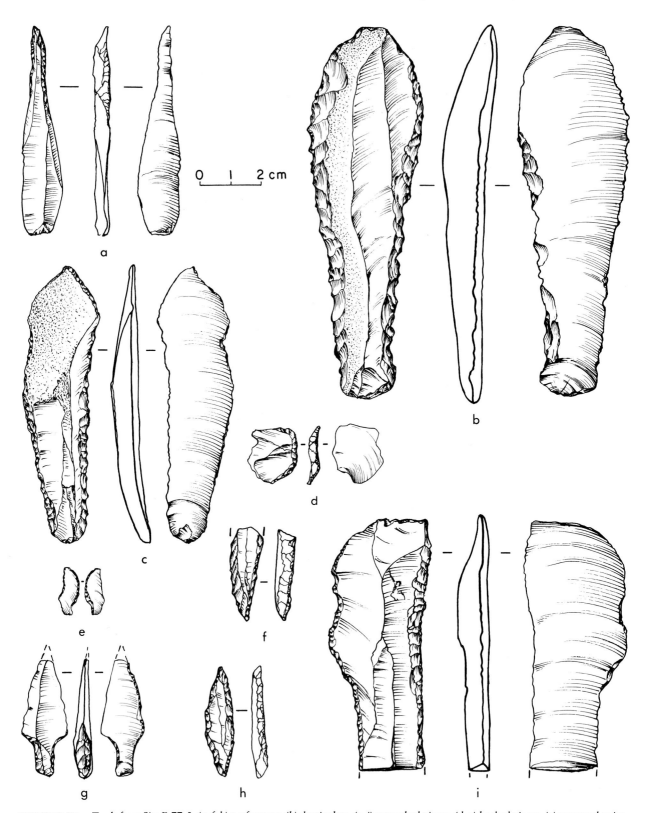

FIGURE 3.87.   *Tools from Site E-77-5: (a, f, h) perforators; (b) denticulate, (c, i) retouched pieces; (d, e) backed pieces; (g) stemmed point.*

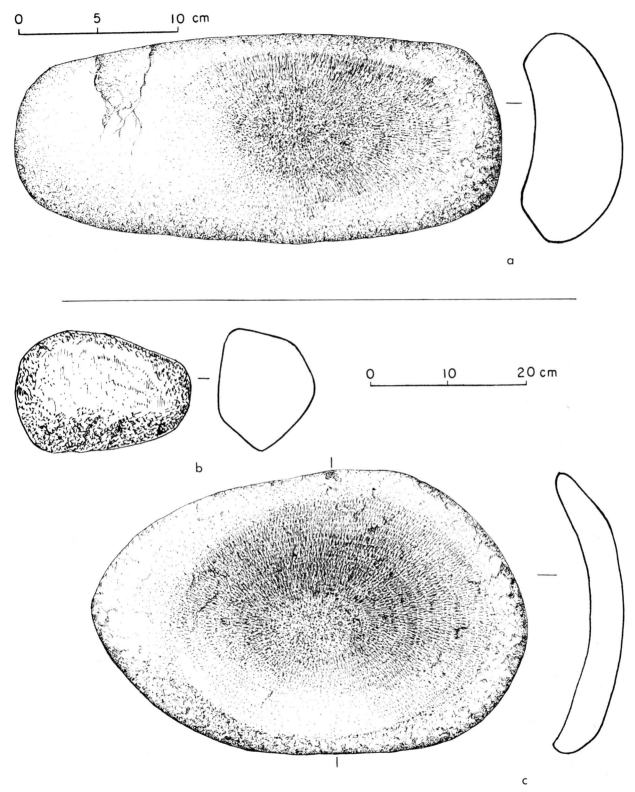

FIGURE 3.88. *Milling stones and hammerstone from Site E-75-8, lower cultural layer (a), and Site E-77-5 (b, c).*

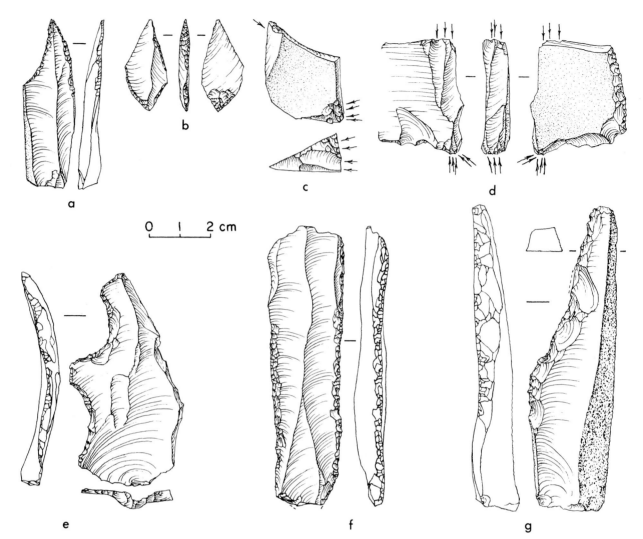

FIGURE 3.89. *Tools from surface of playa and Neolithic pits at Site E-75-7: (a) perforator; (b) point with ogival base; (c) multiple single-blow burin; (d) multiple mixed burin; (e) double-notched flake; (f) retouched blade; (g) shouldered blade, slightly denticulated.*

stratum adjacent to higher remnants of Nubia sandstone. The wells may have been associated with the large extensive Early Khartoum settlement of Site E-75-8, even though the oldest cultural debris of that settlement and the associated silts are at least 2 m higher than the presumed water level in the bottom of the wells. This difference in elevation could have been the result of seasonal fluctuations, or perhaps of a short period of unusually dry years.

Site E-75-8 (E101K3)

The enormous settlement of Site E-75-8, located 300 m north of Site E-75-7 (Figure 3.10), was subjected to limited testing and excavations during the 1975 and 1977 seasons. During both seasons the work was concentrated in the southern portion of the settlement, on a projecting sandy knoll surrounded on three sides by lacustrine sediments. The northern and northeastern portions of the settlement

had been almost completely destroyed by deflation. It is evident that the entire site was significantly modified by deflation, sufficient to remove all sediments of the upper occupational horizons in the area immediately to the north of Pit 1/77 (Figure 3.91). For this reason, only the southernmost tip of the sandy knoll preserves layers associated with the later Neolithic occupations. To the north, the occupational debris that could have been deposited during the later periods is exposed on the surface and mixed with that now eroding from the lowest Neolithic occupations.

The whole area is dotted with deflated or partially deflated rock-lined hearths. Abundant fire-cracked rocks also occurred between the hearths, littering the entire surface as well as the surface of the adjacent lacustrine sediments. These rocks were sufficiently plentiful to armor the top of the knoll and retard its further destruction. The hearths still partially *in situ* contained abundant ash, charcoal powder and flecks, plus occasional burned artifacts and bone.

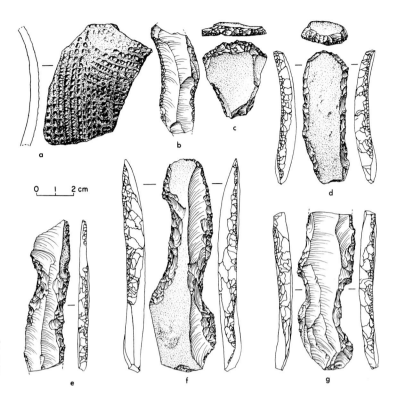

FIGURE 3.90. *Tools from surface of playa and Neolithic pits at Site E-75-7: (a) Early Khartoum sherd from bottom of well (Pit 3); (b, e–g) strangled blades; (c, d) endscrapers.*

Dozens of lower and upper grinding stones occur on the surface, sometimes in inverted or upright positions. A concentration of eight lower grinders and associated handstones was noted near the northwest edge of the studied area (Figure 3.92). Here and there were caches of raw material, quartz pebbles or crystals, thin slabs of chert, and "side-blow" chert flakes frequently worked as sidescrapers (Figure 3.93).

A double burial, heavily truncated by deflation, and almost entirely weathered, occurred on the surface (Figure 3.94) but within the sands of the latest Neolithic occupation (Figure 3.19:5). Another burial was found covered by sandstone slabs and exposed on the surface of the sands to the east of the knoll. Because of the position and geological context (lower sands) of this burial, it was presumably associated with one of the earliest occupations at this site.

By accident, the excavations in 1975 were mostly concentrated in the area where only the lower layer was preserved *in situ*. Four cuts and three trenches were excavated. One cut, 2 by 2 m, was to clear the area around the late double burial (75/3); another, the largest, 5 by 10 m (75/2), was opened in the upper lacustrine sands (Figures 3.16:6b and 3.21:5); the third (75/1), an area 5 by 4 m, and the fourth (75/4), a pit 4 by 4 m, were cut into the lower cultural horizon near the center of the settlement (Figure 3.19:2). The three trenches were all in the northern portion of the worked area; two of them were for stratigraphic purposes where the playa overlapped the dune, and the third was cut through a large mound of fire-cracked rocks.

During the 1977 season, the work was focused at the southern tip of the settlement and limited to the study of its detailed stratigraphy and lithologic setting. Here the excavations consisted of a long trench, 22 by 2 m, connecting two stratigraphic pits (Pit 1, Pit 2, and the Connecting Trench); a second trench, 24 m long and 1 m wide, in the same line as the first but separated from it by an unexcavated area 4 m long; two small pits (Pits 3 and 4), both 2 by 2 m, exposing only the lower occupation level; and two additional stratigraphic trenches, one on the east side of the peninsula (East Trench), and the other on the west side (West Trench). In addition, five 1-m test squares were excavated around the East Trench in an unsuccessful effort to locate an occupational floor associated with the beach, and the trench that had been cut through the large mound of fire-cracked rocks at the north end of the studied area in 1975 was expanded to collect additional charcoal. Several other hearths (A through E) were also examined, and charcoal was collected for radiocarbon dating.

Although the excavated areas constitute only a minute fraction of the total preserved portion of the site, they represent a significant effort because of the depth of the strata, both archaeological and geological. The combined work during both seasons has permitted only an evaluation of the potential of the site, its chronology, its stratigraphy and the lithological context of the cultural layers; and it has provided limited samples of artifacts and faunal and floral remains. The site was occupied over a long period of time, perhaps over 2000 years, and certainly represents several settlements. Our excavations were not sufficiently extensive to permit the isolation of specific settlement units, either

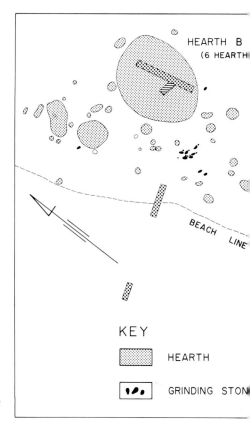

FIGURE 3.91. *Map of southern portion of Site E-75-8 showing location of trenches, hearth mounds, milling stones on surface, and other features.*

FIGURE 3.92. *Site E-75-8 view of grinding-stone cluster on surface of site. Note dense scatter of burned rock.*

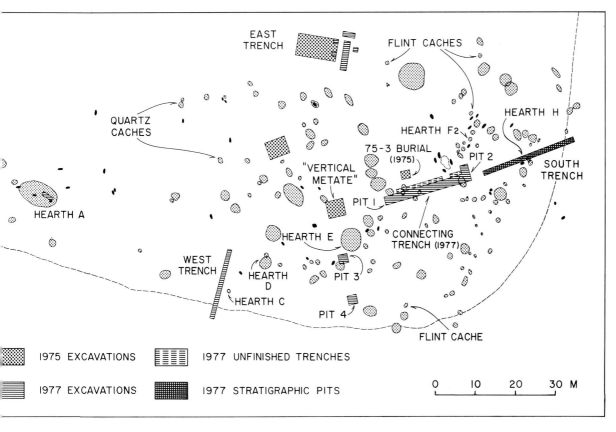

1975 EXCAVATIONS   1977 UNFINISHED TRENCHES

1977 EXCAVATIONS   1977 STRATIGRAPHIC PITS

0   10   20   30 M

horizontally or vertically. A proper study of this complex site would require a multiseason effort with substantial labor, and the opening of very extensive, stratigraphically controlled areas.

Three major stratigraphic–cultural units were recognized. The lowest (Figure 3.20:2), up to 100 cm thick, is a dark layer of sand containing charcoal, fire-cracked rocks, stone-lined hearths, and cultural debris. It rests directly on the dune, and toward the south end it grades into lacustrine silty sand of Playa III. Though the hearths in this layer obviously occur at various levels and witness the presence of multiple, stratified occupations, the limited excavations, which were done by arbitrary layers, make it necessary that all of the data from this horizon be combined. The radiocarbon dates indicate a time range from 7100 to 6700 BP, or about 400 years.

The lithic assemblage from this layer in Pits 1 and 2 and the Connecting Trench is made on a wide variety of raw material, including quartz, quartz crystal, chert, chalcedony, jasper, agate, petrified wood, ferruginous grit sandstone, and granite. Quartz, quartz crystal, and chert were the most common. Most of the chert has a light tan color and an appearance different from that employed in earlier sites; however, its provenience has not been determined. The most common cores are the change-of-orientation and single-platform cores for flakes. Opposed-platform cores for flakes are rare, and bladelet cores are represented by only a few specimens. All cores are heavily exploited and many are reduced to very small pieces (Figure 3.95).

The lithic assemblage contains 395 tools, including 48 grinding stones. By far the most frequent tool group is that of retouched pieces, mostly retouched flakes (30.8%), followed by the notch and denticulate group (27.1%). The latter is composed of notched flakes, the most common, followed by notched blades and bladelets. Denticulates on flakes and bladelets are relatively rare. The next most frequent tool group is that of truncations (17%), mostly microlithic flakes with basal truncations. There are also numerous points made on small flakes, rarely on bladelets, with convex, concave, or straight retouched bases, and lightly retouched pointed tips or lateral edges, the last sometimes approaching backing (10.4%). These points resemble the Bou Saada type when the base is concave (Tixier Type 108), or pointed bladelets with rounded base (Tixier Type 109) when convex. As a population, however, they are much shorter, and fewer are made on bladelets, in contrast to the classic examples occurring in Terminal Paleolithic sites in the Maghreb (Tixier 1955: 94, and 1963). One backed variety present in this collection also occurs in the early Neolithic site of Amekni (Camps 1969a:49) and there they are called "backed points with rounded base" (Figures 3.96 and 3.97).

Perforators and geometrics (both at 5.8%) are next in number. Double-backed perforators are the most common, although only slightly more so than simple examples on

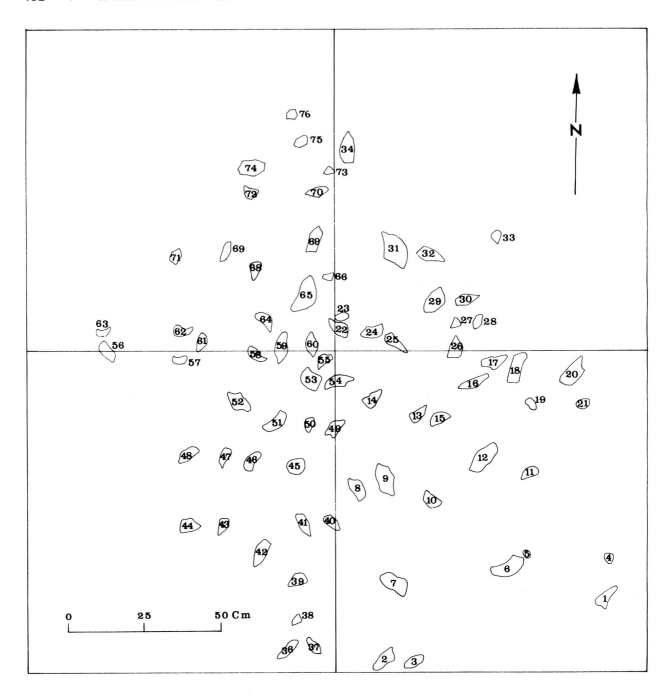

FIGURE 3.93. *Plan of deflated cache of side-blow flakes and sidescrapers, Site E-75-8. Note characteristic gravitational dispersal of artifacts.*

FIGURE 3.94. *View of extensively deflated double burial at Site E-75-8 as first seen.*

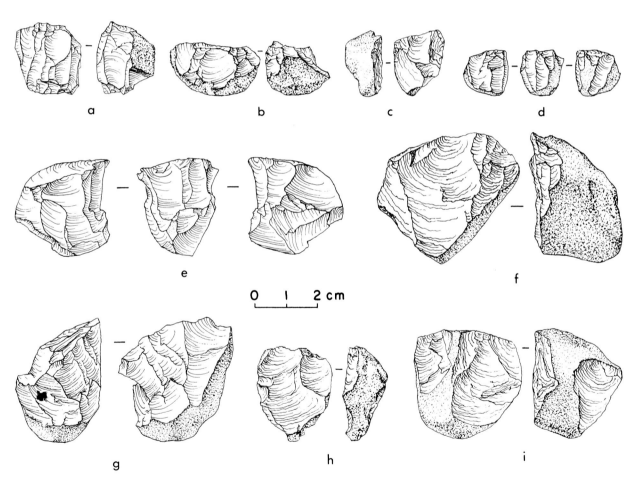

FIGURE 3.95. *Cores from lower Neolithic cultural layer of Site E-75-8: (a) opposed platform; (b–i) single platform.*

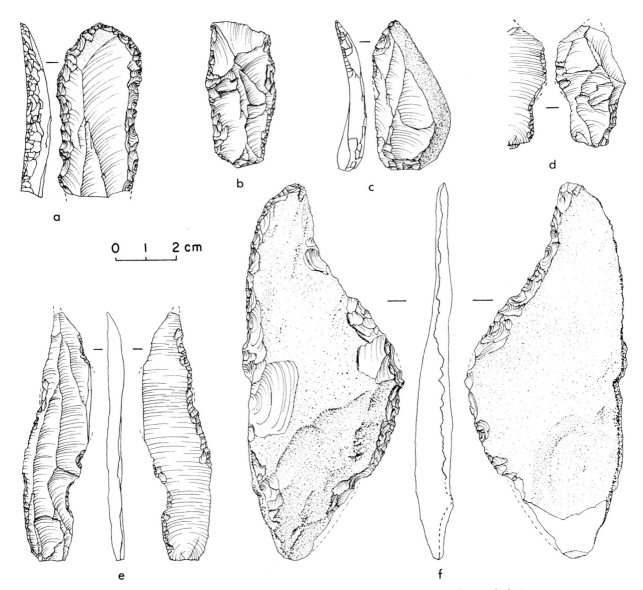

FIGURE 3.96. *Tools from lower Neolithic cultural layer of Site E-75-8: (a–f) retouched pieces.*

flakes. Almost all geometrics are short, small lunates, some of the J-shaped variety, and all have characteristic semi-steep retouch. Triangles and trapezes are present but extremely rare. Bifacial points account for 2.0%. These occur in a variety of forms, including large examples up to 9 cm in length; small, elongated, willow-leaf or lozenge-shaped arrowheads; and barbed and tanged arrowheads with convergent stems.

The remainder of the collection includes eight sidescrapers, an arch-backed bladelet, a shouldered bladelet, an obtuse backed bladelet, and three backed fragments, all accounting for 1.7%. There are also five simple microburins, five endscrapers on flakes, one burin on snap, one polished stone fragment, possibly from a celt, and a double-pointed, polished splinter of petrified wood.

The lower grinders are represented by both whole and

fragmentary specimens. Most are flat sandstone slabs, elongated oval in outline, shaped by pecking, with well-defined grinding surfaces (Figure 3.98). Some have two opposed grinding faces. The handstones, also made on sandstone, are usually oval to circular in outline. They are shaped by pecking and have either one or two opposed convex grinding surfaces. Many display traces of red and yellow ocher pigment.

Ostrich-eggshell fragments, some with incised decorations; finished and unfinished shell beads; a cowrie-shell bead; a fragment of a large bone point; and several pieces of yellow and red ocher were also found.

The plant material recovered from Site E-75-8 came from the early cultural level. Included are numerous roots of a grass and several grains of six-row barley and emmer wheat. Three kinds of weeds and a date palm seed were also

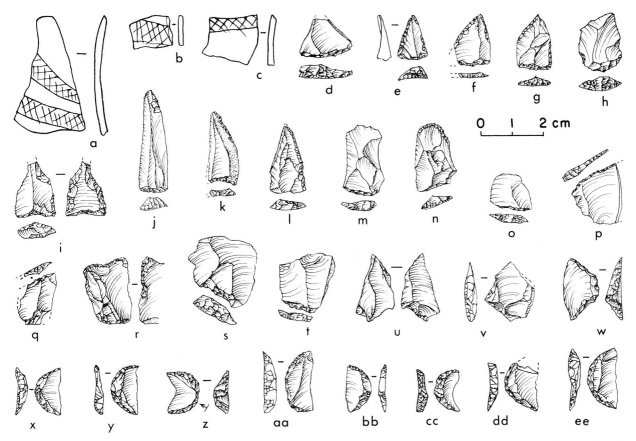

FIGURE 3.97. *Tools and decorated eggshell from lower Neolithic cultural layer at Site E-75-8: (a–c) decorated ostrich eggshell; (d–l) proximal truncations with point; (m, o) proximal truncation with blunt end; (n) proximal truncation with rounded distal end; (p–t) truncations; (u) microburin; (v) atypical triangle; (w) trapeze; (x–ee) lunates.*

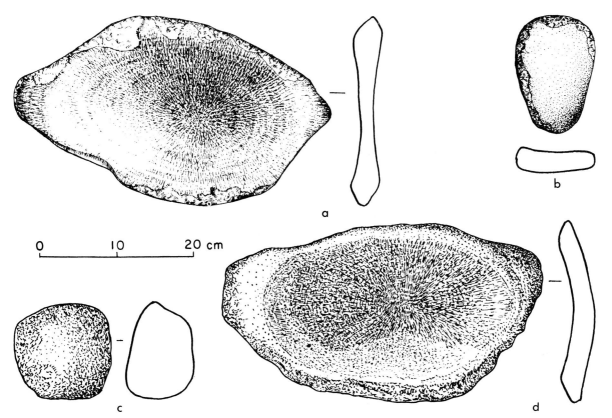

FIGURE 3.98. *Milling stones, handstone, and hammerstone from lower, middle, and upper Neolithic cultural layers at Site E-75-8: (a, b) upper Neolithic Neolithic layer; (c) middle Neolithic layer; (d) lower Neolithic layer.*

present. The last is of special interest, because it may be either a wild tropical African small palm or a modern date palm at an incipient stage of domestication.

The associated pottery is classified as Early Khartoum but is clearly different from that found in the earlier site of E-75-6. Here, the vessels are larger and thicker walled, the paste is more heavily tempered and more friable, and the decorations, usually consisting of a haphazard mat of corded impressions, were partially obliterated while the

clay was still soft (Figure 3.99). The pottery does not appear to be as well executed as that from the earlier site.

Three other excavated units (Pits 75/1 and 75/4, and the East Trench) contained material that clearly belongs to this same period. The collections are small, but the assemblage from Pit 75/1 contains a high frequency of the typical, small points with convex or concave bases, a few lunates and fragments, notches, denticulates, retouched pices, an end-scraper, a perforator, and a few unfinished bifacial pieces.

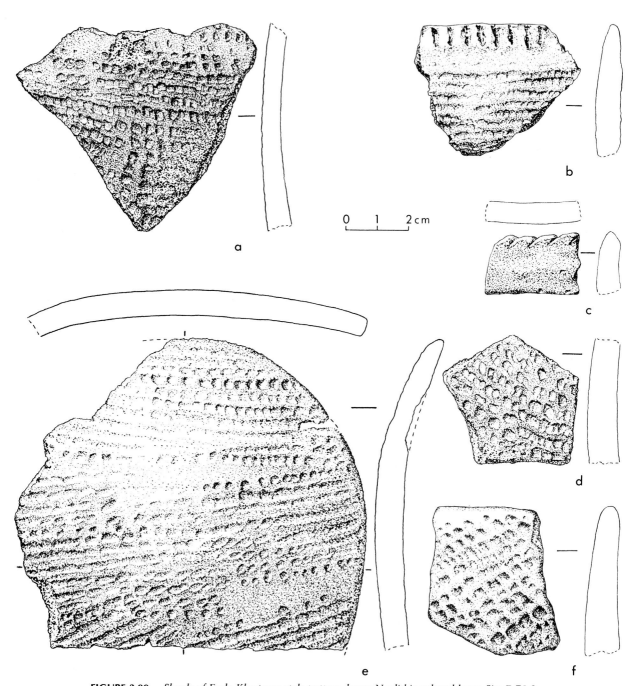

FIGURE 3.99. *Sherds of Early Khartoum style pottery, lower Neolithic cultural layer, Site E-75-8.*

The collection from Pit 75/4 consists of a J-shaped lunate, two points with concave bases, a simple microburin, a fragment of a bifacial point, and an unfinished bifacial piece. Finally, the collection from the East Trench includes seven denticulates, one of which is on a blade, four truncations, three notched pieces, three lunates, a point with straight base, a double-backed perforator, an arch-backed bladelet, a retouched flake, a possible scraper, a retouched slab, and one handstone.

A change in color, degree of induration, and texture distinguishes the following cultural layer from that below. It is preserved only in the southern part of the Connecting Trench, where it is 20 to 30 cm thick, and much lighter in color because of a reduced admixture of organic particles (Figure 3.20:3). It contains a few rock-lined fireplaces at various levels, the lowest of which is dated 6500 BP (SMU-435). It seems likely that two fireplaces and a pit sunk in the top of the lower cultural layer in the northern part of

the Connecting Trench may belong to this phase of occupation; however, the middle layer could not be distinguished in that portion of the trench. The recovered artifacts are scarce and include only 25 tools, 10 of which are grinding stones. The flaked stone tools are mostly notches and denticulates, retouched pieces, four sidescrapers, and two bifacial points, one with convergent stem and a notch on each side of the blade (Figure 3.100d, and Figure 3.101b, c).

The pottery from the middle cultural layer is classified as Early Khartoum, and is identical to that from the lower layer.

The slab-covered burial found in a deflated area at the northwest side of the site cannot be related on either stratigraphic or archaeological grounds to any of the recognized cultural horizons. However, because of the occurrence of the grave in the lower sands and its relatively low elevation, it is likely that it belongs with an Early Khar-

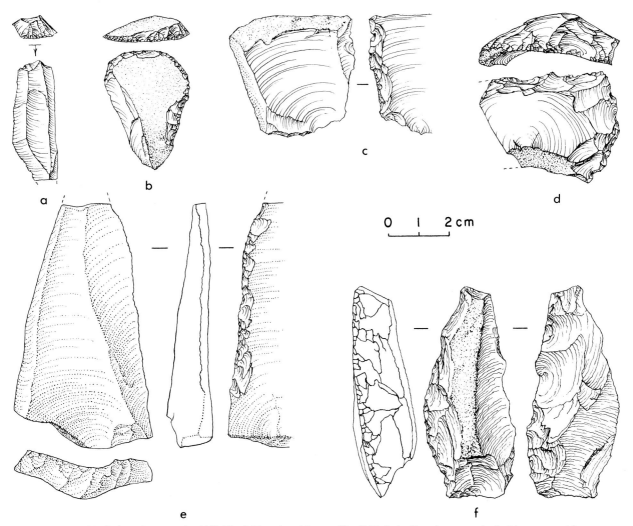

FIGURE 3.100. *Tools from lower and middle Neolithic cultural layers, Site E-75-8: (a, b) endscrapers; (c, f) sidescrapers; (d) transverse sidescraper; (e) sidescraper on old Levallois point. Tools d and f from middle horizon; others from lower horizon.*

toum occupation. The grave was found exposed on the surface and surrounded by large sandstone slabs lying horizontally. The slabs may once have enclosed the grave. The body was placed on its left side, facing north, with hands to face. The position of the legs could not be determined (Fig-

ure 3.102). The bones were badly eroded and only the lower mandible and teeth were in better condition. The study of this mandible (Henneberg *et al.*, this volume) indicates that it belonged to a male, about 35 years of age. The taxonomic comparison shows similarities to modern ne-

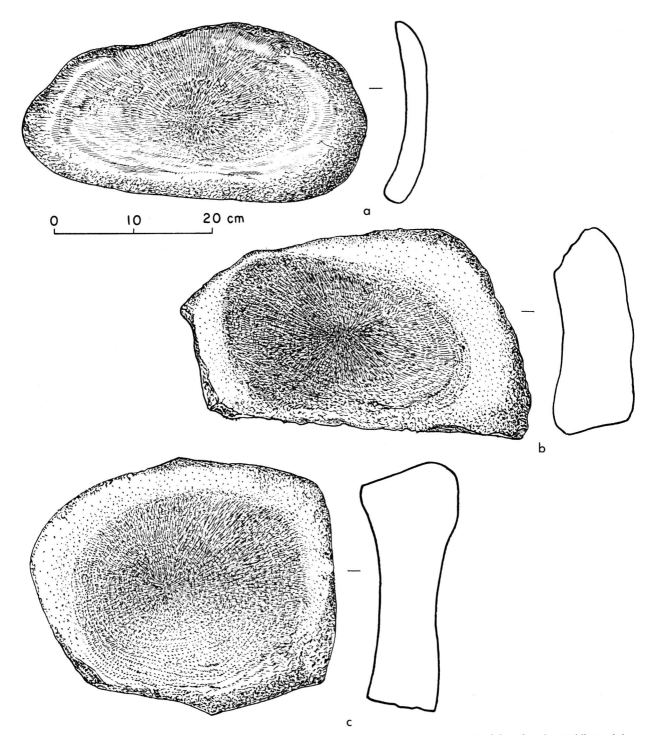

FIGURE 3.101   *Milling stones from middle and upper Neolithic cultural layers, Site E-75-8: (a) upper Neolithic; (b and c) Middle Neolithic.*

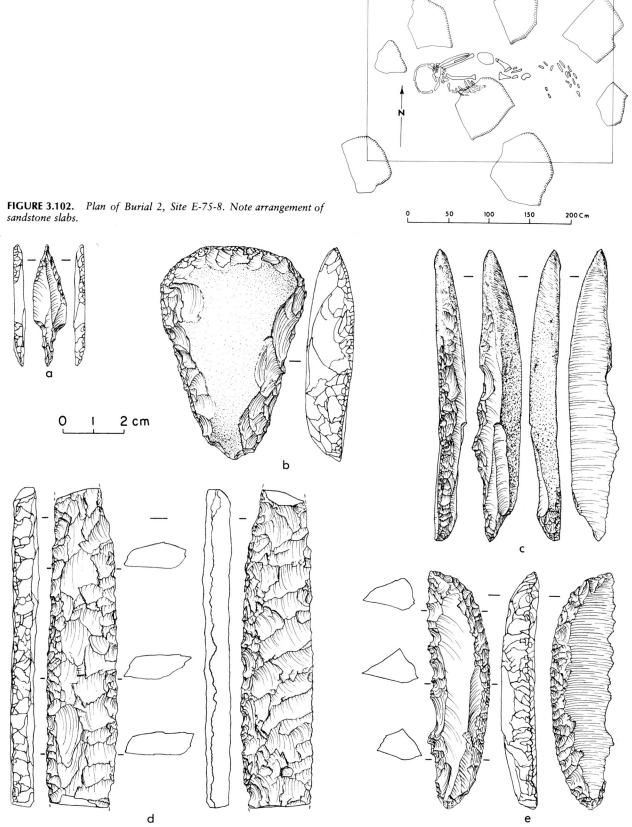

FIGURE 3.102. *Plan of Burial 2, Site E-75-8. Note arrangement of sandstone slabs.*

0   50   100   150   200 Cm

0   1   2 cm

FIGURE 3.103. *Tools from upper Neolithic cultural layer, Site E-75-8: (a) stemmed point; (b) flaked edge; (c) perforator with worn distal end; (d) beveled bifacial piece; (e) crescent piece.*

159

groid populations, and differences from the Late and Terminal Paleolithic Mechta el Arbi populations of North Africa and the Nile Valley.

Another and very fragmentary burial was found in the Connecting Trench, in a pit cut from the middle culture layer, through the lower culture layer into the underlying sand. It may have been a "bundle burial," since the bones occurred piled together and not in anatomical order. Traces of reed matting were noted under the burial. Only scraps of bone remained, including pieces of the pelvis, scapula, radius, and ribs, plus 1 tooth and 20 bones from the feet and hands. These are sufficient only to identify the individual as an adult. Presumably accompanying grave goods include 2 pendants (one made on an unidentified seashell with perforation near the beak, and the other an elongated oval ostrich-eggshell pendant with a hole at one end), 1 carnelian bead, and 10 fragments of an ivory bracelet. The fill of the pit contained 4 tools, 2 cores, 46 chips and flakes, and 2 undecorated Khartoum sherds.

The upper cultural horizon occurs in a loose, pale brown sand, divisible into two units in the middle section of the Connecting Trench. The lower of these units, which is light yellowish-brown and consolidated, shows a distinct mat of vegetation casts (Figure 3.20:4). Charcoal from the top of this lower unit dated 6310 BP (SMU-441). Upslope this lower unit grades into unstratified pale brown sand (Figure 3.20:5), which is indistinguishable from that of the uppermost unit in the midsection of the trench. The top of the uppermost level is dated 5810 BP ± 80 years (SMU-473).

Where the distinction in sand units was clear, the artifacts from the two were collected separately; however, in most areas, particularly in the South Trench and the upper end of the Connecting Trench, they could not be readily distinguished. The entire collection is marginal in size, so the material from the two horizons is combined here. When separated, the assemblages from the two levels did not display any significant differences.

The raw materials utilized have the same range as those

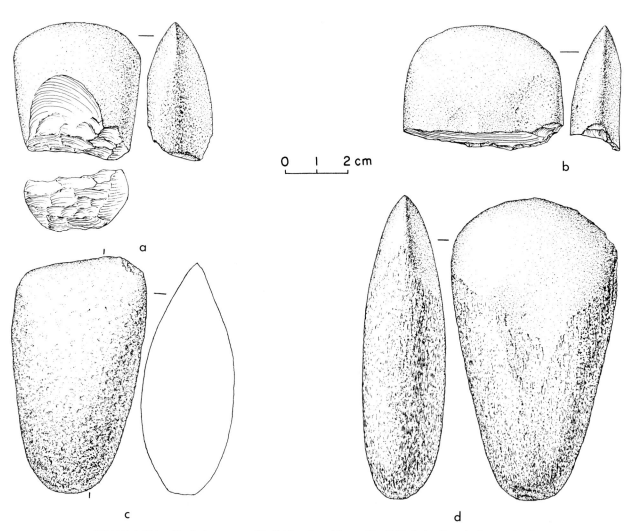

FIGURE 3.104. *Tools from upper Neolithic cultural layer, Site E-75-8: (a–d) pecked ground celts.*

from the lower level, with considerable emphasis on quartz, quartz crystal, and chert. The most common cores, accounting for almost half the collection, are of the change-of-orientation variety for flakes, followed by single-platform cores for flakes. Opposed-platform cores for flakes are represented by a few pieces, and single-platform cores for bladelets are rare. Generally, the preparation of the cores was limited to the striking platform.

The stone tools other than grinders total only 136 pieces. The most numerous group is that of notches and denticulates (39.7%), with notches on flakes largely predominant. Retouched flakes and blades make up the next most important group (33.8%). No other group exceeds 10%, but endscrapers (6.6%), geometrics (6.6%)—mostly lunates with a few trapezes and triangles—and truncations (2.9%) occur. All others are represented by one or two pieces, one of which is a bifacial point and another is a large crescent-shaped artifact with pseudo-Helwan backing along the arc made by alternating fine pressure retouch (Figure 3.103e). The collection includes three ground and polished celts, which are biconvex to oval in cross section

and triangular in outline (Figure 3.104a–c). An eccentric grooved stone was also found.

A cache of 48 unworked, thin, Eocene chert slabs was found buried in this layer, about 10 cm above the lower horizon in the Connecting Trench. Other caches, deflated and exposed on the surface, were noted in the northern part of the site. It is possible that they were associated with the upper cultural layer of the site. They display the typical dispersed patterning due to sliding during deflation. One of these (Figure 3.93) consisted of 76 "side-blow" chert flakes, 23 of which had been retouched into large sidescrapers (Figures 3.105 and 3.106). Another collected cache consisted of 22 quartz crystals.

The grinding stones were represented by 13 specimens, and could not be distinguished from those in the layers below (Figure 3.101c). One large, lower grinding stone was found in the Connecting Trench upside down with the fitting handstone underneath it.

An almost entirely destroyed double burial was found eroding from the upper layer in the southern portion of the site (Figures 3.107 and 3.108). The two individuals had

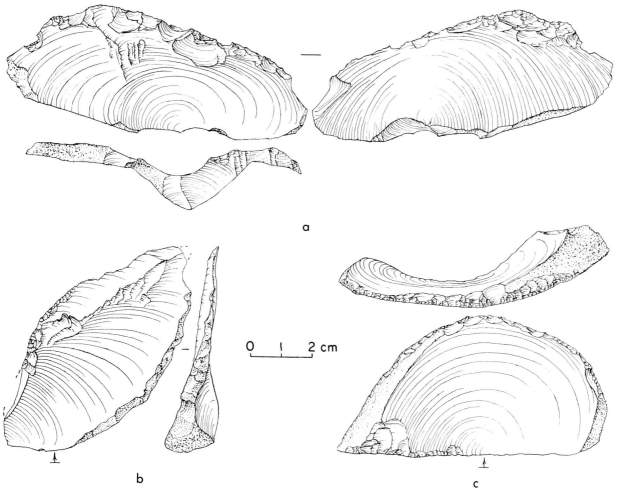

FIGURE 3.105. *Scrapers on side-blow flakes from deflated cache at Site E-75-8.*

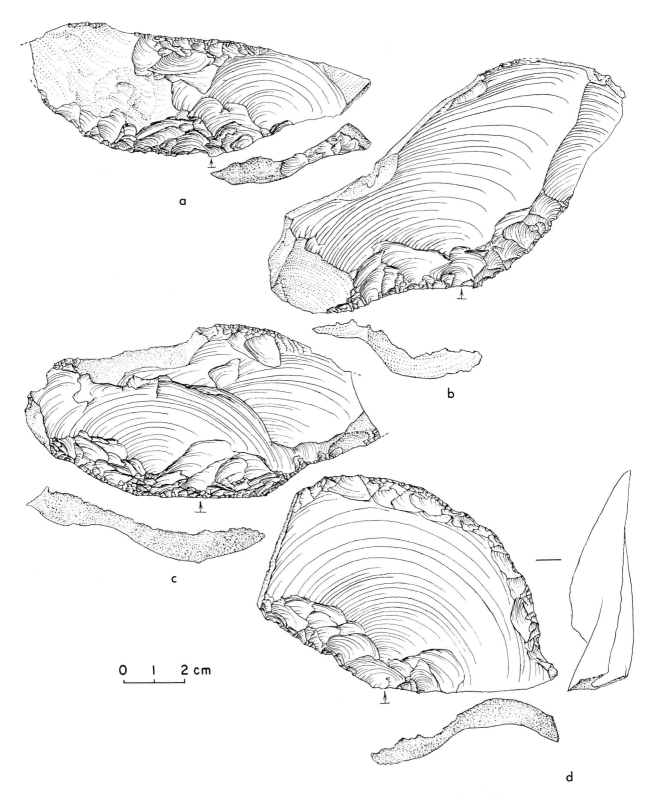

FIGURE 3.106. *Scrapers on side-blow flakes from deflated cache at Site E-75-8.*

FIGURE 3.107. *View of double burial at Site E-75-8 during excavation.*

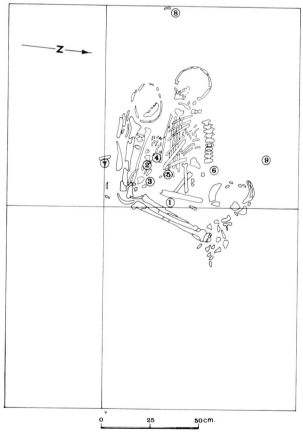

FIGURE 3.108. *Plan of double burial at Site E-75-8. 1 = Round stone; 2 = Green stone; 3 = Ocher; 4 = Clay amulette; 5 = Green stone; 6 = Cowrie shell; 7 = Mica; 8 = Shell object; 9 = Bone point.*

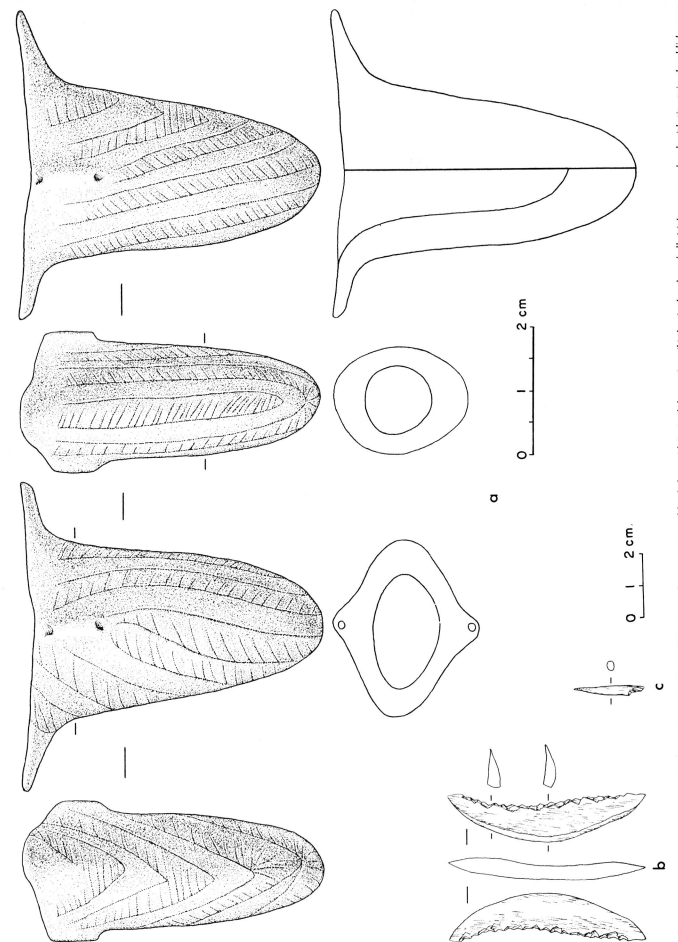

FIGURE 3.109. Grave goods found with double burial, Site E-75-8: (a) pendant container of fired clay, with incised decoration; (b) denticulated seashell; (c) bone arrowhead with tip stained reddish coor.

2 cm

0 1 2 cm.

been placed side by side in a single grave pit, lying on their right sides, facing south, with hands drawn up to the face. One appeared to have fully flexed legs; the legs on the other seemed to be pulled back. One tibia displayed a greenish stain, apparently the result of copper oxidation. The burials were accompanied by pieces of red ocher and mica, a small pottery pendant container with incised designs, a thin cylindrical bone point with red color at the tip, 6 ostrich-eggshell beads, a carnelian bead, a cowrie shell, a piece of worked shell, four green stones, and a round stone (Figure 3.109).

4
The Northern Oases: The Kharga and Dakhla Areas

April is not a pleasant month in the Western Desert. Not only does it frequently have some of the highest temperatures of the year, but there are also occasional sandstorms, the dreaded *hamsiin*. Usually we avoid working during this period, but in 1972 we had already scheduled a long field season in Ethiopia when we received permission to work at Dakhla. Our friends in Egypt had gone to considerable trouble to obtain these permits, so we decided to come to Egypt in early April after the field work in Ethiopia was completed.

Our Dakhla camp was set up near the village of Balat, where two Acheulian-age spring vents had been found. It was a broad, flat, sandy plain, and a good place to camp, although a little too near the village and its swarms of flies. Most of our camps in the desert are located several hundred kilometers from the nearest other humans, and flies, or any other signs of life, are rarely seen.

The excavation at the spring vent and the analysis of the lithic artifacts we recovered there proceeded on schedule despite the flies and heat. Because we knew the Department of Antiquities would want to keep the rich Acheulian collections, we were making every effort to complete our lithic analyses as the work progressed. As the data sheets accumulated, we filed them in a large pocket in one wall of the dining–laboratory tent.

Early one afternoon, we noted that the wind, which had been blowing from first one direction and then another, had died down, leaving a heavy stillness in the air. A few hours later, a heavy, dark brown cloud appeared on the western horizon. The cloud blocked out the sun and extended from the ground into the air for several thousand feet. A big sandstorm was coming our way.

We quickly tightened all the tents, brought all the workers back to camp, and settled in to endure the storm. We knew from our Wadi Halfa days that these storms usually last from 6 to 12 hours. They are accompanied by heavy winds, suffocating dust, and high temperatures.

This one was an unusually strong storm, and many of our tents were soon blown over by the wind, their contents scattered over the plain. One tent that blew down was our dining–laboratory tent. Not only did it collapse, but the refrigerator was turned over and the tables and chairs were scattered. Unfortunately, our manuscript of the data from the previous 2 weeks of analysis had been carelessly left in the tent pocket, and it was scattered to the wind. We later found two or three small shreds of paper, but the analyses all had to be redone. From this experience we learned always to make carbon copies of our manuscripts and to place the copies and the originals in storage boxes in separate tents.

One tent that did not blow over was the one where all the workers had gathered to wait out the storm. It was a happy group; after all, they were not working, and it was a good time to visit or sleep. Suddenly, however, a large cobra slithered into the tent to get out of the storm. Pandemonium broke out: there was only one exit, and the snake was there. Although the walls of the tent had been heavily staked and reinforced with large rocks to withstand the storm, it took only a moment to pull up one wall, and with considerable shouting and pushing, some 20 men fled into the storm and abandoned the tent to the snake.

GENERAL GEOLOGY

There are three oases—Kharga, Dakhla, and Abu Mingar—that occur in a line at the northeastern edge of the Libyan Sand Plain at the foot of the Eocene Libyan plateau. We investigated these oases during the 1972 and 1976 seasons (Figure 4.1). At Dakhla and Abu Mingar, and along the adjacent plateau, an extensive survey failed to disclose important *in situ* prehistoric settlements, except for a few spring remnants just west of the village of Balat, which contained rich late Lower Paleolithic remains. The entire season of 1972 in Egypt was spent at these vents.

The 1976 season was partially devoted to the study of some areas previously investigated by Caton-Thompson at Kharga. These areas were about 10 km north of the town of Kharga and just east of the Kharga airport. The limited goals during this season included a reexamination of Caton-Thompson's spring sequence and the recovery of material suitable for radiocarbon dating. In addition, a nearby series of important Terminal Paleolithic and early Neolithic settlements was studied in association with an early Holocene period of spring activity. An extensive survey of the entire Kharga basin disclosed several other sites, exclusively of three periods: Middle Paleolithic, Terminal Paleolithic, and Neolithic. All of them, however, were extensively deflated, and the surviving surface occurrences held little promise.

Kharga is the easternmost of the three oases and is a long north–south trenchlike basin, about 200 km in length, carved down to the Nubia Formation and sheltered by the

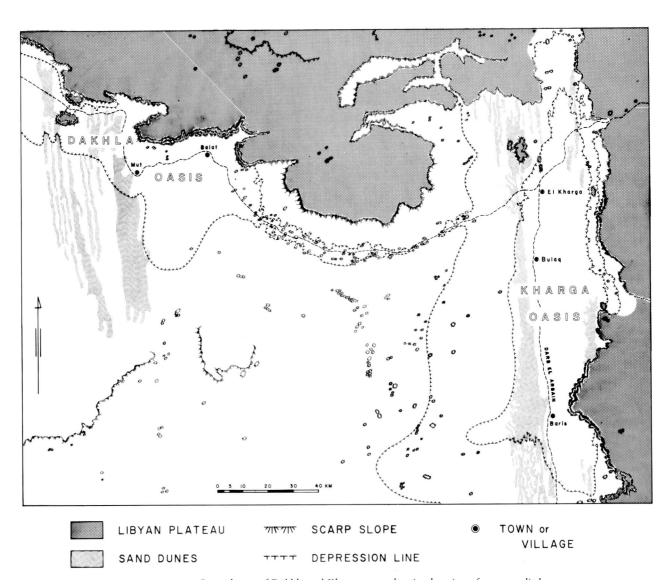

LIBYAN PLATEAU   SCARP SLOPE   ● TOWN or VILLAGE

SAND DUNES   DEPRESSION LINE

FIGURE 4.1. *General map of Dakhla and Kharga areas showing location of areas studied.*

Eocene limestone plateau on the east and north, where the high cliffs form a sharp boundary to the basin. Toward the south and west, however, the edge of the basin merges imperceptibly into the Nubia sandstone desert. The floor of the depression, from 350 to 400 m below the top of the adjacent plateau, is partially covered by several belts of active dunes, moving toward the south, and extending from the foot of the plateau on the north to the south end of the basin.

A string of villages occurs on the floor of the basin along both sides of the Darb el Arbain, the northern portion of which has now been improved and covered with asphalt. Small irrigated fields, orchards, and palm groves surround the villages. Artesian wells, most of which now have to be pumped, supply the water for the fields. This water comes from the deeper of the two near-surface aquifers in the Nubia sandstone, at about 18 m below the surface. Runoff from the fields is collected in saline pools in the lowest part of the depression. These pools are surrounded by marshy vegetation, and their banks and bottoms are made up of the Nubia Formation. The oldest and highest of these ponds are dry and cracked, reminiscent of playa clays.

Ruins of later Pharaonic to Medieval Coptic periods occur in various places in the depression, some in areas that are now desert and lacking in vegetation.

Large, flattish, and deeply dissected silt- and clay-filled basins are seen in various places within the depression, mostly near the north and south ends. In both of these areas of playa accumulation there are numerous fields of yardangs, made up of laminated sands and silts, that contain numerous shells of *Melanoides tuberculata* and less frequent *Bulinus truncatus,* as well as Graeco-Roman pottery, domestic animal remains, and other cultural debris. These yardangs stand up to 10 m high, and seem to be remnants of spring-fed fields and overflow pools fed by artesian water in which the sediments would build up rapidly during use, as they still do today. Beadnell (1909: 110), who first observed these yardangs, believed them to be remnants of lacustrine deposits of an extensive lake. Caton-Thompson and Gardner (1932) and Caton-Thompson (1952) viewed them as historic well deposits, an interpretation quite close to ours.

In the east, the floor of the basin rises toward the foot of the escarpment, and here numerous, dissected, gravel-capped, and indurated benches stand at various elevations. Numerous wadis descend from the foot of the scarp toward the center of the basin, and in a few areas the Nubia Formation bedrock is exposed, usually as ridges, some of which display remnants of fossil springs.

The Quaternary sediments in the Kharga basin have been intensively studied since the beginning of this century (Beadnell 1909) and the accumulated data demonstrate the complexity of the problems involved. This long interest has concentrated not only on the sediments (Caton-Thompson 1952; Caton-Thompson and Gardner 1932; Gardner 1935), but also on the origins of the groundwater (Attia 1954; Ball 1927, 1933; Hellstrom 1940; Murray 1952)

and its age (Degens 1962; Knetsch *et al.* 1962; Munnich and Vogel 1962).

Our preliminary survey of the Kharga basin showed that the Pleistocene sediments in this area are in most cases not associated with archaeological sites, that they are very dissected, and that they are preserved only in limited patches. Furthermore, the sediments that contained earlier Paleolithic archaeology seemed to be limited to isolated spring pools, which could not be readily related to any anticipated regional sequence. These observations convincingly showed that any attempt to conduct a proper investigation of the Pleistocene history of the Kharga basin would be a monumental task, and would require a major effort involving resources not available to the expedition. Also, since there was only limited archaeology, and even this was usually not in primary position, it was outside our interest at the time. Instead, our efforts were concentrated on a series of relatively intact Holocene sites embedded in either lacustrine or spring sediments. These Terminal Paleolithic and Neolithic sites, which were of only marginal interest to Caton-Thompson and Gardner, seemed to provide an opportunity to obtain the first adequate data concerning these periods in the area.

The eastern escarpment of the Eocene plateau displays the following sequence of hard rock units, from the top: Thebes Formation, made up of limestone beds up to 140 m thick, in which there are bands of flint nodules; Esna shale, approximately 80-m-thick beds of green laminated shales; the Tarawan Formation, a chalk unit ranging from 10 to 40 m in thickness and sometimes richly fossiliferous; the Dakhla shale unit, about 80 m thick; a series of phosphatic beds; and the Nubia Formation at the base, the top of which is the Qusseir shale member (or variegated shale), underlain by the Taref sandstone member. Westward along the escarpment, beyond Abu Mingar, the two upper units disappear and the top of the escarpment is formed of chalky limestone of the Tarawan Formation, of Paleocene age (Ball 1900; Beadnell 1909; M. Y. Hassan 1956; Hermina *et al.* 1961; Issawi 1977; Said 1962).

The Quaternary sequence in the Kharga basin and the adjacent plateau was studied and defined by Caton-Thompson (1952) and Gardner. Some of their conclusions and chronological interpretations have been discussed in the literature (e.g., Butzer 1971a: 328–329; Butzer and Hansen 1968; Gautier, this volume). With the exception of our limited tests, there has been no additional work on the sediments since that time. The only important new data come from work on absolute dating of the underground water in the oasis (Knetsch *et al.* 1962; Munnich and Vogel 1962).

The Pleistocene sequence of Caton-Thompson and Gardner consists of several generations of tufas, sheet gravels, wadi terraces, and spring deposits that are grouped into two pluvials, the first being of pre–Upper Acheulian age and the second containing a range of industries from Upper Acheulian through to Neolithic (Caton-Thompson 1952: 5, 144). Some of the lithostratigraphic members of this sequence can be correlated with the Pleistocene sequence observed in the Bir Sahara–Bir Tarfawi and Nabta areas.

Some 150 km west of Kharga is the basin of the oasis of Dakhla, a thin line of villages extending for more than 80 km along the foot of the Eocene plateau. Between Kharga and Dakhla the impressive projecting mass of Abu Tartur breaks the other wise monotonous east–west trend of the scarp. Beyond Dakhla the scarp bends to the northwest and continues in this direction, past the small oasis of Abu Mingar, and then disappears under the Sand Sea.

The floor of Dakhla Oasis is about 100 m above sea level, and is made up of Qusseir or variegated shale in the eastern part and the Taref sandstone member in the western portion. Toward the south the floor of the depression gradually rises until it vanishes beneath the Western Desert. A small scarp, from 10 to 15 m in height, is seen in a few places along the southern margin. More than 10 villages occupy the Dakhla basin and make up the oasis. The adjacent fields are large and covered by luxuriant vegetation, supported by numerous drilled wells, many of which are artesian. The water from these wells is rich in minerals and warm, fluctuating between 24 and 40°C (Abu Al Izz 1971: 210). The aquifer column in the water-bearing sandstone attains a thickness of 1030 m in the Dakhla area, and is one of the largest groundwater reservoirs in the world (Ezzat 1973).

There are only a few active springs in the Dakhla area today, but there is abundant evidence of active springs in the recent past. Extensive basins filled with playa-like red clays and silts are evident at many places within the oasis. Some of these playa-like silts contain Roman or Pharaonic pottery, and it is presumed that these deposits occurred in fields fed by overflow water from either springs or wells. Many dug wells of various ages are evident in the area, appearing as conical hills several meters high, built up of clastic sediments removed during several episodes of reexcavation. In the lowest portion of the depression, as at Kharga, extensive saline ponds collect the runoff from modern irrigation.

Along the foot of the escarpment are thick beds of laminated silts standing up to 20 m above the floor of the sub basins in which they formed. They are today extensively destroyed and deeply dissected by modern wadis that descend from the foot of the scarp. Many exposures of these silts were examined, but none yielded archaeological material *in situ*. Other silt-filled pans occur on the floor of the basin, but their age is unknown since none contained datable archaeological remains. The survey in Abu Mingar was similarly fruitless.

At the eastern end of the Dakhla basin, near the village of Balat and between the Kharga–Dakhla road and the footscarp, is an extensive, dissected bed of boulders,

FIGURE 4.2.   *Variegated shale remnant with Sites E-72-1 and E-72-2 seen from another remnant located farther south; scarp of the Libyan plateau in distance. Note numerous rolled limestone or chert pebbles and boulders in the foreground.*

gravels, and pebbles, which are well rounded and mostly of Eocene limestone. The gravel bed is firmly cemented and sometimes more than 1 m thick, and extends from the scarp toward the south, covering the variegated shale. Hill-like remnants of the shale, still covered by gravel and standing 15 m above the surrounding floor, occur south of the road in an extensively deflated and dissected area (Figure 4.2).

On both sides of the road here are smaller, conical shale hills of various sizes and heights that mark the presence of former spring vents. A few of these have been cut by the road and display reddish and yellow iron and jarosite (potassium iron hydroxy sulfate) stained sediments in the conduits that penetrate through the shale. The flat, deflated sandstone and shale floor between the vents is littered with Middle Paleolithic artifacts that sometimes show secondary concentrations resulting from sliding and runoff dynamics.

Farther south, several large, flat-topped, isolated remnants form a pronounced feature of the landscape. These are remnants of variegated shale, capped and protected from deflation by a bed of tufa more than 1 m thick. The relationship of the tufa, the spring vents, and the boulder–gravel bed could not be properly established on stratigraphic grounds. It is presumed, however, that the tufas are later than the boulder bed, which is also certainly older than the spring vents.

The search for *in situ* archaeology failed to reveal artifacts associated with either the tufas or the gravels; however, several vents had artifacts on the immediate surfaces around the conduits and embedded in the remaining spring sediments. The artifacts associated with these spring remnants are of Acheulian and Middle Paleolithic ages, and in most cases are limited to only a few pieces.

GEOLOGY OF THE SPRING VENTS AT BALAT

Just south and slightly west of the village of Balat is an oval, rounded, boulder-and-cobble-capped prominent knoll of variegated shale, standing some 15 m above the surrounding desert floor. On the south side of the knoll is a cluster of five highly deflated spring conduits, which now appear as low rises at the foot of the knoll (Figures 4.3 and

FIGURE 4.3. *Sites E-72-1 and E-72-2 seen from the top of a nearby remnant. The group of people stands near the vent at Site E-72-1; Site E-72-2 is located behind and slightly to the left of the truck. Numerous spring mounds in background. Rolled limestone and chert pebbles in foreground.*

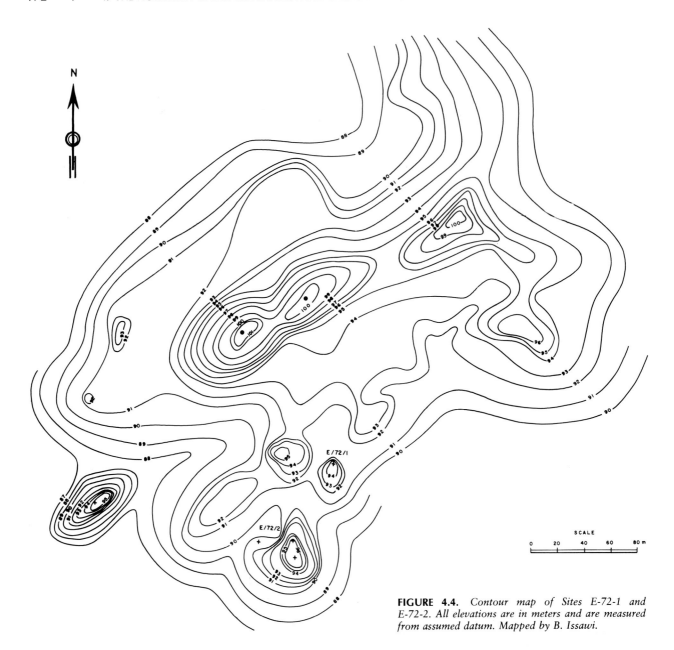

FIGURE 4.4. *Contour map of Sites E-72-1 and E-72-2. All elevations are in meters and are measured from assumed datum. Mapped by B. Issawi.*

4.4). On the surface around these vents were hundreds of bifaces, flakes, cores, and other deflated Early Paleolithic tools with little distinct patterning, but in two apparent spreads, one dispersed around a vent, and the other around a cluster of four conduits. In several of the vents fresh artifacts were seen weathering from the spring deposits. The artifact cluster around the single vent was designated as Site E-72-1 (E67L1), and the other was numbered Site E-72-2 (E67L2). About 200 m southwest of the knoll was another low spring conduit penetrating the variegated shale. Around this vent were several artifacts of Middle Paleolithic aspect. A trench through this vent, designated as Site E-72-3 (E67L3), yielded only a few artifacts embedded in the spring sediments and the excavations were therefore terminated.

Both of the Early Paleolithic sites were collected and scatterpatterned, and three of the conduits were excavated. Only one conduit, that at Site E-72-1, yielded a rich assemblage of artifacts. The other two contained a few artifacts in what proved to be only the bottoms of the vents.

Site E-72-1 (E67L1)

The spring conduit at Site E-72-1 measured 5.5 by 3.5 m, and was irregularly oval in outline (Figure 4.5). The section shows that its base, an obvious aquifer, is formed by Nubia

FIGURE 4.5. *Spring vent at Site E-72-1 after excavation. Note irregular walls and conduit reaching sandstone aquifer indicated by person in center.*

the concentration of sulfates and iron oxides resulting from the breakdown of the shale.

All along the walls of the conduit, filling the numerous fissures, pockets, and benches in the variegated shale, is a relatively thick mantle made up of gravel in a coarse sand matrix, the "sidewall gravels." These gravels are only slightly sorted; usually, the bigger specimens are deposited over the benches and in the pockets. Sulfate and iron oxide staining of the gravels resulted in dusky red (5R 3/4) and brownish yellow colors (25YR 5/4). An isolated, thin horizontal fissure in the eastern wall, on the other hand, was filled with medium-grained sand in which gypsum crystals had formed. The main body of the vent is composed of medium- to coarse-grained sand with occasional diagonal lenses of gravel steeply sloping toward the center, and conformable to the general stratification of the fill. The very center of this fill was unstratified to loose, light gray (2.5Y 7/2) to white in color. Iron oxide and sulfate coloring occurs closer to the sidewalls. There was also a large block of indurated Qusseir shale "floating" in the sediment. An extensive area of jarosite was found deposited in coarse sand over a steep bench in the eastern wall near the base of the conduit. The jarosite was positively identified through x-ray diffraction (analysis by F. A. Servello).

All the sediments, except the lower portion of the basal, reworked, variegated shale, contained artifacts. The gravels at the base yielded 1428 artifacts and the sidewall gravels contained 2356 artifacts. The central sands, although the largest in volume, had only 788 pieces. The area of jarosite and coarse sand had 1157 artifacts, giving a total of 5729 *in situ* pieces for the vent as a whole. Of these, 658 were

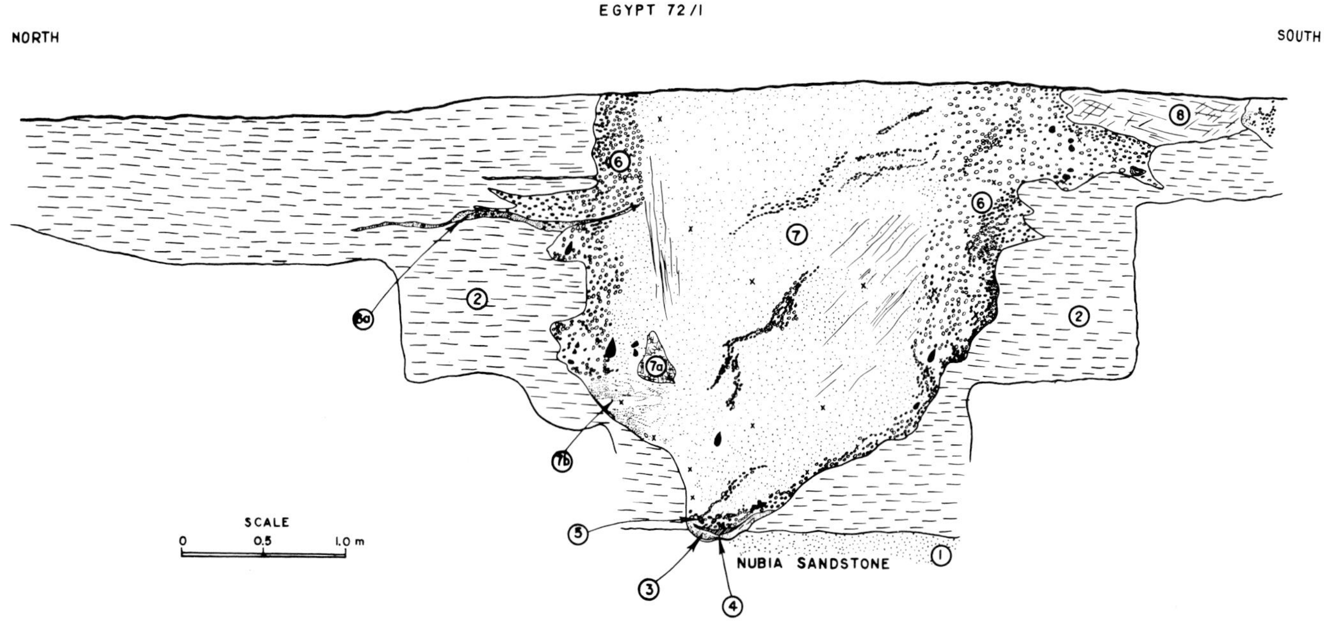

sandstone and that the aquifuge is Qusseir variegated shale. The conduit is cone shaped in cross section, and is filled with loose to cemented sediments (Figure 4.6). The bottom of the core, the lowermost portion of the spring sediments, is made up of a thin layer of reworked variegated shale, cemented and stratified, which coats the base of the conduit. This reworked shale is conformably overlain by a lens of amorphous white clay (10YR 8/1), over which occurs a layer of unstratified gravel and pebbles in a sand matrix. This sediment is loose to cemented, and heavily stained dusky red (5R 3/4) to yellow (10YR 7/8). The stain is due to

EGYPT 72/1

NORTH   SOUTH

SCALE

0   0.5   1.0 m

NUBIA SANDSTONE

FIGURE 4.6. *Section of the vent at Site E-72-1. Key: 1, Nubia sandstone; 2, Qusseir variegated shale; 3, reworked variegated shale; 4, lens of amorphous clay; 5, base gravels; 6, side wall gravel; 6a, gypsum crystals; 7, central gravels and sand; 7a, lump of Qusseir shale; 7b, potassium iron hydroxy sulfate in sand matrix; 8, lump of reworked Qusseir shale. Profile: Servello and Schild.*

handaxes. The surface collection from around the vent contained 1279 artifacts, including 126 handaxes.

The dynamic interpretation of the formation of this conduit fill suggests considerable general sorting of the material. It also suggests that the artifacts that fell in were worked down through constant movement of the water, sediment, and artifacts in the vent. It seems likely that the central portion of the fill records the declining water flow in the later period of the spring's history. The presence of jarosite indicates that the emerging water was at least warm and was highly charged with iron oxides and sulfates, thereby suggesting that the temperature and mineral characteristics of the water were similar to those of the Dakhla wells today.

Statistical analysis of some of the measurements on the artifacts shows that some of the mean values for the pieces in the central sand are significantly smaller than the means for pieces collected from the gravel-loaded sediments in the vent (Schild and Wendorf 1977b: 83). These observations are in accordance with the observed sorting of sands and gravels, as well as with the dynamic interpretations of the conduit history.

In summary, it is evident that the preserved remnants of the spring are in fact only the small, lowermost portion of a once larger conduit leading to a spring, all of which has been removed by deflation. The spring pool was probably originally at the level of the boulder–gravel mantle still partially preserved on the top of the nearby remnant. The mantle of artifacts around the vent doubtless retarded the process of removal and resulted in the preservation of the remaining portion of the conduit.

Site E-72-2 (E67L1)

The series of four vents and surrounding surface area designated Site E-72-2 may once have been connected to form a single spring pool (Figure 4.4). Only two of the vents were excavated. Both were very shallow and contained only a few artifacts within the gravel and sand sediments. The preserved portion of the vents was fragmentary, but not basically different from that seen in the nearby conduit at Site E-72-1.

In Vent 1 the basal sands and gravels contained 1072 artifacts, of which 11 were bifaces. In Vent 3 the total number of artifacts was only 129, including 8 bifaces. The richest collection was from the surrounding surface, totaling 1646 artifacts, among which were 107 bifaces.

SPRING VENTS OF NORTHERN KHARGA

In the northern section of the Kharga depression, north of the town of Kharga, the areas not covered by dunes are characterized by a broken topography obviously controlled by fossil and modern eolian deflation (Figure 4.7). Several elements are represented in this landscape (Figure 4.8). The most pronounced are low ridges of reddish variegated shale (Qusseir Formation), partially mantled by beds of alluvial gravels, presumably of several generations. Two of these ridges have numerous spring mounds along their crests (Figures 4.9 and 4.10), and it was here that most of Caton-Thompson's investigations were made. The ridges are known as Gebel es Shams and Gebel Kharran. Three spring mounds and four sites were tested during the 1976 season at Gebel es Shams (Sites E-76-1, E-76-3, E-76-4, and E-76-5), and at Gebel Kharran one of the trenches at Caton-Thompson's site KO6 was cleaned at her request in a fruitless search for datable material.

Another distinctive feature of this northern portion of the Kharga basin is the extensive, flat area of indurated brownish gray clays and silts, which are remnants of once active playas. The largest of these can be seen on both sides of the road to Assiut between the villages of Ezbet Mohamed Khalil and El Mahariq, and many of the irrigated fields surrounding these villages are on the playa silts. In many areas the playas have been extensively deflated and lowered, with numerous hummocks, small ridges, and yardangs standing as witnesses to the once higher playa surface. The margins of these basins are not clear, and it has not been established whether one basin or several are represented. In the area northeast of Ezbet Mohamed Khalil, the deflated surface of the playa is slightly more than 60 m above sea level. Two deflated prehistoric sites associated with the playa in this area (E-76-2 and E-76-8) were tested during the 1976 season.

Some 500 m west of Gebel es Shams begins an area in which the deflation has formed bedrock basins and has exposed numerous truncated spring vents containing clays and sands. Work in this area was the main effort of the 1976 season. A Terminal Paleolithic and two Neolithic sites were excavated and numerous geological trenches were cut.

Here and there are small, isolated, low gravel ridges, remnants of the once extensive beds that preceded the exposed springs. A trench through one of the alluvial gravel ridges yielded an *in situ* fresh Levallois core of Middle Paleolithic aspect. Beyond the area of small basins and gravel ridges to the west, the ground rises considerably and the surface is formed by flat Qusseir shale, mantled here and there with sand sheets, and stretching westward beyond the Kharga highway.

Immediately north of the spring–bedrock basin is an extensive area of Graeco-Roman, water-laid sand and silts, standing up to around 10 m above the deflational floor, but now heavily deflated themselves and preserved only as yardangs. These Graeco-Roman silts are laminated, containing snails, pottery, and other cultural remains.

The three spring vents selected for testing on the ridge of

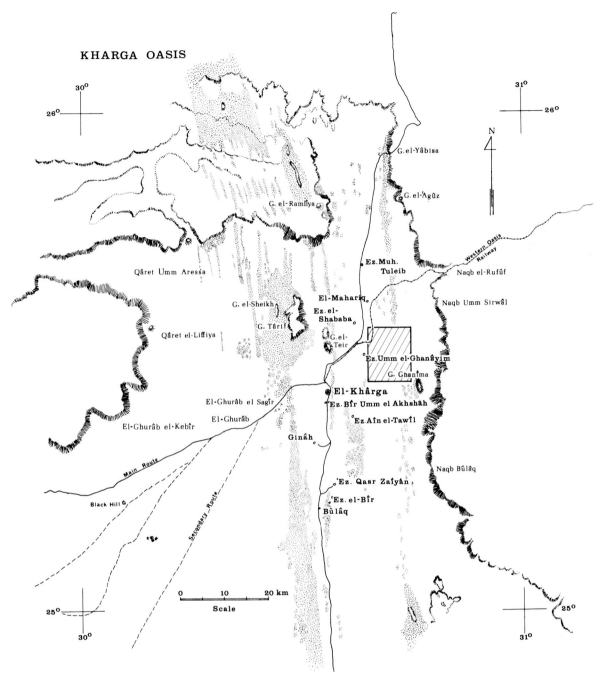

FIGURE 4.7. *Map of northern section of Kharga depression showing major geomorphic features and area of detailed map (shaded), Figure 4.8.*

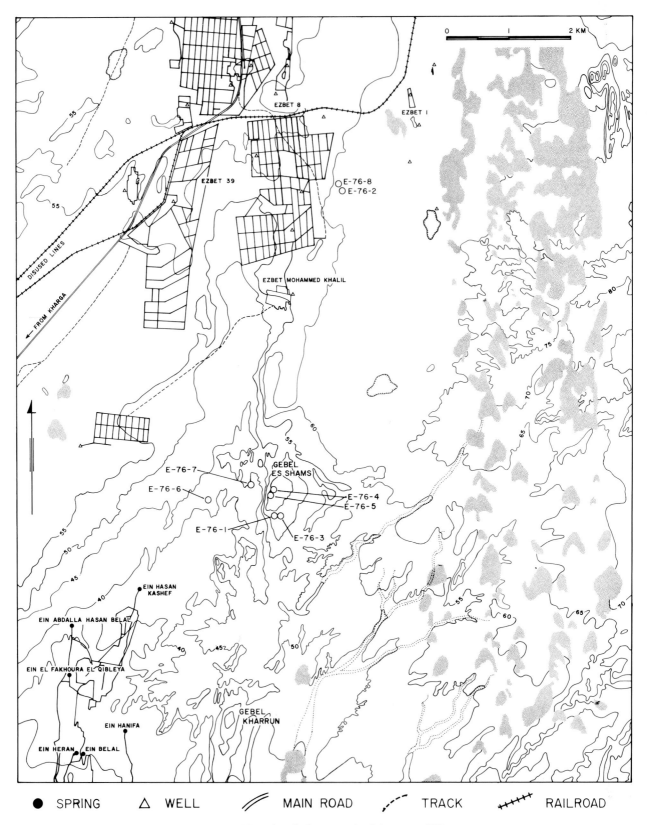

FIGURE 4.8. *Map of studied area north of the town of Kharga.*

FIGURE 4.9. *View of top of Gebel es Shams, looking southeast from Site E-76-1 toward Site E-76-3, the prominent spring mound in the distant center. Both sites were utilized during the Neolithic.*

FIGURE 4.10. *View of top of Gebel es Shams looking south from Aterian Site E-76-4, before excavation, toward Sites E-76-1 and E-76-3, the prominent spring mounds in distant center.*

Gebel es Shams appeared as low, almost circular, flat-topped knolls, from 2 to 3 m high and about 30 m in diameter. The excavations were limited to trenches cut across the mounds, and three selected areas with artifacts on the surface and subsurface were collected and scatter-patterned. Two of the vents contained occasional lithic artifacts of Middle Paleolithic aspect but were primarily of Neolithic or later age. The third vent (Site E-76-4) had an extensive spread of Aterian artifacts on the surface and just eroding out of the spring sand along the east edge of the mound. A large sample of these artifacts was collected. On the top of the spring mound, Neolithic or later pottery and a few lithic artifacts embedded in the deposits witness a later occupation. Because of the various periods of occupation seemingly associated with the spring deposits of single mound, a trench more than 30 m long was excavated to determine their relationships (Figure 4.11).

Site E-76-4

The trench at Site E-76-4 revealed the existence of three separate spring vents, each representing a distinct period of spring discharge. The spring sediments were in stratigraphic sequence separated by pronounced truncations, suggesting that the spring eye was gradually moving toward the west, although the same conduit(s) may have been used. The drift to the west was possibly caused by induration of the preceding spring sediments.

Most of the trench exposed sediments of Spring 1 (Figure 4.12). These sediments consist of a series of intercalating spring sands and clays marking pulsations in the water discharge. The lowest sediment recorded is a mottled, medium- and fine-grained sand, with inconspicuous laminations and lenses of clay of fine to medium blocky structure (Figure 4.12:1a). Its color is light gray (5Y 7/2) to brownish yellow (10YR 6/6). A large lens of gray (5Y 5/1) sandy silt with medium blocky structure (Figure 4.12:1b) separates the sand series into two units. The upper unit (Figure 4.12:1c) is similar in structure to the lower one, but is slightly lighter in color (5Y 8/2 and 2.5Y 7/6). Toward the center this upper unit dips down, but at the margin the bedding becomes horizontal, marking the edge of the spring pool (Figure 4.12:1d). In this marginal section, the very top of the thin sand contained numerous fresh Aterian artifacts. However, the settlement was obviously postdepositional, as was shown by the unconformable position of the cultural horizon with the bedding.

The next series of sediments of this older spring consists of a suite of clay layers and sands, progressively dipping toward the eye of the spring (Figure 4.12:2a–e). The clay layers have medium blocky structure, and the sand is coarse to medium grained. The whole series shows considerable areas of iron reduction, as well as manganese enrichments and oxidized layers of sand, usually following the bedding. The color of the clay layers is light gray (5Y 7/1) to very dark gray (10YR 3/1); the sands are pale yellow to very pale brown (2.5Y 7/4, 10YR 7/4). A small fault displacing some of the sand beds was observed near the center of the spring.

The sands in this suite of spring deposits contained a few very fresh artifacts of Middle Paleolithic aspect, among which a typical Levallois flake and a Levallois core-preparation flake were recognized. It is probable that these sediments are contemporaneous with the Aterian cultural horizon deposited over Layer 1d (Figure 4.12).

The end of the spring activity is recorded in the last series of sediments (Figure 4.12:3a–c), which consists of a thick bed of clay with vertical jointing and blocky structure overlain by laminated mottled sand with reduction/enrichment stains, and manganese concentrations. The clay is gray (5Y 6/1), and the sand is yellow to light gray (2.5Y 7/6, 2.5Y 7/2). The clay contains a relatively rich sample of fresh Middle Paleolithic artifacts with characteristic silt polishing. Among them are a Levallois point and several Levallois core-preparation flakes. The sand above the clay has only a

LEGEND: ▪ Trench   ▪ Sites   ▪ Survey   🌴 Palm Trees   SCALE: 0 1 2 3 1 m

FIGURE 4.11.   *Contour map of Sites E-76-4 and E-76-5, showing spring mound and general topography. Datum assumed.*

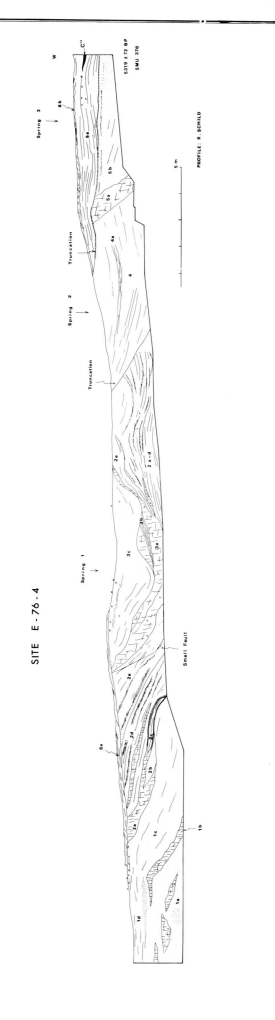

FIGURE 4.12. Cross section through spring conduits at Site E-76-4. Key: Spring 1: 1a, mottled, fine-grained sand; 1b, clay; 1c, laminated sand; 1d, horizontal laminated sand with cultural layer in top; 2a–e, clay and sand beds; 3a–c, beds of clay and laminated sand with fresh artifacts in central portion of vent. Spring 2: 4 and 4a, laminated sands. Spring 3: 5a, clay; 5b, laminated sands with gypsum crystals in top; 6a, coarse laminated dune sand with late Neolithic artifacts and hearth; 6b, sandy, spongy evaporites.

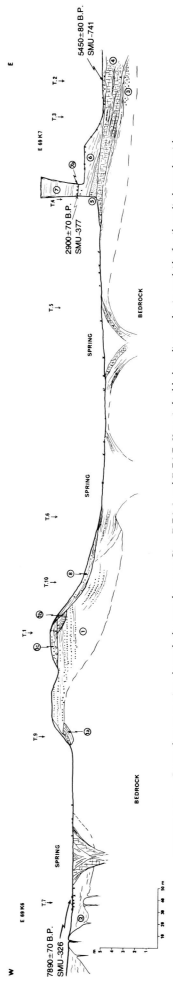

FIGURE 4.13. General cross section through the area between Sites E-76-6 and E-76-7. Key: 1, bedded wadi gravels; 1a and 1b, fossil wadi channels with laminated silts, gravels, and sands; 1c, horizontally bedded silts and gravels with fresh Levallois core at base; 2, laminated sand with Terminal Paleolithic cultural layer in top; 3, laminated sand and gravels; 4, bedded clays with lenses of sand and burnt layers, Terminal Paleolithic (?) at base, Neolithic in upper portion; 5, sand lens; 6, fine silty sand, laminated, Neolithic cultural layer at Site E-76-7; 7a, Graeco-Roman cultural layer over truncation; 7, Graeco-Roman sands and silts; 8, modern slope wash.

few artifacts *in situ* and several on the surface, undoubtedly of mixed age, with those pieces of Middle Paleolithic aspect always eolized.

A pronounced truncation separates the older spring from the sediments of Spring 2. The latter consist of almost horizontally bedded, medium- to coarse-grained sands (Figure 4.12:4 and 4a), which are mottled white to yellow (2.5Y 8/2, 10YR 7/2). These may mark the maximal extension of the pool during its peak of discharge, and are archaeologically sterile.

Unconformably over these sands of Spring 2, and truncating them, is a bed of steeply dipping clay with medium blocky structure. The clay is yellowish brown (10YR 5/6), slightly wet at the bottom of the trench (Figure 4.12:5a), and almost conformably overlain by medium-grained pale yellow (5Y 7/3) sands (Figure 4.12:5b). A line of gypsum crystals developed near the top of the bed and along the truncation separating it from the next unit. Both this clay and the overlying sands of Spring 3 contain no archaeology.

Coarse-bedded sands (Figure 4.12:6a) unconformably overlie the sediments of all three springs, deposited over a deflated surface. They are light yellowish-brown (10YR 6/4) and consolidated to cemented, and they contain fresh Neolithic artifacts, an *in situ* hearth, and some rolled lithic pieces of Middle Paleolithic aspect. Charcoal from the hearth yielded a radiocarbon date of 4650 BP ± 60 years (SMU-412). Conformably over this sand is a thin layer of sandy, spongy evaporites (Figure 4.12:6b), very pale brown in color (10YR 7/4).

The absence of archaeology in the deposits of Springs 2 and 3 handicaps their interpretation, but it seems likely that they might represent only one episode of spring activity, subdivided by a fluctuation in its regimen. The deflation that follows the deposition representing Spring 3 indicates a period of significantly lowered water table, whereas the coarse sand beds and evaporites that overlie this deflated surface may suggest eolian deposition trapped in vegetation during an only slightly wetter oscillation.

Sites E-76-6 and E-76-7

In the deeply deflated area west of Gebel es Shams the erosion exposed bedrock (Qusseir shale), numerous truncated spring conduits, impoverished remnants of spring and overspill clastic deposits, as well as sediments of older alluvial origin. Two extensive sites were investigated in this area. One, a Terminal Paleolithic site designated as E-76-6 (E69K6), was near the western edge of the deflated area; the second, early Neolithic in age and numbered E-76-7 and 7a (E60K7, K7a), was located near the eastern margin. Numerous deflated artifacts, mostly of Neolithic age, littered the ground around all of the truncated springs.

A complex series of bedded gravels and thin silt beds with occasional, often truncated, superimposed channels represents the oldest Quaternary unit recorded in this section of the depression. These sediments are preserved as highly eroded remnants in the form of low, gravel-covered

ridges. Their present morphology is secondary and discontinuous, and cannot therefore serve as the base for reconstructing their history in the Kharga basin. In this particular locality their present surface is about 50 m above sea level, some 20 m or more above the modern deflated surface in the lowest section of Kharga (Figure 4.13:1, 1a, 1b, 1c). This formation may represent more than one period; however, the uppermost recognized unit, a wadi gravel that is horizontally bedded and consists of coarse sand, gravel, and pebbles, yielded a large, entirely fresh, and undoubtedly Middle Paleolithic typical Levallois core at a depth of 40 cm.

The next unit is certainly much younger and was deposited after the gravel cover had been considerably eroded, possibly even to its present morphology. This unit is a bed of sand (Figure 4.13:2) deposited over an eroded and deeply dissected surface of variegated shale. The sand is laminated with the bedding conformable to the eroded shale surface, and fills the basins excavated in the bedrock. It has the appearance of an eolian sand, but it occurs near a spring vent and is therefore either eolian sediment trapped in the vegetation surrounding the spring or else a spring-reworked sand deposit. Its upper section shows typical mottled pseudogley coloring resulting from saturation, and is generally light brown to brownish yellow (7.5YR 6/4, 10YR 6/6). The very top of the sand contains the Terminal Paleolithic settlement of Site E-76-6, which is almost entirely exposed by recent deflation. Large exposed areas of this sand may be seen in the immediate vicinity of the worked site, and traces of other Terminal Paleolithic occurrences are found here. A thin layer of indurated, carbonaceous silt covers this sand in patches, but the origin of this silt is unknown.

Eastward from Site E-76-6, and past the gravel ridge, is a series of heavily deflated spring conduits with Neolithic artifacts on the surface around them. Still farther to the east beyond this basin is an area where tall yardangs of Graeco-Roman sands, covering clays and spring sands of Neolithic age, are preserved, although extensively eroded. Neolithic and younger artifacts litter the surface. Some concentrations were investigated in detail—Sites E-76-7 and E-76-7a (E69K7 and K7a).

The earliest exposed sediments of the springs in this area (bedrock was not reached) contain two subunits. The lower one is composed of coarse-grained sands with small gravel and clay pebbles up to 15 mm in diameter, and is friable to consolidated, has inconspicuous lamination, and dips generally toward the east (Figure 4.13:3); it is pinkish gray (7.5YR 7/2). These sands and gravels are conformably overlain by a bed of laminated white sand, the second subunit. Both subunits are archaeologically sterile.

Conformably overlying the lower sands is a thick bed of mottled, light gray (5Y 7/1) to brownish yellow (10YR 6/6) clay with intercalating lenses of sand and some bedding following the general slope of the base toward the east. The clay bed is cemented, has a blocky structure (Figure 4.13:4), and displays slickensides. At the very base of the clay was a bladelet from a prepared single-platform core of the kind commonly found with the Terminal Paleolithic of the area and never seen in the Neolithic. Near the top of the unit are two burned layers with baked silt and rare, fire-cracked, Neolithic artifacts.

A relatively thick, truncated bed of fine silty sand overlies the clay unit and slopes conformably with it (Figure 4.13:6). This bed is light brown (7.5YR 6/4), contains laminae of silt, and when cleared shows large desiccation polygons. At the bottom of the unit were two concentrations of Neolithic artifacts, pottery, and rare bones designated E-76-7 and E-76-7a. The scattered bones included tooth fragments from a large bovid, and other teeth and postcranial remains from either a gazelle (*Gazella dorcas?*) or a caprovid (sheep/goat; *Ovis ammon* f. aries, *Capra aegragus* f. hircus) (Gautier, this volume). Ostrich eggshells collected from the first of these concentrations gave a radiocarbon date of 5450 BP ± 80 years (SMU-741). The unit contains isolated artifacts throughout, several of which are exposed on the deflated surface. Among these were occasional bones including fragmentary remains of the upper jaws of a bovid that may represent a large breed of domestic cattle.

A thick lens of coarse- to medium-grained, reddish yellow (7.5YR 6/8) sand was observed sandwiched between the clay and silty sand units in the western portion of the section (Figure 4.13:5). It contains rare artifacts, possibly of Neolithic age, and could be of eolian origin.

The thick bed of light brown silty sand is clearly truncated and over this truncation is a bed containing charcoal and historical pottery (Figures 4.13:7a and 4.14). The radiocarbon date on charcoal from the base of this bed is 2900 BP ± 70 years (SMU-377). Over the truncation and the earliest historical bed (Figure 4.14) are at least 5 m of laminated fine sands containing aquatic snail shells, *Melanoides tuberculata* and *Bulinus truncatus* (Gautier, this volume), and historical pottery and other culture remains (Figure 4.13:7). The radiocarbon date on *Melanoides* shells in the upper part of this unit is 18,500 BP ± 170 years (SMU-383). The surprising age indicated for these shells is due to absorption by the snails of old carbonates from the fossil water used in the field. Water from modern wells at Kharga has been dated to around 25,000 to 40,000 BP (Shata *et al.* 1962). Water from the middle aquifer dated 451,000 years ago, and water from the lower aquifer dated 1,580,000 years ago, according to measurements by the helium–argon method (Simons 1973: 443, after Himida 1967). It is presumed that the water used

FIGURE 4.14. *View of a portion of yardang composed of water-laid silts and sands historical in age. Note artifacts on surface.*

during historic times was from the upper aquifer.

The suite of sediments at the eastern portion of this basin seems to reflect two contrasting regimens. The older, represented by Terminal Paleolithic and Neolithic sands and clays, is associated with a large spring-fed pool whose outlines could be still observed on the surface despite subsequent deflation. The burned beds and occupation within the sediments indicate pulsations, possibly seasonal and/or occasional in nature. A thicker lens of presumably eolian sand, on the other hand, may indicate a more pronounced drier episode.

A significant break must have separated the interval of the spring pond from the historical sediments. The latter are believed to have been laid down within and around fields by irrigation water, but it seems likely that the sands and silt particles were wind-borne into the area.

The time gap seen between the spring pond and the historical field deposits may be partially filled by the extensive playa silts observed 6 km to the north and standing nearly 20 m higher. The lithostratigraphy of these playas was not studied, but they do contain settlements that, on the basis of accompanying pottery, could be assigned to a late Neolithic and/or Predynastic period. It is also likely that these playas were deposited in closed basins fed by rainwater. Though they cannot be connected with the early Neolithic spring pool that was studied, they seem to represent a late or final section of the wet Neolithic period, although detailed subdivision of this period is not possible at Kharga with the available data.

ASSOCIATED ARCHAEOLOGY

Archaeological material recovered at Dakhla and Kharga forms an unconnected series of samples from major time sections recognized in both oases. The oldest of these are the Upper Acheulian sites E-72-1 and E-72-2 at Dakhla, both associated with spring vents and neither with preserved living floors, although both were rich in artifacts. The next is a relatively poor Middle Paleolithic workshop of Aterian age, embedded in spring sands at the edge of a pool. No Mousterian material was recovered, although sites of this period have been reported from Kharga by Caton-Thompson (1952). A long time gap separates these Middle Paleolithic occurrences from the subsequent Terminal Paleolithic site at Kharga; slightly later, but in the same climatic episode, is the Neolithic, also at Kharga.

ACHEULIAN

Two closely adjacent localities of the Acheulian period were studied in detail. The first of these was Site E-72-1, an almost totally destroyed, fossil spring vent with artifacts embedded throughout the sediments and also deflated onto the surface surrounding the vent; none of the artifacts was in primary position. Detailed data concerning this site have already been published in a technical report (Schild and Wendorf 1977b), but it will be useful to characterize the site again.

In total, the site yielded a large collection of 7006 pieces, almost all made of the local Eocene chert found in large quantities in the boulder mantle over the Qusseir shale. The preserved, battered, cortical surfaces on some of the artifacts indicate that the raw material was indeed collected from the already deposited boulder mantle. A few artifacts were made of quartzite.

The restricted General Structure shows three peaks in the percentages, formed by biface trimming flakes (38.0%), bifaces (22.4%), and primary flakes (19.5%). Consequently, of the six groups two are dominant: the Initial (I) and the Retouched Tools and Tool-Production Waste (VI) classes. The class of Flake Production (III) is third in importance, the Levallois Group (II) is very low, and the class of Blade Production (IV) is insignificant.

The core technology is based on unprepared, single-platform cores and cores with change of orientation, both globular and flat. Subdiscoidal and discoidal cores are rare, and Levallois specimens are even less frequent (four pieces only). Levallois flakes and blades are accordingly rare.

The tool group in both the surface and excavated collections is dominated by bifaces, which form 82.5% (restricted) of the total. Of the biface group, the most numerous is the class of amygdaloids (34.3%), and of these, the regular specimens with thick butts are the most numerous, followed by short amygdaloids, also with thick butts, and then by regular ones with thinned bases. The next most important group is that of backed bifaces (20.0%), of which the symmetrical examples are the most numerous.

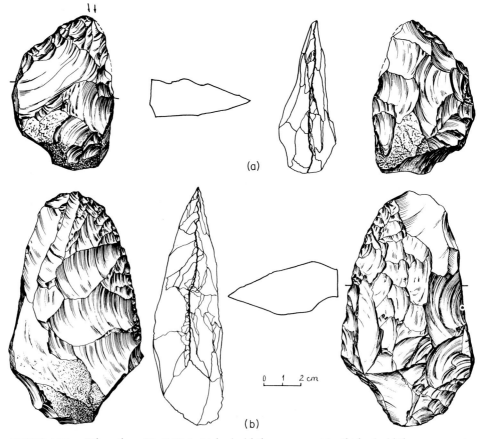

FIGURE 4.15. *Bifaces from Site E-72-1: (a) backed biface, asymmetric; (b) backed biface, symmetric.*

Double-backed bifaces are the third most numerous group (15.6%), immediately followed by subtriangular bifaces (14.6%), of which the regular and elongated pieces with thick butts are the most common. The cordiforms constitute the fifth most important group (8.4%), far behind the others. Ovates and thick elongates are represented by occasional pieces only (Figures 4.15–4.17).

There are only 190 tools other than bifaces in the assemblage. All technological indices are extremely low, since Levallois technology is nearly nonexistent and blades are rare. The Typological Levallois Index is slightly higher (2.6). The non-handaxe tools are dominated by denticulates and notches (Group IV:37.9), followed by sidescrapers, which are below 15%. Among the sidescrapers, the simple convex and bifacial varieties are the most frequent. Other tools are represented by relatively numerous biface-edged pieces, a few naturally backed knives, and an occasional endscraper and burin, both typical and atypical (Figure 4.18).

The nearby surface distribution of artifacts and associated spring vents, which was given the designation E-72-2, covered a larger area than that of Site E-72-1. On the other hand, the total collection of artifacts was considerably smaller, totaling 2847 pieces. Here, too, almost all the artifacts are made on local Eocene chert boulders and pebbles, seemingly collected from the nearby boulder mantle deposited over the variegated shale. A few pieces were made on Nubia sandstone quartzite.

The General Structure (restricted) differs from that at Site E-72-1. Here the primary flakes are most numerous (35.4%), followed by flakes from change-of-orientation cores (17.9%) and biface trimming flakes (14.1%). The Initial Tool (I) and Flake-Production (III) groups are the largest, and the class of Tools and Tool-Production Waste is significantly smaller. As before, the Levallois and Blade-Production groups are negligible. The cores here are similar to those seen at Site E-72-1, with change-of-orientation and single-platform specimens for flakes the most numerous, as well as occasional subdiscoidal pieces. Levallois cores are slightly more numerous and contain one poor, Nubian-type, point core.

The bifaces are again the most important tool group (64.3%). The structuring of the major biface groups is very similar in both sites, except that the cordiforms are here more numerous than the subtriangulars. The amygdaloids form 28.9%, backed bifaces are 20.3%, cordiforms are 16.9%, double backed bifaces compose 16.7%, and the subtriangulars are 13.5%.

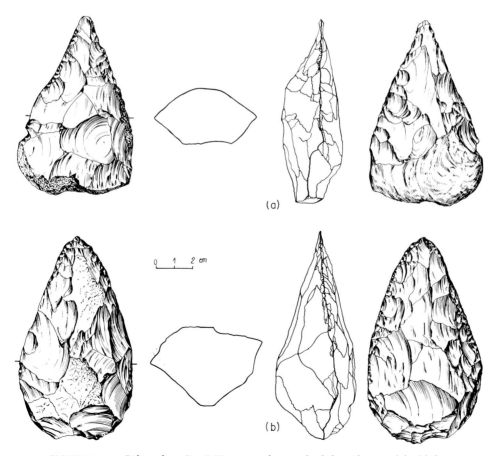

FIGURE 4.16. *Bifaces from Site E-72-1: (a) subtriangular biface; (b) amygdaloid biface.*

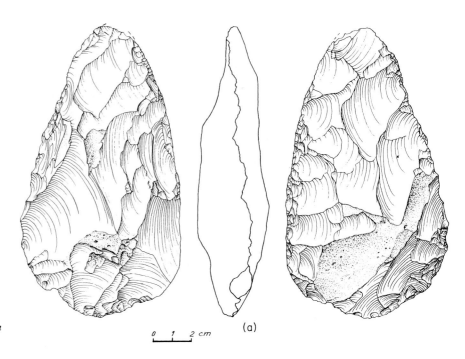

FIGURE 4.17. *Elongated cordiform biface from Site E-72-1.*

0 1 2 cm

(a)

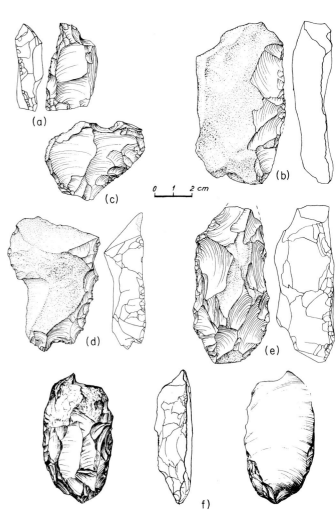

FIGURE 4.18. *Tools from Site E-72-1. All sidescrapers.*

All the technological indices are low or nonexistent, as in the case of the Levallois Index; however, the Blade Index is noteworthy with a value of 4.1.

There are only 70 other tools and most of these are notched and denticulated pieces, accounting for 55.7%. The sidescrapers represent slightly more than 15%. There are also retouched flakes, bifacial edge pieces, and burins.

Both of these Acheulian sites display very pronounced qualitative similarities in morphological and technological features, but the quantitative distributions of some categories are significantly different; specifically, the distributions of the General Structure values and of the biface categories.

The clearly secondary position of the artifacts on the surface and in the sediments of the conduits prohibits analysis of their spatial relationships, and the absence of organic remains further impoverishes the explanatory possibilities of the sites. It is believed, however, that both occurrences resulted from occupations at the margins of spring pools, repeatedly used over a very substantial period of time, most likely throughout the entire period of spring activity. The obviously pulsating margins would facilitate the incorporation of the artifacts into the spring deposits, and some of them would finally be worked down, through the total depth of the conduit. Therefore, both collections presumably form composite samples of artifacts drawn from a long period of time and undoubtedly several occupations. Stylistic differences and chronological trends, if existing, cannot be determined.

At Kharga, Caton-Thompson (1952: 54–73) reported Upper Acheulian closely similar to that of Dakhla from her Site KO10, also a fossil spring vent. Two other similar spring localities recorded by us on the same Es Shams ridge had rare bifaces embedded in their sediments and on the adjacent surfaces. Other Acheulian occurrences were noted by Caton-Thompson (1952: 95–98) in the wadis of Refuf Pass; however, none of these Kharga sites was studied by us.

ATERIAN

During the 1976 season at Kharga, none of the Mousterian localities described by Caton-Thompson was reinvestigated; the surface remains associated with these localities did not seem to be sufficiently promising to warrant further study. Instead, we focused our efforts on the ridge at an Aterian workshop floor, designated Site E-76-4, and nearby surface concentration of Site E-76-5.

When first seen, Site E-76-4 consisted of a very small, dense concentration of artifacts on a small flat bench on the sloping side of a deflated spring vent, adjacent to a thin sand rock unit that mantled the surface of the vent. The artifacts were fresh to semifresh and clearly passed under the thin sand rock deposit, now known to be of relatively late age. The concentration was collected and excavated (Figure 4.19). The artifacts were found partially *in situ* in the very top of laminated spring sands (Figure 4.12:1d), and clearly postdated the deposition of that unit.

FIGURE 4.19. *Excavation of Aterian Site E-76-4, looking south.*

To the south, the limits of the concentration were formed by the sloping and deflated surface of the vent, whereas to the west the edge of the concentration coincided sharply with the clay bed (Figure 4.12:2a); the occupation, therefore, could have preceded the formation of this unit. The boundaries of the living surface do not represent the settlement patterning, but the horizontal distribution of the artifacts seems to be undisturbed on the portion remaining. It was clearly a settlement on the sandy shore of a fluctuating spring pool. Other Aterian artifacts embedded in spring deposits of this vent were clearly later than the collected concentration; however, none of these formed a useful assemblage, nor were they considered to be archaeologically *in situ*. The surface collection at E-76-5, for example, an Aterian occurrence slightly higher up the same spring vent, had clearly been redeposited, as shown by the strongly weathered condition of the artifacts.

The horizontal distribution of artifacts at Site E-76-4 indicates a clustering in the middle of the excavated area, with natural thinning toward the east and north (Figure 4.20). The sharp boundary toward the west, however, may be postdepositional.

The total collection of artifacts from this locality, including chips, is 2364. The surface collection contained 1951 pieces, and the remaining 413 artifacts were from the excavations. Some of the artifacts on the surface were slightly eolized, but the *in situ* specimens were fresh and displayed a light tan patina. In addition to the collection from the workshop floor, 34 chips and flakes and 3 cores were found in various units in the stratigraphic trench, and some of these were chemically altered. The raw material used was exclusively a local, good quality, light gray Eocene chert, occurring as cobbles or nodules in the nearby gravel mantles.

The General Structure of the assemblage is dominated by three elements: Tool-Production Waste Flakes (28.1%), the Levallois Group (26.7%); and the Initial Core-Preparation Group (19.5%). The high percentage of the Tool-Production Waste is caused by the biface trimming flakes, which, in fact, could have been obtained during the final

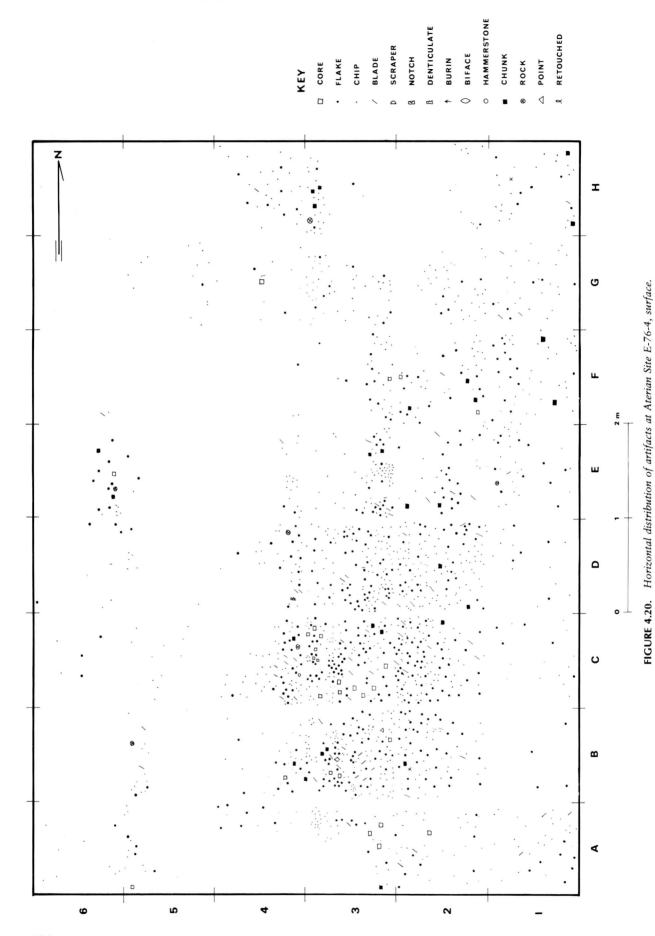

KEY

□ CORE
• FLAKE
· CHIP
/ BLADE
�); SCRAPER
β NOTCH
β DENTICULATE
↑ BURIN
◇ BIFACE
○ HAMMERSTONE
■ CHUNK
⊗ ROCK
◁ POINT
ᔆ RETOUCHED

FIGURE 4.20. *Horizontal distribution of artifacts at Aterian Site E-76-4, surface.*

shaping of the Levallois cores. The Technological Levallois Index is small (IL: 3.7), as is the Blade Index (Ilam: 2.1). Tools are rare and consist mostly of Levallois flakes and blades. The total for retouched tools is only .5%; the Typological Levallois Index is extremely high (ILty: 93.0). Cores are fairly numerous (26 examples), and all but 5 are various Levallois specimens. Of the 6 retouched tools, 2 are bifacial foliates, 3 are Aterian pedunculates on Levallois points, and 1 is a fragment of a denticulate.

The structure of this collection clearly points out the workshop character of the occurrence, concentrated on the preparation of Levallois cores and their limited exploitation, as indicated by the relatively low frequency of Levallois pieces.

The Aterian collection of Caton-Thompson (1952: 88–89) from another spring vent in the vicinity (Site KO6E) seems to be similarly structured and is characterized by a limited number of tools and Levallois pieces in relation to the frequency of cores. The tools are also dominated by Aterian points and bifacial foliates, with only occasional other pieces. The detailed structure of this collection cannot be evaluated because a total count of artifacts was not given.

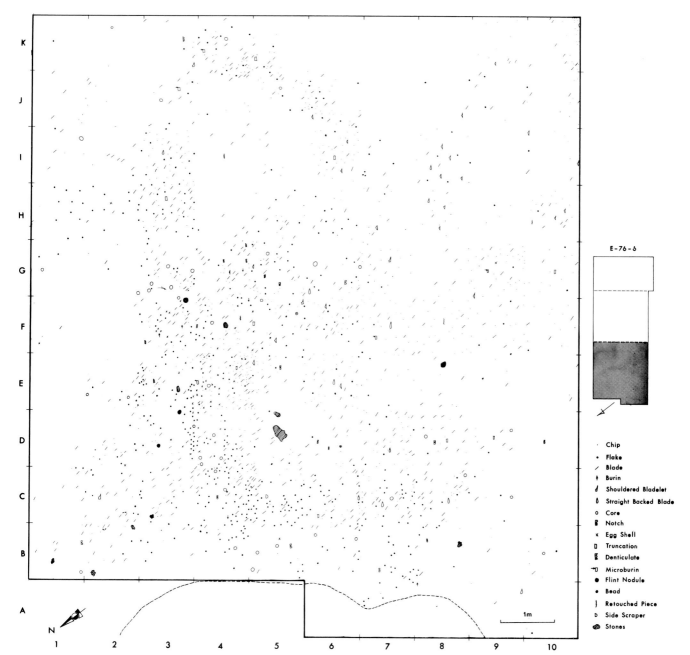

FIGURE 4.21. *Horizontal distribution of artifacts in the northwest portion of Terminal Paleolithic Site E-76-6, surface and subsurface. Note position on key map.*

TERMINAL PALEOLITHIC

The only Terminal Paleolithic locality studied in detail at Kharga was Site E-76-6 (E69K6). When discovered, this site appeared as a large concentration of artifacts, both slightly eolized and fresh, on the surface of and slightly within a bed of indurated, fine, yellowish sand. It is adjacent to an area of spring clays that are part of a truncated vent. A thin crust of indurated, carbonaceous silts covers the yellow sand immediately adjacent to the concentration to the northwest and forms an extensive surface in the vicinity.

The site consists of one major concentration and a few small clusters of artifacts separated from the main body (Figures 4.21–4.23). No other major concentrations of artifacts were observed in the vicinity of the site, but isolated artifacts of Terminal Paleolithic aspect were seen here and there, and other concentrations could have been buried beneath the nearby expanse of silt crust.

The entire concentration and the separated small clusters were collected and excavated over an area of 261 m². The scatterpattern clearly reveals a medium-dense, oval concentration measuring some 10 m in diameter, and three small clusters, ranging from 1 to 4 m in diameter, located southeast of the main body. There are occasional artifacts between the smaller clusters and the main concentration.

There are three radiocarbon dates from Site E-76-6, all on ostrich eggshell. One sample yielded dates of 7850 BP ± 70 years and 7890 BP ± 70 years (two runs, SMU-326), the other dated 7860 BP ± 90 years (SMU-734). These dates indicate that some Terminal Paleolithic overlaps in time with the Neolithic occupation at Site E-75-6 at Nabta Playa.

The raw material from this site is a light tan Eocene chert. The technology is based on single- and opposed-platform cores for blades, which very often show traces of

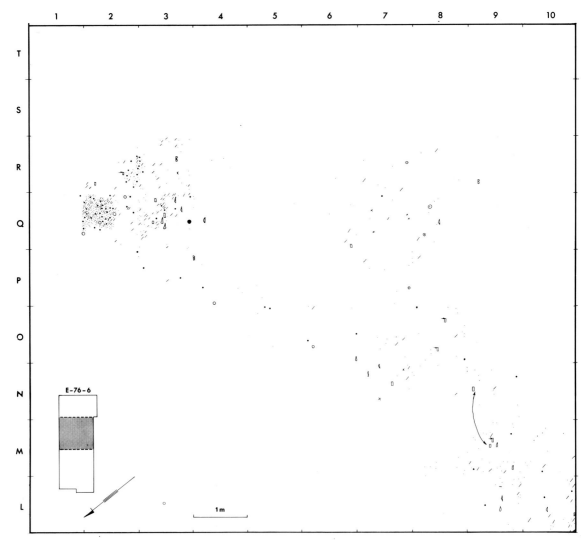

FIGURE 4.22. *Horizontal distribution of artifacts in central portion of Terminal Paleolithic Site E-76-6, surface and subsurface. For key see Figure 4.21.*

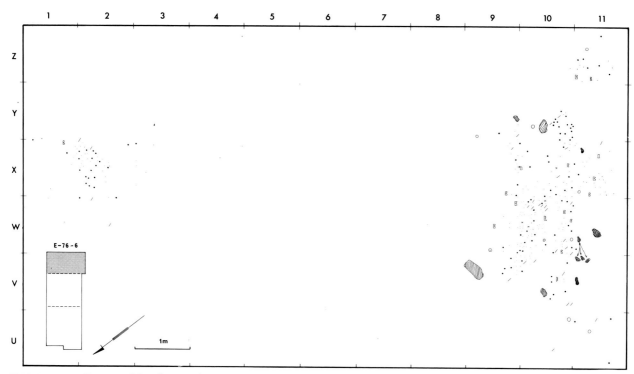

FIGURE 4.23. *Horizontal distribution of artifacts in southeast portion of Terminal Paleolithic Site E-76-6, surface and subsurface. For key see Figure 4.21.*

pre-core preparation of the flaking surfaces (Figure 4.24). The cores for flakes are very rare and are mainly single- or opposed-platform varieties. Change-of-orientation cores for flakes are even less numerous.

The combined tool assemblage is marginal in size, consisting of only 125 retouched pieces. It is dominated by elongated scalene triangles with small short sides, often concave (26.4%). The triangles are followed by notched pieces (25.6%), mostly blades with single and multiple notches. Truncations, both distal and proximal and almost all on bladelets, are next in importance (15.2%), followed by backed bladelets (13.6%), mostly straight and concave, with some shouldered specimens present. There are also isolated arch-backed pieces. Microburins are numerous (8.0%). The index of denticulates and notched pieces is also high (28.0%) and is dominated by notches, denticulated pieces being rather rare (2.4%); retouched pieces are slightly more numerous (4.0%). Burins are present, but rare (1.6%), and endscrapers are totally absent (Figures 4.25 and 4.26).

The collection also includes a number of fragments of ostrich eggshell, as well as beads of the same material in various stages of manufacture. Other organic remains are absent.

It is of interest that no traces of grinding stones occurred, particularly since other localities with very similar assemblages (Site E-72-5 and E-77-6) contained frequent grinding stones.

The tools within the various subclusters are not numer-

ous; however, the one in the south corner has a clearly different tool structure heavily dominated by notched blades (nine) with only a few other tools. Another subcluster, along the northeastern edge of the gridded area, has a tight cluster of flaking debris with an emphasis on truncations and triangles (eight) to the near exclusion of other tools.

NEOLITHIC

Numerous clusters of Neolithic artifacts were observed in the Kharga basin. The recorded sites occurred associated with lacustrine, playa clays near the village of Ezbet Mohamed Khalil (Sites E-76-2 and E-76-8), around truncated spring vents (Sites E-76-7 and E-76-7a), and with spring-related sediments on Gebel es Shams (Sites E-76-1 and E-76-3). The most important collections come from three sites in two areas, Sites E-76-2, E-76-7, and E-76-7a. The localities on Gebel es Shams yielded only insignificant collections.

Site E-76-7 (E69K7) was the earliest Neolithic settlement investigated in the Kharga area. It is a large concentration, slightly over 10 m in diameter, of lithic artifacts with occasional bones and ostrich eggshells, partially exposed and partially embedded in fine spring sand (Figure 4.27). Just beyond the gridded area, a cluster of several pottery sherds was found, also embedded at the same level in the spring sand unit. A hearth area of fire-cracked rocks occurred

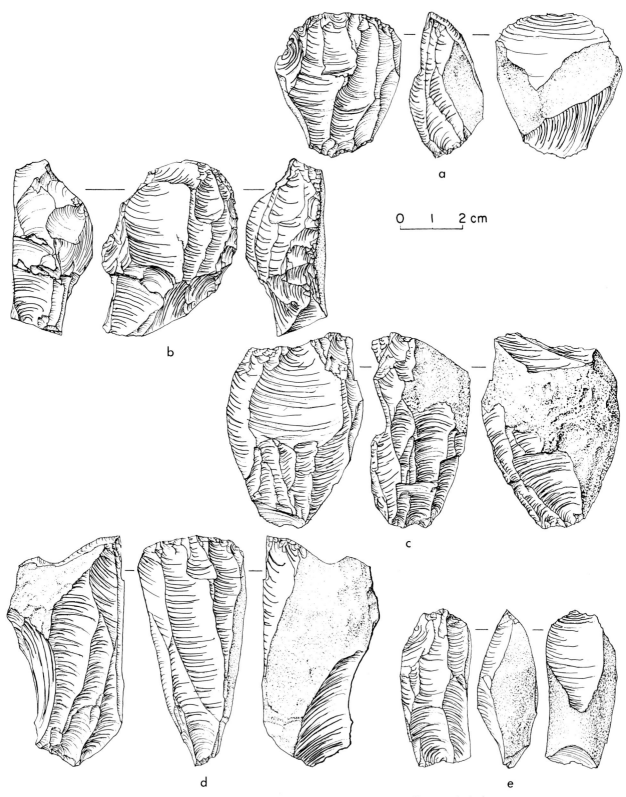

FIGURE 4.24. *Cores from Terminal Paleolithic Site E-76-6. All opposed platform.*

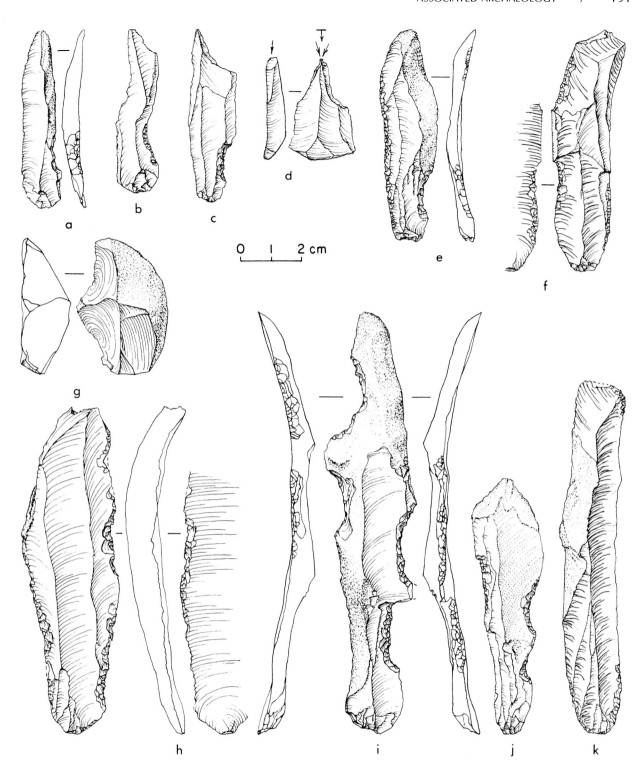

FIGURE 4.25. *Tools from Terminal Paleolithic Site E-76-6: (a–c) notched blades; (d) dihedral burin; (e, f, h, j) notched and retouched blades; (g) single-blow denticulate; (i) multinotch blade; (k) retouched blade.*

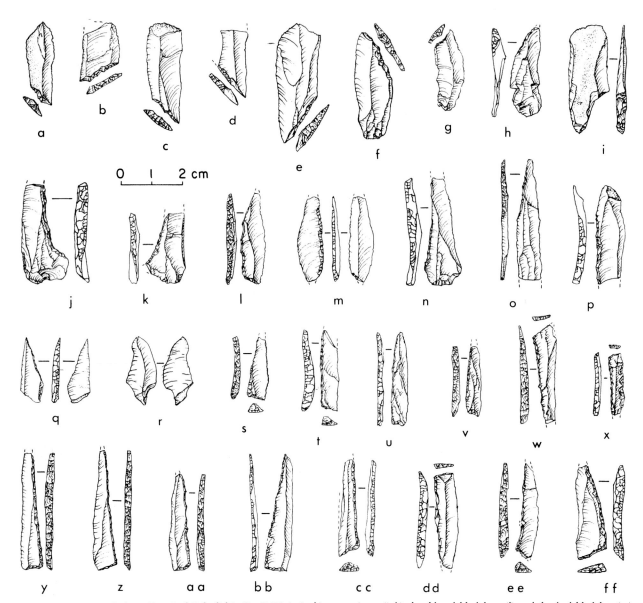

FIGURE 4.26. *Tools from Terminal Paleolithic Site E-76-6: (a–h) truncations; (i–k) shouldered bladelets; (l) arch-backed bladelet; (m) straight-backed bladelet, inversely retouched; (n–p) partially backed bladelets; (q) Krukowski microburin; (r) microburin; (s–ff) triangles.*

partially embedded in the sand at the eastern edge of the collected area. The boundaries of the excavations covered most of the concentration as it appeared on the surface, except for the eastern limit where deeper spring sand was covering the living floor. The settlement appears to consist of a limited occupational unit, certainly not covering an area larger than 100m². There were no structures, pits, or other features in evidence.

The raw material at this locality is primarily a brown to tan, thin, tabular, Eocene chert. A few pieces of gray nodular chert also occurred. The collection includes 68 cores limited to three types, of which the change-of-orientation variety for flakes is the most numerous (60.1%), followed by unprepared single-platform cores for flakes (36.7%).

The remainder are opposed-platform cores for flakes (2.9%).

The collection from Site E-76-7 includes 213 flaked stone tools, 3 hammerstones, and 1 upper grinding stone. Two groups of tools are most numerous: denticulates (26.7%) and perforators (24.4%). The denticulates are made on both flakes and thin chert slabs and occur in a wide variety of forms, using both Clactonian and retouched notches, and seemingly without standardization. The perforators also display a wide range of variation, but almost all are made on flakes, with a few pieces on elongated flakes tending toward blades. The points of the perforators are very diverse, grading from short, wide, and undeveloped to long and well shaped by retouch. Some are symmetrical and

SITE E-76-7

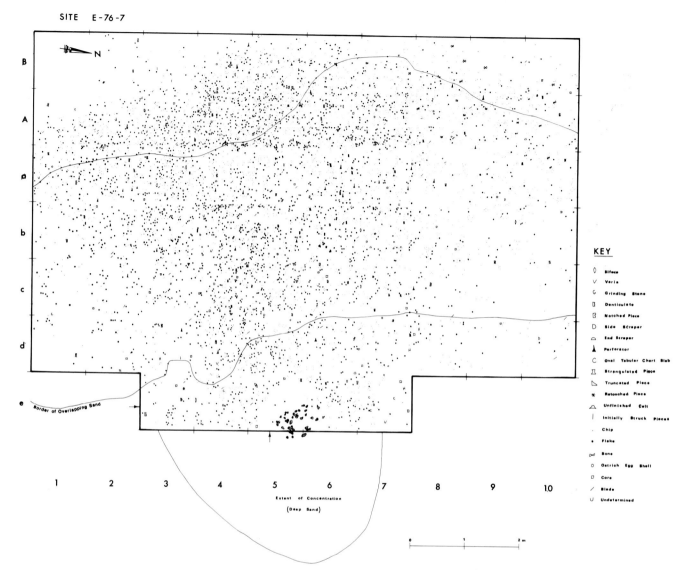

KEY

0	Biface
V	Varia
C	Grinding Stone
ᴗ	Denticulate
ᴖ	Notched Piece
D	Side Scraper
⌒	End Scraper
⏶	Perforator
C	Oval Tabular Chert Slab
Ⅱ	Strangulated Piece
⟍	Truncated Piece
✳	Retouched Piece
⟋	Unfinished Celt
I	Initially Struck Pieces
.	Chip
·	Flake
∞	Bone
O	Ostrich Egg Shell
□	Core
/	Blade
U	Undetermined

Border of Overlapping Sand

Extent of Concentration
(Deep Sand)

FIGURE 4.27. *Horizontal distribution of artifacts from Neolithic Site E-76-7, surface and subsurface.*

others are asymmetrical or have curved (*Zinken*-like) tips. Some of the points are shaped by two single-blow notches, recalling Middle Paleolithic becs; here, however, they are smaller and usually have additional secondary retouch. Classic, double-backed perforators are totally lacking, although one piece displays straight, *sur enclume* retouch along one edge and gibbous, continuous retouch on the other. The axis of this tool is transversal to the axis of the blank on which it is made, a feature not uncommon among the perforators (Figures 4.28–4.30).

Other tools include relatively numerous retouched pieces, both flakes and slabs (8.4%); notches, both retouched and single blow (8.9%); elegant sidescrapers (6.1%); and endscrapers (4.7%). The sidescrapers are well made, usually thin, with semisteep retouch. They have convex, bilateral, transversal, and convergent edges. Most of

the endscrapers are denticulated, but there is one classic, nosed specimen. The less frequent tools include biface fragments (2.3%), initially worked chert slabs (6.1%), and three large flake hoes (?) (1.4%). The hoes are similar to those noted by Caton-Thompson (1952: Plate 117) and called *massive scrapers*. They are characterized by oval shapes, crude endscraper-like fronts, and continuous to occasional retouch along both sides.

The pottery found associated with the settlement is dark gray with carbon-streaked interiors. The paste is very friable and contains abundant quartz-sand temper. The exterior is smoothed, but not polished, and displays no decoration. It is clearly different from both the Early Khartoum and later pottery in the Nabta area.

Site E-76-7 has one radiocarbon date on ostrich eggshells of 5450 BP ± 80 years (SMU-741). This date agrees with

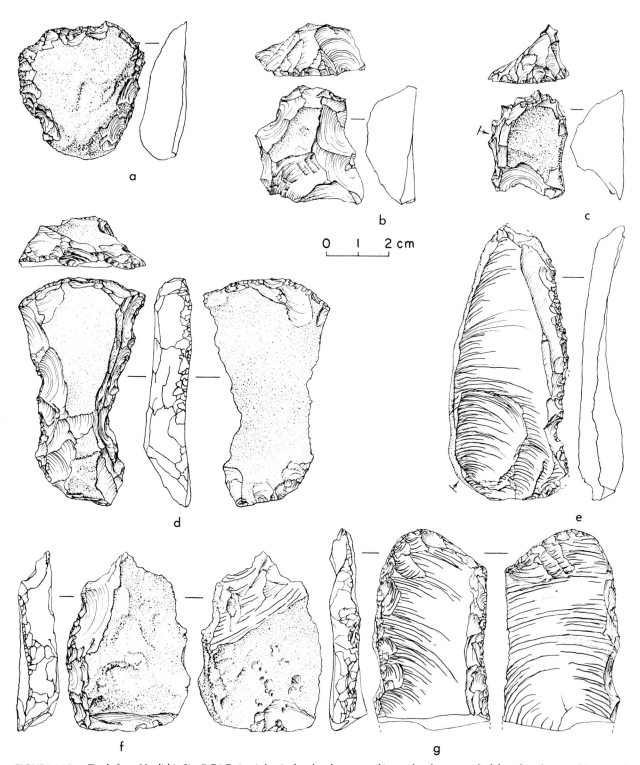

FIGURE 4.28. *Tools from Neolithic Site E-76-7: (a, c) denticulated endscrapers; (b) nosed endscraper; (d) slab with endscraper-like tip and slightly concave retouched sides; (e) convex sidescraper on flake; (f) sidescraper on tablet; (g) bilateral sidescraper.*

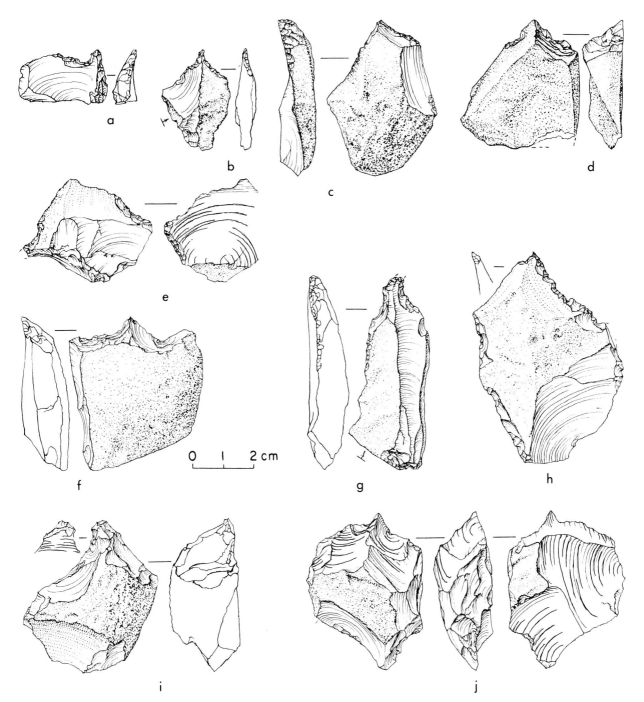

FIGURE 4.29.   *Tools from Neolithic Site E-76-7. All perforators.*

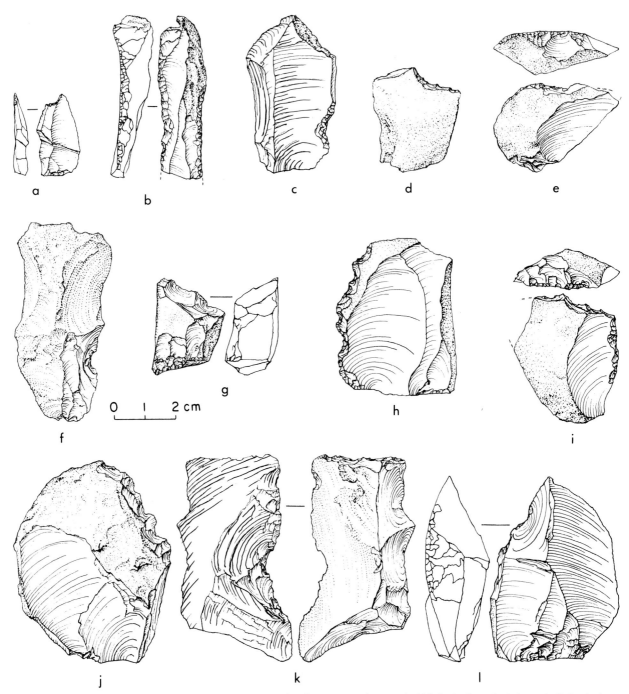

FIGURE 4.30.   *Tools from Neolithic Site E-76-7: (a) concave distal truncation; (b) retouched blade; (c–f) notched pieces; (g–l) denticulates.*

the assessment that the lithic assemblage at this site displays the full characteristics of an advanced Neolithic technology.

Site E-76-7a (E69K7a)

In the same spring sand unit as Site E-76-7 and about 30 m northwest, another small, tight concentration occurred on the surface and partially buried in the sand. The isolated concentration was circular in outline and about 5 m in diameter (Figure 4.31). It consisted of flaked stone debris, pieces of ostrich eggshell, and rare bone fragments. It was

obviously a living floor of a single camp, but excavation failed to reveal any traces of features or pits.

The raw material utilized is identical to that found at Site E-76-7; it is a brown to tan, thin, tabular, Eocene chert. The core types are also similar. Change-of-orientation for flake specimens are the most prevalent type, followed by the single-platform for flake variety. There is only one example of an opposed-platform core for flakes.

The tool collection is small and consists of only 65 pieces, plus 2 hammerstones and 1 fragmentary upper grinder. Here, too, the denticulates are predominant (26.1%), and

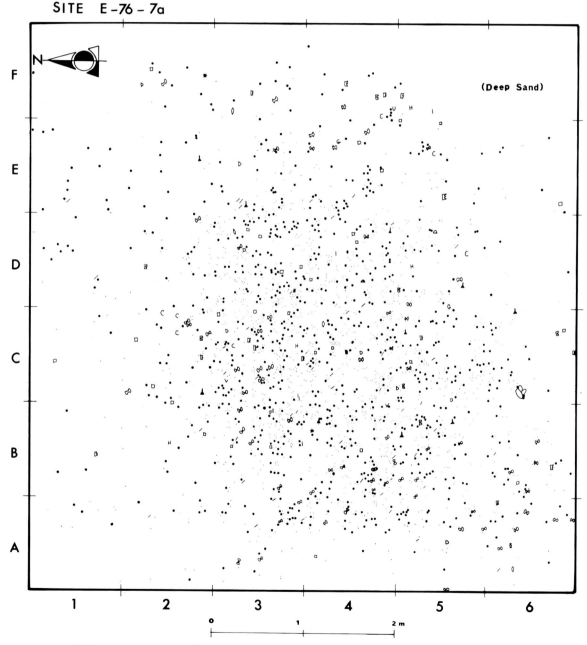

FIGURE 4.31. *Horizontal distribution of artifacts at Neolithic Site E-76-7a. Key as on Figure 4.27.*

the perforators also form a strong group (13.8%); they are, however, slightly less frequent than the large hoe-like specimens on tabular flint (15.4%). Sidescrapers are important (13.8%), and include a large variety of forms. The remaining tools are retouched pieces (6.1%), notched pieces (7.7%), endscrapers (4.6%), initially worked bifacial pieces (4.6%), biface fragments (1.5%), and undetermined fragments (6.1%). Although there are minor differences between the structures of these two assemblages, their qualitative characteristics are identical (Figures 4.32–4.34).

Both Sites E-76-7 and E-76-7a, as well as the adjacent deflated area of spring sands, yielded poorly preserved fragments of tooth enamel and pieces of upper jaws of a big bovid, smaller than *Bos primigenius* and tentatively identified as a large breed of domestic cattle. There were also scattered fragments of bones that could not be definitely identified, but are probably either a gazelle (*Gazella dorcas?*) or a caprovid (sheep/goat) (Gautier, this volume).

Site E-76-2 (E69K2)

About 6 km to the north and partially embedded in the upper section of gray, laminated, playa-like silts was Site E-76-2, obviously in a basin. The silts in this area stand 15 m higher than the deflated spring sediments at the area of Sites E-76-7 and E-76-7a, and the difference in elevation suggests that either the silts of this basin once covered Site E-76-7, or the predepositional topography formed an enclosed basin separated from the spring area. We favor the second hypothesis, but additional field studies would be required to resolve this problem.

When first seen, the site appeared as a heavily deflated and widely dispersed scatter of artifacts covering a roughly circular area about 40 m in diameter (Figure 4.35). There were no evident subclusters, but a group of fire-cracked rocks near the center witnessed the presence of a hearth. Near the hearth, a small, low remnant of silt displayed traces of two thin cultural layers, from 2 to 3 cm thick, separated by 15 cm of sterile silt. The collection therefore combines at least two occupations, but they were probably separated by a relatively short interval of time. Faunal remains were limited to a few scraps of unidentified bone.

A brown to tan, thin, tabular, Eocene chert, the same as that at Sites E-76-7 and E-76-7a, was employed here. Among the cores, change-of-orientation and single-platform for flake varieties are equally numerous, and the opposed-platform for flake cores are represented by only a few pieces.

The tool assemblage is basically the same as the two collections described earlier. Various denticulates form the most numerous group (24.7%), and their importance would be even more pronounced if the unidentified pieces, mostly tabular chert fragments that were broken during manufacture (24.7%), were excluded. The initially worked bifacial pieces, which account for 13.9%, notched pieces (7.5%), and perforators (6.1%) are next in importance. Other significant tool groups include endscrapers (5.4%), sidescrapers (4.3%), retouched pieces (4.3%), and bifacial foliates (2.9%). Other tools are represented by only a few examples: truncated flakes, burins, hoes, a flaked adze, scaled pieces, and several reutilized Middle Paleolithic artifacts. The collection also includes seven hammerstones, two upper grinding stones, and a bone tool (Figures 4.36 and 4.37).

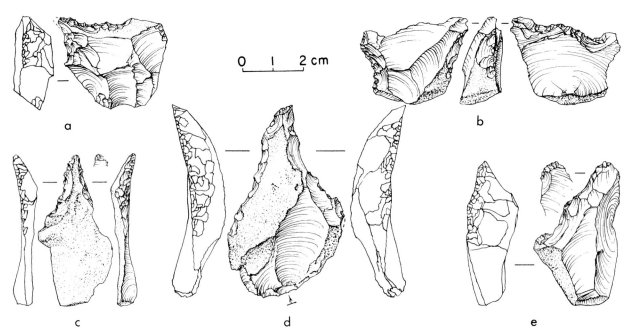

FIGURE 4.32. *Tools from Neolithic Site E-76-7a. All perforators.*

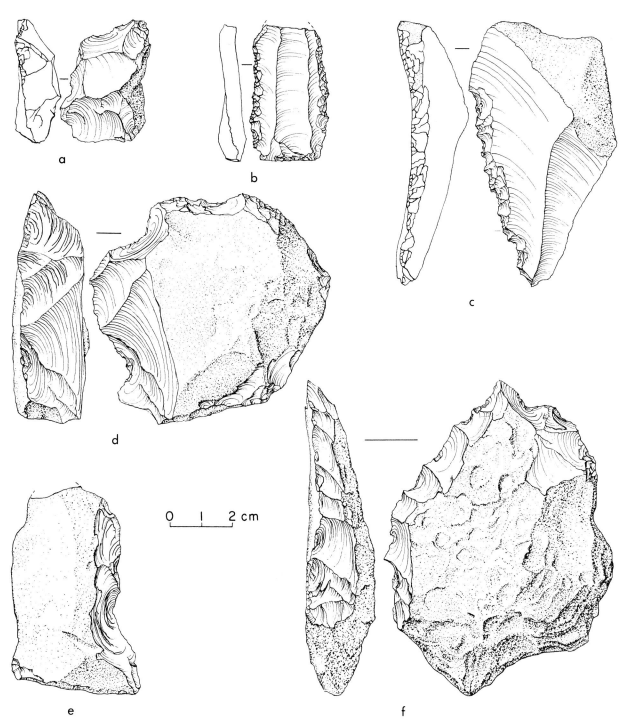

FIGURE 4.33. *Tools from Neolithic Site E-76-7a. All denticulates.*

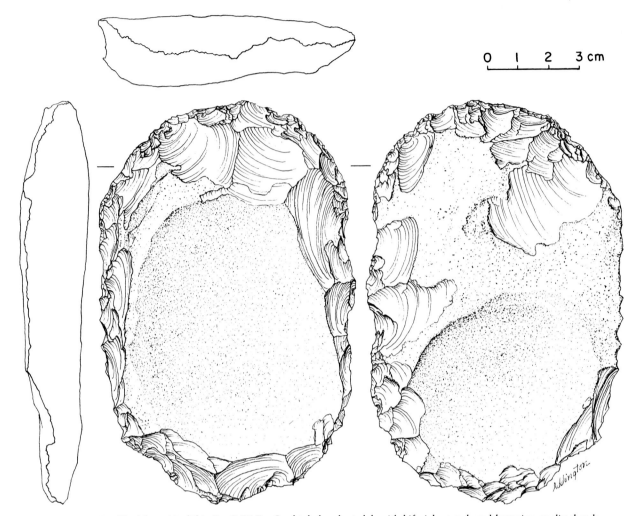

FIGURE 4.34.   *Tool from Neolithic Site E-76-7a. Oval tabular chert slab with bifacial retouch and battering on distal ends.*

FIGURE 4.35.   *View of Site E-76-2. Figure is standing near center of concentration. Note cultivated area in background.*

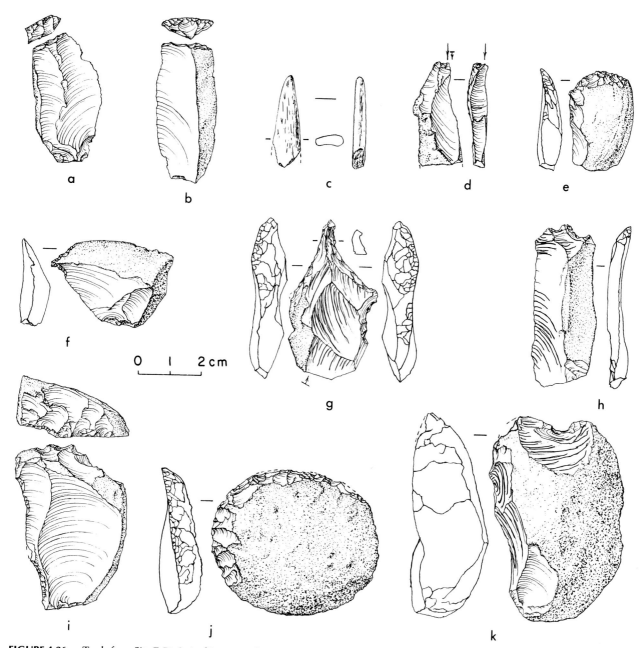

FIGURE 4.36. Tools from Site E-76-2: (a, b) truncated pieces; (c) bone point; (d) burin on truncation; (e) endscraper; (f–h) perforators; (i) denticulated endscraper; (j) endscraper; (k) single-blow notched piece.

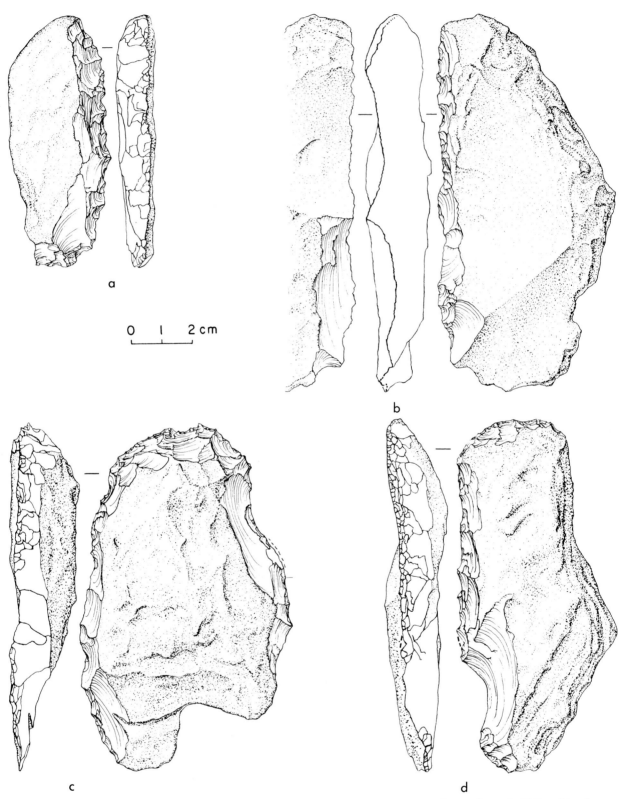

0   1   2 cm

FIGURE 4.37. *Tools from Site E-76-2 (retouched tabular pieces): (a) lateral convex sidescraper; (b) initially worked biface; (c) endscraper-like tip and denticulated sides; (d) endscraper-like tip and one side retouched and notched.*

SUMMARY OF NEOLITHIC

It seems that all the Neolithic collections from Kharga represent a single taxonomic unit that is characterized by simple core technology, limited to unprepared flake cores, and by a stress on the working of tabular chert into bifacial tools, foliates, and large, oval, hoe-like pieces with an endscraper edge and unifacially or bifacially retouched sides. The quality of the tabular chert was mediocre and the collections therefore include many failed pieces abandoned at various stages of manufacture. The major elements in the tool kit are the denticulates followed by perforators, both of them occurring in a wide variety of forms. Sidescrapers are frequent and always well made. Endscrapers and notches are present, as are occasional burins and truncated flakes. A characteristic trait is the total lack of cores for bladelets, of bladelets themselves, and of any form of microlithic tools, including geometrics. The sites also contain rare sherds of undecorated, coarse-tempered pottery, which in no way resembles the Early Khartoum pottery seen to the south at Nabta. The occurrences appear to be small with no suggestion of long-term camps or of structures. Larger sites, like that of E-76-2, undoubtedly result from a combination of multiple occupations and postdepositional scattering through erosion. Elements of the same taxonomic entity were previously collected by Caton-Thompson (1952: 36–40) in the Kharga area and described under the name of Peasant Neolithic.

5
Miscellaneous Investigations

The Gilf el Kebir is an extensive upland area in the southwest corner of Egypt. It is the most desolate and remote part of the country, totally devoid of water, and rarely visited in modern times. The English had been there in the days before World War II, and they had reported Acheulian and Neolithic sites there (Bagnold 1933). From our earliest days in Egypt we had often talked about going to the Gilf, but the logistical problems seemed insurmountable.

In 1975, however, we had just received three new Volkswagen 181s, and since they were air cooled and required a minimum of gasoline we decided to use them to make a quick survey of the Gilf. Our base camp that year was at Nabta, 500 km east of the Gilf, and we arranged for the Geological Survey to leave two barrels of gasoline at Bir Sahara, which is about halfway to the Gilf and is the nearest available water. We carefully calculated our fuel requirements and purchased sufficient jerry cans so each vehicle could carry enough fuel to go from Bir Sahara to the Gilf and back, plus some extra for safety. To cut down on weight we bought three lightweight tents and six sleeping bags, and laid in a supply of dried food. It was to be a Spartan adventure.

In addition to the authors, the designated survey team consisted of Rushdi Said, then Vice Minister for Mining and Mineral Resources; our senior geologist, C. Vance Haynes; Eyde, our guide; and a mechanic. The day before we were to leave Haynes and Eyde took one of the new Volkswagens out into the desert to see how it behaved on difficult ground. Very shortly it was deeply mired in soft sand, and Haynes put it in reverse and immediately stripped the rear gear.

Eventually they got the vehicle unstuck and came back to camp. Haynes was dejected over the accident, and Eyde was deeply worried. He was about to take three foreigners and his boss several hundred kilometers across some very rough terrain, with no local water and little possibility of help if there was difficulty. Clearly to him these pretty little cars might not have the stamina for the task ahead. In a few minutes he announced his decision: He would not go unless we also took along a lorry, which he knew from many trips into the desert might take a longer time, but it got there and it could carry extra fuel and water; also, if one of the fancy new cars broke down, the lorry could carry it back. All arguments failed. Eyde was adamant, and so we left camp with three Volkswagens and a big Russian lorry.

We did, however, decided to make some changes in our gear. We no longer had to worry about weight, so we took along someone to cook, a table, and chairs. All that talk about a hard, no-frills trip to the Gilf rapidly vanished, and Eyde enjoyed a pleasant, worry-free excursion.

We reached the Gilf near its northeast corner and traveled down along the spectacular vertical cliffs that form the east face of this huge sandstone mass. At Wadi Bakht, a vast crevasse that cuts back into the Gilf, we turned west up the wadi to the foot of an enormous dune, which at one time had completely blocked the wadi but was now breached near the center with a deep gully. Bagnold's group had reported a large Neolithic site in a playa behind the dune. We parked the vehicles in the wadi below and two of us made a quick check of the dune to see if our Volkswagens could move over it safely. The dune, however, was soft and thus a good place to get stuck. This was reported, and we began moving our equipment on foot to the archaeological site some 2 km away. One of us, who will remain unidentified, thought that the dune on the other bank of the

205

wadi looked firmer, and so he decided, against all urging, to drive his Volkswagen over the dune in that area. There was a clear place where he gathered speed to carry him across the dune, nearly half a kilometer wide. At first it went very well, but some 200 m inside the dune the car came to a halt in a great cloud of dust. There was a shout for help, but only Eyde went over to give assistance; the rest of us proceeded with the work we had come so far to do. Besides, he had been warned. It took over 4 hours of pushing, carrying rocks, and digging to get the Volkswagen back on hard ground. Things were a little tense around camp that evening, but never again did any of us knowingly drive the cars into soft areas.

As it turned out, the lorry really was not necessary. The Volkswagens made the entire trip without incident, using only the fuel they carried, and there would have been plenty of water. Subsequently, the 181s have traveled throughout the desert with us and have proven their worth as reconnaissance vehicles.

As part of its general survey of the Western Desert, the Combined Prehistoric Expedition undertook a brief examination of two areas, the Dyke area and the Gilf el Kebir. The first area is 175 km south of the village of Balat at Dakhla. Detailed maps are not available for this area, but it is distinguished by a prominent system of dykes extending toward the northwest from the Nusab el Balgum igneous mound of the Precambrian mass of El Tawila (Issawi 1971). The second area, visited very briefly, is that of the western portion of the Gilf el Kebir, where the Bagnold expedition of 1938 worked several important sites, two of which were located.

THE DYKE AREA

The area surveyed in the Dyke area was just west of and adjacent to the line of dykes in a generally flat, stony, and sandy desert characterized by broad exposed surfaces of Nubia sandstone in which are numerous, rather small basins filled with both fossil and modern sand. A few of the basins were very extensive, but the fill had been reworked and the stone floors exposed in all of the larger basins that were examined. Drainage lines are very inconspicuous here, and appear only in the immediate vicinity of the basins. Comblike conical sandstone gebels spot the area here and there, and give the region a desolate and forbidding character. No traces of fossil springs were seen in the vicinity, and the nearest surface water today is at Bir Murr on the Darb el Arbain about 100 km to the southeast, and, slightly farther, at the southern most part of Kharga to the northeast.

Traces of several occupations were noted in this area, but only two of the better sites were worked from a "flying camp" (minimum equipment only) in March 1972. One of the sites was Mousterian, and the other was Terminal Paleolithic. Remnants of later occupations, possibly of Neolithic or Old Kingdom age, were noted elsewhere in the vicinity, but were always found to be extensively destroyed.

Site E-72-4 (E78M1)

The Mousterian settlement consisted of a thin scatter of lithic artifacts near the center of a small, irregular basin some 500 m in diameter. Three other, much thinner scatters of uncharacteristic chipping debris occurred in the same basin, but these were not studied.

The basin is filled with indurated, coarse-grained sand with occasional pebbles, all apparently derived from the Nubia sandstone. The sand is shallow and reddish yellow (5YR 6/6), and it is not laminated. Its base rests on the Nubia sandstone, which slopes gently toward the center of the basin. All the artifacts were on the surface, deflated from their original bed, but most pieces had fresh ground-ward faces, suggesting a relatively recent exposure and minimal displacement. The upper surfaces were moderately wind abraded and polished.

The horizontal distribution of artifacts shows three inconspicuous, small, and thin concentrations of debris, tools, and cores with a large block of Nubia sandstone in the center (Figures 5.1 and 5.2). Although their distribution suggests separation of the concentrations, a sidescraper from Concentration 2 articulates with a pseudodenticulate and another sidescraper fragment from Concentration 1. The three pieces, in fact, form a bilateral sidescraper with one of the edges denticulated.

The collection from the site totals 417 pieces, of which 41 are tools and 5 are cores. The material utilized is exclusively quartzitic, Nubia grit sandstone of two varieties: one more ferruginous and metamorphosed, and the other more fine grained, brown in color, and favored for tools. Of the 5

FIGURE 5.1. *View of Site E-72-4, Dyke area, looking north across sand pan with Middle Paleolithic concentrations in fore-ground.*

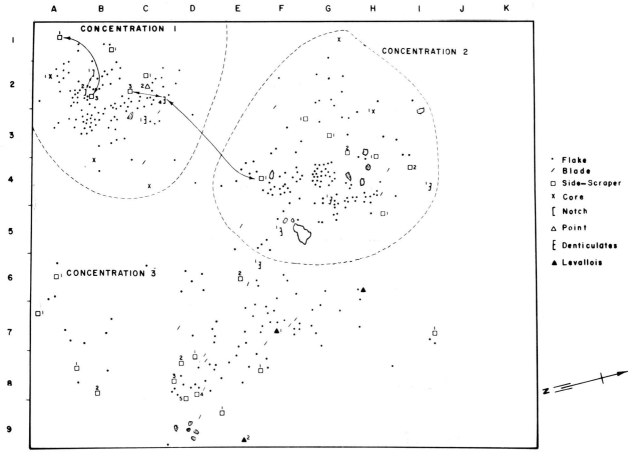

FIGURE 5.2. *Horizontal distribution of artifacts at Site E-72-4. Sandstone blocks indicated by shaded areas.*

cores found in the site, 2 are globular change of orientation for flakes, 1 is single platform for flakes, and 1 is single platform for flakes made on a flake. One core is undetermined.

Levallois technology is poorly represented (IL: .9), although blades are relatively numerous (Ilam: 8.0). Levallois unworked pieces are present. Of the retouched tools by far the most numerous are sidescrapers, which account for more than 50%. The denticulates are rare, and there are only two Mousterian points, one of which is on a Levallois point. The tools are large; some of them have lengths of nearly 30 cm (Figures 5.3 and 5.4).

The distribution of the artifacts and the size of the collection suggest a single short-lived camp made by a small group. The local geomorphology and data from elsewhere in the Western Desert clearly indicate that the occupation at Site E-72-4 was associated with a temporary source of water collected in a relatively small enclosed basin and obviously derived from local rainfall.

Site E-72-5 (E79A1)

The subsequent settlement in this area is also associated with an oval, slightly irregular, shallow enclosed basin,

measuring approximately 400 by 600 m, which is located some 18 km south of Site E-72-4. The basin is filled with clastic sediments and is surrounded by exposed areas of Nubia sandstone, which are often covered by modern sand sheets. The deflated surface of the basin fill shows numerous varied concentrations of artifacts and clusters of fire-cracked rocks in the lower, central portion of the basin as well as near its edges. There seem to be two different kinds of concentrations. Clusters of the first type are rich, dense, and relatively small in size. Clusters of the second type are large, poorly delimited, and highly deflated; these low-density clusters are made up of heavily eolized artifacts, which occur most commonly at slightly higher elevations around the margin of the basin. The first type of concentration is definitely Terminal Paleolithic in age, whereas the other type contains occasional bifacial pieces made on thin chert slabs and is believed to be Neolithic–Predynastic or Early Kingdom in age (Figure 5.5).

The largest and best defined Terminal Paleolithic clusters were two adjacent, similarly sized concentrations, located slightly west of the deepest portion of the basin. The less deflated of these was selected for more detailed investigation. A grid measuring 10 by 11 m was laid down over the area of the concentration and all the surface artifacts were

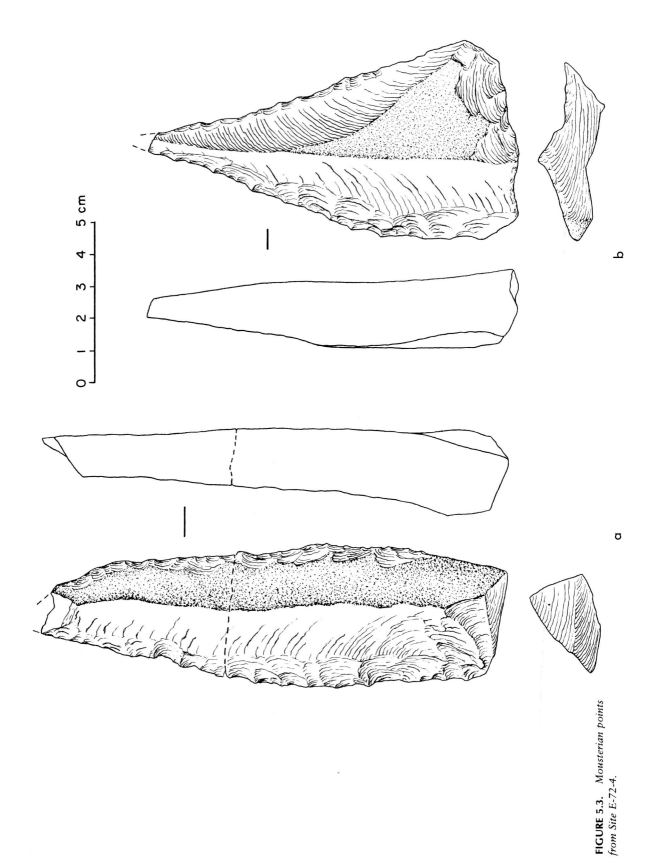

FIGURE 5.3. *Mousterian points from Site E-72-4.*

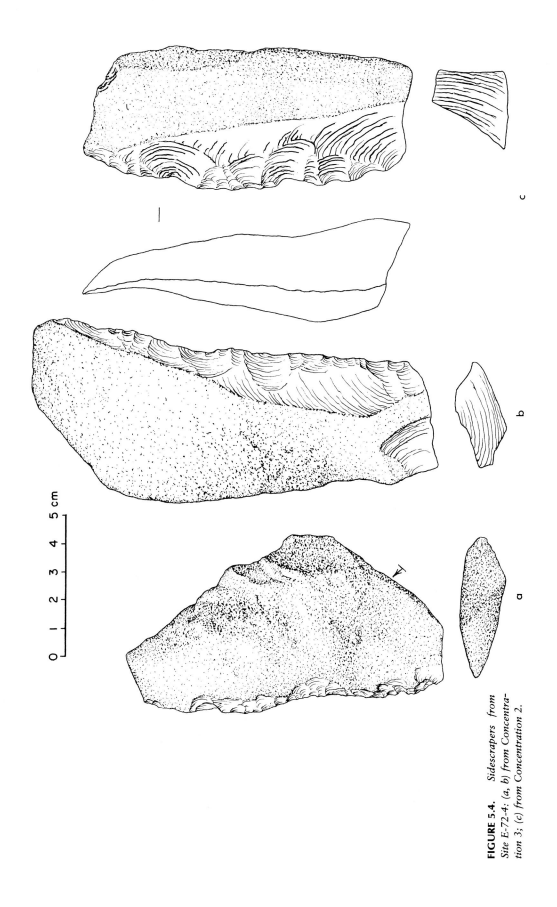

FIGURE 5.4. *Sidescrapers from Site E-72-4: (a, b) from Concentration 3; (c) from Concentration 2.*

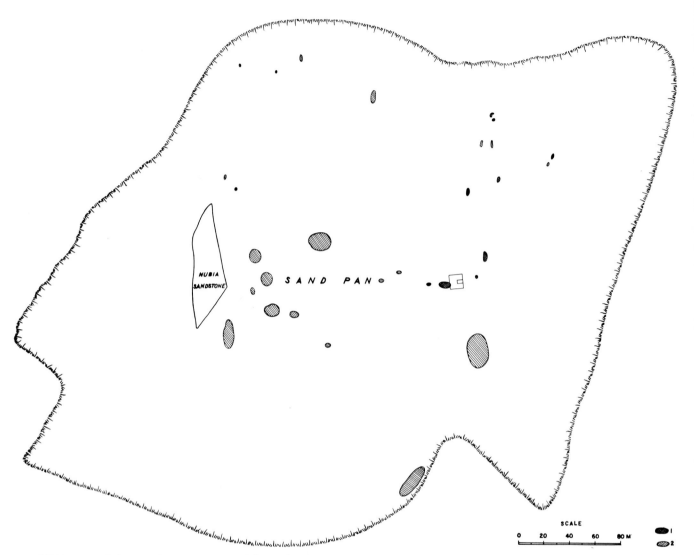

FIGURE 5.5. *Dyke area, Site E-72-5. Map of the sand pan containing Site E-72-5. Key: 1, Terminal Paleolithic/Epipaleolithic concentrations; 2, Neolithic and/or Early Kingdom clusters. Collected area indicated by rectangle. Mapped by B. Issawi.*

scatterpatterned. In addition, a trench 3 by 4 m was excavated at the eastern edge of the concentration. Three other stratigraphic trenches were cut to the sandstone floor of the basin in a line toward its deepest portion, which was near the eastern edge of the remaining clastic fill (Figures 5.6 and 5.7).

The trenches revealed the cultural layer of the concentration embedded in the top of a shallow sand–silt fill. The sand is laminated, flaky, and pink (5 YR 7/4), and fluctuates in thickness from 40 cm near the site to less than 1 m in the lowermost portion of the basin. The lamination is pseudorhythmic, with coarse-grained and silty laminae, generally conformable with the dip of the sandstone floor. Numerous small swales and wavy bedding sections are observed throughout the sediment. The sand grains are well rounded and polished, and are derived from the Nubia sandstone (Figure 5.8).

The sand fill of the deflational basin carved into the Nubia sandstone floor was obviously deposited by local rainfall wash, and the lack of any trace of significant drainage around the basin also indicates surface runoff. The alterations and the coarser- and finer-grained laminae could indicate a diffused surface wash alternating with more violent transport from which an eolian factor cannot be excluded. The presence of certainly later occupations in the basin strongly suggests that the period of local rainfall extended in time far beyond the Terminal Paleolithic occupations.

The surficial scatter of artifacts at the concentration studied (Figure 5.9) shows a very dense occurrence of chipped stones almost totally confined within a semicircular area delineated by more than 50 large to small sandstone blocks, some of them greater than 30 cm in length. The results of nearest-neighbor analysis using a Wroclaw dendrite indi-

FIGURE 5.6. *Site E-72-5 after collection, looking north. Note the beginning of the next concentration in the left center of photograph.*

cate that the distribution of these blocks is not random (Schild and Wendorf 1977b: 120; for discussion of technique, see Florek *et al.* 1951 and Kostrubiec 1971). The heaviest concentration of the blocks forms a semicircle extending from the west to the north and the east sides. Within the area delineated by the blocks, and close to the

FIGURE 5.7. *View of sand pan in Dyke area, looking west across Site E-72-5 in foreground, before collection was taken.*

edge of the concentration, are several large flat milling stones. It seems probable that the blocks of sandstone mark a large circular or semicircular structure, perhaps a tent whose walls were held down by the stones, a standard practice in today's desert camping (Figure 5.10).

There are two collections from Site E-72-5; the first is from the surface, and the second is from the cultural layer in the trench. They differ significantly in several respects. The surface collection yielded 2647 pieces, of which 156 are tools and 196 are cores. Two major types of raw material were used. Predominant was a quartzitic, fine-grained sandstone (51.9%), frequently represented by larger pieces, with chert next in importance (41.5%). The remainder was quartzitic grit sandstone (4.2%) and fossil wood (1.7%).

The excavated collection contains 1246 pieces, including 140 tools and only 96 cores. The raw materials are the same as those from the surface, but the frequencies are significantly different. Here, the chert is dominant (85.5%), followed by quartzitic sandstone (10.01%), with quartzitic grit sandstone at 3.9%, and only one piece made of fossil wood.

Among the cores there are no significant differences in the types represented in the two collections, taking into account the small size of the excavated group. The most

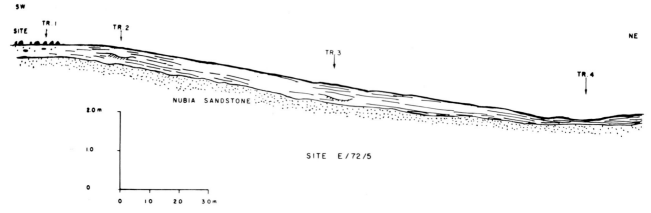

FIGURE 5.8. *Cross section through Site E-72-5 toward pan center.*

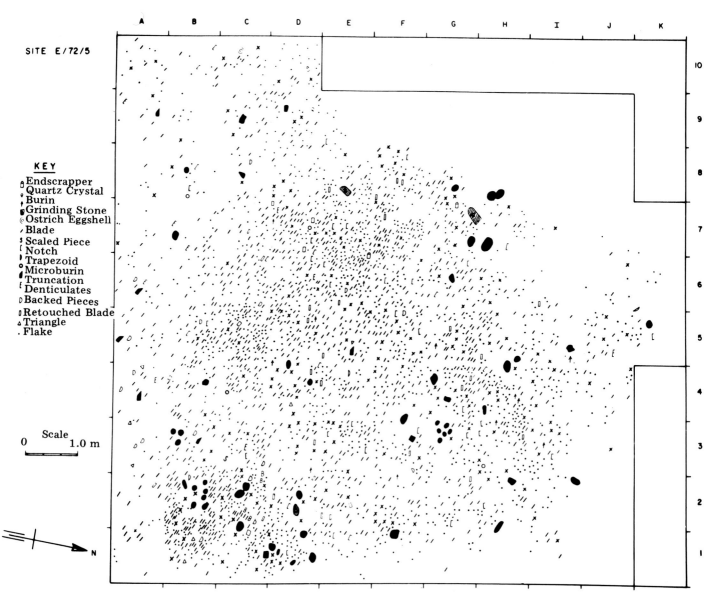

FIGURE 5.9. *Horizontal distribution of artifacts at Site E-72-5. Milling stones shaded; sandstone slabs blackened.*

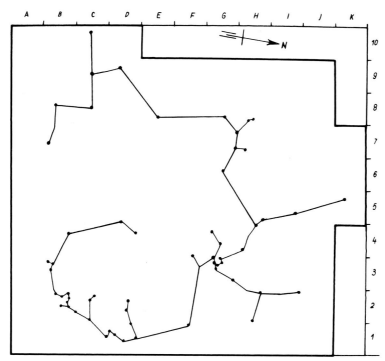

FIGURE 5.10. *Dyke area of Site E-72-5. Wroclaw dendrite spread over sandstone blocks treated as points. Ranks of connection are not indicated.*

numerous are single-platform cores for blades and bladelets, followed by change-of-orientation cores, also for blades and bladelets (Figure 5.11). Third in importance are change-of-orientation cores for flakes. Considerably less frequent are opposed-platform cores for blades or bladelets, single-platform cores for flakes, opposed-platform cores for flakes, prepared pre-cores, and initially struck pieces.

The tools in the surface collection are dominated by notches and denticulates, usually on blades and bladelets (39.8%), with retouched pieces as the second group (19.8%). Geometrics are third (10.9%) and are composed mainly of elongated scalene triangles with small short sides. Trapezes are represented by only two examples, and neither segments nor lunates are present. The fourth most important group is that of burins (10.3%), followed by backed bladelets (8.3%), many of which are shouldered specimens. Endscrapers (1.3%), truncations (1.9%), and scaled pieces (.6%) are rare, but present. Microburins are present (5.1%) and include only the simple variety.

The structure of the excavated collection is very different (Figure 3.37), although notches and denticulates are still the most important (28.6%). The geometrics, exclusively elongated scalene triangles with small short sides, are almost as frequent (24.3%), backed bladelets are now third (13.6%), and microburins are relatively common (12.1%). Retouched pieces fall to 4.3%, and the same value (4.3%) is recorded for truncations. Endscrapers are absent, and burins are low (2.1%) (Figures 5.12 and 5.13).

The evident and statistically significant differences be-

tween the structures of the two collections in the frequencies of cores, debitage, and tools, the percentages of various raw materials, and the proportions of various tool groups can be explained as a result of postdepositional alteration of the surface collection through wind action. The surface collection is impoverished in small pieces, such as the geometrics, backed bladelets, and small pieces of chert, whereas the larger and heavier pieces, like cores and artifacts of quartzitic sandstone, were overrepresented. The dichotomy between the two collections clearly illustrates the selective process that affects sites exposed for prolonged periods in this hyperarid environment. Numerous grinding stones, both milling stones and handstones, occur at the site. The milling stones are made of large, flat, Nubia sandstone slabs, and display a broad, shallow grinding area on one face. Some of the larger ones are rather more than 40 cm in length. The handstones are oval in outline and have slightly convex cross sections.

This locality seems to represent either several reoccupations of exactly the same spot or a long and unbroken occupation, which seems unlikely considering the lithostratigraphic situation of the debris—close to the central portion of a periodically flooded basin. The phenomenon of reoccupation at precisely the same spot may be explained by the presence of a structure, indicated by the alignment of large stones, and the occurrence of large, untransportable milling equipment. The occurrence of another and apparently very similar occupational unit in the immediate vicinity would suggest a settlement composed of two social and/or task units.

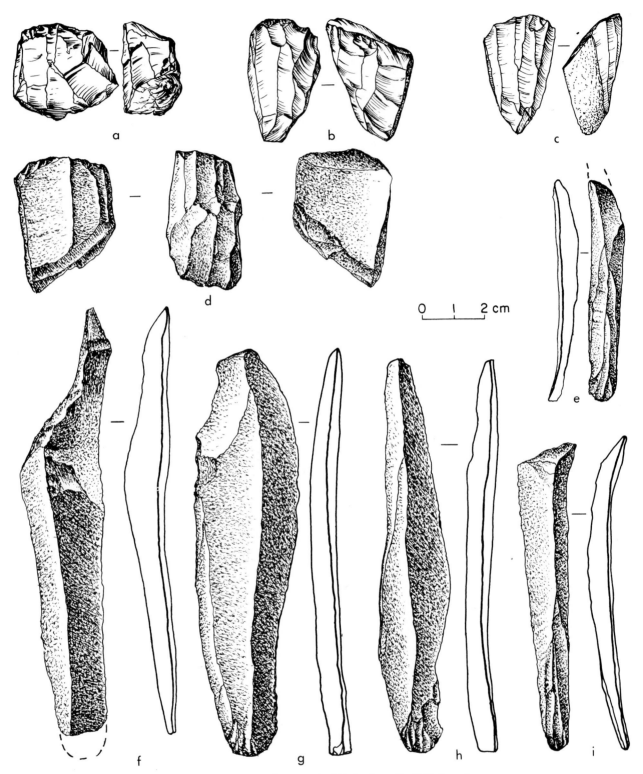

FIGURE 5.11. *Cores and unretouched blades from Site E-72-5, surface.*

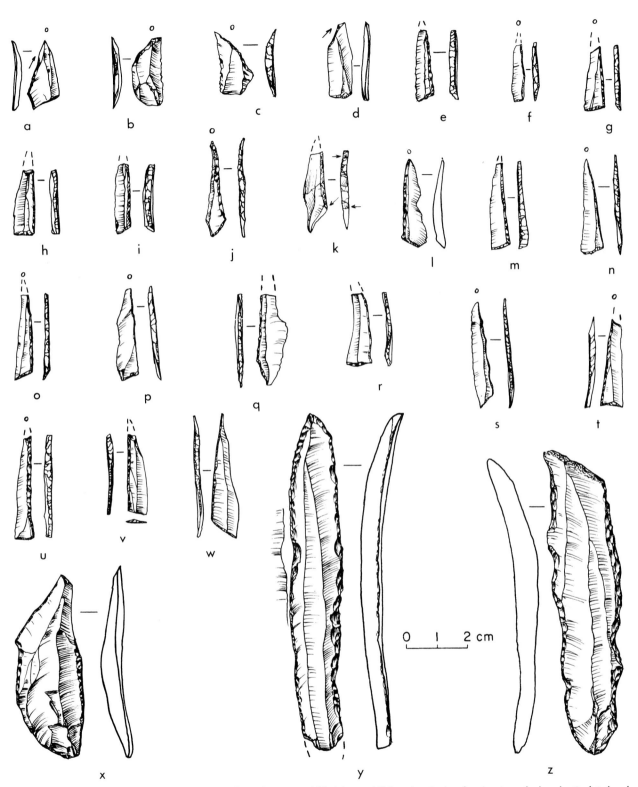

FIGURE 5.12. *Tools from Site E-72-5, excavated: (a–d) truncated bladelets and flakes; (e–w) triangles; (x–z) notched or denticulated and retouched pieces.*

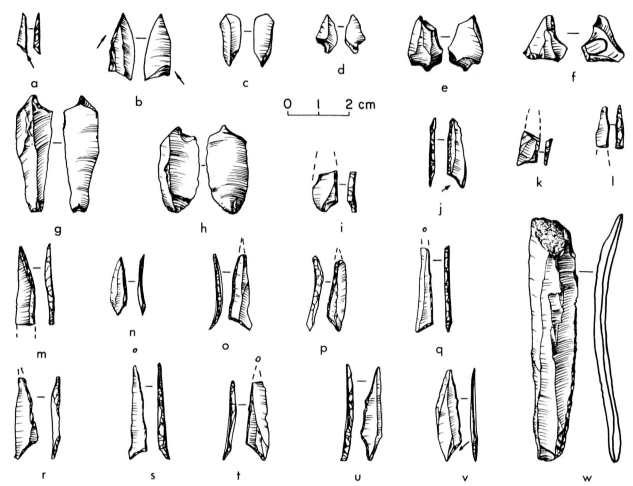

FIGURE 5.13. *Tools from Site E-72-5, excavated: (a, b) Krukowski microburins; (c, d) distal microburins; (e–h) proximal microburins; (i–v) triangles; (w) retouched blade.*

THE GILF EL KEBIR

In the far southwestern corner of Egypt is a large, high plateau with vertical escarpments on all sides. It is dissected by numerous canyon-like wadis opening onto the surrounding plain. This plateau, known as the Gilf el Kebir, was first discovered in 1925 by Prince Kemal el Din (1928) and John Ball. It is the most remote portion of Egypt and the most difficult to reach. It is totally lacking in surface water, although some of the wadis on the north and west side have vegetation in their lower courses.

Following the initial discovery, the area was visited by several European explorers (Bagnold 1931, 1933; Bagnold *et al.* 1931; Clayton 1933, 1937). The first archaeological work in the area was done in 1933, 1934, and 1935 by Frobenius, who focused principally on the rock art (Rhotert 1952). In 1938 an expedition to the area led by R. A. Bagnold had two prehistorians on its staff: O. H. Myers, who studied three major prehistoric sites, and H. A. Winkler, who recorded the rock art in the southern Gilf and at

Gebel Uweinat (Bagnold *et al.* 1939; Peel 1939; Peel and Bagnold 1939; Winkler 1938–1939). During World War II the British Long-Range Desert Group under Bagnold operated extensively near the Gilf and maintained a base at Uweinat (Shaw 1945).

Myers' collections from the Gilf el Kebir were never fully studied until the late 1960s, when the materials from one of the sites (Wadi Bakht), then in storage at the Musée de l'Homme in Paris, were examined by W. P. McHugh for his doctoral dissertation, and summarized in a separate article (McHugh 1975).

The reported occurrences of Early Paleolithic and Neolithic sites at the Gilf el Kebir led the Combined Prehistoric Expedition to undertake a reconnaissance trip in February 1975 to evaluate the archaeological potential of the area, as mentioned earlier in this chapter. The survey resulted in a short visit to two sites previously discovered and worked by Myers: one, a Late Acheulian, located near the

Bagnold camp, and the other, in Wadi Bakht. Small "grab sample" collections were made at both localities and a sketch profile was drawn of Wadi Bakht. No other sites were located and the situation does not seem promising for major archaeological work, particularly considering the extremely difficult logistical problems confronting any large group that might seek to operate in the area.

The geology of the area was studied by R. F. Peel, a member of the Bagnold party (Peel 1939, 1941). The Gilf is a huge block of Nubia sandstone that stands from 200 to 300 m above the surrounding plain. The top of the Gilf is flat except for a few basalt flows, and dips gently to the north and east. It is covered with a thick red soil. Our survey was limited to the southeastern portion, the area most dissected by numerous canyon-like wadis. These wadis are filled with alluvial sediments, which form several generations of extensive fans at their mouths.

Myers' Site 1000

The extensive scatter of Late Acheulian artifacts near Bagnold's base camp was designated Site 1000 by Myers (Bagnold *et al.* 1939). The site is on the surface of a gravelly alluvial fan, at the foot of the plateau, about 3 km from the scarp face. It was the only Acheulian site intensively worked by him although several other occurrences of Acheulian artifacts were noted in the area. The trenches opened by Myers were still evident in 1975 and one portion was cleaned and a small area extended into the undisturbed sediment.

Most of Myers' collection apparently came from the surface, although some material was within the sediment. Our observations confirmed this and it seems that the Acheulian artifacts form a part of the alluvial fan. The stratigraphy of the alluvial sediments has not been studied because of the

limited time spent in the area. It seemed evident, however, that a Late Acheulian occupation must have been contemporaneous with a period of increased wadi discharge draining the plateau.

The collection made in 1975 included only a few bifaces, all either amygdaloidal or cordiform, and was not adequate for a study of the taxonomic structure of the occupation (Figure 5.14).

Wadi Bakht

This canyon-like wadi is located at the southeastern edge of the Gilf and is one of the largest wadis in the area (Figure 5.15). About 10 km above the mouth the wadi narrows considerably and is blocked by an enormous falling dune, now breached. Below the dune the floor of the wadi supports numerous small bushes and occasional clumps of grass. The surface of the dune on both sides of the wadi is littered by thousands of stone artifacts. Above the dune a bed of silts several meters thick accumulated in a lake dammed by the dune (Figure 5.16). The area of silt extends across the canyon and some 500 m up the wadi. On the north side the silts interfinger with dune sand, and behind the breached dune the erosional wadi head cut through several meters of lake deposits. Lithic artifacts, grinding stones, pottery, ostrich eggshell, and bone occur throughout the silt (Figure 5.17).

Myers spent considerable time at this site and assembled four surface collections, each from a 64 m² block (McHugh 1971). Two of these were from the upper and lower slope of the dune on the north side, and two were from the surface of the lake silts, one on the southern side close to the dam, and the other upstream several hundred meters from the barrier.

Our examination was limited to a brief study of the

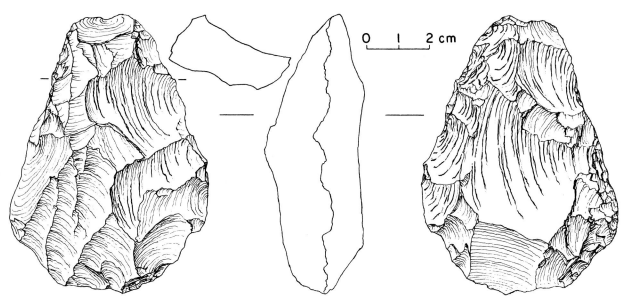

FIGURE 5.14. *Amygdaloid biface from Myers' site near Bagnold's camp.*

FIGURE 5.15. *View up Wadi Bakht. Note high cliffs of Gilf el Kebir in the distance.*

FIGURE 5.16. *View of falling dune blocking upper end of Wadi Bakht, Neolithic artifacts occur on dune and within playa sediments behind dune.*

lithostratigraphic situation and a relatively limited collection of artifacts from a surface concentration on the silts adjacent to the dune barrier on the north side of the lake. At this spot deflation had begun to erode the silts and exposed traces of many settlements in both the dune and the silts. Our collection is therefore a composite of several occupations and possibly has some time depth. In addition to the lithics, the collection includes bone material and ostrich eggshell. A date of 6980 BP ± 80 years (SMU-273) was obtained on these shells, and this probably refers to a later segment of the occupation at this locality.

The restudy of the Myers collections by McHugh has shown that over 80% of the artifacts were made of local

quartzitic sandstone, and about 18% were of various other materials, including silica glass, chalcedony, chert, agate, basalt, siltstone, and quartz. Although there were differences between the four collections, they seem to be minor, and the four will be discussed here as a single group. The collection includes 106 cores, of which the most important are of the single-platform variety. The tool assemblage totals 377 pieces, the most numerous being retouched pieces (28.1%, recalculated from McHugh 1975). The next group is formed by denticulates (18.8%), closely followed by notched blades and flakes (17.5%). Endscrapers are well represented (14.6%), and the remaining categories are much less frequent. Of these minor tools, perforators are the most numerous (7.7%), followed by backed elements (3.9%). Burins are rare (2.9%), as are lunates and segments (2.1%), and truncated pieces (1.3%). Sidescrapers, corescrapers, pedunculated pieces, trapezoids, scaled pieces, and varia are represented by only one or two specimens each.

The Myers collection also includes 21 milling stones, but no handstones, and there is a fragment of a ground and polished celt or axe. Seven hammerstones and three choppers are also reported. The associated pottery was represented by a collection of over 700 sherds, but almost all the rims and decorated sherds were removed by Myers and subsequently lost. The remaining sherds seem to fall into two classes, one a thick ware, the other much thinner and smoother.

Our collection from Wadi Bakht contains 105 tools and 13 cores. The latter include change-of-orientation globular

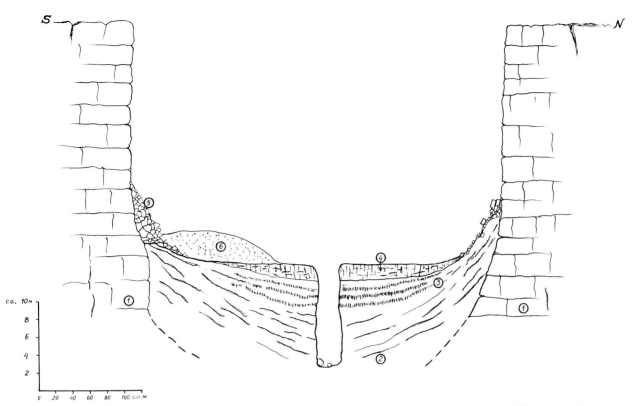

FIGURE 5.17. *Schematic profile through playa in Wadi Bakht immediately behind the dune barrier. Height of cliffs not to scale. Key: 1, Nubia sandstone; 2, dune sands; 3, silt layers sandwiched between dune sand in upper portion of dune, occasional archaeology throughout; 5, Nubia sandstone slope rubble; 6, modern dune.*

cores as the most important, followed by single-platform cores for flakes, with semidiscoidal and conical cores for bladelets each represented by a single example. Of the retouched tools the most important group is that of denticulates (55.2%), which include unilateral on flake as most common, followed by unilateral on blades, bilateral on blades and flakes, convergent symmetrical on blades, convergent on flakes, and transversal on flakes. Endscrapers are the next group (13.3%), of which the denticulated, flat endscrapers on flakes are the most numerous. The remaining endscrapers include specimens on retouched blades and flakes, shouldered, carinated, and simple on flakes. Retouched pieces form the third group, usually made on blades. Sidescrapers are next in importance, and are either simple or bilateral, on flakes or blades. Notched pieces account for 5.7%, perforators are rare (3.8%), and burins are represented by only three examples (Figures 5.18 and 5.19). There is one varia, an enormous doubled endscraper on a bilaterally retouched flake, 12.1 cm in length. The collection also includes two handstones with encircling grooves.

Our collection included 117 sherds, many of them decorated with a variety of incised and impressed designs, and a few of them reminiscent of Early Khartoum with masses of cord impressions. They are, however, not Khartoum, and no true Early Khartoum pottery is represented. Most of the

pottery is thin, wih polished exterior and with dense, well-fired paste, reddish brown in color, and tempered with fine sand. Vessel shapes include hemispherical bowls and necked jars; rim shapes include simple and direct, as well as slightly lipped and thickened, varieties. The decorations are finely executed impressions made by combs, cords, and roulettes, and incised lines forming simple V-patterns or massed in zones separated by smoothed areas (Figure 5.20).

The faunal remains collected by Myers, now in the British Museum, were preliminarily identified by Bate and Jackson (McHugh, 1975), and include ? *Elephas* sp., *Bos* sp., *Addax*, *Damaliscus* sp., *Gazella* sp., ? *Capra* sp. (goat), *Canis* cf. *anthus* (jackal), ostrich, and *Equus asinus*. The exact provenience of these remains is unknown, but most of them probably came from Wadi Bakht.

Our faunal collection was very limited and consists of only 2 bones from a large domestic dog, 3 bones of *Gazella dorcas*, 8 bones from sheep and/or goat, and 25 bones from domestic cattle (Gautier, this volume).

The Wadi Bakht occupation undoubtedly represents a considerable time depth and the radiocarbon date obtained may be an average of a section of the total time span. It is possible that the formation of the dune that preceded the lake and actually caused the later empondment of the water was contemporaneous with the dry arid episode separating Playas I and II at the Nabta area. The dam probably did

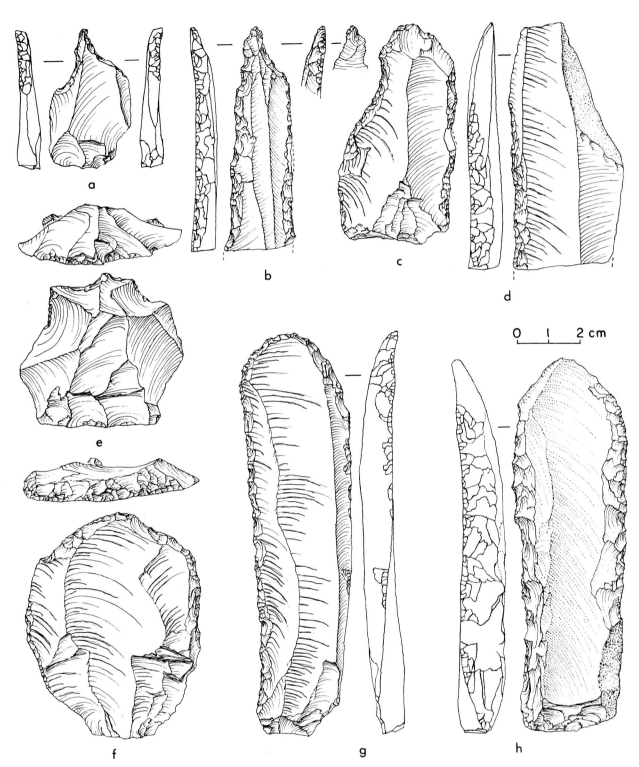

FIGURE 5.18. *Tools from Neolithic site at Wadi Bakht: (a, b) perforators; (c) notch on retouched piece; (d, h) retouched blades; (e) denticulated endscraper; (f) endscraper; (g) endscraper on retouched blade.*

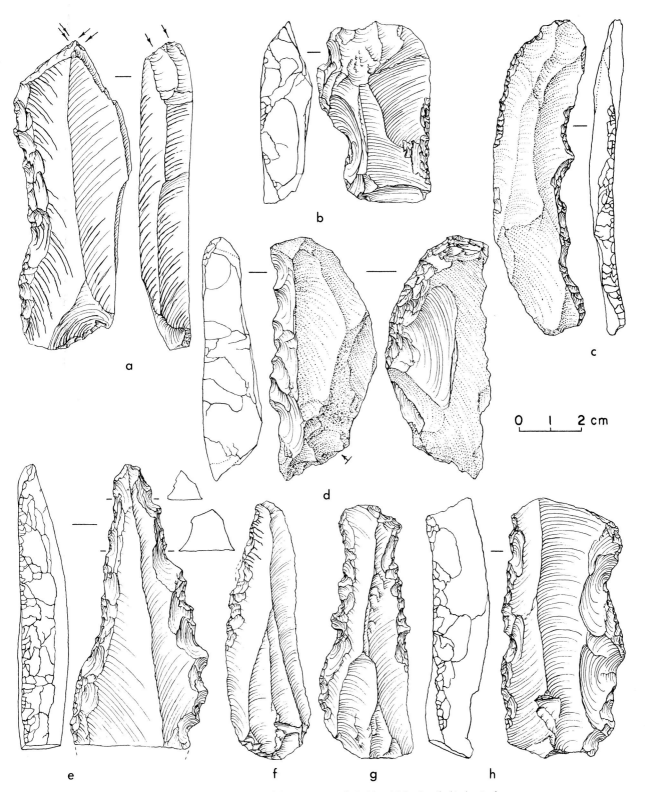

FIGURE 5.19. *Tools from Neolithic site at Wadi Bakht: (a) burin; (b–h) denticulates.*

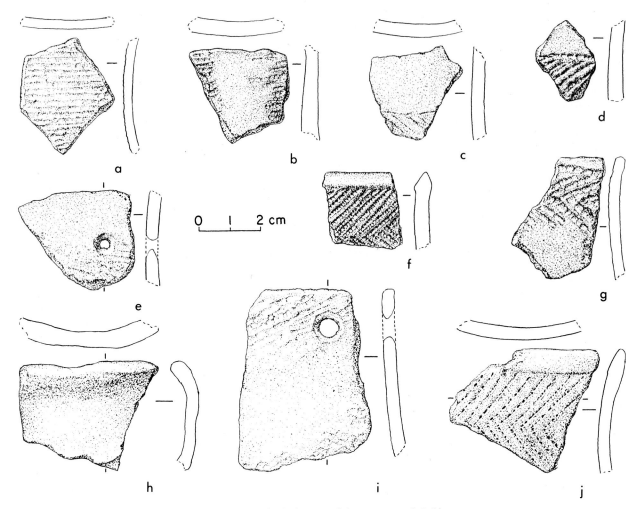

FIGURE 5.20. *Sherds from Neolithic site in Wadi Bakht.*

not exist earlier, as there are no evident Terminal Paleolithic occupations and a pond would surely have existed had the dam been in place. The sedimentation of the lake is, therefore, possibly contemporaneous with Playas II and III. The breaching of the dune barrier is not likely to have any climatic significance, since it probably occurred when the lake sediments built up to a height permitting an overflow. On the other hand, the dissection of the lake sediments at the breach point has not proceeded very far, thereby suggesting a relatively arid climate since that time. It seems likely that occupation occurred throughout the life span of the lake.

6
Paleoenvironment of the Western Desert of Egypt

The work described thus far in this volume and that of earlier investigators show that the Western Desert of Egypt, today one of the driest areas of the Sahara, has undergone several dramatic environmental changes in the past. These changes had profound effects on the floral, faunal, and human life in this part of the world, and should be viewed as a part of the variability of past climates in the Sahara as a whole. The record of past climatic changes, which is preserved in the form of sediments and associated fossils, is, as a result of their dynamics, very limited. The record is not continuous and only sections of it are preserved today. In no single locality is a continuous sequence of events preserved, and consequently any reconstruction must be based on several isolated portions of each sequence.

The best evidence for past climates is always associated with wetter episodes. The arid phases, which tend to obliterate the preceding evidence, are represented either by no record at all or only by erosion and/or eolian sediments. The record becomes progressively more complete through time, not only because of much greater preservation, but also because of the availability of radiocarbon dating and other techniques that provide better absolute and relative chronologies. For these reasons the paleoclimatic reconstruction is not equal for all periods, and the later ones appear to be much more complex than the earlier, although the actual complexity of the earlier periods may well have been at least as great.

The physiographic character of the Western Desert also had a strong effect on both the preservation and the kinds of evidence available. The total lack of surface drainage, except adjacent to the Nile, has precluded the occurrences of wadi sediments similar to those that have been so important in the development of the fossil record elsewhere in the Sahara, such as the Saoura drainage system; nor were there large lake basins like those of Lake Chad and at Ahmet; nor huge ergs, as are found in central and northwestern Sahara. Mountains, which are sensitive to climatic changes, are also lacking. Instead, the most important evidence for past environments in the Western Desert comes from relatively small, enclosed basins, either spring or rain fed, and from the deposits of fossil artesian springs, both of which are believed to respond to major climatic changes. Another factor that undoubtedly has contributed to the character of the preserved record is the permeability of the pre-Quaternary sediments: The Nubia sandstones, instead of encouraging the development of drainage systems, absorbed the available moisture, leading to the formation of one of the world's largest subterranean water reservoirs only a short distance below the surface.

It seems likely that the atmospheric phenomena, which are responsible for this area's being the most arid portion of the Sahara today, may also have played an important role in the past, in that even during moist phases the area was probably relatively drier than other parts of this great desert.

The assembled data indicate at least four major, wetter periods in the Egyptian Sahara during the past. There are some indications of preceding wetter intervals, but these are inconclusive and never well dated. Also, each of these four major periods may be composed of several pulsations. The wetter periods have been given informal names that reflect either their predominant archaeological association (Late Acheulian, Mousterian, and Aterian) or their chronological position in the Quaternary sequence when the latter is well established (early Holocene).

EVIDENCE FOR PRE–LATE ACHEULIAN ENVIRONMENTS

The physical evidence for pre–Late Acheulian sedimentation is confined to a few areas only, limited to small fragments, and never conclusively dated. The fragmentary data are preserved as plateau and wadi tufas in the larger oasis basins, such as at Dakhla (Schild and Wendorf 1977b), Kharga (Caton-Thompson 1952; Caton-Thompson and Gardner 1932; Gardner 1932, 1935), Kurkur (Butzer 1964, 1965, 1971b; Butzer and Hansen 1968; Hester and Hoebler 1969; Issawi 1968; Reed 1964; Said 1969), and Dungul (Hester and Hoebler 1969; Said 1969; Said and Issawi 1965). They also occur in the oldest, eolian, basin-fill sediments at Bir Sahara (Schild and Wendorf 1975).

Extensive remnants of plateau tufas, composed of freshwater limestone, travertine, and flowstones of cryptocrystalline calcite, all with inclusions of gravels and sands, are found in similar geomorphic situations at Kharga, Dungul, and Kurkur (Butzer and Hansen 1968:360; Hester and Hoebler 1969:133). These plateau tufas are deposited on chalk near the edges of the basins and at elevations between 340 and 375 m. In Kurkur the plateau tufas are seen as extensive beds along the northern and western margins of the oasis and cover an area of 12 km². They reach a maximum thickness of 15 m and are composed of several beds, among which two major units are evident. At Kharga, the plateau tufas are present near the top of the scarp along the eastern edge and on the northwest side. The best developed areas are at Bulaq Pass, where they cover an area of more than 2 km² and are about 10 m thick, and at Rizeikat Pass, where they cover a surface of about 8 km². The tufas were first described by Zittel (1883) and Ball (1900), and were studied in some detail by Caton-Thompson and Gardner (1932). At Dungul the tufas are at an elevation of 295 m, some 45 m above Dungul Well. They are found as hillocks, 10 to 15 m high, composed of unbedded, crystalline, carbonate rock, and cover large areas southeast of the well.

None of the plateau tufa exposures has yielded macrofossils, or cultural remains, except for impressions of *Ficus ingens* and *F. sycomorus* (Said 1962:76). Pollen analysis performed on two samples from the upper member at Kurkur yielded Tertiary boreal and montane elements, subtropical and tropical xerophytic or mesohygrophytic pollen, as well as numerous *Gramineae*, xerophytic, and halophytic components (Van Campo *et al.* 1968:517). The pollen frequencies in the two samples are different, suggesting a significant change in the climate during the deposition of an upper portion of the tufa. The later samples show a decline in arboreal elements representing east Mediterranean and boreal environments and a significant increase in forms preferring drier and warmer conditions. Both samples have very significant components of relict Tertiary elements and these are attributed to the presence of Tertiary forest vegetation in the area.

It cannot be determined if the plateau tufas are of final Pliocene or of early Pleistocene age. They certainly represent a very long and not uniform period of deposition, but the detailed environment of deposition is vague. Butzer and Hansen (1968:363) attribute their formation to fluvial activity, alluviation, and spring action through several distinct environmental phases. Clearly they do not indicate hyperarid conditions but suggest a significant local precipitation.

The plateau tufas are the oldest Plio–Pleistocene sediments of the Western Desert. The next preserved deposition is certainly much younger, although the time depth involved is unknown. Undoubtedly, a major period of dissection occurring sometime after the plateau tufa contributes to the very patchy character of the evidence. In Kharga there are no known sediments between the plateau tufas and the upper sheet gravels with the Upper Acheulian, except for scraps of pre–upper sheet gravels at various elevations at Refuf Pass and Umm-ed-Dabadib, well below the plateau tufas (Caton-Thompson 1952:5). At Kurkur, Butzer and Hansen (1968:363) recognize several steps in this dissection reaching a total vertical distance of over 140 m. It is not known if the entire span is a huge period of downcutting and removal of sediments, or a complex multifaceted interval whose real character is masked by the prevailing tendency for dissection.

After this is the deposition of pre–Late Acheulian Wadi Tufas at Kurkur and Dungul. These deposits are gravels, silts, and calcareous sediments—the last sometimes of organic formation—and are laid down in channels of complex alluvial, lacustrine, and evaporitic origin. The various beds of gravels deposited as sheets over underlying eroded bedrock at Kharga and Dakhla are a second kind of sediment. The relationship between the sheet gravels and the wadi tufas is unknown; however, both antedate the Late Acheulian and they seem to represent two significantly different environments.

The two pre–Acheulian wadi tufas (Tufa I and Tufa II) at Kurkur occur as terraces at 25 to 30 m and 16 to 20 m, respectively. They represent two wadi aggradations separated and followed by periods of dissection. Their formation is attributed to pluvial erosion of the uplands followed by spring activity. The climatic implications are a minimum of torrential discharge, a dense vegetation cover, and a high groundwater table maintained by seasonal rainfall (Butzer and Hansen 1968:363, 386). Pollen analysis of a sample of Wadi Tufa I, in contrast to the samples from the plateau tufa, indicates drier conditions than previously, as expressed by an increase of xerophytic elements (53%) and a decrease of boreal and montane Mediterranean pollen (4%). Lowland Mediterranean types form only 9% (Van Campo *et al.* 1968:517).

At Dungul, mounds of tufa that postdate the deposition of plateau tufa (Tufa I) are believed to be contemporaneous with Wadi Tufa I at Kurkur (Hester and Hoebler 1969:138). A complex series of sediments composed of brecciated boulders, a thin layer of marl, black fossil soil, and an extensive sheet of Tufa II is possibly contemporaneous with the formation of the Wadi Tufa II complex in Kurkur. It also indicates a changing depositional environment (Said, in Hester and Hoebler 1069:11, 138).

The sheet gravels at Dakhla and Kharga are made up of relatively thick (up to 1 m at Dakhla) beds of boulders and gravels in an unsorted, pinkish sand matrix. At Kharga, the pre–upper sheet gravels are deposited at two different levels, one 25 to 30 m above the upper sheet gravels, and another 34 to 40 m above the wadi floor (Caton-Thompson 1952:5). At Dakhla, they are seen along the foot of the cliff, north of Balat, and westward from there (Hermina *et al.* 1961; Schild and Wendorf 1977b). These extensive sheet washes are culturally sterile and heavily dissected. They seem to represent massive gravitational movement over a broad area following torrential rainfall on surfaces that were relatively free of vegetation.

Butzer and Hansen (1968) attribute Wadi Tufas I and II to the middle Pleistocene, and a generally similar date is suggested by the fact that both the pre–upper sheet washes at Kharga and the sheet gravels at Dakhla precede the Late Acheulian.

Another possible Quaternary pre–Late Acheulian deposit is the sand fill of the Bir Sahara–Bir Tarfawi basin. The enormous, almost circular basin, quite possibly controlled by the uplifting of the El Tawila basement complex, is filled with sands, at least in its upper portion. The depth of the fill is unknown, but it is certainly deeper than the modern depressions and the largest bore holes sunk into their floors, all totaling some 16 m. This sand may represent only the upper portion of the fill, and the true composition of the remainder is unknown. It is presumably of eolian origin, as is the portion that was examined, but it might contain a complex sequence of other kinds of sediments. The question cannot be resolved without extensive deep drilling. The upper portion of the fill clearly represents an arid period antedating the Late Acheulian.

In summary, although the evidence for the pre–Late Acheulian history of the desert is exceedingly limited, it indicates an enormous variability of climates: a relatively moist final Pliocene–lower Pleistocene; a much drier middle Pleistocene, sometimes semiarid with torrential rainfall and scarce vegetation, and at other times with seasonal rainfall, and considerable continuous (or almost continuous) water flow. These moist intervals were presumably separated by hyperarid periods of dissection and erosion such as that recorded in the upper fill of the Bir Sahara–Bir Tarfawi basin.

Although no archaeology has been found associated with these sediments, an adequate search has not really been made. Elsewhere in the Sahara, particularly in the northwestern portion, several occurrences of presumably lower and middle Pleistocene artifacts have been reported (Camps 1974a:12–15; Chavaillon 1964; Ramendo 1963), and further search of the deposits of this period in the Egyptian Sahara is obviously needed.

ACHEULIAN ENVIRONMENTS

The best evidence for the Late Acheulian environments in the Western Desert comes from the basin oases of Dakhla, Kharga, and Kurkur; from the wells of Bir Sahara and Bir Tarfawi, in the Gilf el Kebir, and from several sites along the Nile in Nubia. In both Dakhla and Kharga the Late Acheulian is contemporaneous with a period of artesian spring discharge, and at Kharga it occurs with upper sheet gravels. At Kurkur, the Acheulian occurs with Tufa III (Hester and Hoebler 1969), whereas in Bir Sahara and Bir Tarfawi the Late Acheulian is found with lacustrine sediments and sand plain carbonates, and the Final Acheulian is found with spring vents inside the depression and at a slightly lower elevation than the surrounding sand plain. In the Gilf, the Acheulian is embedded in alluvial fans, and along the Nile it is found either in the sediments of wadis discharging into the Nile Valley or in older Nile silts.

The discontinuous nature and varied character of these occurrences and the almost complete absence of any faunal and floral remains as well as of absolute dates prevent a firm correlation, and the only suggestion of a sequence within the Acheulian is at Bir Sahara. Although archaeology alone is not an adequate means for correlating these sediments, in this instance it provides the only link between them. Undoubtedly, the sediments represent a large period of time and considerable environmental variability.

At Bir Sahara the sites on the sand plain seem to be associated with deflated carbonates of pedogenic origin, suggested by their irregular nodular shape and the high sand content of the nodules. They could represent one of the K horizons of the semiarid soils, whose optimal environment varies between 250 and 600 mm of precipitation per year (Cooke and Warren 1973:104).

The largest accumulations of deflated Late Acheulian artifacts in this area occur at Bir Tarfawi around ponds slightly below the level of the surrounding sand plain. Single artifacts are still embedded in the lacustrine limestones of these ponds. The detailed stratigraphy of the lakes is yet to be studied, but it seems likely that they were fed by springs in much the same fashion as were later lakes in the area. A period of deflation possibly separates these lakes and the formation of the spring pool at Bir Sahara, which contains Final Acheulian and some indications of *Equus* and ostrich.

The evidence from Bir Sahara–Bir Tarfawi leads us to infer a threefold sequence of moister episodes, each with a slightly different water table, that are separated by two minor periods of deflation and presumed aridity. The highest water table was with the occupations on the sand plains. This is followed by that of the ponds at Bir Tarfawi, and finally by the Final Acheulian spring at Bir Sahara. An open savanna or grassland, perhaps a semiarid environment with seasonal precipitation, is indicated for the area during this period.

In both Kharga and Dakhla, the Acheulian in the spring vents indicates no more than the presence of spring discharge and a clustering of human occupations around the artesian pools. A different picture, however, emerges from the association of Acheulian artifacts with alluvial gravels at Kharga. In Refuf Pass the Acheulian is embedded in two series of gravels, each capped with tufas (Caton-Thompson 1952: 98), which certainly represent associations of gravel and calcareous deposits similar to those described by Butzer and Hansen (1968:376) at Kurkur. In the Refuf Pass sequence the lower Acheulian occurrence is classified as "Evolved Acheulian," whereas the upper one is classified as "Acheulio-Levalloisian" (Caton-Thompson 1952: 94). The tufaceous caps over the Acheulian gravels are called Tufas I and II. A complete list of fauna and flora found by Gardner (1935) and Caton-Thompson in the tufaceous cap at Kharga is discussed elsewhere (Gautier, this volume).

In the oasis of Kurkur, Butzer and Hansen (1968:370) recognized a threefold sequence of tufas, marls, and gravels termed *intermediate wadi tufas* or the Tufa III complex. The Tufa III complex is subdivided into three wadi aggradations with a period of marked dissection and eolian deposition between units IIIb and IIIc. Tufa IIIa contained freshwater *Melanoides* shells, as well as rare *Zootecus insularis* land snails, and it yielded two Late Acheulian bifaces (Hester and Hoebler 1969: 139). A radiocarbon date of >39,900 BP (I-2063) was obtained on a sample of marl from the middle of Tufa IIIa. Tufa IIIb yielded shells of *Melanoides* and *Pupoides coenopictus* (Leigh 1968: 513). None of these snails permits a detailed environmental reconstruction. Butzer and Hansen (1968: 376) correlate Tufas IIIa and IIIb with the lower sheet gravels and Wadi Tufa III (Lower Levalloisian) and IV (Upper Levalloisian) from the Refuf and Matana passes at Kharga; however, the associated archaeology indicates a correlation with Tufas I and II of Refuf Pass.

The investigations of Hester and Hoebler (1969:135) at Kurkur resulted in a different interpretation of the Tufa III sequence. Their excavations seem to indicate that Wadi Tufa IIIc of Butzer and Hansen is a downstream facies of Wadi Tufa IIIa.

At Dungul, the Tufa III complex composed of a series of conglomerate capped by an extensive tufa sheet is seen as similar to the Wadi Tufa III complex at Kurkur. Eolized Middle Paleolithic artifacts occur on the surface of Tufa III at Dungul (Hester and Hoebler 1969: 35).

The sequence of wadi tufas and gravels at Kharga suggests that each unit of gravel represents an initial period of increased wadi deposition in high-velocity streams, implying torrential discharge and relatively scarce vegetation,

followed by a period when fine clastic materials and carbonates were formed in ponds and slowly moving water, or springs. This differs considerably from the interpretation of the wadi tufas at Kurkur where all gravels, silts, marls, and tufas are seen to form integrated units and are attributed to facies changes. The presence of gravel complexes in the Kurkur foreland, apparently contemporaneous with Tufa IIIa/b units in the oasis, would seem to testify to the occurrence of torrential discharge and high stream carrying-capacity during at least some parts of this period; in Dungul the conglomerate depositions seem always to precede the formation of tufas.

The rather rich faunal and floral remains in the wadi tufa at Kharga (Gardner 1935) provide the best environmental evidence for the phases of reduced stream discharge and increased spring activity. Unfortunately, the reports on the faunal and floral collections from wadi tufas fail to specify their exact stratigraphic and chronological position, so the assemblages might represent the combined environments of Late and Final Acheulian, Mousterian, and Aterian depositions. However, Gardner noted that the richest faunal collection, and the one yielding most of the exotics, is from the silts below the lowest tufa, possibly of Final Acheulian age (Gardner 1935:495). Gardner notes three outstanding features of the molluscan fauna: (a) the poverty of genera represented, (b) the high proportion of land snails, and (c) the peculiar composition of the aquatic fauna (Gardner 1935:492). Of the 14 species represented among the land snails, half are paleoarctic. Around one-fourth today live farther south, and only one-fifth are present Egyptian forms. On the other hand, the aquatic snails, represented by 12 species, are entirely Egyptian except for one southern form. The presence of paleoarctic forms certainly indicates considerably cooler summer temperatures. A similar conclusion is suggested by the $^{18}O-^{16}O$ isotopic temperature determination on snail shells from the Kharga wadi tufa, done by Degens (1962), who suggested a mean annual temperature 6°C cooler than today. On the other hand, the presence of tropical forms would imply warmer winters than today, and thus the climate would have been more equable and with less seasonal variation than today. The presence of fig and hackberry indicates an annual rainfall of between 200 and 400 mm per year (Caton-Thompson 1952), considerably more than is received today in Egypt along the Mediterranean coast. If most of the exotic snail species can indeed be attributed to the tufas chronologically associated with a Final Acheulian, then the environmental reconstruction offered here will be valid for that period.

On both sides of the Nile, between Abu Simbel and Ineiba, are numerous gravel ridges of several generations standing more than 20 m above the Nubia sandstone floor. When seen from the air, the ridges appear as discontinuous meandering courses flowing toward the Nile. These inverted streambeds (Figure 6.1) were investigated in some detail by Giegengack (1968), who terms them *wadi conglomerate*. The observations made by Giegengack suggest the presence of many episodes of deposition and induration

FIGURE 6.1. *Aerial view of inverted wadis along the west bank of the Nile, north of Abu Simbel.*

by iron oxides. Despite an extensive search for associated archaeology, only half a dozen artifacts were found, including one handaxe of Late Acheulian appearance. Indirect sedimentary evidence led Giegengack to believe that these wadi conglomerates are younger than this oldest Nile unit, the early Nile gravels, which contained geologically *in situ* sites of Acheulian age. A description of the sites has not been published, but a preliminary statement by Kleindienst (in Giegengack 1968:77–79) attributes them to a non-Levallois Acheulian and, although not precisely placed, not one of its latest phases. Giegengack assigns the early Nile gravels to the Riss glaciation; the wadi conglomerate is regarded as early Würm, following a traditional theory that correlates African pluvials with European glaciation.

The chronological evidence as reported by Giegengack must be regarded as inconclusive. The association of archaeology with wadi conglomerate is not firmly established by the presence of one handaxe, which could have been introduced after deposition. In addition, it was not possible to demonstrate a direct stratigraphic relationship with the early Nile gravels, which themselves may represent several units.

Although we have not worked these inverted wadis, we feel that they probably date considerably before the Late Acheulian since the nearby extensive Late Acheulian site of Arkin 8 occurs *in situ* on the desert floor within sediments associated with a wadi of relatively modern morphology (Chmielewski 1968).

Fragments of similar inverted wadis were also seen on the slopes of Gebel Nabta, not far below its summit and high above the desert floor. These also failed to yield associated archaeology, but occasional Late Acheulian bifaces do occur in the same area on pediments that are lower than the inverted channels.

The morphology of the inverted wadis near the Nile indicates that considerable deflational changes have occurred since their deposition. The clearly meandering character of the wadis suggests a high base of erosion, a low gradient, and perhaps sufficient moisture to sustain perennial flow. This observation seems to be contradicted by the apparently high velocity of the streams that is indicated by the gravel-loaded beds. It seems likely, however, that the gravel remnants are in fact the highest-velocity portions of the main streams of the rivers and that the finer sediments are totally removed. The inverted wadis clearly need further investigation before their chronological, lithological, environmental, and stratigraphic status can be established.

Elsewhere in the Nile Valley, traces of a Late Acheulian with Levallois technology were found on and within old Nile silts near Dandara at Site E61O1, just north of Luxor (Wendorf and Schild 1976b: 97). Neither the silts nor the sites were investigated, but Said (1975:25) places the deposits within his Pre-Nile system as the Dandara silts. The early Nile gravels of Giegengack are identified by Said with the Idfu gravels of his Proto-Nile (1975:21). Here again, firm evidence is entirely lacking, although it is possible to infer that a Late Acheulian was contemporary with a Nile aggradation. Quite recently, between Assiut and Nag Hammadi, at Nag Ahmed Khalifa, a small assemblage of several bifaces and cleavers was found within the Nile gravels about 11 m above the modern floodplain. No Levallois technology is reported (Vermeersch *et al.* 1977: 124). It is impossible to relate these Acheulian-bearing deposits to any of the Acheulian episodes in the Western Desert.

It is evident that the climate during the Upper Acheulian was very complex, and included more than one period of aridity and intervening semiarid and moister phases. At least two such cycles and possibly more are indicated by the sequences at Bir Sahara–Bir Tarfawi, Kharga, Dungul, and Kurkur.

The evidence for paleoclimates of this time range elsewhere in the Sahara is very poor, and correlations can be based only on the typological identification of the associated archaeology, a process that is open to many objections. Despite this handicap, however, there are some data supporting moister climates in the time range preceding the Middle Paleolithic and contemporaneous with the Late to Final Acheulian.

In the central Sahara, extensive beds of lacustrine diatomaceous formations associated with Late Acheulian and rich fauna are reported from the Armadrar Plain at the foot of the Tassili Mountains (Arambourg 1948; Arambourg and Balout 1952; Reygasse 1935). The fauna contained white rhinoceros, *Elephas recki, Equus mauritanicus, Homoioceras antiquus, Alcelaphus bubalis,* and various antelopes. In total, the faunal assemblage appears to reflect savanna and lacustrine conditions.

At Adrar Bous, also in the central Sahara, Late Acheulian artifacts are associated with basal gravels at the Agorass n'Essoui lake depression, and both Levallois and non-Levallois Late Acheulian occur with loams and lacustrine sands of the level plains (Clark *et al.* 1973). No fauna is reported.

In the Saoura Basin in the northwestern Sahara, the Late Acheulian sites are associated with Ougartian VI, in particular with VIb, marked by a humid climate as indicated by the formation of small lakes in valleys and on the plateau. At the Anchal site (Mount Ougarta) an extensive Final Acheulian site was found in fine, lacustrine sands (Chavaillon 1964:151). Again no fauna is reported.

In the classic region of Morocco, Late Acheulian artifacts occur with the Tensiftian and Pre-Soltanian continental cycles, both characterized by a "Sudanese" type of fauna and the latter also by the arrival of the first paleoarctic elements (*Sus scrofa*) (Biberson 1961a, b; Freeman 1975; Jaeger 1975). The associated molluscan fauna indicates a temperate climate, cooler than today. Presumably, the Anfatian and Harounian transgressions are contemporaneous with late stages of Acheulian. It is not possible to correlate the age of the Late Acheulian moist phases in the Western Desert precisely with the Moroccan sequence because of the absence of absolute dating in both areas; however, the typological impression is that all of the Acheulian occurrences in the Western Desert could be quite close to Biberson's Stage VIII of Acheulian development and therefore could be placed somewhere close to the time range of the Harounian and Pre-Soltanian.

In Tunisia, the Acheulian site of Sidi Zin, near Kef, excavated by Gobert (1950), may be roughly compared to the Late Acheulian of the Western Desert of Egypt in general development but not in the details of tool taxonomy. Sidi Zin was covered by spring tufa deposits and contained a "Sudanese" faunal assemblage of a savanna type; a climatic inference similar to that in Morocco is suggested.

The existing evidence from the Sahara indicates a widespread humid episode contemporaneous with a Late and Final Acheulian. This episode was certainly multifaceted and characterized by at least two and possibly three humid pulsations separated by periods of aridity. The evidence for paleoclimates along the Mediterranean and Atlantic littorals during this time is inconclusive, and it is impossible to ascertain the exact correlation of the wet Late Acheulian periods in the Sahara with the transgressions of the sea. It is also impossible to determine whether the wet episodes in the southern and eastern belts of the Sahara were in phase with increased precipitation in the northern fringe of the desert. The moister episode of Ougartian VIb in the Saoura

Basin, associated with Final Acheulian, suggests that at least this event was synchronous in both areas.

A similar problem exists in comparisons with the Nile. With the data at hand it is impossible to establish whether a Late or Final Acheulian high siltation, and therefore Nile aggradation, is strictly contemporaneous with one of the recorded wet pulsations in the Western Desert; however, such a correlation seems likely, since similar events during the Holocene seem to be closely related.

From the preceding discussion it is evident that a variety of environments prevailed in the Egyptian Sahara during the period of the Late Acheulian. In some of the oases, such as Kharga, Dakhla, and Bir Sahara, the Late and Final Acheulian occur associated with spring pools. At Bir Tarfawi and in the central Sahara, the Late Acheulian occurs with lakes. Along the Nile at Arkin 8, in the Gilf el Kebir, at Kharga, and at Kurkur, Late and Final Acheulian sites are found along the banks of wadis. This evidence indicates that the local rainfall, which was responsible for the flow of the wadis, the emergence of the springs, and the formation of the lakes, must have been of considerable magnitude. Rainfall in more distant areas could not have produced all these phenomena. It is impossible to estimate the annual rate of local precipitation because of the lack of critical floral and faunal evidence; however, the megafauna (either zebra or wild ass and ostrich) and the invertebrate fauna suggest the presence of at least a grassland, with arboreal vegetation around localities with surface water and bushes and shrubs in the wadis. The occurrence of paleoarctic species of molluscs requires significantly cooler summer temperatures; the winters during this period seem to have been warmer than at present, thus producing a more equable year-round climate.

A wide variety of environments was present. The wadi bottoms and the areas around the lakes and spring ponds must have been quite wooded, possibly dominated by acacia, hackberry, fig, and palm. The flat areas of today's high desert were probably essentially Sahelian grasslands. The vegetation in the Nile Valley is likely to have been even more luxuriant than that found in the wadis, but there are no data available that would permit a detailed reconstruction.

EVIDENCE FOR MIDDLE PALEOLITHIC ENVIRONMENTS

A long and certainly hyperarid period separates the wet episode of the Late and Final Acheulian from the next wet cycle. The extent of hyperaridity is measured by the excavation of the deep deflational basins at Bir Sahara and Bir Tarfawi. The deflation of these basins required a lowering of the water table to a level below that of today.

The forerunner of the next wet cycle is the formation of phytogenic dunes in the lower portions of these depressions, indicating a rising water table, although prevailing conditions were still semiarid at best. The earliest known

Mousterian settlements are contemporaneous with this semidesert environment.

A further considerable rise in the water table led first to the formation of swamplike basins, and then to the development of relatively large lakes with well-aerated waters containing abundant plant life. This rising water table is seen as reflecting an increase in local rainfall. Even during the moist phase, however, fluctuations of the water table are evident, implying variations in the local rainfall. These are shown by the lithological character of the silts, which display erosional contacts and beds of burned sediments, caused by fires among the dry, near-shore vegetation, and also by the occurrence of Mousterian settlements within water-laid sediments.

The return of aridity is signaled by the formation of evaporites in dense vegetation and in algae growing in very shallow water, and by the appearance of eolian sediments interfingering with the evaporites. The cycle of aridity became more intense and a new hyperarid interval is recorded by the deflation of the earlier lake sediments at Bir Sahara and the excavation of the northern portion of the Bir Tarfawi basin. The record from Bir Tarfawi suggests that the water table must have again dropped to a level below that of today.

The next new wet period is once more heralded by the formation of phytogenic dunes in the bottoms of the basins, and the rising water table eventually results in the formation of lakes in both basins. Fluctuations in the water table are again indicated by several lithostratigraphic features. The formation of soil in the top of the lacustrine silts at Bir Sahara marks the end of this Aterian wet phase. Radiocarbon dates indicate an age for both the Mousterian and Aterian wet phases of greater than 40,000 years ago.

The faunas associated with the sediments of both wet periods recorded at Bir Sahara and Bir Tarfawi are closely similar, and this, together with the resemblances in lithology, suggests that basically similar environments prevailed during each period. The presence of white rhinoceros, extinct buffalo, *dama* and red-fronted gazelles, and extinct camel indicates a grassland. The red-fronted gazelle and camel, moreover, show that it was a dry savanna or steppe, perhaps an environment similar to that found today in central Sudan and Chad (Gautier, this volume). The warthog, on the other hand, is usually found in well-watered environments, and must therefore have been limited to the area in the immediate vicinity of the lakes. Such a reconstruction of the vegetation is perhaps too conservative. The occurrence of species preferring drier conditions (red-fronted gazelle and camel) together with those requiring a wetter and more wooded environment might indicate an environment similar to those found today south of the Sahel in the southern range of the red-fronted gazelle; still within the dry savanna belt, but with rainfall in excess of 400 mm per year and with extensive stands of acacia.

None of the invertebrates is indicative of a specific environment; all tolerate a wide range of environments and today are found in Egypt and in adjacent areas (Gautier, this volume). This invertebrate fauna differs significantly from the assemblages recovered from the wadi tufas at Kharga, which contained notable proportions of paleoarctic and tropical forms (Gardner 1935). Although the latter assemblages cannot be assigned to specific periods of deposition, some of them could well be contemporary with the Bir Sahara–Bir Tarfawi fauna, and some of the differences may be due to the microenvironments of small streams and pools fed by water originating on the high scarp. Most of the exotic forms at Kharga, however, are terrestrial, and the

fauna from Bir Sahara and Bir Tarfawi contains only a few land snails.

The modern geomorphology of the Bir Sahara–Bir Tarfawi sand plain indicates that only the depressions had water in abundance. Thus, reconstruction of the landscape would include more dry steppic plain, possibly wooded with acacia, with more luxuriant, nonarboreal vegetation present only during and after the seasonal rains. The basins, on the other hand, undoubtedly enjoyed a lusher vegetation characterized by the presence of deciduous trees and woodlands.

This record and the succession of events at Bir Sahara–Bir Tarfawi are unique and the most explicit in their environmental significance. The enclosed basins associated with the Middle Paleolithic elsewhere in the Western Desert provide some further evidence for local rainfall, and for the occasional presence of water within the basins. However, most of the deposits in these Middle Paleolithic basins have been destroyed by deflation, and the intensity and extent of sedimentation in the basins therefore cannot be evaluated. Nevertheless, there is no doubt that the landscape in the areas of the small, internal drainage basins was different from that of today and from that which prevailed at the same time as the Bir Sahara and Bir Tarfawi sand plain. The basins were obviously temporary reservoirs of water or moisture, providing a prolonged water supply for both flora and fauna well beyond the rainfall season, and in this respect they were probably quite similar to the small basins found today in the African dry savanna belt.

As with Late Acheulian, the appearance of new spring pools in the oases indicates a recharging of the subterranean water reservoir, and sediments again forming in the wadis. The spring vents of Kharga and Dakhla do not yield evidence for the twofold character of the Middle Paleolithic wet phase documented at Bir Sahara and Bir Tarfawi; however, changes in lithology of the Aterian spring at Site E-76-4 at Kharga do suggest fluctuations in the activity of these artesian wells, an observation also noted by Caton-Thompson (1952:8) and Gardner.

The character of the archaeological remains in the spring vents at Kharga does not permit a reliable chronological subdivision of the Middle Paleolithic springs. Basically, Mousterian and Aterian assemblages cannot be distinguished except by the presence of pedunculates or biface foliates in the latter, and the sometimes low frequencies of these Aterian tools prevent a firm distinction when samples are small. Consequently, the lack of Aterian elements in the "Levalloisian" spring of KO8A (Caton-Thompson 1952: 73) cannot be considered as absolute evidence for its pre-Aterian age. Caton-Thompson, nevertheless, recognized two and possibly three ages of spring activity: Levalloisian (Site KO8A), Aterian (Site KO6E), and ? Epi-Levalloisian (Site KO5) (Caton-Thompson 1952: 9).

A much more complex sequence is seen by Caton-Thompson for the deposition of wadi sediments. Two tufa terraces (III and IV) are assigned to the Lower and Upper Levalloisian; a period of erosion separates these from the

Levalloiso-Khargan wadi gravels; and another, minor erosion is believed to occur between the Levalloiso-Khargan wadi gravels and a period of Aterian wadi siltation. This sequence was developed from observations made at many different localities, but in only one instance does an Aterian floor occur stratigraphically above a Levalloiso-Khargan assemblage (Site Bulaq A), and this is within a single 7-m wadi terrace. The occurence of both assemblages in the same terrace prevents their assignation into two separate, major climatic events. Our impression of the Levalloiso-Khargan and Khargan is that of a Middle Paleolithic industry with a high frequency of naturally retouched pieces. It is quite possible, however, that this complex might be composed of Mousterian assemblages of unknown taxonomic affiliations.

The floral and faunal remains from the wadi tufas at Kharga that were discussed in the previous section on Late Acheulian environments may also include species from the wadi tufas associated with the Middle Paleolithic. The climatic inferences given for the Late Acheulian may therefore apply to this period as well.

Caton-Thompson (1952:28) also reports the presence of small basins, both on the adjacent plateau and on tufas along the scarp, which are associated with Aterian and Khargan. Some of these small basins are over 3 m deep and contain fine silts and sands. They are clearly analogous to the Middle Paleolithic sand pans in the high desert.

Within the Kharga depression, the Middle Paleolithic is not only associated with spring vents, but also seems to occur embedded in the water-laid sediments such as those between Sites E-76-6 and E-76-7. The remnants of this complex series of gravels are too limited for an evaluation of the environment and dynamics of the system. It is certainly composed of several channels, but its stratigraphic and chronological relationships with the Middle Paleolithic springs are unknown.

At Kurkur some of the younger wadi gravels and tufas reported by Butzer and Hansen (1968) may belong to this period. None of them has a clear association with archaeology. A radiocarbon date of > 39,900 BP (I-2064) was obtained on marl from the middle of Bed B of Tufa III (Butzer and Hansen 1968:377). A "Khargan" industry is reported from the surface of Tufa IV (Hester and Hoebler 1969:140), and there is another date of 31,800 BP ± 70-0 years (I-2062) obtained on calcite crust from the top of Tufa IV. A denticulate also was found in the gravel bed assigned to this complex (Butzer and Hansen 1968: 378). Tufa III is a complex series of gravel and silt deposits capped by dark brown tufa, and Khargan tools are reported by Hester and Hoebler (1969: 137) as occurring on the surface of this tufa. It is certain that the dates from these tufas are too late, and the samples presumably were contaminated by more recent carbonates.

As was the case with the Late Acheulian, the wadi tufas in all these oases display closely similar patterns of sedimentation, including gravels, silts, and sands that are usually cemented or capped by tufaceous, carbonaceous formations, or both. Although there is variability among these sediments, some of which can be explained by changes in facies, the overall impression is that it is the environment responsible for the formation of tufas that always closes the cycle. The gravels and unsorted sands represent high-velocity currents, and the marls, silts, and fine sands were deposited in ponds with quiet, stagnant water, an indication further documented by the accompanying molluscan fauna (Butzer and Hansen 1968:377; Leigh 1968:514). The exact environment responsible for the tufa caps, however, cannot be reconstructed. Various possibilities are suggested (Butzer and Hansen 1968:385), including surface washing by lime-charged water and deposition in shallow pools with abundant vegetation. It should be noted that the tufas have a variety of physical appearances and thus may record differing environmental situations. The fact that the wadi cycles are almost always terminated by the formation of tufas and followed by a cycle of downcutting is certainly of environmental significance.

The sequence at Bir Sahara and Bir Tarfawi indicated considerable complexity for the two Middle Paleolithic wetter periods, each being composed of several pulsations. It is tempting to propose that the wadi beds in the oases also reflect the same complexities in the variability of their sediments. However, the wadi sediments have not been examined extensively enough to determine if this is so. Indeed, it is not even established that these tufas are of Middle Paleolithic age, although this seems most likely.

In the Nile Valley, most of the known early Middle Paleolithic sites occur on the tops of inselbergs or embedded within sediments away from the Nile channel. It is therefore impossible to infer the behavior of the Nile during most of this period. Only one early Middle Paleolithic site (440) occurred in stratigraphic relationship with Nile sediments. It was located in the Khor Musa in the Second Cataract (de Heinzelin 1968: atlas Figure 15; Wendorf and Schild 1976b:237). There, two Middle Paleolithic living floors occurred in a dune both underlain and overlain by Nile silts and gravels. The relatively poor assemblages included a bifacial foliate, thus implying an Aterian age (Shiner 1968c; 637). Charcoal from the upper layer gave a date of 14,340 BP ± 500 years (WSU-290), which is undoubtedly too recent. Mammalian remains were most frequent in the lower level and fish dominated the upper (Shiner 1968c: 634). The materials included 48 identified fragments of wild cattle (*Bos primigenius*), 2 pieces of red-fronted gazelle (*G. rufifrons*), and 1 fragment each from a wild ass (*Equus asinus africanus*), and hippopotamus (*H. amphibius*) (Gautier 1968: 98). A variety of fish were present: *Clarias, Bagrus, Synodotis, Barbus* ?, *Tilapia*, and *Lates*, all typical modern Nilotic forms (Greenwood 1968: 109).

The nearby environment beyond the floodplain of the Nile Valley during the time of these two settlements cannot be determined either from the lithology or from the faunal assemblages. It has not been established whether the dune was of local, fluviatile origin, or was of blown-in, low desert sands. The faunal assemblage points to a dry, open, arid grassland to a light wooded landscape (Gautier 1968:97); however, this may refer only to the floodplain and wadi mouth environments of the Nile Valley. The archaeology and other available data do not permit a direct correlation of the events at the site with the sequence established at Bir Sahara and Bir Tarfawi. It could be presumed that the site is chronologically closer to the Aterian episode, although whether it precedes, dates within, or postdates the lake episode at Bir Tarfawi cannot be established. In any event, the Nile at the time of these settlements in the Khor Musa was very low, possibly similar to the modern level. The overlying silts that indicate a Nile aggradation are also of unknown age, but a Late Middle Paleolithic site (Khormusan industry) is found nearby within apparently similar silts.

During the Late Middle Paleolithic several sites classified as Khormusan (Marks 1968b:315) occur with high silts marking a Nile aggradation (Sites 1017, ANW-3, and 2004), or at the edge of the valley in eolian sands derived from the low desert and covered by high silts (Sites 34, Industry A, and 34, Industry D). Although initially regarded as Late Paleolithic, largely because of two radiocarbon dates ranging between 21,000 and 18,000 BP, the Khormusan is technologically and typologically Middle Paleolithic. The radiocarbon chronology has recently been revised by rerunning one of the initial samples and adding two new dates. The rerun of the remaining portion of the processed WSU-203 sample from Site 1017 dated > 36,750 BP ± 3350 years (SMU-245) (Wendorf and Schild 1976b: 239. Charcoal from another Khormusan site excavated by the University of Colorado gave a date of > 36,000 BP (GXO-409) (Irwin et al. 1968). Finally, a sample of charcoal from Site 34, Industry D, regarded by Marks as one of the most recent Khormusan sites, dated > 41,490 BP (SMU-107).

The silts and sands in which the Khormusan sites occur cannot be closely correlated with the sequence at Bir Sahara and Bir Tarfawi. The taxonomic classification of the archaeology is clearly different from either Mousterian or Aterian. Although it cannot be directly established, it seems likely that the silts covering Site 440 are contemporaneous with the silts at the same elevation in which the Khormusan assemblage of Site 1017 occurs, located about 1 km away. These high silts were previously regarded as representing the Dibeira-Jer Formation (de Heinzelin 1968); a unit now seen as much more complex (Wendorf and Schild 1976b).

Abundant faunal remains occur with three of the Khormusan sites. All of them are again dominated by *Bos primigenius*, whose frequency fluctuates between 80 and 85% of all identifiable bones. It is of interest that the high frequency of *Bos* in the lower level at Site 440 and in the Khormusan is unique in the Nile Valley. Though the details of the environment cannot be reconstructed, it is likely that the high siltation of the Khormusan is contemporaneous with relative aridity in the low and high desert. This is suggested by the presence of low desert dunes during this

period at Site 34, and by the absolute confinement of Khormusan settlements to the floodplain of the river.

The picture emerging from these limited data is an unstable river regimen with certainly more than one period of high siltation and aggradation, and one episode of recession. The period of high siltation is possibly younger than the Aterian wet phase at Bir Tarfawi, but the level of the Nile during both of the wet phases at Bir Sahara and Bir Tarfawi is really not known.

In the Chad basin numerous exposures of lacustrine sediments indicate the presence of an extensive series of lakes (sometimes referred to as the Aterian Lakes), which may be contemporaneous with either one or both of the Bir Sahara–Bir Tarfawi wet periods. The exact chronology of these lakes is not well established, but the estimated ages are between 40,000 and 20,000 BC (Conrad 1969, 1972; Fauré 1966; Maley 1976; Pias 1970; Rognon and Williams 1977; Servant 1973). There is no direct association of this lacustrine period with the Aterian, but such is inferred from the distribution of Aterian cultural material (Hugot 1966).

Lake Chad itself was hydrologically connected with the intertropical drainage zone, which certainly contributed to its high stand. There were, however, numerous isolated lakes in the Chad basin, in Nigeria, and in Mauritania that required considerable local rainfall. No published data are available on the environment of these lakes, but several radiocarbon dates seem to be associated with their sediments. During this period a shallow lacustrine series is reported overlying deep eolian sands at about 15°N. The radiocarbon dates obtained from these lake sediments fall between 38,000 and 41,000 BP (Servant and Servant-Vildary 1972:87). A supposedly more recent lacustrine series is reported from the Bahr el Ghazal area, with five radiocarbon dates on limestone ranging from 30,000 to 22,000 BP (Servant and Servant-Vildary 1972:88).

In the Adrar Bous of the central Sahara, Clark and others (1973:264) report an early Middle Stone Age industry with Levallois technology *in situ* in olive green calcareous loams, obviously of lacustrine origin. In the same area Aterian artifacts are associated with a sequence of sediments that seem to indicate a drier period with some eolian activity, although the depressions were still filled with water and swamp (Clark et al. 1973:265).

In the lacustrine depression at the border of the Armadrar Plain, on the footslopes of the Tassili Mountains within the Erg Tihodaine, extensive Aterian sites appear to be associated with the lacustrine littoral, but no artifacts were seen embedded in lake sediments (Arambourg and Balout 1952:285).

In the western part of the central Sahara, in the Erg Chech, extensive beds of lacustrine sediments with ostracods are reported. Aterian is said to be associated with these lacustrine sediments (J. Chavaillon 1964:195; N. Chavaillon 1973: Figure 4). There are three radiocarbon dates believed to belong with the late Pleistocene lake formations of this erg, although their relationship with the archaeology is unknown. The oldest of these, on calcareous sandstone with ostracods, is 24,200 BP ± 630 years (I-2375). The second date, on calcareous tufa, is 17,700 BP ± 290 years (I-2376), and the third, much younger, on limestone, is 10,100 BP ± 200 years (I-1645) (Conrad 1969: 445–446).

In the same general area, the basin of Ahnet–Mouydir contains extensive and thick late Pleistocene lake sediments. Here, no associated archaeology has been reported but there are three radiocarbon dates, all from one section and all on shells of *Cardium*. The uppermost sample dated 35,500 BP ± 2300–1800 years (I-1817). The middle sample, collected about 2 m lower in the section, gave a date of 18,800 BP ± 400 years (I-1779). The lowest sample, taken more than 4 m below the upper one, dated 33,700 BP + 4300–2700 years (I-1649) (Conrad 1972:346–348).

Farther west toward the coast, in inland Mauritania, a lacustrine transgression is reported in the *sebkha* of Chemchane from which calcareous nodules were radiocarbon dated at around 23,000 BP (Beaudet *et al.* 1976: 164).

In the northwest Sahara, in the Saoura Basin, the Aterian occurs in numerous surface and subsurface sites and embedded in secondary position within the lower sediments of the Saouran alluvial complex (N. Chavaillon 1971, 1973). The most common lithologic associations of the redeposited Aterian are the sandy alluvia of the Saouran II, but the true chronological position is believed to be within the end of the Saouran erosional period and the very beginning of the Saouran accumulation sequence (J. Chavaillon 1964: 195). Two radiocarbon dates are reported to be associated with the beginning or the early part of the Saouran accumulation in the middle Saoura valley. The first date, on "peaty sand" at Bou Hadid, is > 39,900 BP (I-1787), and the second, from slightly higher in the sequence at the same locality, is > 38,000 BP (I-1761). At El Ouata, two other radiocarbon dates are reported from a section believed to be slightly later in the Saouran accumulation. *Limnea* shells from a freshwater limestone layer gave a date of 33,900 BP ± 1900 years (DF-143, T-428). Higher in the section another sample of *Limnea* shells dated 32,700 BP ± 1700 years (DF-143, T-429) (Conrad 1969: 445; 1972: 343–349).

Several pollen spectra have been obtained from the Saouran alluvial complex. Initially these samples were regarded as promising indicators of the climate during the period (Butzer 1971b: 349–387), but research in modern pollen rain in the Sahara indicates that considerable caution should be used in the interpretation of fossil pollen spectra (Schulz 1976; Van Campo 1975). The pollen spectra from the lacustrine sediments of the Saouran alluvia contain no tropical elements and are predominantly composed of sub-Mediterranean and Mediterranean desertic taxa with some temperate and Mediterranean elements. This suggests a climatic deterioration in comparison with preceding periods (Beucher 1972:11).

Beyond the Sahara on the Mediterranean littoral of the Maghreb, information concerning past vegetation comes from the two Mousterian and one Aterian sites at El Guet-

tar, Wadi Akarit, and Wadi Djouf el Djemel. Pollen analysis of a sample from the lower layer at El Guettar, south Tunisia, shows a complete lack of xerophytic vegetation and a predominance of green oak. The next two higher layers, on the other hand, contain the first indications of the arrival of xerophytes (*Ephedra*) on the plain, and the presence of cedar and juniper woodland in the hills. All three layers are Mousterian. Still higher in the section, the pollen spectra indicate that the arboreal vegetation totally disappeared from the area. The cultural association of this upper layer is unknown, but it is certainly post-Mousterian and is believed to be of an Upper Paleolithic character (Gruet 1955b, 1958–1959; Leroi-Gourham 1957; Van Campo 1958; Van Campo and Coque 1960).

At Wadi Akarit, near the Mediterranean littoral, pollen from the middle layer of the "gray clays," associated with the richest Mousterian industry at that site, shows the presence of numerous herbs and grasses, indicating a steppic environment with tamarisk bushes and rare Mediterranean trees (Camps 1974a: 48–51; Van Campo and Coque 1960), conditions generally similar to those of today.

The Aterian site of Djouf el Djemel did not yield pollen, but it did contain charcoal of the diamorphic ash tree (*Fraxinus xanthoxyloides*), and this is believed to indicate a more humid and colder climate (Balout 1955).

The coastal area of North Africa has yielded a number of Middle Paleolithic sites with abundant fauna. These sites appear to represent two major taxonomic units, both within the same technocomplex but distinguished by the presence of pedunculates and bifacial foliates in one of them (the Aterian). Weak stratigraphic evidence suggests that the Aterian is the more recent. The key locality for this is the cave of Taforalt in eastern Morocco where a Middle Paleolithic layer without pedunculates or bifacial foliates occurs at the base of the Middle Paleolithic sequence (Roche 1972, 1976). Also, in the cave of Mugharet el 'Aliya there is a suggestion of a Levallois Mousterian preceding an Aterian (Howe 1967). Unfortunately, there are only a few good, non-Aterian, Middle Paleolithic assemblages from the Maghreb, and the best of these, such as Jebel Irhoud in Morocco and Retaimia in Algeria, are poorly known (Balout 1965; Dalloni 1955; Ennouchi 1966). Only one of these non-Aterian Middle Paleolithic sites is dated and this is Jebel Irhoud, which gave a date of 32,000 BP (NY-72) (Ennouchi 1966).

Several Middle Paleolithic sites have been found associated with beach features along the Mediterranean and Atlantic coasts. At Mugharet el 'Aliya, in Tangiers, sediments containing traces of a Levalloiso-Mousterian type of industry and some possible Aterian elements are believed to be contemporaneous with a sea level of +5 m (Howe 1967; Stearns 1967). Several Aterian occurrences are reported to be connected with marine sediments of the classic Tipasa–Tenes belt of undeformed shoreline at about +5 m (Hey 1971). At Camp Franchet, near Algiers, fresh Middle Paleolithic artifacts believed to be Aterian but lacking the diagnostic tools of that industry are found embedded in the top section of the indurated beach sediments containing *Strombus* shells, close to the modern sea level (Camps 1955: 22). The artifacts are believed to be later than the beach and to have been worked down into the sediments before they became indurated. Also, in the same area, at Karouba, Roubet (1947, 1966) reported Aterian artifacts in a similar beach. Marine shells from a sediment believed to be equivalent to the basal portion of this beach gave a Th/U date of 140,000 BP ± 10,000 years (Roubet 1972; Stearns and Thurber 1965). It should be noted, however, that the connection between the dated sample and the Aterian beach has not been established. At other localities in this same general area west of Algiers, Aterian occurs in reddish colluvial sediments above beach features believed to be equivalent to that at Karouba (Roubet 1972). There is a radiocarbon date on shells from one of these Aterian sites of 31,800 BP ± 1900 years (I-3951) (Hebrard 1970).

The Mediterranean beach sequence is extremely complicated and far from being understood. However, it seems likely that these beaches are relatively late within the Neo-Tyrrhenian transgression, which is now believed to be contemporaneous with deep-sea cycle number 5 and the most recent of the Eemian transgressions (Butzer 1975).

Several radiocarbon dates are reported from Aterian contexts. At the caves of Dar es Soltan, Morocco, there are two dates; charcoal from the upper layer gave a date of 27,000 BP (UCLA-678B), whereas the lower layer is dated at 30,000 BP (UCLA-378A). In the cave of Taforalt, *Helix* shells from the top of the Aterian level dated 32,370 BP + 1890–2470 years (Gif-2276) (Roche 1976:158). Another date of 34,550 BP is reported from the Aterian level in the same cave (Camps 1974b).

At the cave of Contrebandiers (Temara), in Morocco, there are four radiocarbon dates, all on bone. These range from 24,500 BP ± 600 years (Gif-2582) from Layer 11 (the lowest) to 12,320 BP ± 400 years (Gif-2580) from Layer 10. In this instance, the dated samples may have been contaminated by later admixture from the overlying occupation, and the dates are regarded as too recent.

At the site of Ain Maarouf in western Morocco, *Limnea* shells from a terrace with an Aterian level near the top gave a date of 32,000 BP ± 600 years (GrN-3165) (Choubert *et al.* 1967:435).

Significant faunal remains have been reported from many of these Middle Paleolithic sites in the Maghreb (Balout 1955; Camps 1974a; Vaufrey 1955). The collections represent a variety of physiographic situations, but the available data do not permit a statistical evaluation that might reflect the differing environmental situations. In general, the fauna has a clear Ethiopian savanna-type character, with *Homoioceras antiquus, Connochoetes taurinus, Alcelaphus buselaphus, Gazella atlantica,* and *Equus mauritanicus* as the most common and present in almost all sites. Several paleoarctic species also occur: *Bos primigenius, Megaceroides algericus, Rhinoceros mercki,* and the wild boar *Sus scrofa,* all of which seem to be adapted to a variety of environments.

Other indications of past climates during the Mousterian and Aterian periods in this area have been inferred from cave sediments at Mugharet el Aliya (Stearns 1967). A series of calcareous crusts and rubified sediments are seen as reflecting alternating cool and warm humid climates. Here a Levallois Mousterian (?) postdates the formation of a thick stalagmitic layer, and this in turn is followed by the rubification of the sediments, a process regarded as an indication of a warmer and more humid climate. The earliest Aterian in this cave occurs on the rubified surface and is covered by a calcareous crust over which another layer of "full Aterian" is deposited. The calcareous crust is believed to represent a cool phase of Würm, and the lowermost stalagmite is seen as the maximum coolness corresponding to an early Weichsel (Stearns 1967:34).

Undoubtedly these Middle Paleolithic occurrences in the Maghreb cover a large span of time and a variety of environments. In general it seems to be colder and more humid, although the pollen assemblages in some instances suggest relative aridity.

Farther east along the Mediterranean coast, at Hajj Creiem in Cyrenaica, beach deposits are overlain by a series of wadi tufas with Levalloiso-Mousterian artifacts. Above the tufas are alluvial sediments with artifacts of Middle Paleolithic character (McBurney 1975; McBurney and Hey 1955).

The nearby cave of the Haua Fteah contained an impressive sequence of Middle Paleolithic occupations. Using oxygen isotopic data, mammalian fauna, and the sedimentology of the cave deposits, McBurney (1967, 1975) associates the earliest Levalloiso-Mousterian (Layer XXXIV) with a temperate climate. The overlying layers (XXXII to XXVIII) are seen as reflecting a short period with a cold climate. Above this there is a brief return to temperate conditions and then a maximum cold. The last is believed to represent the main Würm (McBurney 1967: 28; 1975:419). All these layers are seen as Levalloiso-Mousterian, although a single bifacial foliate suggests the possible presence of Aterian (McBurney 1967:139). Throughout the Levalloiso-Mousterian complex, and in contrast to most of the following Upper Paleolithic Dabban culture, the fauna is dominated by large bovids. There are two radiocarbon dates on charcoal from the Levalloiso-Mousterian layers in Haua Fteah. The lowest sample dated 47,000 BP ± 3200 years (GrN-2023), and the second dated 43,400 BP ± 1300 years (GrN-2564).

Summary of the Middle Paleolithic

The problem of chronology is obviously critical to an adequate understanding of the Middle Paleolithic in North Africa. Without proper dating it is impossible to see the extent and duration of the environmental changes, and their chronological relationship with other areas. In the Middle Paleolithic the only certain thing is that at some time or times during this period some areas of the Sahara were receiving more precipitation than today. A relatively large number of radiocarbon dates places significant lacustrine sedimentation in the vicinity of 30,000 years ago and others around 20,000 years ago. Theoretically, these dates can be considered contemporaneous with those few obtained in the same time range for both Mousterian and Aterian assemblages in North Africa.

This conclusion, however, is not acceptable in the light of some of the radiocarbon dates and the enormous time depth indicated for the total Middle Paleolithic development in the Nile valley and the Western desert, where the youngest of the taxonomic–time units, the Khormusan, is apparently more than 40,000 years old. Furthermore, if we accept the tentative evidence linking a Middle Paleolithic, possibly Aterian, with undisturbed Mediterranean beaches of the Tipasa–Ténès belt of Algeria, it cannot be later than the last of the Tyrrhenian transgressions. According to both Th/U dates and age estimates based on uniform sedimentation rates, this event cannot possibly be younger than about 80,000 years ago and could easily be considerably older (Butzer 1975; Shackleton 1975; Stearns, 1970).

The evaluation of many of the radiocarbon dates from North Africa is a geochemical problem that as yet has not received adequate attention. The magnitude of this problem is well illustrated by the series of dates obtained at Bir Sahara and Bir Tarfawi, where only the slightest traces of carbonates or even brief surface exposure are seen to affect the dates obtained significantly. It is believed that the age of these sediments is beyond the reach of present radiocarbon technology; and those samples where carbonate contamination could be reduced to a minimum gave dates confirming this age estimate. It therefore seems reasonable to reject all absolute dates for the earliest reported lacustrine sediments of Chad, Erg Chech, Saoura, the lowlands of Ahnet, Chemchane, and the several absolute dates on the Aterian. The older absolute dates from Haua Fteah present a problem because they are both on charcoal. Perhaps they should be regarded as minimal for this period.

The available environmental data pose a similar problem. With the data at hand the fauna cannot be statistically evaluated and related to the microenvironments of the sites. Even if this were possible, the absence of a firm, relative, chronological placement prevents any deduction concerning environmental changes through time. In the absence of chronological controls, a series of long, local sequences providing environmental data could serve as a basis for such a reconstruction; but, with the possible exception of El Guettar, the existing data are inadequate beyond banal observations that it was wetter and/or cooler.

Seen from the perspective of the sequence at Bir Sahara and Bir Tarfawi, it is possible to hypothesize that some of the southern and central Saharan lakes are Middle Paleolithic in age and probably represent more than one moist fluctuation. It is impossible to establish whether these wet phases in the southern and central Sahara are contemporaneous with an increase in precipitation in the northern belt. The fauna appear to be closely similar except for the lack of several paleoarctic forms in the Bir Sahara–Bir Tarfawi and Nile Valley areas, but this may be due to sampling errors.

The relationship between the fluctuations in the level of the Nile and the high lake stands in the Western Desert cannot be determined. At this stage of research, therefore, it is impossible to establish whether local precipitation was in phase with a high Nile or not. These questions could be resolved by a special program of studies of the Nile and related wadi sediments of this age, but such is yet to be done. We are inclined to believe, but cannot properly demonstrate, that the high lake levels in the Sahara resulting from local rainfall were caused by a northward shift of the monsoonal summer rain. This hypothesis would agree with the observation at Bir Tarfawi that the better developed wave beach features are on the northern portion of the lake, supposedly a result of strong southerly winds. If this area was indeed well within the monsoonal belt, then strong seasonal variations in precipitation also could be inferred. This would strongly affect both animal and human populations.

─ENVIRONMENT DURING THE POST-ATERIAN HYPERARID INTERVAL─

The firm evidence from the Bir Sahara–Bir Tarfawi area indicates that a long and pronounced period of increased eolian activity and a hyperarid rainless environment followed immediately after the Aterian lake and continued until the early Holocene. Nowhere in the Western Desert is there any evidence for significantly increased precipitation, spring activity, or even the presence of human occupation that might be related to the time span between the Middle Paleolithic and the Terminal Paleolithic.

The geochemical problems involved in the radiocarbon dates for the Middle Paleolithic discussed previously are also applicable here. It is for this reason that we reject the dates on Tufa IV in Kurkur and Dungul, as well as those that seem to indicate the presence of lacustrine episodes around 20,000 years ago in the Chad basin, Erg Chech, Ahnet, and Sebkha Chemchane.

It was formerly believed that several episodes of aggradation occurred in the Nile Valley during this period. Two of these were the Ballana–Masmas and the Sahaba–Darau aggradations, dating 26,000 to 17,000 BP and 15,000 to 12,000 BP, respectively (Wendorf and Schild 1976b). The initial separation of this event into two separate aggradations originated in Sudanese Nubia and was based largely on radiocarbon dates that have been shown to be in error (the Khormusan, once regarded as dating about 19,000 to 17,000 BP, is now dated earlier than 40,000 years ago). Farther north, near Isna and Idfu, the evidence was less conclusive, but despite this, the original subdivision was followed (Wendorf and Schild 1976b). Recent extensive excavations and accompanying geological and radiocarbon research in the large mouth of Wadi Kubbaniya, on the west bank below Aswan, suggest major revisions of this scheme. It is believed that the over-20-m-thick suite of Quaternary sediments in the mouth of this wadi records the significant events in the Nile Valley chronologically placed between about 19,000 and 10,000 BP. The whole section consists of Nile silts, vertisols, dune sediments, and lacustrine deposits, the latter formed in blocked seepage ponds. There appears to be no major break in the sequence of rising Nile silts throughout this period; thus, only a single major aggradation is postulated for this time span. The aggradation is strictly contemporaneous with pronounced eolian activity throughout, with constant dune accumulation in the wadi mouth, proceeding from the northern escarpment, and ultimately blocking the wadi. At no point did the wadi contribute any sediments to the sequence, nor is there evidence for a pronounced decline of the Nile until after 10,000 years ago. There may well have been minor fluctuations within this long aggradational event, but they were of no consequence.

It is difficult to explain the dynamic processes in the sedimentation of this episode of Nile aggradation. It would seem logical to expect heavy rains in the headwaters of the Nile during the periods of silt accumulation; however, the available evidence suggests low or very low lake levels for several millenia prior to 11,000 BP in East Africa (Butzer et al. 1972; Gasse 1976:203).

There is, however, evidence for wadi activity during the periods of silt accumulation, observed exclusively on the east bank of the river. One of these is in southern Egyptian Nubia where five separate wadi gravel intrusions occur in an otherwise monotonous siltation (Giegengack 1968). Slightly farther north, at Kom Ombo, the first phase of the Ineiba wadi formation is believed to be contemporaneous with the Sahaba-Darau silts. Still farther north, in the Dishna area, and still on the east bank, wadi sediments are interstratified at the base of massive Sahaba–Darau silts. No evidence for wadi activity was observed with the earlier phase, the Ballana–Masmas aggradation. The evidence for wadi activity suggests that the Red Sea Hills were receiving some rain during this period. None of the wadis along the west bank of the Nile seems to have been active.

On the west bank of the Nile eolian phenomena are seen throughout this period of the last final Pleistocene aggradation. They are present in the form of massive dune fields interfingering with silts in the area between Isna and Armant in Upper Egypt (Wendorf and Schild 1976b), at Ballana (Wendorf 1968:791–855), as well as at Kubbaniya.

The atmospheric circulation responsible for this situation is not known, but it is possible that the rains over the Red Sea Hills were a result of the movement of depressions along the Red Sea during the winter. These are believed to result in turn from the occurrence of discontinuities between adjacent high-pressure cells, meridional heat exchanges, and inland movement of moist unstable air (De

Planhol and Rognon 1970; Rognon and Williams 1977: 293). Such circulation, typical for a hyperarid period, occurs today and is responsible for the occasional heavy rains over the Red Sea Hills.

This hyperarid period in the Western Desert is reported from a broad belt of sub-Saharan Africa as a desertic episode expressed in greatly increased eolian activity, the formation and movement of dunes, and deforestation. In some instances, it is believed that the desert shifted southward from 4 to 5°, or around 500 km below its southern boundary today (Beaudet et al. 1976: 158). During that time in the Chad basin, eolian sands and dunes formed over lacustrine sediments (Servant and Servant-Vildary 1972: 88), and the second erg formed (Pias 1970:297). Throughout the Sahara the lakes seem to disappear (Chamard 1973a and 1973b; Rognon, 1976). In Mali and Niger the red dunes of Ogolian formed a continuous belt (Beaudet et al. 1976; Michel et al. 1968), and the basin of the White Nile was invaded by dunes (Williams and Adamson 1974). The abundant evidence for this hyperarid period in sub-Saharan Africa has been synthesized by Rognon and Williams (1977).

Other evidence for an increased aridity comes from deep-sea cores off the West African coast, which recorded an increase in windblown sand (Parmenter and Folger 1974). Another series of cores from the Red Sea and the Gulf of Aden displays changes in foraminifera, which are believed to indicate, indirectly, conditions of aridity (Deuser et al. 1976).

Climatic evidence from the Maghreb and the Mediterranean littoral of Africa is practically nonexistent for this interval. After the Aterian the area seems not to have been occupied except for the Cyrenaican coast, and possibly El Guettar, until the Iberomaurusian, the earliest of which is dated around 20,000 BP (Roche 1976:156). Even for the Iberomaurusian the climatic indications are inconclusive. The fauna is abundant but cosmopolitan in this geographic situation. In the Maghreb, in only one site, Tamar Hat, are the relative frequencies of the fauna available and here the most common species is the Barbary sheep (Ammotragus lervia) (Saxon et al. 1974). The other species common with the Iberomaurusian are zebra (Equus mauritanicus), and large antelopes, particularly the hartebeest (Alcelaphus buselaphus), together with the common predators, such as lion, hyena, and jackal. Rhinoceros and extinct buffalo (Homoioceras antiquus) are rare. Three paleoarctic species are also noted. These are brown bear, present in all cave sites, a large deer [Cervus (megaceroides) algericus], and small Barbary deer (Cervus elaphus barbarus) (Camps 1974a: 90).

Floral remains accompanying the Iberomaurusian are known from five sites only and are defined on the basis of charcoal and some pollen studies (Camps 1974a). The forms identified include nine deciduous species and six conifers. Of these, two, the black pine (Pinus nigra laricio) and cedar (Cedrus atlantica) are considered as indicators of a cooler climate on the Algerian littoral because they presumably occur only at much higher elevations, above 1400 m.

The climatic implication of black pine has been questioned by Couvert (1969) and is explained as selection through human activity, even though the site on which this was based lies at a very low altitude (about 20 m) (Saxon *et al.* 1974).

In the same site (Tamar Hat) the oxygen isotopic analysis of edible shells (*Monodonta turbinata*) gave an inkling of climatic fluctuation in the form of a warm pulsation in Layers 15 to 31. There is a radiocarbon date from Layer 15 of 17,040 BP ± 400 years (MC-812) (Saxon *et al.* 1974:50).

In Cyrenaica there is a long sequence of isotopic temperature readings on shells from the Haua Fteah in the layers assigned to the Dabban culture and the Eastern Oranian, the latter a local equivalent of the Iberomaurusian. For the Dabban, an Upper Paleolithic industry that is dated at another cave (Hagfet Ed Dabba) as beginning around 40,000 years ago, the temperature indicated a cooling phase at the beginning, leading into a colder period. Unfortunately, the record is not continuous, but in the succeeding layers, assigned to the Eastern Oranian beginning around 18,000 years ago (Saxon *et al.* 1974: 50), the indicated temperatures are still cold, although they became warmer by the end of this period.

Throughout North Africa there are no firm data available on precipitation during this period. The significant confinement of occupation sites to the littoral and the adjacent mountains suggests an uninhabitable environment beyond, in the northwest fringes of the Sahara (Camps 1974a: 60). Only two sites, El Hamel and El Haouita, located in the steppe and desert belt, seem to contradict this statement. However, both of these are much younger, dating between 8000 and 6000 BC (Camps 1975), and thus are almost certainly contemporary with the early Holocene period of increased moisture in the Sahara.

HOLOCENE WET INTERVAL

The data on the Holocene wet interval in the Western Desert come primarily from the Nabta, Kharga, and Dyke areas in the southern and central portion, and from Siwa Oasis and the Qattara Depression in the north. Another source of useful data is the Nile Valley; less significant information comes from the Gilf el Kebir and Uweinat.

The most complete sequence of events during this complex period comes from the series of enclosed drainage basins just south of the Kiseiba scarp in the southern, central portion of the Western Desert of Egypt. Around Nabta several extensive deflational basins, probably hollowed out during the preceding hyperarid phase, were hydrologically active because of local rainfall during the early part of the Holocene.

The playas south of the Kiseiba scarp are characterized by smooth, hard surfaces, a lack of salt crusts, and apparent impermeability due to fine-grained, clastic sediments within the group of clay and silts. The aggradation of these playas was clearly caused by deposition from surface floods and eolian activity, the latter particularly during the early phases of their formation. This type of playa, according to the classification of Motts (1965), is a "total surface-water discharge playa." These playas are often characterized by the distribution of vegetation in a ring around the periphery of the basin. The central area is barren, since the contraction of the clays in the central portion, caused by alternating wet and dry seasons, prevents vegetational growth. Playas of this type are seen today in Egypt in the northwestern desert, south of the littoral dune belt and north of the Qattara Depression, in an area of weak (about 50 mm per annum) winter rainfall.

The lithostratigraphy of the playas reflects pronounced environmental fluctuations in this area. There is clear evidence for three episodes of increased rainfall separated by intervals of hyperaridity. The approximate chronology of these events is as follows:

Playa I	9000–8500 BP
First arid interval	8500–8200 BP
Playa II	8200–7900 BP
Second arid interval	7900–7700 BP
Playa III	7700–5800 BP

The reconstruction of the environment in this area is based on limited evidence, such as the faunal components of associated archaeological occurrences, which may have been subjected to cultural selection, and plant remains, also from archaeological sites within the playas and therefore reflecting only the playa environment. Because of the limited floral sample recovered, no quantification of these data has been possible.

The relatively rich faunal sample clearly indicates the dominance of small ruminants whose environment today is that of the desert (*Gazella dorcas*) or semidesert (*Gazella rufifrons*), and the lagomorph, *Lepus capensis,* which is found today throughout Africa and the Iberian peninsula. These three dominant species obviously indicate a semiarid environment for the area. The absence of megafauna, except for presumably domestic *Bos,* supports this interpretation; the presence of a single example of warthog, which usually requires a more humid environment, could be explained by the playas. It is interesting to note that *G. dorcas* and *G. rufifrons* occur together only in the central, western Sudan near the latitude of Khartoum, where the northernmost ranges of *rufifrons* and the southern limit of *dorcas* overlap (Niethammer 1971:516). The rainfall in this overlap area today is between about 100 mm per annum in the north and 300–400 mm per annum in the south. The ostrich, characteristic of semiarid regions south of the Sahara, was also present in the playa area, to judge from the occurrence of numerous eggshell fragments.

The limited floral evidence indicates the presence of acacia, salsola, tamarisk, dom palm, and date palm, as well as several varieties of grasses, weeds, and cereals. Except for the cereals, and some of the weeds, all of the plants are southern forms.

The available data suggest that the area below the Kiseiba scarp lay in a zone that today would be classified as the semidesert of Sudan. According to Barbour (1961), the semidesert of Sudan is confined between the southern limit of the desert, around 16°N to 17.5°N (in the west), and around 14°N. Its northern limit coincides with the 80- to 90-mm isohyet, whereas the southern limit is between the 300- and 400-mm isohyets. The vegetation in this zone is composed mainly of acacia shrubs, grasses, herbs, and rare larger trees, the latter usually occurring along watercourses.

A reconstruction of the landscape during the early Holocene moist phases, according to both the modern distributions of the flora and fauna and the geomorphology, would show the playas surrounded by semi-woodland vegetation, shrubs and grasses, occasional permanent pools (as indicated by the rare presence of catfish), and extensive grassland on the sandy plain beyond the playas. Barren, exposed surfaces of Nubia sandstone and Eocene limestone on the gebels dotted the landscape.

This general reconstruction seems to be applicable to all three playa phases, but it is probable that there were differences between them that we cannot yet adequately document. For example, there are some indications that the earliest moist phase was not as wet as the later two, as is indicated by the higher proportion of eolian elements in the sediments.

North of Kiseiba there is only limited evidence from the peneplain surface between the scarp and Dakhla–Kharga. A small playa basin in the Dyke area (Site E-72-5) showed a considerable element of eolian activity during the formation of this surface water-discharge playa (Schild and Wendorf 1977b:146).

At Kharga, the available data are much less conclusive than those from south of Kiseiba. There is no doubt that the early Holocene wet phase marks the beginning of the natural artesian spring discharge at Sites E-76-6, E-76-7, and E-76-4, and the formation of large silty playas (Site E-76-2) in the Kharga basin and small playas on the Eocene plateau (Caton-Thompson 1952: 162). The data indicate no more than an increased precipitation refilling the underground reservoir and forming playas; the amount of this precipitation cannot be determined.

As in the Great Oases, the data from the Gilf el Kebir show increasing precipitation near the end of the desert phase, which was responsible for the accumulation of the large dune that blocked Wadi Bakht. The basin behind the dune was filled first with alternating silts and eolian sands, and later by the deposition of silts only. The very special geomorphic situation of this basin prohibits any overall reconstruction of the local environment. Today, similar

blocked wadis, descending eastward from the Eocene plateau in the vicinity of Idfu, have accumulated thick silt deposits and permitted occasional agriculture as recently as 30 years ago. It seems clear, therefore, that even in the almost rainless desert special geomorphic conditions may result in playa accumulation.

The fauna recovered from Wadi Bakht is, in itself, too limited to permit further discussion of the environment, but a more extensive faunal assemblage for this area is suggested by the prehistoric rock drawings that occur here and at nearby Uweinat (Rhotert 1952; Winkler 1938–1939). At the Gilf el Kebir, and elsewhere in the Western Desert of Egypt, there are rare prehistoric drawings of elephants and giraffes, which are considered to indicate a more luxuriant environment, according to the most recent analysis of these pictorial representations (McHugh 1971, 1974). In Wadi Hamra, in the Gilf area, there are only two dubious representations of elephants, but many giraffes. A few elephants, together with giraffes, ibex, and antelope, are present in the prehistoric rock art of Dakhla (McHugh 1971; Winkler 1938–1939), and another representation of an elephant is reported from the area between Dakhla and Kharga. No representations of elephants seem to be reported from Uweinat, but there are numerous giraffes. Despite these scattered illustrations of elephants and giraffes, however, no bones of either of these forms have been reported from anywhere in the Western Desert. These rare drawings, therefore, may record occasional incursion of giraffe and elephant into areas that were then at the northern limit of their range.

The rarity of giraffe and elephant representations in the rock art of the Western Desert is in contrast with the frequencies reported from several localities in the central Sahara. There, the most common illustrated wild animals are elephant, giraffe, rhinoceros, antelope, and bovid (*Homoioceras*) (Camps 1974a), which may reflect ecological differences between this area and the Western Desert. Although both elephant and giraffe are known to require luxuriant environments, their extreme range in modern times (near Lake Chad, in the vicinity of Kanem) has extended northward to an area where the rainfall is in the range of 150 mm per annum (Huard 1972: 208). Similarly, giraffe, whose ecological preference is today south of 12°N in the Chad area, are sporadically reported ranging up to the southeast border of Ennedi at 16°N. It is believed that the extreme ecological limit is around 50 mm of rainfall per annum.

These data have been variously interpreted. Butzer 1958, 1961), in a series of articles, saw the Gilf el Kebir, Uweinat, Dakhla, and Kharga areas as lying within the 50-mm isohyet, and most of the rest of the Western Desert as receiving less than 50 mm per annum. McHugh (1974), on the other hand, basing his argument on the same data, placed the Gilf el Kebir between 400 and 500 mm of annual rainfall, and Uweinat at around 600 mm. Hester and Hoebler (1969), using the same data and the presence of playas and archaeological remains in the Western Desert, made estimates between these two extremes. All these reconstructions, however, are based on essentially undated evidence, but make an implicit assumption of contemporaneity with the Holocene wet phase.

In northern Egypt, along the Mediterranean littoral and in the Qattara, Siwa, and Garra depressions, which today receive more rainfall than the southern portion of the Western Desert and are within the belt of winter rainfall, traces of early Holocene occupation are extremely scarce, and present only in the areas of modern oases, as in Siwa and Garra (F. A. Hassan 1976, 1978). The survey undertaken by the Combined Prehistoric Expedition along the Mediterranean littoral, between Marsa Matruh and Alexandria, and along the northern portion of the Qattara Depression, failed to disclose any traces of early Holocene settlements and indicated that sediments of this period are practically nonexistent. The only evident late Quaternary and/or early Holocene sediments along the northern cliffs of the Qattara Depression are dissected alluvial fans, and the enclosed basin on the floor of the depression and those on the adjacent plateau are being filled by silts of modern playas. Most of the Quaternary deposits within the depression consist of modern sand dunes, *sebkhas*, and thin sheets of gravel. Similarly, the colluvial sediments and wadi fills immediately adjacent to the littoral often contain wheel-made pottery at their base.

These observations in the northern portion of the Western Desert are in striking contrast to those from the southern portion and obviously indicate a relative scarcity of precipitation in the early Holocene.

On the basis of preliminary reports concerning the work at Siwa and Garra oases (F. A. Hassan 1976, 1978), it appears that the upper Pleistocene hyperarid period was locally followed by an interval of very moist conditions and the formation of upper loamy deposits between around 8400 and 8600 BP. This period of maximum moisture was preceded by an interval of "more vigorous thunder showers" dated between 9000 and 8500 BP. A period of aridity and erosion in which there was a shrinking of the groundwater-fed lake and an advancement of the dunes is placed between 8000–7000 BP and 4500 BP, and progressively more arid conditions are seen between 4500 and 2500 BP, when salt crusts formed on the dunes in the pans. A brief and slight increase in moisture occurred around 2500 BP when *Tamarix* colonized the dunes.

From the available data, it seems obvious that the northern portion of the Western Desert was much more arid than the southern during the early Holocene. The available dates from Siwa and Garra are not sufficient for precise correlation, but they suggest that the period of maximum moisture, dated between 8400 and 8600 BP, may coincide with the first Holocene arid interval between Playas I and II at Nabta, whereas the increased aridity in Siwa and Garra, generally dated between 8000 and 4500 BP, is contemporaneous with the maximum moist phases of Playas II and III. Evidently, the northward shift of the summer rains and the monsoonal belt, which is seen as responsible for the

moist phases in the southern desert, did not extend as far north as Siwa. On the contrary, the cyclonic winter rainfalls along the Mediterranean littoral were weak and apparently out of phase with the monsoonal rains in the south. This conclusion is very different from that of Butzer (1966), based on evidence from Nubia, that the Neolithic wet period was primarily due to winter rainfall.

To the west of the Western Desert of Egypt in the central and southern Sahara, the most significant and complete records of the environment in this interval come from two areas. The first is the Chad basin where extensive geological and palynological investigations have permitted detailed environmental reconstructions (Maley 1976, 1977a, b; Rognon 1976; Rognon and Williams 1977; Servant and Servant-Vildary 1972). The second important area is the Tibesti (Geyh and Jäkel 1974; Jäkel and Schulz 1972; Maley 1977b; Messerli 1972; review in B. D. Shaw 1976).

The Chad basin can be fed by runoff from the central Saharan highlands, by local rainfall, and by the influx of water in the rivers flowing from the south. The geological and palynological studies of this area have been concerned with the complex interaction of these three sources of water, each of which carries a distinctive suite of pollen.

The geological, palynological, and diatom studies have resulted in the subdivision of the early Holocene into several episodes. After the late Pleistocene period of hyperaridity, the first of these occur at Kanem and in the eastern section of the basin and are represented by three weak expansions of the lake, each separated by arid stages, the latter sometimes accompanied by eolian action. According to Servant (Maley 1977a:188), the first transgression is dated between about 12,900 and 12,500 BP, the second between about 11,800 and 11,000 BP, and the third between about 10,200 and 9700 BP. Servant parallels the first two transgressions with the last two Pleistocene warmer oscillations of Bolling and Allerod, and the third with the Preboreal. The dating for the first transgression, however, is slightly older than the Bolling oscillation *sensu stricto* on the North European Plain (12,400–12,000 BP).

Following these early events is a complex period of multiple transgressions extending from about 9200 BP to the present. There are five transgressions during this period, not all of which were accompanied by local rainfall. Lake II_1, dated at 9200–8500 BP, was synchronous with local rains as well as influxes of water both from Tibesti and from the south. Between 8500 and 8400 BP is a short interval of local aridity, followed (8400 and 7800 BP) by a transgression (Lake II_2), caused by an increasing influx of water from the south accompanied by a decrease of water from the Tibesti source. Within this period there is a small fluctuation, dated between 8200 and 8100 BP. The next transgression (Lake II_3), dated between 7700 and 7300 BP, was caused only by water coming from the south, accompanied by locally arid conditions. The fourth expansion (Lake II_4) is preceded by a considerable recession of the lake during which the paleo-Chad became almost completely dry (7300–7100 BP) with no influx from either the south or the north. The Lake II$_4$ transgression (7100–5000 BP) was accompanied by local rainfall resulting from the northward shift of the summer rain belt, together with an influx of water from both the Tibesti area and the south. The maximum of the Tibesti influx is placed between about 7200 and 6600 BP, and is believed to disappear after about 5500 BP (Maley 1977a:195).

A long regression, between 5000 and 3900 BP, is reported to precede the last Chad transgression (Lake II$_5$), dating between 3900 BP and the present. This last transgression is a complex period composed of several minor fluctuations in the lake and changes in the local environment (Maley 1977a: 195).

A summary of the data from the Tibesti and comparison with results of the pollen analysis from the Chad (Maley 1977b) has suggested the presence of six periods of increased moisture during the early Holocene, all dated between about 9000 and 2000 BP, as follows:

Phases	Approximate Dates BP	Conditions
H	4000–1000	Terrace accumulation
G	5500–4000	Erosion
F	6400–5500	Sahelian optimum
	6400	Change of climatic regimens
E	7200–6500	Optimum
D	7700–7200	Aridity
C	8100–7700	Optimum
	8250–8100	Aridity
B	8400–8250	Optimum
	8550–8400	Aridity
A	9000–8550	Optimum
	9300–9000	Aridity

The detailed chronology proposed by Maley both for the Chad and Tibesti areas is based in large part on the projection of radiocarbon dates from many localities onto two main pollen diagrams, and may therefore be subject to some error. A comparison of the early Holocene paleoecological events at Nabta and those from the Chad basin and Tibesti shows several areas of similarity as well as certain differences. The Lake II$_1$ transgression in the Chad and the first wet phase at Tibesti seem to be generally contemporaneous with Playa I at Nabta. The succeeding arid phase at Nabta, which is not well dated, is certainly of short duration, and may be contemporaneous either with the regression of paleo-Chad between Lake II$_1$ and Lake II$_2$, or with a short episode of aridity in the Sahelian zone in this area, dated between 8200 and 8100 BP.

Playa II at Nabta must be considered as largely contemporaneous with the Lake II$_2$ transgression of the paleo-Chad during which the Tibesti influx apparently declined. The quite pronounced aridity separating Playa II and Playa III at Nabta, dating before 7500 BP, is apparently contemporaneous with Lake II$_3$ at Chad when there was no local rainfall and the expansion of the lake was due entirely to the influx of water from the south. It also seems to be at least partially contemporaneous with the Phase D period of aridity at Tibesti. Playa III at Nabta, on the other hand,

from 7500 to < 6300 BP, seems to be only partially contemporaneous with the moist phase of Lake II$_4$ at Chad and Phases E and F in the Tibesti.

It cannot be determined if the evident, but basically minor, discrepancies between the Nabta and the Chad–Tibesti sequences are due to errors in dating or to local variations in atmospheric circulation. We suspect, however, the former. Nevertheless, in broad terms, the coincidence of Sahelian maxima in the Chad area with playa expansion in the southern Western Desert strongly supports the hypothesis that the increased precipitation in this portion of the eastern Sahara was caused mainly by the northward shift of the summer monsoonal rains.

Along stream channels that drain to the north from the Tibesti, numerous hearths have been recorded by Gabriel (1977b). Many of these hearths have been radiocarbon dated and several of them also have associated faunal remains. The faunas include numerous *Bos,* many of which are identified as domestic (on the basis of size), and also occasional sheep. Nondomestic animals include elephant, buffalo, giraffe, and antelope. Gabriel believes that these sites were occupied by Neolithic cattle-herders. Two phases are recognized. The first is dated between 7500 and 5700 BP; the second, when the main occupation occurred, is dated from 5700 to 5400 BP. An earlier phase may be represented at one site that contained Early Khartoum style pottery ("dotted wavy line") and was dated 8065 BP ± 100 years (Hv 2748; Gabriel 1977b: 80). Although only the earliest of the defined phases is represented in the Nabta sequence, and seems to coincide with Playa III, these finds are of considerable importance because they confirm that a vegetative cover favorable for cattle and other large mammals existed on the central Saharan plains during this period. Gabriel estimates a mean annual rainfall in that area between 300 and 400 mm.

Elsewhere in the Sahara the available data are not as full as those from the Chad and Tibesti. The evidence for a Holocene wet period appears to occur throughout the Sahara, although there are few dates and nowhere else is there a complete reconstruction of a complex sequence covering several millenia. This situation prevents any precise estimate of the possible displacement through time of either the cyclonic polar front or the monsoonal belt. In most cases, the extent of the changes in the environment is practically unknown, except for the simple statement that it was wetter than today.

In central Sudan, west of Khartoum, a series of shallow lakes, fed by rainfall, is reported to have existed between about 8500 and 7000 years BP. They contain a molluscan fauna, indicating an "acacia–tall grass" environment, requiring at least twice as much rainfall as is found there today (Williams and Clark 1976:52).

In the foothills of the Hoggar, pollen from the site of Amekni (Camps 1969a, 1974a) indicates more moist conditions, beginning well before 8000 BP, and shows the presence of *Typha,* evergreen oak, hackberry, Judas tree, and other Mediterranean elements. Also, local rainfall and/or runoff from the Hoggar was obviously sufficient to support wadis and pools containing fish. The pollen evidence and the fauna are interpreted as indicating the presence of gallery forests, savanna, and basins with permanent water. It is not clear if the Mediterranean flora indicates primarily winter rainfall, or if summer rains were also important.

In the Acacus foothills of the Fezzan in Libya the excavations by Mori (1965a, b) at the rockshelter of Muhuggiag, with radiocarbon dates ranging from 7400 to 4700 BP, yielded a pollen and macrofloral remains sequence that shows at the base a dominance of *Typha,* grasses, and rare trees, indicating the presence of permanent, possibly stagnant water. After about 6000 BP an arid phase is indicated, followed by an interval of slightly wetter conditions than today, but with xerophytes dominant in the vegetal cover.

Elsewhere in the Sahara there are data from several Neolithic sites, such as Meniet in the Hoggar (Hugot 1963) and Wadi Amded in the Adrar Tiouiyne (Camps 1974a: 236–237), which shed further light on this period. At the site of Meniet the recovered pollen included a high frequency of arboreal, Mediterranean elements; the associated macrobotanical remains were dominated by xerophytic species, such as grasses and sedges. This situation is typical for the pollen rain for the Sahara where long-distance pollen transport is a major problem (Cour and Duzer 1976; Van Campo 1975). At the Neolithic site in Wadi Amded fish remains were sufficiently numerous to have been one of the major food resources, and indicate permanent water.

In the western Sahara, in the lower Senegal, a humid phase is reported dating between 11,000 and 8000 BP, followed by an arid interval dating 8000 and 7000 or 6000 BP, in turn followed by another humid phase from 6000 to 2500 BP (Beaudet *et al.* 1976: 158). In inland Mauretania a pluvial phase (Pluvial II) is recognized between 10,000 and 3300 BP (Beaudet *et al.* 1976: 163).

Lacustrine sediments implying a wetter climate are also reported from the northwestern Sahara, in the Erg Chech and the valley of Saoura, dating between about 9000 and 3400 BP. The pollen contemporaneous with the Neolithic wet phase at Saoura, however, indicates the presence of basically modern local flora, although possibly more abundant (Beucher 1972; Van Campo 1975:51).

A series of marshy soils in the lacustrine basins at the border of the Great Western Erg and Erg Er-Raoui, again suggesting more moist conditions, gave a series of dates ranging from around 6200 to 5300 BP (Conrad 1969: 445).

The northern margin of the Sahara, in the area of Ouargla Oasis, has also yielded some indications of climatic fluctuations during the Neolithic. A drier phase, contemporaneous with a regression of the *sebkha* and a Terminal Paleolithic occupation dating 8600 BP (Camps 1974b: 275), is reported from the site of the Hassi Mouilah (Aumassip 1972: 276; Marmier and Trécolle 1968). This is followed by dune accumulation and then by a humid phase just preceding a Neolithic occupation dated 5300 BP (Camps 1974b:278). Elsewhere in the Ouargla area, the Neolithic sites are usually located at the very edge of *seb-*

khas or inside them. This situation is interpreted by Camps (1974a:341) as indicating some drying of the *sebkhas* during the Neolithic, and a biotope possibly close to that of today, with vegetation more dense near watercourses. This would be not unlike the reconstruction by Beucher for the Saoura.

In the Maghreb, along the littoral and within the Atlas Mountains, the data are very inconclusive. The work of Lubell and others (1975, 1976) in the Tlidjene Valley in eastern Algeria has indicated that the period from around 9800 to 6000 BP was generally cooler and more moist than today, and was interrupted by a warmer and drier pulsation between 8200 and 7600 BP.

At the site of Medjez II, in Algeria, a colder and more humid climate is suggested for the oldest phase of occupation, dating between 8800 and 8600 BP (Camps 1974a; Camps-Fabrer 1975; Couvert 1972). On the basis of studies of Capsian charcoal, Couvert (1972) has postulated the existence of two weak Holocene humid phases, dating between 8500 and 7500 years BP and 6500 to 5000 years BP, which interrupt a general trend toward more aridity (Couvert 1972; Rognon 1976: 267; Rognon and Williams 1977:305).

Clearly, the data from the southern and central Sahara, from the northern fringe of the desert, and from the Mediterranean littoral are inadequate for comparison with those from the Chad, Tibesti, and the southwestern desert of Egypt. It may, however, be noted that throughout this period the northern belt does not seem to have been much wetter than it is today, thereby strongly contrasting with the southern margin and central portions of the desert. Furthermore, it appears that the events in the northern fringe (such as the arid pulsations at Siwa and Tlidjene) and those in the southern and central areas were not entirely in phase. This would indicate the considerable importance of monsoonal rains in the southern and central portions of the Sahara, but very limited southward displacement of the cyclonic front. If this is true, it is very different from the short-term (nineteenth century) record of climatic variations in the Sahara, which indicates coincidence of climatic phenomena in the northern and southern margins of the Sahara (Dorize 1976:227). The increasing importance of the monsoonal rains during the period between about 9000 and about 5000 BP over the southern and central portion of the Sahara seems to have been caused by the cooling of the Antarctic, which, in turn, reinforced the Saint Helen anticyclone and strengthened the summer monsoons in the Sahel (Maley 1973; Rognon and Williams 1977:310). The north Saharan anticyclone belt in that time was possibly located farther to the north (Rognon and Williams 1977: 317).

Comparison of the events in the Western Desert of Egypt with fluctuations of the Nile River and of the Nile-controlled lake in the Fayum shows several remarkable similarities (Wendorf and Schild 1976b). The first early Holocene aggradation, the Arkin, dating around 9000 to 9500 BP, seems to be partially contemporaneous with Playa

I of Nabta; the following recession, dated in the Fayum as before 8100 BP, appears to be equivalent to the arid interval separating Playas I and II. Similarly, the aggradation of the Premoeris Lake, with radiocarbon dates between 8100 and 7600 BP, falls within Playa II. The same aggradation is reflected along the Nile in the silts at El Kab and at DIW-51. The arid phase separating Playas II and III at Nabta coincides with the major decline in the Fayum separating the Premoeris and Protomoeris lakes dating around 7600 BP. Playa III, on the other hand, clearly corresponds to the Protomoeris Lake, with a single date of around 7200 BP, and to the high Nile floods recorded at Catfish Cave. It seems likely that the truncation of the record at Nabta after around 6300 BP may have occurred at the same time as the decline that separates the Protomoeris and Moeris lakes. There are no available data from Nabta that can be correlated with the Moeris Lake aggradation, but it should be noted that during the Old Kingdom there was extensive exploitation of the nearby Chephren diorite quarry, suggesting some source of available water. Playa activity may therefore have occurred during this period, for which the record was not preserved at Nabta.

Surprisingly, there are no known Terminal Paleolithic or Neolithic occupations or sediments at Bir Sahara or Bir Tarfawi. Old Kingdom sites are known from both basins at elevations close to those of the modern wells, thus implying only a slightly higher water table during that period. None of these sites yielded significant biological data, except for ostrich eggshells. Today this area is well beyond the northern range of the ostrich, although it was present in modern times at the better-watered Uweinat. We can offer no explanation for the puzzling absence of early Holocene sediments in this area.

After the late Pleistocene arid interval when dunes blocked the White Nile, Lakes Victoria and Albert increased in size during the Holocene and again overflowed into it. At the same time the Blue Nile changed its regimen from a braided stream depositing sands through the Gezira Plain to a meandering stream with suspended load, which was responsible for the formation of silts downstream from Khartoum (Williams and Adamson 1974; Wiliams et al. 1975). Clearly these changes indicate a major shift toward increased rainfall in the headwaters of the Nile.

Although there are few radiocarbon dates for the Holocene aggradations of the Nile, and thus their beginnings and ends can only be estimated, the wet pulsations in the south of the Western Desert and the Nile aggradations are generally synchronous. In theory, the onset of increased rainfall in the headwaters and the beginning of aggradation downstream could have preceded slightly the increase of local precipitation in the desert. In general, however, the wet phases in the Western Desert, Nile aggradation, and the lacustrine transgressions in east and tropical Africa all seem to occur at about the same time (Butzer 1976; Butzer et al. 1972; Rognon and Williams 1977; Van Zinderen Bakker and Coetzee 1972; Wendorf and Schild 1976b).

A somewhat different interpretation of the source of the local rains has been offered by Butzer (1966, 1976) and Butzer and Hansen (1968, 1972). They observed evidence for increased Holocene wadi activity during two major periods: between 11,200 and 8000 BP (Ineiba Formation, late phase), and between 6000 and 5000 BP (Shaturma Formation). The sediments representing wadi discharge, mostly observed on the eastern bank of the Nile, are believed to be out of phase with the sediments of the summer Nile floods, and therefore to indicate local winter rains.

Today the Red Sea Hills receive most of their precipitation between November and January; the monsoonal rains in the Sahelian belt occur between July and September. It is unlikely, however, that a northward shift of the monsoonal belt would not have influenced the winter rains on the Red Sea Hills and that at least a large portion of the precipitation there would not have resulted from this shift. The alternating layers of silts and sands observed in the Khor Adimar on the east bank of the Nile, and interpreted as evidence that Nile and wadi sedimentations were out of phase, might also be viewed as resulting either from summer rains preceding the maximal mid-August stand of the Nile, or from the violent discharge of wadi sediments into the inundated floodplain, thus briefly interrupting the deposition of fine silts. It seems that this problem cannot be resolved without further extensive field studies and additional radiocarbon dates.

Regardless of whether the Red Sea Hills received winter or summer rains or both, the Western Desert was undoubtedly fed by monsoonal rains that resulted from a northward shift of the belt during each of the recognized humid pulsations. The extent of the displacements cannot be firmly established, but the presence of numerous playas on the limestone plateau near Kharga and in the depression itself suggests that they extended at least to the line of Kharga and the Gilf el Kebir. We feel that the evidence is not adequate for precise estimates of the amount of rainfall represented.

These Holocene events bring to a close the Quaternary sequence for the Western Desert of Egypt, and the sequence provides the necessary chronological and environmental framework for understanding the complex cultural developments occurring in these areas of the Sahara, which are so remote today.

7

Human Exploitation
of the Western Desert

ACHEULIAN

The earliest known human occupation of the Western Desert is Acheulian, which in the whole of North Africa and the Sahara (Freeman 1975) is the least known, large taxonomic entity. The detailed chronology is extremely sketchy, behavioral data are almost nonexistent, associated fauna is very limited at best, and the physical environment is not well understood. This situation results from several factors, of which two are possibly the most important. First, recent archaeological work, both along the Nile and in the Western Desert, has concentrated on late Pleistocene and early Holocene settlements because they seemed to offer much more potential for complex interdisciplinary research. Second, the Acheulian is a remote period, and thus subject to greater destruction both in the past and today.

CHRONOLOGY

There are no known stratified Acheulian sites anywhere in the Western Desert or along the Nile; there are no absolute dates or firm, detailed, lithostratigraphic placements; and inferences about relative chronology are based only on the unclear geomorphic situations of some of the sites. In the Bir Sahara basin there is an indication of a limited sequence, possibly representing two or three chronological phases, but of these, only the latest was studied in some detail (Site BS-14) and furnished an adequate sample for statistical treatment and taxonomic comparisons. A very similar situation exists along the Nile; even the studies done during the Nubian campaign (Chmielewski 1968; Guichard and Guichard 1965, 1968; Kleindienst 1972),

although dealing with a larger number of occurrences, never yielded any reliable chronological data.

In the Western Desert the Acheulian occurrences seem always to be associated with a wetter phase or phases. The relative dating of the sites studied is based primarily on rather weak taxonomic indications. The assemblages from the two sites in Dakhla (E-72-1 and E-72-2) seem to be similar to those isolated Acheulian finds associated with surfaces that precede the assemblage in the spring vent of Site BS-14. This impression is reinforced by the fact that the spring vent of Site BS-14 represented the last event before a hyperarid period when the Bir Sahara basin was deflated to a level below that of the modern water table. The earlier occurrences are regarded as being Late Acheulian in age, and the last is classified as Final Acheulian.

Only typology could provide any basis for chronological comparisons between the Acheulian of the Western Desert and that of the Nile Valley, but the two areas are so very different in typology that even that seems hopeless.

TAXONOMIC SETTING

Two clear taxonomic units have been defined on the basis of the comparisons of both qualitative and quantitative differences in the group of bifaces from four assemblages (E-72-1, E-72-2, BS-14, KO8). A third group, on the surface of the Bir Sahara plain, may exist, although it cannot be fully documented.

The non-biface tools and debitage of these sites cannot be compared, as only two similar sites yielded any significant

243

number of tools and cores, a fact resulting from the limited excavation and *in situ* material from Site BS-14 (Figure 7.1).

The differences between the two taxonomic entities are shown by the structure of the biface group (Figure 7.2), indicating the dominance of amygdaloidal, cordiform, and backed bifaces in the Late Acheulian Kharga–Dakhla unit, and, in contrast, the emphasis on the group of subtriangular, and asymmetrical cordiform bifaces in the Final Acheulian of Site BS-14. Although made of very different raw materials—Eocene chert in Dakhla and Kharga and quartzitic sandstone at Bir Sahara—the bifaces from Bir Sahara are in general much better made. They are thinner and display a high level of craftsmanship that, in North Africa, can be compared only with some of the finest bifaces from the surface site of El Ma El Abiod (Vaufrey 1955:57). It is also not unlikely that the "Acheulio-Levalloisian" from the site at Refuf Pass near Kharga (Caton-Thompson 1952:99), with fine bifaces, could be classified within this group.

Both entities seem to be formally different from the Acheulian along the Nile in Nubia, although all are characterized by a complete lack of cleavers, which are common in Northwest Africa, the central Sahara, and farther south in the Nile Valley at Khor Abu Anga. The material from Site Arkin 8, also Late Acheulian, stands apart in that it contains a large number of ovates and limandes, and numerous choppers and chopping tools, an assemblage type peculiar to this site (Chmielewski 1968). Other collections from Nubia usually contain significant numbers of thick elongates (such as lanceolates) (Guichard and Guichard 1968).

It seems obvious that the period represented by the Acheulian in the Western Desert and along the Nile is very long, and the variability of the microenvironments could have been considerable. For those reasons, it is not now possible to evaluate the relative importances of cultural, chronological, environmental, and functional factors in the enormous diversity of the North African Acheulian. Indeed, the outlook for resolving these basic questions is not good, since suitable sites seem to be lacking.

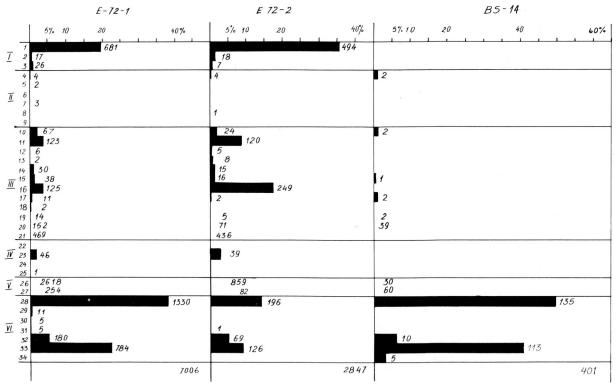

FIGURE 7.1. *Restricted General Structure of inventories from Sites E-72-1, E-72-2, and BS-14. Figures indicate number of pieces in each category. Key: Group I (Initial): 1, primary flakes; 2, primary blades; 3, initially struck cores. Group II (Levallois): 4, Levallois flake cores; 5, Levallois flakes; 6, Levallois blade cores; 7, Levallois blades; 8, Levallois point cores; 9, Levallois points. Group III (Flake): 10, single-platform flake cores; 11, flakes from single-platform cores; 12, opposed-platform flake cores; 13, flakes from opposed-platform cores; 14, change-of-orientation flake cores, flat; 15, change-of-orientation flake cores, globular; 16, flakes from change-of-orientation cores; 17, subdiscoidal cores; 18, flakes from subdiscoidal (discoidal) cores; 19, fragments of undetermined flake cores; 20, undetermined flakes; 21, rolled, undetermined flakes. Group IV (Blade): 22, single-platform blade cores; 23, blades from single-platform cores; 24, opposed-platform blade cores; 25, blades from opposed-platform cores. Group V (Chip): 26, simple chips; 27, crushed chips. Group VI (Tools and Tool-Production Waste): 28, biface trimming flakes and chips; 29, notch spalls; 30, resharpening spalls; 31, naturally backed knives; 32, retouched tools plus burins; 33, bifaces; 34, spheroids. Categories 19, 20, 21, 26, and 27 are excluded from the restricted percentages.*

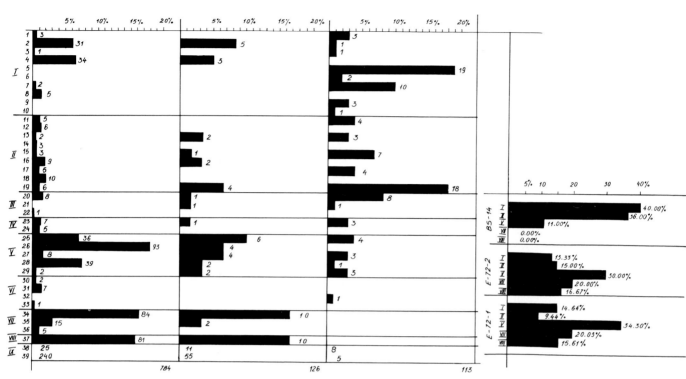

FIGURE 7.2. *Quantitative distribution of biface categories and their main groups at Sites E-72-1, E-72-2, and BS-14. Key: Group I (Subtriangulars): 1, subtriangular with thinned butt; 2, subtriangular with thick butt; 3, subtriangular, elongated, with thinned butt; 4, subtriangular, elongated, with thick butt; 5, ogivo-triangular with thinned butt; 6, ogivo-triangular with thick butt; 7, pelecyform with thinned butt; 8, pelecyform with thick butt; 9, shark-tooth with thinned butt; 10, shark-tooth with thick butt. Group II (Cordiforms): 11, cordiform with thinned butt; 12, cordiform with thick butt; 13, cordiform, elongated, with thinned butt; 14, cordiform, elongated, with thick butt; 15, subcordiform with thinned butt; 16, subcordiform with thick butt; 17, subcordiform elongated with thinned butt; 18, subcordiform, elongated with thick butt; 19, subcordiform with oblique thinned butt. Group III (Ovals): 20, discoidal; 21, oval; 22, limande. Group IV (Thick Elongates): 23, lanceolate; 24, atypical Micoquian. Group V (Amygdaloids): 25, amygdaloid with thinned butt; 26, amygdaloid with thick butt; 27, amygdaloid, short, with thinned butt; 28, amygdaloid, short, with thick butt; 29, amygdaloid with oblique thinned butt. Group VI (Diverse): 30, protolimande; 31, cleaver–biface; 32, ficron; 33, rostro-carinate. Group VII (Backed Bifaces): 34, backed symmetric; 35, backed asymmetric, thick; 36, backed asymmetric, thin. Group VIII (Double-Backed Bifaces): 37, short-tipped. Group IX (Other): 38, undeterminate plus fragments; 39, unfinished. Figures indicate number of pieces or percentages.*

SETTLEMENT SITUATIONS

The three Acheulian sites investigated by us, and Site KO8 studied by Caton-Thompson, are all of a single type of settlement situation, namely that of the spring vent. It is believed that these sites represent settlements or camps at the edges of spring pools, and that the artifacts were subsequently incorporated into the pool sediments, most of which were later destroyed, and into the spring deposits within the conduit itself. The spring-vent camps, which seem so important in number, may well have been much less important in the total Acheulian settlement pattern. Spring vents, with their firmly cemented deposits or calcareous evaporitic seals, were certainly among the better protected from destruction.

Each of the spring-pool localities may represent multiple occupations occurring throughout the total period of the spring's activity, perhaps several thousand years or more.

The spring pools were among the few places where permanent water was present, and may therefore have served as base camps (Figure 7.3).

A second settlement situation is represented by the large but thin concentrations of Acheulian artifacts on the sand plain of the Bir Sahara–Bir Tarfawi area. These clusters are impoverished as a result of deflation, and weathering and destruction of the smaller pieces. Their environmental associations are not certain, although the occasional proximity of carbonate crusts of evaporitic appearance could indicate the presence of waterlogged areas. However, since none of these sites was studied, more detailed suggestions cannot be advanced.

Another quite different microenvironmental situation is that of the lakeshore occurrences seen at the southern end of Bir Tarfawi. Here, again, extensive destruction of the original landscape prevents a detailed reconstruction. Very few artifacts—specifically, those embedded in indurated, water-laid sediments—are still in place. Obviously even

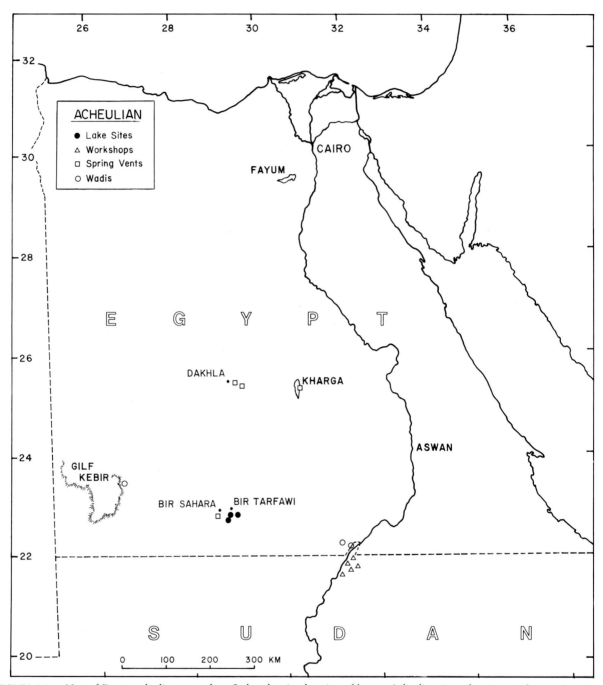

FIGURE 7.3. *Map of Egypt and adjacent northern Sudan showing location of known Acheulian sites of various settlement situations.*

these are not in primary context. Even when the destruction and considerable displacement are taken into account, however, the relative scarcity of artifacts must reflect a function for these lake localities quite different from that of the spring pools.

Wadi courses were yet another setting for settlements, although such are rarely found in the Western Desert because of the local geomorphology. They are known from the Kharga scarp and the wadi fans of the eastern face of

the Gilf el Kebir (site near Bagnold's camp). None of these sites is *in situ*.

In a similar situation is the enormous site of Arkin 8, perhaps the largest ever found in this part of Africa (Chmielewski 1968). Situated on a wadi bordering the western fringe of the Nile Valley in Nubia, this locality undoubtedly reflects multiple occupations. To judge from the size of the area and the density of artifacts, it could also represent several thousand years.

The Nile Valley contains specialized activity localities of Acheulian age in the form of extensive workshops located in the immediate vicinity of outcrops of quartzitic sandstone, either on the tops of the gebels or on the pediment slopes. These too are always extremely rich in tools and debitage, and undoubtedly represent many occurrences (Guichard and Guichard 1968). Scattered finds of Acheulian handaxes have been reported embedded in Nile sediments, in most cases derived from unknown sediments. Their primary geomorphic settings are unknown, except that they occur in the valley (Bovier-Lapièrre 1926; Giegengack 1968; Huzayyin 1941; Kleindienst 1972; Sandford and Arkell 1939; Wendorf and Schild 1976b).

Isolated Acheulian artifacts are also found in lag positions in the southern portion of the Western Desert of Egypt, in the area where the greatest geomorphic change has occurred. These areas had no wadi, lake, or spring remnants, and their general geomorphology indicates that playa-like, internally drained basins may have existed here during the wet phases of the Acheulian.

It seems evident that practically all microenvironments in which water was present were exploited. Although some differences in such microenvironments are apparent, and their significance could in part be appreciated (such as between spring pools and lakes), the cultural implications of the remainder are still almost totally unknown.

EXPLOITATION OF ENVIRONMENT AND LOCAL RESOURCES

None of the Acheulian sites in either the Western Desert or along the Nile has yielded sufficient fauna to permit detailed reconstructions of the exploitation and subsistence patterns. The character of the environment, a semiarid savanna or bush, suggests seasonality resulting from changes in the availability of water and grazing grounds for the megafauna. This seasonality is not evident in any of the sites that have been studied, although those localities that contain limited numbers of artifacts and those associated with the seasonally active, shallow basins may well represent such occupations.

At Site BS-14, the occurrence of ostrich-eggshell fragments (one of the earliest occurrences known in North Africa) and the mammal remains imply a rather large range of exploitation.

One characteristic of all of the Acheulian occurrences is that the utilized raw material was always the nearest available. From this we can infer that there was no trade in stone and that the toolmaking and disposal economy was based on expendability. Tools were probably made for short-term goals and were not taken from the area of one raw material into that of another, even if the first raw material was much better in quality.

MIDDLE PALEOLITHIC

A basically different order of data is available for the Middle Paleolithic in the Western Desert. The sites, though not numerous, contain in situ living floors and relatively rich associated faunal assemblages, both of which permit greater insights into the prehistoric societies. Along the Nile, however, only the latest section of the Middle Paleolithic, the Khormusan, has an equivalent record, and even for this period the studied sites are not numerous; they were preserved in situ in only a few limited areas. The quality of the data on the Middle Paleolithic of the Western Desert also differs strikingly from that associated with the same period in the Maghreb and elsewhere in the Sahara. For example, the sites in the Western Desert are the only ones yielding information on the horizontal distributions of artifacts and fauna on Middle Paleolithic floors. They are also the only open-air sites, except for El Guettar in Tunisia, yielding stratigraphy and relative chronology. Nevertheless, this must be viewed as only an initial study of the Middle Paleolithic in the Sahara; the number of mapped floors is not sufficient for statistical testing of hypotheses concerning details of social structuring, camp organization, subsistence patterns, or exploitation of the environment. The relative chronology also is not complete and there is no absolute chronology, except perhaps for the latest Middle Paleolithic development in the Nile Valley (Khormusan).

CHRONOLOGY

The Middle Paleolithic of the Western Desert and the Nile Valley is composed of three clear, large, taxonomic entities, each of which occupies a distinct chronological position. The two oldest of these are found both in the Western Desert and in the Nile Valley, each confined to separate wetter pulsations: Mousterian and Aterian. The youngest, the Khormusan, occurs only in the Nile Valley and seems to be contemporaneous with the beginning of a hyperarid phase in the Western Desert. This basic outline is the only firm statement that can be offered concerning the chronology. Even here, there is no direct superposition of Aterian over Mousterian; there is, however, clear evidence for two distinct periods of increased lacustrine activity in the Bir Sahara–Bir Tarfawi area, and it is most likely that the Aterian is contemporaneous with the later one.

Within the Mousterian, the Bir Sahara sequence yielded five periods of occupation, of which the latest has no identified lithics. There are no apparent continuous trends within the four earlier Mousterian sections that could indicate a unidirectional change through time. The only element that might suggest a chronological trend is the appearance of a single, poorly defined pedunculate on a Levallois point with the fourth Mousterian period at Bir Sahara.

This site is also characterized by the diminished size of both blanks and tools; however, this cannot be viewed as a trend in light of the succeeding Aterian in which the artifacts are of a size closely comparable to those of the Mousterian.

There is no firm basis for chronological comparison of the Mousterian of the Western Desert with that of the Nile Valley, the central Sahara, the Maghreb, or Cyrenaica, but they probably were generally contemporaneous. The Mousterian has not been reported from the Sahara (Balout 1965c; Camps 1974a), except for a "Middle Stone Age" occurrence apparently preceding the Aterian in the Adrar Bous area (Clark *et al.* 1973). In the Maghreb, there are a few sites containing thick Mousterian cultural deposits, as those at Gebel Irhoud in Morocco (Arambourg 1965; Ennouchi 1966) and Retaimia (Dalloni 1955), but nothing is known of their cultural stratification and content. The Nile Valley also lacks any basis for chronological subdivision of the Mousterian.

The Aterian in the Bir Sahara–Bir Tarfawi area probably represents an early section of the Aterian development in North Africa, as indicated by its association with an early part of the second lacusterine sequence there. As with the Mousterian, there is no possibility of a chronological comparison of this Aterian with that of Kharga and Aterian-related sites in the Nile Valley. It is quite possible that the early Aterian from Bir Tarfawi is chronologically close to the earliest Aterian sites of the Algerian littoral, such as Mugharet el'Aliya (the Aterian on the surface of Layer 9; Howe 1967), Dar es Soltan (the Aterian on the surface of Layer 1; Ruhlmann 1952), Camp Franchet (Camps 1955:22), and Karouba (Roubet 1947, 1966). If this is correct then the apparently late occurrences of the Aterian in the Maghreb, such as Dar es Soltan, Layer F (Ruhlmann 1952), and Mugharet el 'Aliya, Layer 5 (Howe 1967), would be later than any of the Bir Tarfawi sites.

The radiocarbon dates from the Bir Sahara and Bir Tarfawi basins indicate that the Mousterian and Aterian are beyond the range of the laboratory method and are older than 43,000 years. The radiocarbon date obtained from modern water in Bir Sahara (287 BP ± 69 years; SMU-433) demonstrates a fast recharge of the aquifer by modern rains. This implies a similar, or even faster, recharge during wet periods in the Western Desert, and excludes the theoretical possibility of contamination of the dated snail samples by much older, fossil water. Thus Bir Sahara and Bir Tarfawi differ significantly from Kharga where shells from Graeco-Roman wells were dated as 18,000 years old, a result of contamination from fossil water. The Kharga wells, however, may well have been dug down to a buried aquifer.

We believe that the exact ages of the Mousterian and Aterian are unknown, not only in the Western Desert, but also elsewhere in North Africa, and that all of the absolute dates attributed to the Mousterian and Aterian should, in fact, be much older. This conclusion is in agreement with evidence from East Africa indicating a far greater absolute age for the Middle Paleolithic in that area than was pre-viously believed (Evernden and Curtis 1965; Schild and Wendorf 1977a; Wendorf *et al.* 1975).

TAXONOMIC SETTING

The taxonomy of the North African Middle Paleolithic has been generally based on the system developed by Bourgon and Bordes (Bordes 1961; Bordes and Bourgon 1951; Bourgon 1957), applied to some sites in the Maghreb, such as El Guettar (Gruet 1955a,b, 1958–1959), Taforalt (Roche 1972), and Ain Fritissa (Tixier 1960); in the northwestern Sahara (the Saoura Basin—N. Chavaillon, 1971, 1973); and in the Nile Valley (Guichard and Guichard 1965, 1968; Marks 1968c). Most of the published Middle Paleolithic collections, however, have not been analyzed by this method.

Almost all of the variation found in the Middle Paleolithic of North Africa can be described by the classification system designed by Bordes for the French Mousterian. It is obvious, however, that several of Bordes' "types" actually subsume entire groups of forms. The most striking examples of this are the pedunculated tools and bifacial foliates, whose enormous formal and stylistic variability is concealed by Bordes' typology, as was shown by Tixier (1967). Similar observations could be made about many of Bordes' other more complex types. For this reason it must be recognized that the use of this taxonomy primarily brings out a general tool structure of an assemblage, not its stylistic characteristics. Nevertheless, the fact that Bordes' system can be used in North Africa, unlike some Middle Paleolithic entities such as the post-Micoquian of Central Europe, demonstrates a certain cultural, classificatory value for the system, although possibly of only a very large order.

We believe that the present state of research and the limitations imposed by Bordes' system prevent the identification of stylistic taxonomic units, and thus definitions such as Denticulate Mousterian and Denticulate Aterian or Typical Mousterian and Typical Aterian are nothing more than statements of the General Structure of the tool kit. Also, it should be emphasized that even the broad-scale subdivision of the Middle Paleolithic of North Africa into the two major categories of Mousterian and Aterian is based only on the presence or absence of two groups of tools—bifacial foliates and pedunculated pieces. Undoubtedly, there are stylistic differences, and therefore smaller taxonomic units within these two large entities, inklings of which can occasionally be seen (the variability in the Levallois retouched points from the Aterian of Kharga and the Moroccan pedunculate points), but the current methodology is not adequate to isolate these.

The tool structure of the Mousterian assemblages from the Western Desert (Figures 7.4–7.6) indicates that almost all of these could be classified as Denticulate Mousterian; that is, denticulated tools occur in high frequencies. Only two small assemblages, Site E-72-4 and a portion of Site

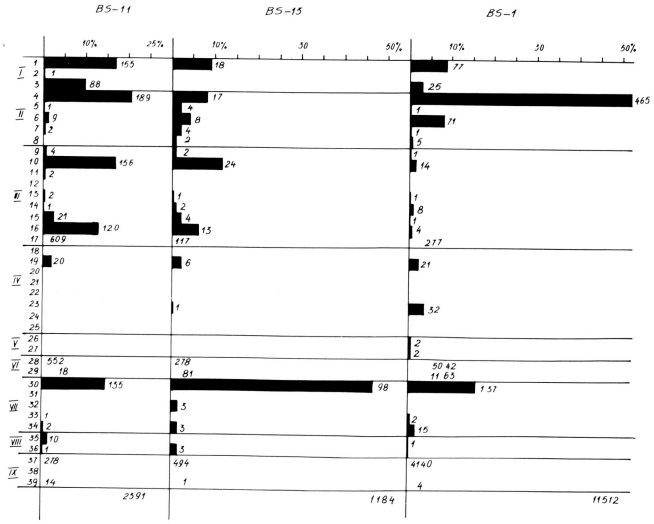

FIGURE 7.4. *Restricted General Structure of inventories from Sites BS-11, BS-13, and BS-1. Key: Group I (Initial): 1, primary flakes; 2, primary blades; 3, early-stage core-preparation flakes. Group II (Levallois): 4, Levallois core-preparation flakes; 5, Levallois cores; 6, Levallois flakes; 7, Levallois blades; 8, Levallois points. Group III (Flake): 9, single-platform flake cores; 10, flakes from single-platform cores; 11, opposed-platform flake cores; 12, flakes from opposed-platform flake cores; 13, discoidal cores; 14, flakes from discoidal cores; 15, change-of-orientation cores; 16, flakes from change-of-orientation cores; 17, undetermined flakes. Group IV (Blade): 18, single-platform blade cores; 19, blades from single-platform cores; 20, opposed-platform blade cores; 21, flakes from opposed-platform blade cores; 22, single-platform bladelet cores; 23, bladelets from single-platform cores; 24, opposed-platform bladelet cores; 25, bladelets from opposed-platform cores. Group V (Core Rejuvenation and Early Removal from Pre-cores): 26, core tablets; 27, core "trimming" blades. Group VI (Chip): 28, regular chips; 29, retouch chips. Group VII (Tools and Tool-Production Waste): 30, retouched tools; 31, resharpening (longitudinal) spalls; 32, biface trimming flakes and chips; 33, burin spalls; 34, notch spalls. Group VIII (Hammerstone): 35, spheroidal hammerstones (?); 36, regular hammerstones. Group IX (Undetermined): 37, crushed chips; 38, chunks; 39, undetermined cores. Categories 28, 29, 37, 38, and 39 are excluded from the restricted percentages.*

BS-13, are reminiscent of the Typical Mousterian, where non-Quina and nontransversal sidescrapers and Mousterian points dominate. The Levallois technology is present in all of the assemblages, but the intensity of its application varies.

A seemingly stylistic trait is seen in the diminished size of tools and blanks at Site BS-1 in comparison to all other Bir Sahara Mousterian assemblages. This reduction in size does not appear to have been imposed by the raw material, and may represent stylistic drift, although, if so, it did not carry over into the Aterian.

For the Mousterian-like "Levalloisian" from Kharga, meaningful comparisons are extremely difficult because of the limited sample size of these assemblages. Caton-Thompson (1952) recognized several taxonomic entities in the spring vents, wadis, and mud pans of the Kharga depression and its immediate vicinity. Beside the Levalloisian and Aterian, there were two entirely new units defined as the Levalloiso-Khargan and Khargan, both preceding the Aterian and following the Levalloisian. These are essentially Mousterian, distinguished by the smaller size of the

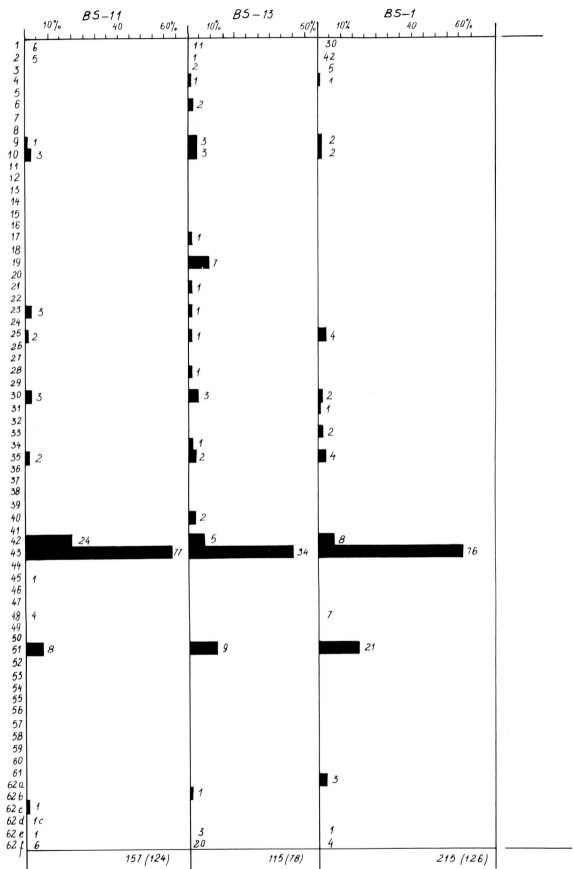

FIGURE 7.5. *Quantitative distribution of tools from Sites BS-11, BS-13, and BS-1 (restricted percentages). Categories 1 to 61 according to type list of F. Bordes; 62a, undetermined sidescrapers; 62b, bifacial triangular points; 62c, bifacial edge pieces; 62d, spheroids; 62e, regular hammerstones; 62f, undetermined and fragments. Figures indicate number of pieces in each category. Figures in parentheses at base give restricted totals.*

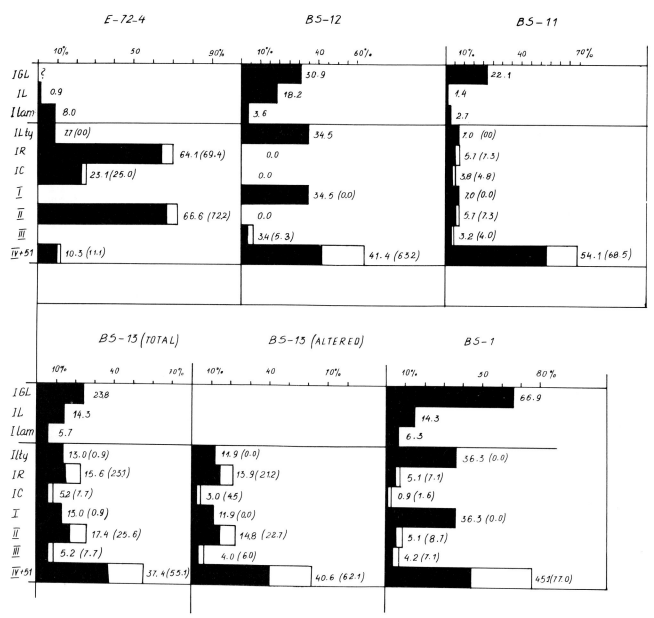

FIGURE 7.6. *Main indices of assemblages from Sites E-72-4, BS-12, BS-11, BS-13 (total altered by removal of tools from supposed activity cluster), and BS-1. Black bars indicate large percentages; white bars show restricted percentages if these are bigger than large ones. Figures without parentheses give large percentages; restricted percentages are shown in parentheses.*

blanks and tools and by the presence of more or less random, steep and semisteep, sometimes slightly denticulated, retouch on flakes. Except for Kharga and the Dungul area, the latter reported by Hester and Hoebler (1969), neither of these Khargan entities seems to occur elsewhere in the Western Desert. Others (McBurney 1960:155–158) have suggested that these particular tools may have resulted from natural retouching of the blanks.

In the Nile Valley in Nubia, the known Mousterian assemblages (Marks 1968c), some of which were originally reported to occur with rare handaxes (but cf. Wendorf and

Schild 1976a), are classified predominantly as Typical Mousterian of Levallois facies. Denticulate Mousterian is present, but rare. The significance of this observation will be discussed in a later section.

The structure of the Aterian in the Bir Tarfawi basin is similar to that of the Mousterian. Thus, most of the assemblages are denticulate oriented, and only one small concentration is clearly oriented toward the Typical Mousterian. The quantitative characteristics of the Aterian assemblages from the spring vents at Kharga (KO6E) differ significantly from those for the Bir Tarfawi Aterian. At

Kharga the assemblages are high in Levallois, with numerous retouched Levallois points, including distinctive specimens with thinned butts, and they are dominated by pedunculates or bifacial foliates. The values for these two groups far exceed the frequencies of any other retouched tool category. The Aterian assemblage from the spring vent at Site E-76-4, on the other hand, is almost totally composed of Levallois preparation flakes and a few tools. The sample is obviously too small to permit meaningful comparisons (Figures 7.7–7.9).

The second Middle Paleolithic complex along the Nubian Nile, one that seems to be related to the Aterian, is the series of sites assigned to the Middle Stone Age. All these assemblages are made on quartzitic sandstone, high in Levallois, and tend to be rather poor in tools. Classic Aterian pedunculates are not present, but bifacial foliates form a significant tool group. These bifacial foliates are also present in the upper, poorly known assemblages from the site of Khor Abu Anga near Khartoum (Arkell 1949; Carlson 1967). An Aterian site, located on the west bank of the Nile near the Second Cataracts, has been reported, but the lithic artifacts have not yet been described (Carlson and Sigstad 1973).

The classic Nubia Middle Stone Age sites, such as Arkin 14 and Gebel Brinikol, seem to be specialized workshops, characterized by heavy indices of bifaces of various shapes, most of which are probably unfinished bifacial foliates abandoned in various stages of completion. This functional emphasis makes any comparisons difficult, and it cannot be absolutely determined whether they are indeed part of the Aterian technocomplex or if they are somehow associated with the Sangoan, a huge, poorly defined entity with bifacial foliates in sub-Saharan Africa. The geographical and environmental setting for the Nubian Stone Age, however, would tend to place it closer to the Aterian.

The only clear living site of this time range in the Nile Valley in Nubia seems to be Site 440, in the Khor Musa. The assemblages recovered from the two floors at this site are both made on quartzitic sandstone and Precambrian rock, are very limited in tools, and are dominated by denticulates. The collection includes a single bifacial foliate. Both assemblages could fall well within the range of variability of the Aterian at Bir Tarfawi, but closer comparisons cannot be made because of the sample size.

SETTLEMENT SITUATIONS

Because of the similarity in the settlement locations of the Mousterian and Aterian, these two entities will be discussed together (Figure 7.10).

As with the Acheulian, all of the geomorphic settings

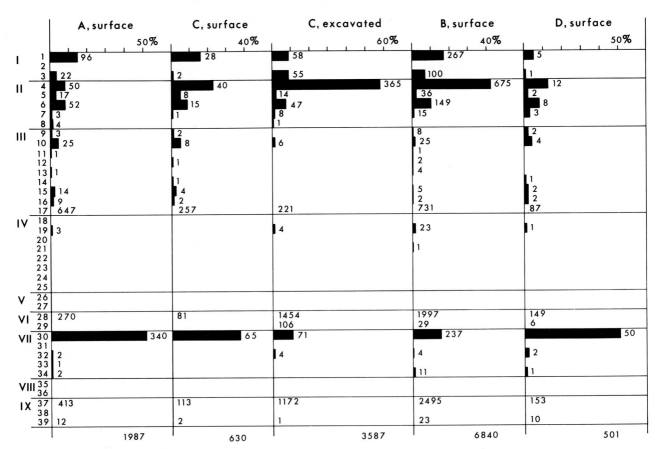

FIGURE 7.7. *Restricted General Structure of inventories from Aterian localities at Site BT-14. For key, see caption, Figure 7.4.*

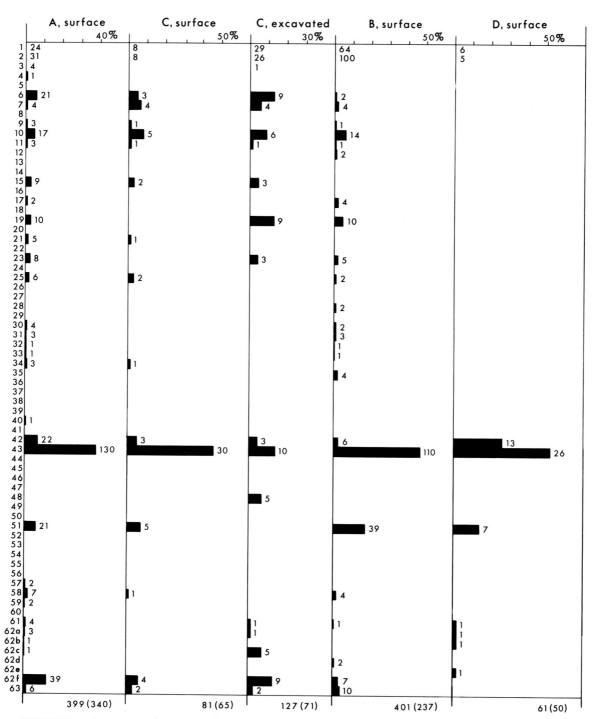

FIGURE 7.8. *Quantitative distribution of tools from Aterian localities at Site BT-14. For key, see caption, Figure 7.5.*

where water was available were exploited during the Middle Paleolithic, although the way in which they were exploited may have been quite different. There are numerous sites closely associated with lakeshores in the Bir Sahara and Bir Tarfawi basins. Other sites are found in the areas where internally drained basins and playas developed; some occur with spring-fed pools. Wadi courses and several niches in the Nile Valley were also utilized.

The basins of Bir Tarfawi and Bir Sahara contain several sites for which the inferred functions are different. The most obvious of these are the kill and butchery localities in the shallow lake bottom at Site BT-14, Area A. These are characterized by a high intensity of residual animal bone, a very low density of artifacts, including tools, and poorly defined boundaries. This is in contrast with the small, tight, and realtively dense concentration at Site BT-14, Area C,

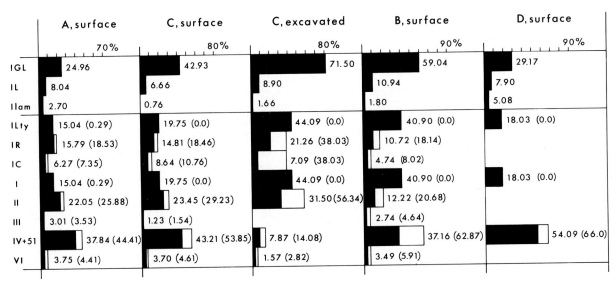

FIGURE 7.9. *Main indices of Aterian assemblages from Site BT-14. For key, see caption, Figure 7.6.*

embedded in the same silt as the nearby butchery localities, but presumably occupied during a dry phase, possibly seasonal. Area C is believed to be a living camp. The distributions of the lithic artifacts and bones are different at these two kinds of sites, and they also have drastically varying tool and debitage structures. The butchery area is dominated by various denticulates, whereas the living site yielded numerous sidescrapers and Mousterian points, and a high frequency of Levallois preparation elements.

A similar dichotomy is suggested for Bir Sahara. Here, two dense and well-limited, although larger, clusters of artifacts occur on a sandy beach some distance from the shore (Site BS-1), and several vague and relatively poor concentrations were found adjacent to the water's edge where they were undoubtedly subject to seasonal flooding (BS-11, BS-12, and BS-13). Unfortunately, the scarcity of directly associated faunal remains in clear-cut butchery situations prevents the certain determination of site function. Unlike Bir Tarfawi, all of the sites are denticulate dominated.

The two dense concentrations at Site BS-1 seem best explained as repeatedly occupied areas whose precise function cannot at present be established. The other localities, all near the edge of the lake, most closely resemble sections of the huge butchery site of BT-14, Area A; at Bir Sahara, however, the concentrations seem to represent not the actual place of the kill, but perhaps an adjacent activity area. This is suggested by a "Typical Mousterian" subcluster within an otherwise denticulate-dominated assemblage at Site BS-13; the presence of this subcluster indicates an area of function different from that carried on in the remainder of the site.

The dense and large cluster of BT-14, Area B, located on the adjacent lakeshore at Bir Tarfawi, may also have been similar in function to the water-edge concentrations at Bir Sahara. In this instance, however, the locality was used repeatedly over a period of time and the resulting mass of

artifacts effectively conceals any functional subclusters that might have existed.

In both lake basins, there was also occupation of the dunes that preceded the formation of the lakes. These settlements have been destroyed by wind and there is no basis for estimating their sizes, their functions, or the spatial distributions of the artifacts, but their locations do suggest camps on dunes adjacent to water holes.

Unfortunately, the data from Bir Sahara and Bir Tarfawi are limited in number of occurrences and in associated fauna, and comparable data are not available from any other areas in the Western Desert. The hypotheses generated, therefore, must be viewed as tentative, and require additional testing.

Only one relatively intact site was found in the geomorphic area of the internally drained basins (E-72-4). This is a thin, small, extremely poor concentration of artifacts composed of three subclusters that may form a single homogeneous occupational unit. The search for evidence of Middle Paleolithic occupations in other internally drained basins yielded occasional artifacts, but always in lag position and never in large numbers. We assume, therefore, that these areas were never heavily utilized, and that the settlements there were similar in size and density to Site E-72-4. They seem to be seasonal camps, which were reoccupied but never for extended periods of time.

The available data on occupations around spring pools are restricted to Kharga. Only a few of these localities have yielded fairly rich assemblages, indicating only sporadic use of this niche. No data on spatial distributions or fauna are available for these sites, so neither the sizes of the settlements nor their functions can be guessed.

A similar situation obtains for those localities found in the wadis and with the limestone plateau mud pans. The wadi occurrences are probably not entirely *in situ*, and the situation in the pans may well have been similar to that at

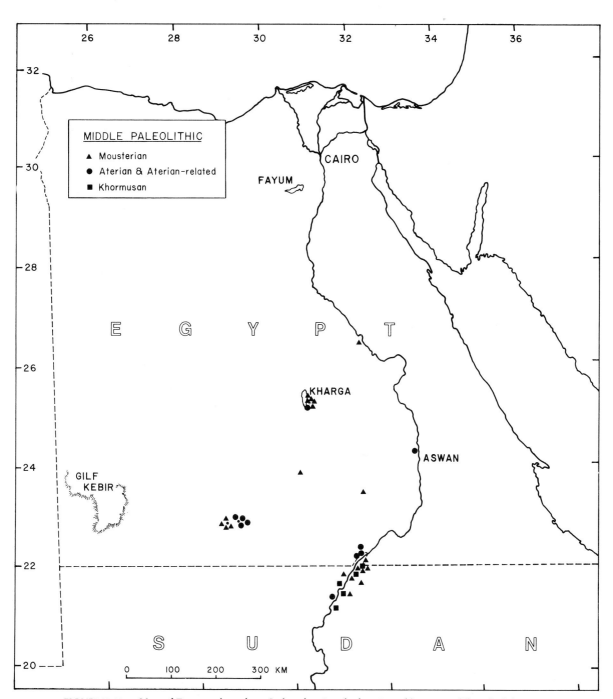

FIGURE 7.10. *Map of Egypt and northern Sudan showing the location of known Middle Paleolithic sites.*

Site E-72-4, representing only small and brief seasonal occupations.

In the Nile Valley two layers at Site 440 obviously represent occupations on dunes near the bottom of a wadi close to the river. These are the only definite living sites of this period in the valley, and they are assigned to the Aterian-related Middle Paleolithic. All other known Middle Paleolithic occurrences in the Nile Valley in Nubia occur in one of two geomorphic settings, both of which probably reflect a strong emphasis on workshop-related activities, in that they are always close to outcrops of quartzitic sandstone and are often far from any apparent water source. One of these settings is represented by sites on top of gebels where sometimes thick accumulations of artifacts occur; sites found in slope colluvia and pediments make up the second group (Guichard and Guichard 1965, 1968).

The sites in both groups are high in Levallois and yielded varying proportions of the elements normally associated with workshop activities.

The third and latest large Middle Paleolithic entity, the Khormusan, is presently known only from the Nile Valley. This restricted distribution may indicate that the Khormusan dates from the period of hyperaridity in the Western Desert that followed the Aterian. Although at least six Khormusan sites are known (ANW-3, 2004, 6G30, 1017, 34A, and 34D), and several radiocarbon dates are available, information is limited concerning settlement size, their detailed structuring, or their functional variability. All are associated with Nile sediments and seem to be near-shore occupations, probably living sites, and many of them are believed to have been repeatedly occupied (Marks 1968b).

When compared with the Acheulian, greater variability in site situation, artifact and faunal distributions, and size of occurrences is evident for the Middle Paleolithic. For the most part, this increased variability is due to the larger number of sites available and to their better preservation, but it also reflects a more complex economy and subsistence pattern during the Middle Paleolithic. Nevertheless, the data are not really sufficient for well-founded hypotheses concerning the settlement patterns and their variability through the long period of time represented by the Middle Paleolithic.

EXPLOITATION OF ENVIRONMENT AND LOCAL RESOURCES

The composition of the Middle Paleolithic fauna in the Western Desert, dominated by white rhinoceros, extinct buffalo, and extinct camel, and containing *Gazella dama*, *Gazella rufifrons*, and a zebra, indicates a more luxuriant environment than that of even the Holocene wet periods. The frequent presence of white rhinoceros, which is highly specific as a herbivore and is known to move readily in search of desirable grazing areas, implies savanna conditions moister than those found today near Lake Chad; only the black rhinoceros, which is more tolerant, lived in an exceptionally marshy microenvironment of Bahr el Ghazal (Huard 1972:208). How moist may be indicated by the present distributions of *Gazella dama* and *Gazella rufifrons*, which occur together as far south as the northern fringe of the humid tropical climate in Guinea, and at the southern limit of the semiarid belt well south of Khartoum in Sudan (Niethammer 1971:516). The annual rainfall in this southern zone varies from 300 mm in the north to 500 mm in the south, and it supports acacia woodlands and open grasslands classified as "low rainfall, woodland savannah" (Barbour 1961).

There was surely seasonality in the pattern of rainfall over the Western Desert, but whether winter or summer rains prevailed is not established. The rather tenuous evidence of beach development on the northern shore of the lake at Bir Tarfawi, however, would suggest prevailing southerly winds and thus a northward shift of the summer rainfall monsoonal belt. The animal and human populations doubtless responded to the seasonal changes in the vegetation, so that the areas with small internally drained basins would be available to the Middle Paleolithic hunters only for very restricted intervals shortly after the rains. This is a likely explanation for the low density of Middle Paleolithic sites and artifacts in these areas.

The lake areas of Bir Sahara and Bir Tarfawi, on the other hand, were a unique microenvironment in the Western Desert, with relatively large bodies of permanent open water and more luxuriant surrounding vegetation. These served as magnets to both man and the animals he hunted, particularly during the drier phases of the year. The entire desert was open for movement after the rains, but for the rest of the year the nearest permanent water may have been as far away as the natural wells existing today, the nearest of which, Bir Sheb, is at a distance of about 70 km. It seems that it was during the dry periods that animals were concentrated around the lakes and that most of the human exploitation of these areas occurred, as is indicated by the kill site of Bir Tarfawi, which was apparently simultaneous with low-water stages of the lake. These observations imply considerable mobility for the human groups.

One of the more striking aspects of the pattern of hunting is the emphasis placed upon large mammals to the exclusion of the smaller animals, such as lagomorphs, birds, fish, reptiles, and rodents. Most of the meat was provided by rhinoceros and camel, which are not only the largest animals but also the most commonly killed.

A clearly different economic emphasis is suggested for the Middle Paleolithic sites along the Nile. Data available are only for two floors from an Aterian-related Middle Paleolithic and for the Khormusan. The Aterian-related examples, both from Site 440 in the Khor Musa, show strong emphases on fishing in one instance, and on *Bos* hunting in the other, a dichotomy that may imply seasonality. In any event, the concentration on fish is one of the oldest known examples of intensive fishing. [Another example is that of the Georgian cave site of Kudaro, of Late Acheulian age (Lubin 1977).] In the Khormusan few animals other than *Bos* were hunted, an emphasis that can only be due to deliberate specialization.

Analyses of the tools and debitage from the Middle Paleolithic sites in the Western Desert suggest complex raw-material and tool economies. Although the raw-material assemblage is always dominated by varieties from local sources, there are some indications of long distance transport, such as the presence of Thebes Formation flint in the assemblage from Site BS-13—the nearest outcrop of this material is over 200 km away. This limited occurrence is taken not to suggest traffic in raw materials, but to indicate the mobility of and the distances covered by groups during the Middle Paleolithic.

Dynamic technological analysis of several Middle Stone Age assemblages from Bir Sahara and Bir Tarfawi indicated varying structures, especially in the Levallois group. Some of the assemblages, such as BS-1, show low values for the initial core-preparation group, high percentages of Levallois flakes, very few Levallois cores, but high frequencies of Levallois flakes. This situation, combined with the data on artifact distributions and site location, is believed to suggest a living site where cores that had been initially prepared at the raw-material source were finally prepared, partially exploited, and then taken elsewhere.

The assemblage from Site BS-11, a low-density scatter adjacent to the shore, was characterized by higher values for both the initial core-preparation debris and flakes from the preparation of Levallois cores, and by low frequencies of Levallois pieces (flakes, blades, points, and cores). This site is seen as a temporary stop where a number of Levallois cores were blocked out, prepared, and then taken elsewhere.

Site BS-13, on the other hand, a similar low-density scatter adjacent to the shore, has a low stress on those elements associated with both initial and advanced core preparation, and a more pronounced emphasis on finished Levallois pieces and retouched tools. In this instance Levallois pieces were brought to the site already made, were used there, and were then left. The thin, limited site of E-72-4 in the internal drainage basin in the Dyke area is somewhat similar to Site BS-13, although low in Levallois. It contained almost no cores, generally few flakes, and proportionally numerous tools.

Similar complexity in the raw material economy and in the pattern of tool production and discard characterizes the Aterian assemblages from Bir Tarfawi. Furthermore, at the kill locus of BT-14, Area A, very few stone artifacts occurred with the clusters of butchering remains, and these are composed mostly of finished and broken tools, believed in the majority of cases to have been made elsewhere, although perhaps nearby on the shore.

These data indicate a raw material and tool economy much more complex than the simple "expendable versus curating" strategies proposed by Binford (1973). Unlike the Acheulian, a considerable amount of planning is evident, involving both curating and expenditure. Site functions are obviously complex and cannot be expressed in such simplistic terms as base camps, workshops, quarries, task-group stops, or hunting camps.

Information concerning social structure and group size is extremely limited. Most of the sites were reoccupied, so that individual occupational units are masked, but there are two indications of rather small group sizes. Sites BT-14, Area C, and E-72-4 are both believed to represent single occupations, and both are characterized by small areas of activity as outlined by the scatter of artifacts. In neither instance, however, is it possible to determine if the units represented are kin, task, or social groups. We can only determine that they were relatively small.

TERMINAL PALEOLITHIC

The Aterian found in the Western Desert seems everywhere to have been associated with the last Pleistocene wet pulsation preceding the long hyperarid period that did not end until the early Holocene. The exact duration of the hyperarid period is not known because of problems of dating for the Aterian, but in any case it seems to have lasted more than 30,000 years. Nowhere in the Western Desert, or for that matter in the entire Sahara, is there firm evidence for local rainfall or spring activity during this long, dry episode. There are no traces of human occupation, except in the Nile Valley, where possibly the latest Middle Paleolithic entity, the Khormusan, and certainly several Late Paleolithic complexes, occurred (Figure 7.11).

The earliest Holocene human colonization of the Western Desert is that of the Terminal Paleolithic, which seems to have begun immediately after the onset of slightly more moist conditions. A relatively large number of sites of this period have been studied in some detail (Sites E-72-5; E-75-6, lower layer; E-75-7, lower layer; E-75-9; E-76-6; E-77-3; E-77-6; and E-77-7) from three widely separated areas representing two different geomorphic settings. One site was near spring vents in the Kharga area, and the others were all with internally drained basins, in the Dyke area or at Nabta. Several of the sites have associated radiocarbon dates, and most can be placed within local stratigraphic sequences.

CHRONOLOGY

The earliest sites seem to be contemporaneous with the beginning of Holocene playa formation in the Western Desert and do not seem to have persisted after the more arid interval separating Playas I and II. Associated radiocarbon dates place the beginning of the Terminal Paleolithic occupation at around 9000 BP, and the latest dates are at about 8300 BP; however, the site that is most recent stratigraphically (E-77-6) is not dated and it is possible that it, and some of those found farther north in the Dyke area, and at Kharga, may be contemporary with the earliest Neolithic in the south, a conclusion that is reinforced by the two radiocarbon dates of 7850 BP and 7855 BP from Site E-76-6 at Kharga.

At least three distinct taxonomic entities have been defined within the Terminal Paleolithic of the Western Desert, all of them dated. The precise chronological relationships between these entities are not known, although it seems likely that the earliest has been identified (Site E-77-7), as well as the latest (E-76-6).

The absolute chronology of the Terminal Paleolithic in the southern and central portions of the Western Desert places it as contemporaneous with the earliest Siwan assemblages in northern Egypt, dated to 8800 and 8400 BP (F. A. Hassan 1976, 1978), and with the late Arkinian

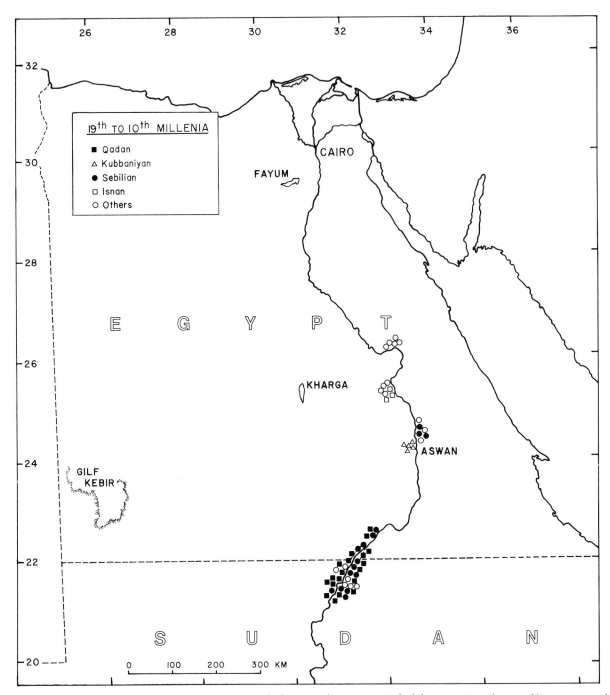

FIGURE 7.11. *Map of Egypt and northern Sudan showing the location of known Late Paleolithic sites. Note absence of known sites in the Western Desert.*

industry along the Nile, dating after 9400 BP (Schild *et al.* 1968). All but the latest Terminal Paleolithic entity in the Western Desert seem to precede the earliest Shamarkian, El Kabian, and Qarunian, dated between 8200 and 7200 BP (Wendorf and Schild 1976b). In the Maghreb during this period one finds the earliest Typical Capsian, the oldest

occurrences of the three basic facies of the Upper Capsian (the Tébessian, the Sétifian, and the Méridional), and the oldest Mellalian in the Ouargla area (Camps 1974b:274–275). In short, the Terminal Paleolithic in the Western Desert seems to date after the Iberomaurusian, and with the earliest Capsian and Capsian-related units of the Maghreb.

TAXONOMIC SETTING

The three taxonomic entities defined for the Terminal Paleolithic in the Western Desert are differentiated by their varying qualitative and quantitative characteristics, specifically the presence or absence or frequencies of certain geometric forms, backed bladelets, stemmed points, and notches and denticulates.

The oldest entity, which unfortunately is represented by only one poor assemblage (Site E-77-7), contains a high percentage of backed bladelets, mostly straight backed and arched. There are no geometrics and the notches and denticulates have moderately high values (Figure 7.12).

The second entity, found at three sites (E-77-3; E-75-6, lower layer; E-75-7, lower layer), is characterized by high frequencies of arch-, straight-, and shoulder-backed bladelets; high values for notches and denticulates and retouched pieces; low to medium indices for geometrics (both trapezes and triangles); and the presence of numerous Ounan or Harif stemmed points (Figure 7.13).

The third and most recent group, also found at three sites (E-72-5, E-76-6, and E-77-6), is distinguished by high proportions of three tool classes: triangles, almost all of the elongated variety with small short sides; denticulated and notched blades; and retouched blades. Backed bladelets are low to moderate in frequency, and stemmed points are lacking. Caton-Thompson's "Bedouin Microlithic" sites at Kharga (1952) may also belong to this group. They are all surface sites and seem to be mixed with Neolithic elements, but do contain numerous, elongated scalene triangles with small, short sides (Figure 7.14).

In addition, the assemblage from Site E-75-9 seems to be so different that it cannot be assigned to any of the three groups, although it does show some features reminiscent of the first. The assemblage is dominated by arch-backed bladelets, but there are moderate to high values for geometrics (triangles and lunates), and notches and denticulates are well represented (Figure 7.12).

All of these entities have low frequencies for burins, endscrapers, and perforators (except for Site E-77-7 where burins are slightly more numerous).

The meaning of this variation is not known. In part it may be chronological (Site E-77-7 is certainly the oldest according to its radiocarbon date), and it is possibly of geographical significance: The third group seems to have its greatest density north of the Kiseiba scarp where two of our sites and the "Bedouin Microlithic" are located. There is no basis for evaluating the functional diversity that may be represented in these groups. Nevertheless, regardless of the internal variability, all of the assemblages fall well within the Terminal Paleolithic technocomplex of North Africa. All the tool forms found in the Western Desert are well represented in almost all of the Terminal Paleolithic groups in North Africa as a whole.

On the northern fringe of the Western Desert, recent work at Siwa (F. A. Hassan 1976, 1978) has yielded several Terminal Paleolithic assemblages that share some elements with those in the central and southern portions of the Western Desert, but they are clearly different. The Siwa assemblages are composed of backed bladelets, low percentages of geometrics, and high proportions of burins. Hassan sees the closest parallels in the Qarunian assemblages from the Fayum, and the Libyco-Capsian and Neolithic of the Haua Fteah in Libya. It is interesting to note, however, that at least some of the Siwan assemblages contain elongated scalene triangles with small short sides. Apart from the emphasis on burins, and the occasional presence of bifacial elements, which may be later, the oldest Siwan assemblages seem to be generally comparable to the third and northernmost entity.

Comparison with the Terminal Paleolithic in the Nile Valley and the Fayum shows significant differences from all approximately contemporary assemblages (Arkinian, Shamarkian, El Kabian, and Qarunian). The Nilotic industries are characterized by high percentages of backed bladelets and low values for geometrics, and in this respect the oldest Western Desert entity is possibly the closest to those found along the Nile. This could be taken to suggest a Nilotic origin for the early colonization of this newly available area, but typological studies (Schild and Wendorf 1975) suggest that the later Terminal Paleolithic entities of the Western Desert had a closer relationship with the Upper Capsian in the Maghreb. This may imply a broad zone of very general cultural similarity across the semiarid early Holocene Sahara.

There is also a quite remarkable similarity between one of the Western Desert groups and certain sites in northern and central Sinai and the western Negev, but this similarity is in only one form, the stemmed point of the Harif type (Bar Yosef 1975; Bar Yosef and Phillips 1977; Bar Yosef et al. 1974; Marks and Scott 1976). Otherwise, the Harifian has a totally different tool structure, as well as basic typological differences in the groups of geometrics, truncations, and backed pieces. The Harifian also seems to be older, since all of the available radiocarbon dates place it slightly before 10,000 BP.

The stemmed points from the Western Desert seem stylistically close to the Harifian points, but some also share a certain similarity with the Ounan points of the Maghreb (Tixier 1963) and the central Sahara (Camps 1974a; Clark et al. 1973). There, the Ounan points occur within assemblages that are typologically and structurally diverse and also differ from those in the Western Desert. This would indicate a long-lasting, broad, supracultural distribution of this element, which may have been associated with a specific function.

SETTLEMENT SITUATIONS

A radically different settlement situation is evident for the Terminal Paleolithic of the Western Desert in comparison with those of earlier periods. Only two basic geomorphic associations are known: sites associated with inter-

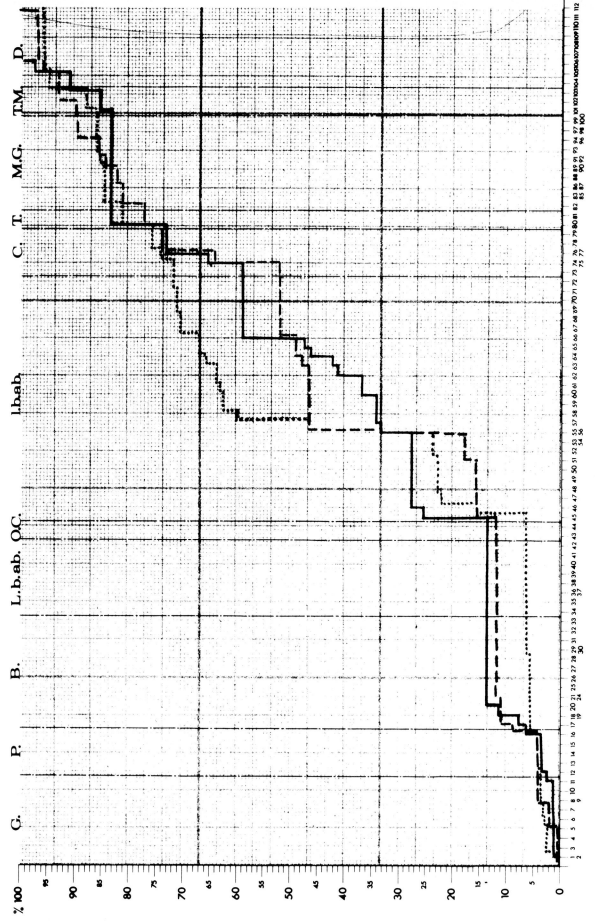

FIGURE 7.12. *Cumulative graphs comparing Site E-77-7 and Site E-75-9 in the Western Desert with the Shamarkian at Debeira West 51. Key: continuous line, Site E-77-7 (90 pieces); dashed line, DIW-51, southern part (622 pieces). Based on Tixier (1963) typology.*

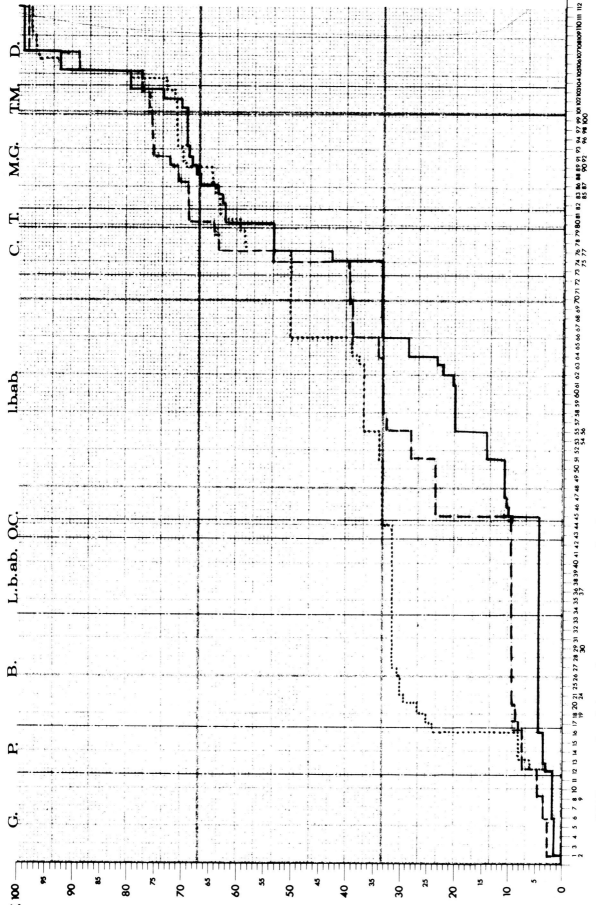

FIGURE 7.13. Cumulative graph comparing sites assigned to the second Terminal Paleolithic taxonomic group with the earliest Neolithic in the Western Desert. Key: continuous line, Site E-77-3 (431 pieces); dashed line, Site E-75-6, Terminal Paleolithic (146 pieces); dotted line, Site E-75-6, Neolithic (312 pieces). Based on Tixier (1963) typology.

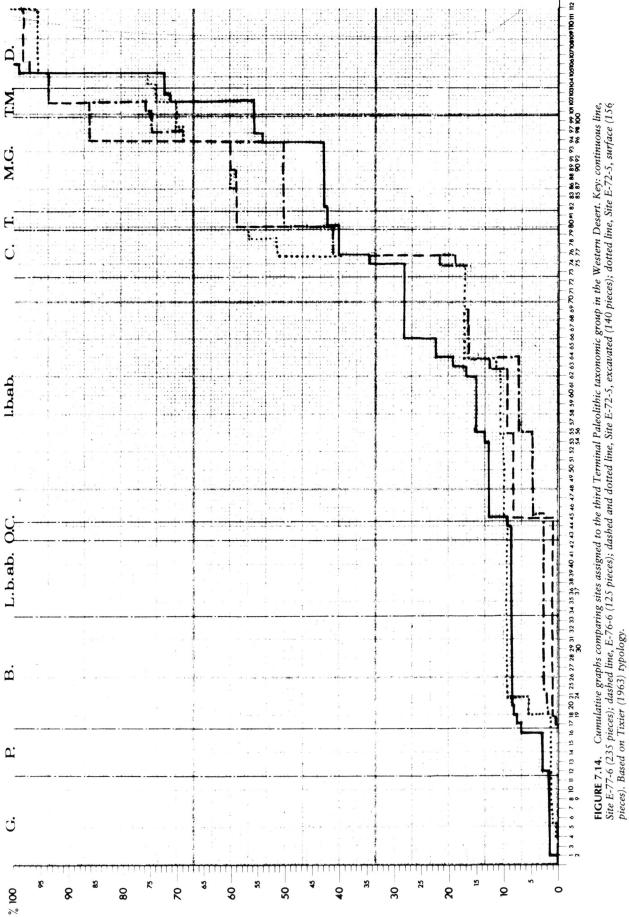

FIGURE 7.14. *Cumulative graphs comparing sites assigned to the third Terminal Paleolithic taxonomic group in the Western Desert. Key: continuous line, Site E-77-6 (235 pieces); dashed line, E-76-6 (125 pieces); dashed and dotted line, Site E-72-5, excavated (140 pieces); dotted line, Site E-72-5, surface (156 pieces). Based on Tixier (1963) typology.*

nally drained basins or playas, and sites around springs (Figure 7.15).

Sites associated with the playas are evenly distributed between two slightly different settings: (a) on dunes or on sandy eolian or playa sediments near the edge of the water (Sites E-75-6, lower layer; E-75-7; E-75-9; and E-77-3); and (b) closer to the center of the playas and on the playa silts (Sites E-72-5, E-77-6, and E-77-7). The sites of the "Bedouin Microlithic" (Caton-Thompson 1952) fall within this general group, although they cannot be placed specifically, and the Terminal Paleolithic sites at Siwa also seem to occur with internally drained basins (F. A. Hassan 1976:20).

Only one site (E-76-6) and one additional occurrence (Site E-76-7, lower layer) are associated with active artesian springs, and both are at Kharga. Apparently, and for reasons not yet understood, the geomorphic setting at Kharga permitted a reactivation of the springs sooner than else-

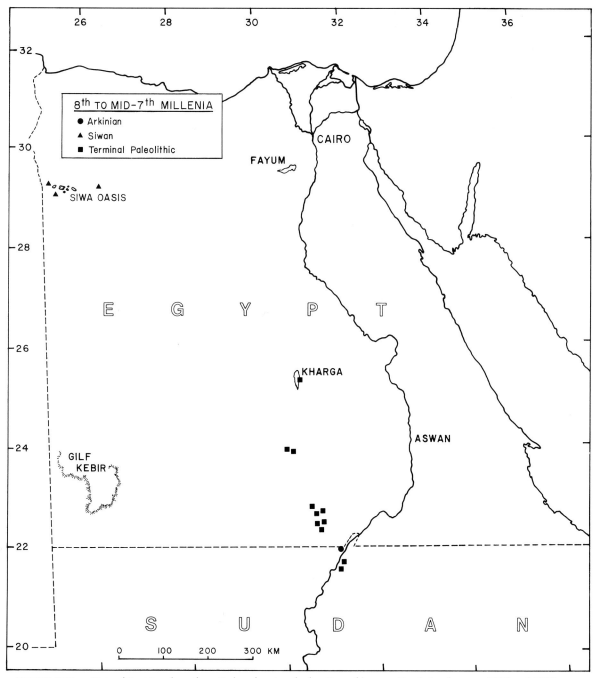

FIGURE 7.15. *Map of Egypt and northern Sudan showing the location of known sites dating between 8000 and 6500* B.C.

where in the Western Desert, where spring vents of this age are otherwise unknown. Similarly, there are no sites associated with wadi sediments, or even located near the wadis, or in the spring-fed basins of the Bir Sahara–Bir Tarfawi area.

The sites located on sandy sediments near the water's edge in the internally drained basins are always characterized by the presence of several concentrations, each presumably representing an occupational unit. It is not clear whether these are multiunit settlements or reoccupations by smaller groups, but the latter seems the more likely. All of these sites contain fauna, indicating some dependence on the hunting of small animals, possibly all that was available in the area, and they also contain grinding stones in varying frequencies.

The sites found on the playa sediments are all either single-unit settlements (Site E-77-7) or multiunit occurrences (Site E-72-5 and E-77-6), and except for one site (E-77-7) all have dense and very rich occupational debris. One of them, Site E-72-5, yielded traces of a large circular tentlike house structure. The fact that these sites were located on seasonally flooded surfaces and yet contained dense debris indicates multiple reoccupations of the same spot. Two of the sites contained numerous grinding stones, some on large, unshaped sandstone slabs that would not be easily transportable.

The only fairly rich spring site, E-76-6 at Kharga, seems to differ in a variety of ways from those with the internally drained basins. Here the site consists of a series of very small (except for one) concentrations, some of which heavily emphasize notched and denticulated blades and may be specific activity areas. There are no traces of grinding stones, a feature strikingly different from the occurrences with the internally drained basins.

EXPLOITATION OF ENVIRONMENT AND LOCAL RESOURCES

The semidry environment of the early Holocene in the Western Desert apparently could not support the megafauna characteristic of the moist phases during the Middle Paleolithic, nor was it wet enough to sustain the *large* herbivores that occurred in the littoral Maghreb in the early Holocene. Greater stress was therefore placed on lagomorphs and gazelle. It is now obvious, however, that the hunting of small animals was not the only source of food. The locations of sites and the constant presence of numerous grinding stones with large grinding surfaces demonstrate a certain dependence on cereals and/or grasses, which were harvested during dry periods, probably in the winter. The playas were the only place where there was sufficient moisture and area to support large colonies of either domesticated or wild edible grasses, a situation that today is paralleled in the Sahel (Nicolaisen 1963). The relative importances of grain and hunting are unknown, but this problem will be discussed in detail in the section on the Neolithic.

The raw-material economy of the Terminal Paleolithic is also strikingly different from that of the Middle Paleolithic. Although most sites contain a few pieces of immediately available materials (such as quartz and igneous rocks at Nabta), the overwhelming majority of lithic artifacts were made on the finest stone of the Western Desert: Eocene chert, which had to be transported large distances. A slightly different situation was seen at the Dyke area (Site E-72-5), where the most commonly used material consisted of metamorphosed rocks (chalcedony) obtained in the vicinity and quartzitic sandstone, which could also have been locally derived. Analysis of the debitage from these two materials shows strikingly different economies. The cores of metamorphic rock were prepared and exploited at the site, but almost all the cores of quartzitic sandstone were prepared elsewhere, brought in as shaped pre-cores, and then exploited (Schild and Wendorf 1977b).

The raw material economy of the Terminal Paleolithic strongly suggests that great value was attached to the quality of the raw material, thus implying either extensive trade or high mobility of groups or both.

NEOLITHIC

The largest body of data, and perhaps the most interesting, concerns the Neolithic occupation of the Western Desert. Except for isolated finds of the so-called "Peasant Neolithic" at Kharga (Caton-Thompson 1952) and those of the Libyan culture at Dungul and the playas nearby (Hester and Hoebler 1969), it has long been totally unknown, and neither of these studies of isolated surface finds could provide more than a glimpse of the full extent and significance of the early food-producing societies of northern Africa.

Early Neolithic settlements, together with those of the pre-pottery Neolithic, in the Western Desert are extremely important for the understanding of the human and environmental mechanisms responsible for the development of agriculture, for its spread, and for the shift toward increasing dependence on food production. They record the presence of developed food-producing societies in the southern Western Desert several thousand years before their appearance in the nearby Nile Valley, which would seem to be a better environment. They also record societies very differently structured from those that immediately preceded them in the same area. The example of these Western Desert societies further confirms the complexity of the development of agriculture and domestication, and of human adaptation to diverse environments. It was undoubtedly an optimal adaptation to this specific semiarid environment.

CHRONOLOGY

There are at least two playa episodes associated with the early Neolithic of the Western Desert (Playa II and Playa III). The oldest Neolithic site (E-75-6, upper layer) seems to be confined to the onset of Playa II and is securely dated by more than 10 radiocarbon dates that are within one standard deviation of 8100 BP. The dates associated with the Neolithic assigned to Playa III (Site E-77-5) show that this event began at about 7500 BP and ended after 6300 BP.

Within this period, at least four taxonomic units are recognized. The earliest, at Site E-75-6, upper layer, is associated only with early Playa II; the second is confined to an early part of Playa III (E-75-8, Layers 1 and 2; and E-77-5/5A); and the third occurs late in Playa III (Site E-75-8, Layer 3). Contemporary with an early part of Playa III is another unit found only in the Gilf el Kebir (Wadi Bakht).

The earliest Neolithic in the Western Desert is contemporary with the earliest Neolithic sites of the so-called "Sahara–Sudanese Neolithic" of the central Sahara. In the Hoggar, the earliest Neolithic dates are at Amekni, 8050 BP ± 80 years (UW-87), and at Timidouin, 8100 BP ± 130 years (Mc-484) (Camps 1974b:276). In the Tassili, at the site of Fozzigiaren, the first impressed pottery occurs just above the level dated 8072 BP ± 100 years, and in the Tibesti, at the site of Gabrong in Enneri Dirennao, pottery was found in a layer dated 8065 BP ± 100 years (Hv-2748) (Gabriel 1977b). In the Libyan Acacus Mountains, at Site Ti-n-Torha West, a series of early human occupations containing pottery has been reported. Four layers are reported. The lowest, Layer 4, dated 9080 BP ± 70 years, is without pottery. The oldest surely dated occurrence of pottery is in Layer 3, dated 8640 BP ± 70 years and 8540 BP ± 140 years. The pottery is "dotted wavy line," Early Khartoum style (Barich 1974). There are also two sites with pottery, one in the Hoggar (Site Launey), the other in the southern Sahara in Nigeria (Tamaya Mellet), with dates of 9210 BP ± 115 years (UW-97) and 9350 BP ± 170 years (Gif-1728), respectively, which have been considered too old (Camps 1974b:269). It is possible that these samples, like the one that gave the abnormally early date at Site E-75-6, are statistical anomalies or were contaminated; however, in light of recent discoveries the dates are not entirely impossible. All the remaining dates show a remarkable contemporaneity for the first appearance of pottery, in fully developed agricultural and pastoral societies, at about 8100 BP throughout a huge area across the Sahelian belt of the Sahara.

It seems likely that the earliest Neolithic settlements in the Western Desert overlap the Terminal Paleolithic for a period of at least 200 years, as indicated by the three dates between 7800 and 7900 BP from Site E-76-6 at Kharga. The stratigraphic evidence tends to confirm this conclusion. Site E-77-6 dates either to the arid phase between Playas I and II, or the very beginning of Playa II, and in the latter case it would be contemporary with the earliest Neolithic occupation of Site E-75-6, upper layer. In any event, only a few years could separate these two sites.

Farther north, at Kharga, there is a date of 5450 BP ± 80 years (SMU-741) on ostrich eggshell from a small Neolithic settlement associated with a spring vent (Site E-76-7). The materials recovered from this site, and from a series of similar spring vents and playas in the same area, all form a taxonomic unit that is totally different in technology, typology, and pottery from the early Neolithic of the southern Western Desert. It appears to be a fully developed Neolithic, and it occurs near the end of the playa formation and a period of natural spring discharge at Kharga. This and another date of 4650 BP ± 60 years (SMU-412), from the spring vent of Site E-76-4 where similar tools occurred, indicate a post-Neolithic, Early Kingdom age for this entity.

In the Nile Valley, the Terminal Paleolithic certainly persisted until the very end of the sixth millenium, and probably later. The two earliest Neolithic units from Nabta, therefore, are contemporaneous with the early Shamarkian, El Kabian, and Qarunian (Vermeersch 1976; Wendorf and Schild 1976b), and they precede the earliest Neolithic in the lower Nile Valley (Merimda Beni Salams; Derricourt 1971) and Fayum A with dates of 6391 BP ± 180 years (C-550 and C-551), 6064 BP ± 250 years (C-457), 5810 BP ± 115 years (I-4127), and 5160 BP ± 110 years (I-3469) (Barker et al. 1971; Caton-Thompson and Gardner 1934; Libby 1952; Wendorf and Schild 1976b) by nearly 2000 years.

The second and fourth Neolithic units in the Western Desert have radiocarbon dates between 7500 and 6600 BP and are contemporaneous with numerous Sahara–Sudanese sites ranging from the Tassili in the east, through the Hoggar, the Ténéré, and the Tibesti and Ennedi in the west. They are also contemporaneous with the earliest ceramic sites of the Neolithic of Capsian tradition of the northern Sahara and the Atlas Mountains, with the oldest sites of the Mediterranean Neolithic of the Algerian littoral, and with the oldest Neolithic of Haua Fteah in Cyrenaica (Camps 1974a; McBurney 1967). Thus, throughout the Sahara from its southern fringes to the Algerian littoral there were pottery-using people, some of whom were partially contemporaneous with the latest Epipaleolithic of the Maghreb, and with the final Terminal Paleolithic at Kharga and in the Nile Valley. In Nubia, a date of 6540 BP ± 110 years (Tx-1155) from the Khartoum-related site of DIW-5 reveals sporadic occurrences of this kind of Neolithic in the valley in Nubia (Shiner 1968b; personal communication).

The third Neolithic unit in the Western Desert, known only from one site at Nabta (Site E-75-8, Layer 3), dates from about 6500 BP until after 5800 BP. The close resemblance between the pottery of this unit and that of Abkan of Sudanese Nubia (with dates ranging from 5960 BP to 4470 BP; Derricourt 1971) suggests either that a typical Nilotic

Neolithic existed by this time both in the Nubian Nile Valley and in the adjacent desert and the earliest occurrence is not yet dated in the valley, or that the Sahara version preceded that found along the Nile. In any case, the Saharan unit is clearly older than the earliest dated Neolithic of the lower Nile Valley. For the latter, there are two sets of dates for Fayum A, one set obtained by the solid carbon method by Libby (1952) of 6391 BP and 6064 BP and a more recent series ranging from 5160 BP to 5810 BP (Barker *et al.* 1971; Wendorf and Schild 1976b); the solid carbon dates are consistently older and are therefore generally rejected. There is also a long series of dates from Merimda, ranging from 6250 BP to 4690 BP (Derricourt 1971).

TAXONOMIC SETTING

There are four taxonomic entities evident in the Neolithic of the Western Desert of Egypt. Three of these occur in the dated stratigraphic sequence at Nabta, and the fourth is known only from the Gilf el Kebir. A fifth entity might be represented at Kharga, but this is believed to be post-Neolithic in age (Figure 7.16).

The oldest Neolithic complex is known only from one site (E-75-6, upper layer). This is a large, organized settlement with houses, storage pits, and wells. It shows a pronounced typological similarity to a preceding Terminal Paleolithic, although the structuring of the tool kit differs in several important aspects. Here, perforators form the most important group and this tends to distort the remainder of the frequencies. The group of backed bladelets is second in importance, followed by notches, denticulates, and geometrics (among which triangles are dominant). Burins also are numerous, endscrapers are rare, and the microburin technology is present. Bladelet cores of the single- and opposed-platform varieties and change-of-orientation flake cores form the most important technological group, and in this respect, the material closely resembles the local Terminal Paleolithic. There is no trace of either bifacial retouch or polished celts. There are numerous, large, shaped, grinding stones, oval in outline and with large, deep-grinding surfaces. They differ from those of the Terminal Paleolithic in that the latter were unshaped, but the handstones in both groups are similar.

The pottery, some of the earliest known in Africa, is extremely rare but well made. The shapes are simple, the vessels are small, and the exteriors are covered by dense, impressed decorations that can be duplicated with catfish spines (Banks, this volume). It is clearly within the Early Khartoum or Sahara–Sudanese tradition. Closely similar motifs occurred at Early Khartoum where it was described as "atypical micaceous ware" (Arkell 1949: Plate 82); the paste at Nabta, however, is not micaceous.

The second Neolithic group is known from two sites: E-75-8 and E-77-5/5A. Two different types of houses are present. One is a small, slab-lined structure, and the other is closely similar to the shallow basin houses of the earliest Neolithic. There were also numerous, shallow, stone-lined

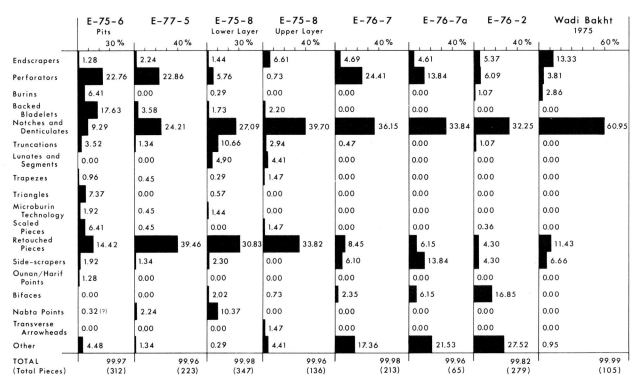

	E-75-6 Pits 30%	E-77-5 40%	E-75-8 Lower Layer 30%	E-75-8 Upper Layer 40%	E-76-7 40%	E-76-7a 40%	E-76-2 40%	Wadi Bakht 1975 60%
Endscrapers	1.28	2.24	1.44	6.61	4.69	4.61	5.37	13.33
Perforators	22.76	22.86	5.76	0.73	24.41	13.84	6.09	3.81
Burins	6.41	0.00	0.29	0.00	0.00	0.00	1.07	2.86
Backed Bladelets	17.63	3.58	1.73	2.20	0.00	0.00	0.00	0.00
Notches and Denticulates	9.29	24.21	27.09	39.70	36.15	33.84	32.25	60.95
Truncations	3.52	1.34	10.66	2.94	0.47	0.00	1.07	0.00
Lunates and Segments	0.00	0.00	4.90	4.41	0.00	0.00	0.00	0.00
Trapezes	0.96	0.45	0.29	1.47	0.00	0.00	0.00	0.00
Triangles	7.37	0.00	0.57	0.00	0.00	0.00	0.00	0.00
Microburin Technology	1.92	0.45	1.44	0.00	0.00	0.00	0.00	0.00
Scaled Pieces	6.41	0.45	0.00	1.47	0.00	0.00	0.36	0.00
Retouched Pieces	14.42	39.46	30.83	33.82	8.45	6.15	4.30	11.43
Side-scrapers	1.92	1.34	2.30	0.00	6.10	13.84	4.30	6.66
Ounan/Harif Points	1.28	0.00	0.00	0.00	0.00	0.00	0.00	0.00
Bifaces	0.00	0.00	2.02	0.73	2.35	6.15	16.85	0.00
Nabta Points	0.32 (?)	2.24	10.37	0.00	0.00	0.00	0.00	0.00
Transverse Arrowheads	0.00	0.00	0.00	1.47	0.00	0.00	0.00	0.00
Other	4.48	1.34	0.29	4.41	17.36	21.53	27.52	0.95
TOTAL (Total Pieces)	99.97 (312)	99.96 (223)	99.98 (347)	99.96 (136)	99.98 (213)	99.96 (65)	99.82 (279)	99.99 (105)

FIGURE 7.16. *Frequencies of major tool groups in several early Neolithic sites in the Western Desert.*

hearths. The associated lithic assemblage is very different from that seen before. The tool kit is dominated by two groups: retouched pieces, and notches and denticulates. Perforators are quite numerous, but geometrics are almost absent and are virtually limited to broad lunates, often with semisteep retouch. Backed bladelets occur, but are very rare, and there are only a few microburins. A characteristic group is the series of points formed by truncated bases, with either naturally pointed or retouched tips. There are also rare bifacial points and a few stemmed points, sometimes with bifacial retouch. Pecked and polished stone celts occur. The grinding stones cannot be distinguished from those in the earliest Neolithic.

The pottery, although still within the "Khartoum–Sahara–Sudanese" tradition, is radically different. It is noticeably more friable than that of the earliest Neolithic, and two major groups are represented. The more numerous is decorated with various kinds of smeared impressions, including woven mat, dragged comb, and punctates. The second variety of pottery is a plainware, thicker than the decorated and lighter in color. The vessels seem to be limited to large bowls, and decorations, when they occur, are confined to the upper portion.

As has been already observed (Camps 1974a; Hays 1971, 1975), although there is a very general resemblance in pottery style across a huge area, the Sahara–Sudanese Neolithic is composed of numerous individual taxonomic units, each with distinctive ceramic and lithic features. This would suggest that many different cultural groups may have been involved in the introduction of the earliest Neolithic into the southern and central Sahara (Kobusiewicz 1976).

The third unit, found only in the upper portion of Site E-75-8, is represented by a poor lithic assemblage containing mainly notches and denticulates and retouched pieces indistinguishable from those found within the second unit. Geometrics are very rare and are limited to a few lunates and trapezes. Transverse arrowheads are also occasionally present, and only a few fragments of backed bladelets occur. There is no trace of microburin technology. Bifacial points are found, but rarely. Pecked and polished celts are present, and there are numerous grinding stones similar to those in the lower layers. Caches of side-blow flakes and various sidescrapers seem to be associated with this level.

The pottery shows no resemblance to that of the Sahara–Sudanese tradition. It is well made, hard, and includes some burnished and some smudged and burnished examples, and a buff-colored ware with incised straight lines parallel to the rim. There are no painted decorations. The closest parallel to this pottery seems to be that from the Abkan Neolithic in the Nubian Nile Valley (Ware Groups M, and one example; Ware Group K—in Nordström 1972, and personal communication).

The fourth Neolithic entity in the Western Desert, found only at Wadi Bakht in the Gilf el Kebir, is represented in our collection by a "grab sample" that probably derived from several different settlements covering an unknown period of time. It differs from the material from another location in the same, blocked wadi, which was collected by Myers (Bagnold et al. 1939) and studied by McHugh (1971).

The lithic artifacts in our sample are heavily dominated by denticulates, mostly denticulated blades. Endscrapers, retouched pieces, and sidescrapers are the three next most important forms, and geometrics and backed elements are absent. Bifacial pieces and polished celts also seem to be lacking.

The Myers collections are from three localities: two across the wadi from our site and the other upstream from it near the upper edge of the playa. Retouched pieces are the most numerous, followed by denticulates, notches, endscrapers, and perforators. Geometrics and backed bladelets also occur, but bifacial pieces and celts are absent (McHugh 1971).

The pottery from our locality seems to be generally similar to that described by McHugh. All of it is well made and includes three varieties of burnished wares: simple burnished, smudged and burnished, and burnished and impressed. Other pieces have incised or comb-impressed decorations. Vessel forms are more complex than those of Early Khartoum, and include outward flaring rims and constricted necks. Traces of either fiber temper or plant inclusions in the clay are also evident on most sherds. Similar design motifs have been reported on pottery from southern Libya, west of the Gilf el Kebir (Vita-Finzi and Kennedy 1965) and from Uweinat (de Heinzelin et al. 1969; Van Noten, personal communication).

The fifth taxonomic unit, previously described as "Peasant Neolithic," but regarded by us as probably later and of Dynastic Age, is represented at several sites near Kharga. The lithic assemblages are dominated by notches and denticulates, with endscrapers, sidescrapers, and perforators also frequent. Bifacial pieces of various sizes, usually unfinished, are also important. Large, chipped stone "hoes" are characteristic of all the assemblages in this group. The technology is based on various flake cores, and the working of thin chert slabs.

The associated pottery is handmade, hard, and tempered with either coarse sand or fine sand. It is sometimes red-slipped or smudged, but is never otherwise decorated. It would seem to be different from all other pottery known from the Western Desert.

SETTLEMENT SITUATIONS

Although there is an extensive body of data available from the Neolithic of the Western Desert, the number of localities studied is small compared with that of the Terminal Paleolithic. This situation does not reflect the number of sites, for Neolithic sites were undoubtedly the most numerous and apparently the most extensive in the desert. Unfortunately, most of them are heavily deflated and destroyed. The few good sites found required the excavation of large areas, consuming a great deal of time, so that altogether fewer sites were excavated, even though the greater part of three seasons was devoted to this period (Figures 7.17 and 7.18).

Almost all of the Neolithic sites are related to playas or playa-like situations; there are a few sites at Kharga that are associated with springs and spring pools. No sites were found associated with wadis. As with the Terminal Paleolithic, there are two different geomorphic situations within the playas: The first of these is the settlements near the water's edge (Site E-75-6 and E-75-8); the second is on playa silts, often near the center (E-77-5/5A). Wadi Bakht must be seen essentially as a playa, albeit somewhat different since it occurs in a relatively narrow wadi, which

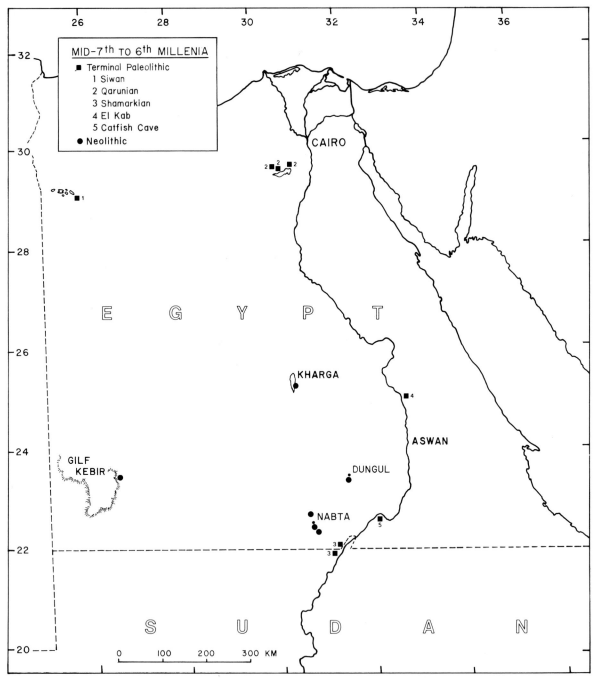

FIGURE 7.17. *Map of Egypt and southern Sudan showing the location of known sites dating between 6500 and 5000* B.C. *Note occurrence of several Terminal Paleolithic entities in the Nile Valley and northern desert during this period, contemporary with the early Neolithic in the southern Western Desert.*

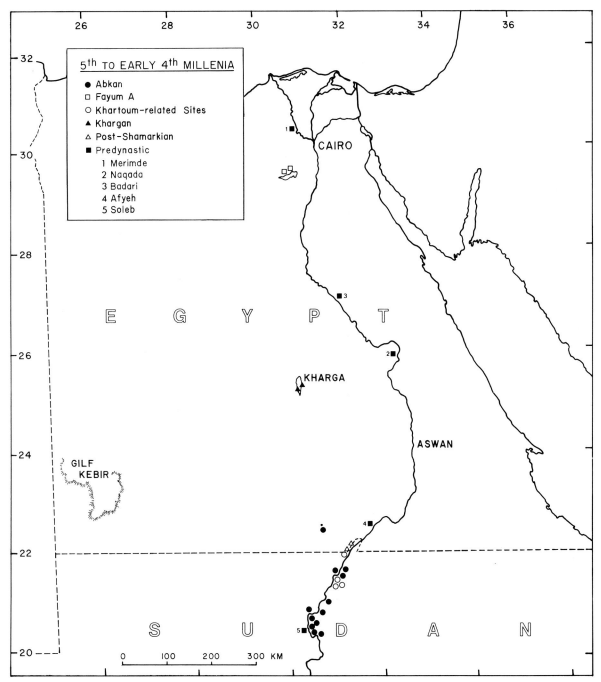

FIGURE 7.18. *Map of Egypt and northern Sudan showing the location of Neolithic sites occupied between 5000 and 3000 B.C. Note shift of the Neolithic to the Nile Valley.*

limits the area suitable for habitation, and artifacts occur throughout: at the edge of the playa; on the playa silts; on slope wash adjacent to the cliffs; and on dunes blocking the wadi. Our collection and, probably, those of Myers come from the edge of the playa.

The two studied sites that were located at the edge of playas seem to represent organized settlements, possibly of permanent or semipermanent nature and perhaps most

closely resembling a small village or hamlet. At Site E-75-6 this is indicated by the planned, logical arrangement of houses and storage pits; the number of houses and their organization indicate a relatively large and disciplined community. The settlement obviously had a certain duration, and the storage pits, most of which are granaries, must have been located above groundwater level throughout the period of their use.

At Site E-75-8 the situation could have been closely similar. In this case, however, the site was repeatedly occupied for a much longer time, as is indicated by the series of superimposed hearths in the test trench, and the excavations, though extensive, did not open a sufficiently large area to reveal the kind of settlement organization. Here also storage pits are present, heavy grinding stones are numerous, and large pottery storage jars are frequent.

On the playa silts the character of occupation is radically different, and is not uniform. There are two kinds of houses and two kinds of cultural debris accumulations. The first is represented by slab-lined houses occurring singly or in small groups, and characterized by a minimal number of associated stone artifacts and pottery. The second situation is represented by shallow basin houses or tent floors, also occurring singularly or in small groups, but associated with relatively rich lithic debris. Pottery is present, but not numerous, and there are few large grinding stones. These playa settlements must be regarded as seasonal, not merely because of their character, but primarily because of their location in areas that were seasonally flooded.

Our observations in many other playas below the Kiseiba scarp, at sites that were not excavated, indicate that this basic dichotomy in settlement character occurs throughout. The larger and richer sites always occur on rises within the playas or at their edges, whereas the smaller, poorer occurrences are found on the playa silts.

The southern Western Desert is strewn with thousands of deflated concentrations of burned rocks. In most cases these occur in small, shallow sand pans, either without any associated artifacts or with only a few, uncharacteristic pieces. Pottery never occurs, probably because of eolian destruction. These deflated hearths received only our most casual attention, and thus we have no data on their distribution or possible cultural associations. Similar deflated hearths in the eastern central Sahara, however, have been studied by Gabriel (1973, 1976, 1977a, 1977b). There are 19 radiocarbon dates (mostly on collagen) from these hearths, ranging from 9880 BP ± 70 years (Hv-5485) to 3375 BP ± 140 years (Hv-5620) (Gabriel 1977a:28), and three chronological phases are defined: Early (7500 to 5700 BP), Main (5700 to 5400 BP), and Final (5400 to 4100 BP). They are interpreted as brief stops by nomadic pastoralists during the Neolithic.

Although deflated hearths seem to occur almost everywhere in the Western Desert, large and dense Neolithic settlements are present only south of the Kiseiba scarp. This may reflect both the physiography of the area—that is, the apparent absence in the north of large internally drained basins, except those at Dakhla and Kharga—and the diminishing gradient of rainfall toward the north.

At Kharga the situation is entirely different from that seen farther south. Near the springs and spring pools (Sites E-76-1 and E-76-7/7A), the occurrences are relatively small, but dense. There are no traces of architecture or pits, and large grinding stones are rare to absent. Those located in the playa silts (Sites E-76-2 and E-76-8) are also small and dense. An entirely different subsistence system and settlement organization seem likely for these sites.

EXPLOITATION OF ENVIRONMENT AND LOCAL RESOURCES

The subsistence economy of the Neolithic included three major elements: hunting of small animals (gazelle and lagomorphs), agriculture (plus gathering), and cattle husbandry. The relative importance of each of these elements cannot be determined, although the character of the settlements suggests a considerable stress on agriculture, barley and wheat for the most part. The importance of cattle husbandry is unknown, but its existence is shown by the occasional presence of *Bos* bones, which are interpreted, because of both size and occurrence in this ecological situation, as most probably from domesticated forms. The rare presence of these bones should not necessarily be taken to indicate either their scarcity or their low importance in the economy; it is probable that the cattle were not utilized for meat, but for milk and blood, a pattern that is widespread in Africa today. The common occurrence of hare and gazelle in all Neolithic sites indicated that these were the major sources of meat, and the varying frequencies of these two forms are believed to reflect ecological changes. The role of gathering is suggested by the presence of dom and date palm, and a number of wild grasses may also have been harvested, as they are today in the Sahel belt of Africa.

The available data permit only a rather simple model for early Neolithic exploitation of the Western Desert. Although the data are from several sites occurring in different areas, and over a considerable span of time, no two are quite alike; if they had been, this might have provided some confirmation of the proposed model. The dichotomy observed in the location of the sites, which is paralleled by differences in structure, indicates the existence of permanent or semipermanent villages or hamlets near the playas, located on high ground beyond the reach of the water's seasonal fluctuations, and of small, obviously seasonal camps on the playa surfaces. The simplest interpretation of this is that the small sites on the playas were occupied during planting or harvesting, or possibly both. The large sites, on the other hand, seem to represent the main settlements, which were socially structured, and where the major food preparation and storage occurred. The ground plan of Site E-75-6, with two lines of separate small households and associated granaries, strongly suggests that the basic unit of the society was that of the nuclear family.

No such organization is apparent in the playa sites, and their small size and isolation may suggest either single-family units or task groups. Regardless of the social implications of these small playa sites, however, the simplest model calls for their use as seasonal camps either during late summer after the playa had become sufficiently dry for cultivation, or during the winter harvest. There are no means of determining the relationships between any of the permanent settlements and the small playa sites, so it is not known if permanent settlements dispatched groups to the nearby playa only, or if a wide area and several playas were utilized simultaneously. The extent of nomadism imposed by the intensity of cattle husbandry may have been considerable, to judge from modern ethnographic analogies.

There is a large body of data available from a number of modern pastoralist and agricultural societies in northern sub-Saharan Africa (Cunnison 1966; Dyson-Hudson and Dyson-Hudson 1969; Evans-Pritchard 1940). These provide a very wide range of variation in the exploitation of basically similar environments. Thus almost any combination of social and economic patterns could be applied to the interpretation of the early Neolithic in the Western Desert. We will try to avoid this temptation, but there are basic resemblances shared by almost all of the Sahelian and sub-Sahelian groups.

One feature that all of them seem to share is some degree of nomadism, the extent of which is determined by the availability of water for the cattle. Water, in turn, is dependent not only on the amount of rainfall but also on the local geomorphology and soil lithology. Another shared feature is varying dependence on seasonal agriculture and gathering. For example, the Humr of the Baggara Arabs of southwestern Kordofan maintain millet and cotton gardens in areas of the northern range of their annual migration. These are planted in June and July and harvested in December. The cattle are pastured throughout the area during this period, and are then moved back south after the harvest (Cunnison 1966).

A study of modern cattle distribution and its relation to annual rainfall in the Sudan (McHugh 1971, 1974) has indicated that cattle can be successfully raised in the semiarid belt that receives rainfall between 400 and 625 mm per year. In areas of lower rainfall, between 200 and 400 mm, cattle can be maintained only where there are permanent sources of water. Goats, sheep, and camels can be raised where the rainfall is between 100 and 200 mm per year, but, again, only when permanent water is available. There is no doubt that permanent water was available in the larger playas throughout most of the Holocene wet phases, either on the surface after the rains or by digging wells. Cattle could, therefore, be maintained with the rainfall inferred for the southern portion of the Western Desert.

Another example of seasonal desert agriculture is found among the Bedouin now settled along the Nile in central Egypt, in the Isna–Idfu area. These groups utilize playas and blocked, silt-filled wadis in front of and within the adjacent Eocene plateau. At least six such localities were recently utilized and owned by one kin band, and all contain fine-grained, silt sediments of playa character.

Detailed data are available for the wadi of Ramdiin, which has been used during the last 200 years by the Mariif kin group of the Awazim tribe. The wadi is blocked by a dune and provides a cultivable area of about 4 feddans (1 feddan equals 1.038 acres). Nearby unblocked wadis were used for goat and sheep grazing. Although Wadi Ramdiin has not been used for the past 30 years, allegedly because of lack of rainfall, when last cultivated it apparently produced crops greater than would be produced on the equivalent surface on the Nile floodplain. It was used after rains, winter or summer, once every 3 to 5 years. A group of up to 20 people would be dispatched from the main settlement near Isna 2 to 3 days after rain was observed above the Eocene plateau. The trip to the wadi took 1 or 2 days, either on foot or by camel. The group remained there about 1 month, camping nearby (but erecting no structures) and obtaining their drinking water from natural limestone pools. No fertilizer was used, the land was not plowed, and the seed was planted in holes dug with hoes. The crop planted depended on the season of the year. After summer rains they planted maize and melons; in the winter, wheat and barley. The harvest, which occurred from 2 to 4 months later, was done by a smaller group, composed entirely of men, and required about 1 month until all of the grain was in sacks ready to transport back to the village on the Nile. Grinding of the grain was limited to that needed for use by the harvesting group, and prehistoric grinding stones were often used for this purpose. According to Eyde Mariif, who participated in the last few harvests at Wadi Ramdiin, the yield was about 8 *ardabs* (each *ardab* is 144 kg) per feddan for wheat, and 12 to 15 *ardabs* per feddan for barley. This was considerably higher than the yield from their land on the floodplain near Isna, which gave only from 5 to 6 *ardabs* of wheat and 10 *ardabs* of barley per feddan. On a recent visit to Wadi Ramdiin, we found that stalks of maize were still visible on the playa surface even though the area had not been used for over 30 years (Figure 7.19).

The Bedouin model, if combined with pastoralism and considerable north–south seasonal displacements, might bear some resemblance to the Neolithic pattern of playa and desert use in the Western Desert, although it appears

FIGURE 7.19. *Playa and cultivated area behind dune blocking Wadi Ramdiin. Figure is holding stalks of maize.*

that the Nile was not utilized during dry periods and that there was much more dependence on hunting during the Neolithic.

The data from Kharga are inconclusive. The small size of the occupations, the lack of structures, the scarcity of pottery, and the rarity of grinding stones all suggest a different subsistence and/or social pattern for these sites. These differences may indicate either specialized activities, as for sites located on the playas at Nabta, or perhaps different economic stress with more emphasis on pastoralism and less on agriculture. Our perception of these sites might have to be revised, however, if the large stone "hoes" were indeed used for agricultural purposes.

Elsewhere in the southern and central Sahara the available data concerning patterns of exploitation and settlement structuring in early Neolithic are rather poor. The earliest indications of agriculture are two pollen grains of millet found at Amekni (Camps 1969a, 1974a). In Libya, north of the Tibesti, several localities have yielded seemingly domestic Bos associated with human occupation. These sites have several radiocarbon dates between about 8000 and 2600 BP (Gabriel 1977b:51–54). The earliest certainly domestic Bos are from Uan Muhuggiag in the Acacus foothills in southwestern Fezzan, Libya, dated to about 4000 BC, and from Agorass-in-Tast, in Adrar Bous, Niger, at about the same date; both of these are short-horned cattle. There are no traces of barley or settlement organization until the latest Neolithic at sites such as Tichit-Oualta (Camps 1974a).

Data concerning settlement sizes, their structuring, variability, and the geomorphic microenvironments utilized in this area are also scarce. Most of the sites have been only tested. Many of them have not yet been described in detail, and some of the most important ones are caves or rockshelters. At present, therefore, it is not possible to propose a model for the Neolithic adaptations to the physiographically diverse areas of the central and southern Sahara. There must have been some variability, as is indicated, for example, by the presence of fish at some sites and their absence at others, but how this might have been related to the micro- and macroenvironments of the area is unknown.

The raw-material economy of the earliest Neolithic differs significantly from that found in the later Neolithic. The earliest Neolithic is very similar to the Terminal Paleolithic in this respect, except for a significant increase in the use of quartz and quartz crystals, which occur in the nearby basement rocks. The flint was obtained from the Eocene plateau, a considerable distance away, and is almost all of excellent quality.

The Neolithic associated with Playa III differs significantly not only in tool structure but also in raw material. Although a small amount of the excellent Eocene flint is still used, quartz is the major raw material, accompanied by silicified limestone, jasper, chalcedony, agate, and other metamorphic rocks that occur in the Western Desert as small pebbles. Toward the end of Playa III, stress is placed on the use of natural, thin, Eocene chert slabs as witnessed

by the frequent occurrence of caches of this material at several sites of the period.

This increased use of quartz and other poor-quality material in the Neolithic of Playa III recalls the similar shift accompanying the appearance of early Neolithic settlements in the Nile Valley of Nubia, in late Shamarkian, Khartoum-related, Abkan, and A-Group assemblages (Nordström 1972; Schild et al. 1968; Shiner 1968a). These technological changes, and the accompanying decrease in the frequencies of geometrics, backed elements, and other tools requiring the production of bladelets, may accompany a changing economic structure within the early Neolithic societies in both the Nile Valley and the Western Desert, perhaps the increasing dependence on food production. The progression of this shift can be traced through the early Neolithic sequence in the Western Desert, from Site E-75-6 to E-77-5 to E-75-8. In the Nile Valley, on the other hand, the earliest Neolithic settlements seem already to have made this shift, probably a reflection of their younger age.

PHYSICAL TYPE OF EARLY NEOLITHIC POPULATIONS

Human osteological remains from the Western Desert are extremely scarce, but tantalizing. Despite the obviously dense Neolithic population in this area, no cemeteries were found, and only four burials were seen, of which only one was sufficiently well preserved for analysis. Another double burial was found just below the surface of the uppermost layer of Site E-75-8, but this was not analyzed and its date cannot be determined. Stains of copper on one arm bone may indicate that it postdates the latest recognized occupation of the site. The one analyzed burial cannot be placed precisely within the sequence of Site E-75-8, but its geomorphic location suggests an association with the earliest occupation of the site. Analysis of the lower jaw has been interpreted as showing close resemblances to Negroidal populations (Henneberg et al., this volume).

This observation agrees with several previous physical determinations on early Neolithic populations from the central and southern Sahara. From Khartoum in the south, and from there westward across the Sahara, skeletal remains of at least two types of Negroidal populations are believed to occur: one is gracile, and the other is more robust and is called "Sudanese" (Camps 1969b; Chamla 1968). In the Nubian Nile Valley, the Neolithic population in all of the recognized groups is believed to be also Negroid, and is clearly different from the robust Mechtoid skeletons found associated with the Late Paleolithic there. Several Mechtoid graveyards and individual graves are reported from near Isna in the north to Gebel Sahaba in the south, ranging in age from about 18,000 to 12,000 BP. They are associated with both Fakhurian and Qadan industries (Anderson 1968; Armelagos et al. 1965; Butler 1974). There are no skeletal remains from the Terminal Paleolithic in either the Nile Valley or the Western Desert.

8

Some Thoughts on the Origin of Food Production in Northeast Africa

The problem of the origin of food production has been a major focus of scholarly interest for more than two decades. Most of this interest has been concentrated on the Near East, long believed to be the earliest center of domestication for both animals and grain, and a number of theories have been advanced.

One such is the "Oasis Theory" of Childe (1936), which had, in fact, been suggested by Peake in 1928. This holds that the increased aridity during the late Quaternary confined human groups and the as-yet-undomesticated grasses and animals within certain moister, but limited, areas. Rather later, Braidwood (1960) proposed, in his "Hilly Flanks" theory, that the first domestication of cereals must have occurred in the area where the wild relatives of these grow today. Implicit in this theory was the assumption that there had been no significant change in the climate of the area since the early Holocene.

A number of authors have advanced slightly varying explanations for the origins of agriculture in the Near East, all of which share a more or less pronounced stress on population pressure as the most decisive factor (Binford 1968; Flannery 1969; Reed 1977; Smith 1972; Smith and Young 1972). Perhaps the most extreme presentation of this view was by Cohen (1975, 1977). All of these seem to have been stimulated by Boserup (1965) and her study of the effects of population pressure upon agricultural production (but see also Farris 1975; Spooner 1972). A number of criticisms have been voiced against these rather simplistic explanations, of which the most notable are those of Bronson (1972, 1975) and Polgar (1975), who advocate a complex interaction of many agencies in the origins of agriculture.

Several explanations have also been offered for the appearance of food production in northern Africa, the Nile Valley, and the Sahara (Butzer 1976; Clark 1971, 1976; Harlan et al. 1976; B. D. Shaw 1976; Smith 1972). Clark sees domestic animals spreading from the Nile Valley and gradually diffusing from there throughout Africa. Local grains, on the other hand, were not domesticated prior to around 2000 BC, when the increasing desiccation forced the desert population to turn toward agriculture (Clark 1976:79). Shaw has a somewhat similar view, postulating the importance of population pressure due to increased aridity, a modification of the Oasis Theory of Childe. Smith has proposed that changes in population pressure resulting from fluctuations in population density in relation to resources were a causal factor. Harlan et al. suggest multiple origins for African domesticates, but also infer that the desiccation of the Sahara forced hunter–gatherers to move southward into zones already intensively exploited, which resulted in stresses leading to manipulation of the plant populations (1976:18). Butzer (1971a:591, 1976:9) believes in a late date for the appearance of agriculture in the Nile Valley and suggests that it failed to develop there earlier because the broad spectrum hunting-and-gathering economies were so well adapted to the local environment that they successfully resisted the introduction of food production.

Our own interest in the beginning of food production in the Nile Valley began in a late phase of the Nubian Salvage Campaign when the first sites containing numerous shaped grinding stones and lustrous edged pieces (presumably sickles) were found near Tushka in Egyptian Nubia in a site with a radiocarbon date on charcoal of 14,550 BP ± 490 years (WSU-315). Several more recent dates on carbonates from the site are believed to be contaminated and have been rejected since they conflict with the stratigraphic setting of the site (Wendorf 1968:940; Wendorf and Schild 1976b:275). At about the same time, the Yale Expedition excavated another site with numerous grinding stones at Kom Ombo (Gebel Silsila IIB, Area 1), which has dates of 13,560 BP ± 120 years (Y-1447, on *Unio*) and 13,070 BP ± 120 years (Y-1375, on charcoal) (Butzer and Hansen 1968:140; Reed 1966). Subsequently, during our work farther north in Egypt near Isna, another series of sites with grinding stones and sickle blades was excavated and found to date between 12,600 to 12,000 BP (Wendorf and Schild 1976b:289). All three of these cases are associated with drastically different taxonomic units: the first is Qadan; the second most closely resembles the Afian (Phillips, personal communication); and the last is Isnan.

Our interpretation of these discoveries (Wendorf and Schild 1976c) has undergone considerable change, particularly in the light of work in the Western Desert, which has provided a much better understanding of the environmental fluctuations in the Nile Valley and surrounding areas. Furthermore, the discovery of food-producing societies at an early date in the Western Desert necessitated a considerable rethinking of the Nilotic data.

All three known occurrences of grain-dependent societies are securely located within the "Sahaba–Darau" aggradation of the Nile, which is dated between 14,500 and 12,000 BP. Except for the site at Kom Ombo, which is not yet adequately described, the other areas, Tushka and Isna, are on the west bank and are in generally similar microenvironmental settings. They are located in valley embayments and existed during a period of high Nile. This high Nile greatly reduced the area of the floodplain along the main channel in those areas where the cliffs abut the river, but extended it up the wadis and embayments. The sites are all associated with accumulating dunes, interdunal seepage ponds, or with floodplain immediately adjacent to the dunes in areas where moisture would remain trapped after the flood had receded. The absence of tropical diatom flora and the presence of a few paleoarctic forms in one of these ponds near Isna suggest cooler summer temperatures than those of today.

The evidence accumulated from the Western Desert for this interval shows that the entire high desert of Egypt was hyperarid and almost certainly drier than today. Along the Nile, this hyperarid climate is reflected in the accumulation of massive dune-fields in the embayments and wadis along the west bank from Ballana in Egyptian Nubia (see Wendorf 1968:829) at least to Isna, where some of the dune sands were initially interpreted as beach deposits (Wendorf and Schild 1976b:65).

In none of these sites were actual grains of the utilized grasses found. At Tushka, however, pollen of large unidentified grasses and wheat rust spores were recovered from the interdunal pond sediments containing the grinding stones and lustrous edged pieces of the Qadan industry (Wendorf 1968:940–946). The best clue to the identity of the utilized grasses came from another interdunal pond at Isna, where relatively numerous fossil pollen grains were present in the diatomaceous sediment. The pollen assemblage included some boreal types, which obviously resulted from long-distance transport, but pollen of aquatic plants was absent, thus indicating the ephemeral character of the ponds, and the remaining elements suggested a grassland environment. Throughout the diatomaceous pond-sediments were occasional large, grass, pollen grains of cereal type, which have been tentatively identified as barley (Dabrowski, in Wendorf and Schild 1976b:73–74). These become suddenly numerous (between 10% and 15% of the total pollen) near the top of the sequence, coinciding with the beginning of a nearby occupation (Site E71K14, D) of the Isnan industry. Sites assigned to the Isnan industry are numerous, large, and rich, and contain grinding stones and frequent pieces with lustrous edges, showing microscopic traces of wear typical for flint sickle-blades (Wendorf and Schild 1976b:391–392).

The dramatic increase in the cereal-type pollen and the synchronous arrival of the Isnan industry may be interpreted either as the introducing of planted cereals by man, or as reflecting the effects of human protection of naturally occurring cereals and the elimination of their competition. In our initial interpretation we favored the second possibility, but more recent data demand some reevaluation.

Important among these new data is that the adjacent desert, or the Western Desert at least, was almost certainly hyperarid with no local rainfall. The Eastern Desert may have been slightly different: There is some evidence of wadi activity during this period along the east bank (Butzer and Hansen 1968; Giegengack 1968; Wendorf and Schild 1976b:146–149), but it should be noted that these wadis drain from the Red Sea Hills, which, because of their high altitude and the patterns of atmospheric circulation, receive comparatively high rainfall even today (Rognon and Williams 1977:293). Thus, the only available moisture along the western bank of the Nile Valley came from the summer floods and the seepage ponds adjacent to the floodplain, where water was retained for longer periods. This situation of a hyperarid climate and summer flooding is of considerable importance if the cereal-type pollen has been correctly identified as barley. The natural habitat of barley today, as known from Cyrenaica, the Egyptian littoral, and the upland areas of the Near East, is confined to areas that receive winter rainfall (Harlan and Zohary 1966). Wild barley normally cannot compete successfully with other grasses under conditions of summer rainfall. It is believed, however, that with cool summer temperatures and late summer moisture, wild barley could well flourish (Harlan, *in litt.*).

These problems were paramount in our minds when we returned, in 1978, to the Nile Valley at Wadi Kubbaniya where we had previously (in 1967) located extensive Late Paleolithic settlements having grinding stones, mortars, and pestles. The excavation of these sites, together with extensive geological work and accompanying radiocarbon measurements, yielded intriguing new data concerning early plant domestication.

All of the Kubbaniya sites containing grinding equipment are located in the lower portion of silts and interfingering dunes of the early final Pleistocene Nile aggradation (Figure 8.1). A series of eight radiocarbon dates ranging from 18,250 BP ± 290 years (SMU-591) to 16,960 BP ± 210 years (SMU-599) places these occupations within the earliest known Late Paleolithic occurrences in the Nile Valley. The reconstruction of the paleoenvironment based on lithostratigraphy and morphology indicates a microenvironment of accumulating dunes adjacent to a rising Nile floodplain. Seasonal seepage ponds formed in the interdunal lows and behind the dune barrier. The wadi was dry throughout this period and contributed no sediments. The Western Desert was the immediate source of the dunes, which were invading the wadi from the north, just as they do today. The total setting clearly indicated an environmental situation where the only source of moisture was the Nile floods, and the desert was hyperarid, perhaps even drier than today.

The associated archaeology is dominated by partially backed bladelets with Ouchtata retouch, with rare scaled pieces, burins, endscrapers, retouched pieces, notches, and denticulates. The technology is based on single- and opposed-platform bladelet cores, with rare change-of-orientation cores, and occasional Levallois and Halfan type specimens. Typological and stylistic analysis of the assemblages indicates close resemblances with Site E71K13 near Isna, 150 km to the north (Phillips 1973), and slightly more distant parallels with some Halfan sites near Wadi Halfa, in Sudanese Nubia. The resemblances to Site E71K13 are further reinforced by the rare use and curation of an identical variety of Egyptian flint in both localities.

The faunal remains include wild cattle (*Bos primigenius*) and hartebeest (*Alcelaphus buselaphus*) as the most common, as well as gazelle and occasional hippopotamus bones. Fish were very numerous at the sites in the dunes, and birds were frequent. The latter are of particular interest because they include species that are winter visitors to Egypt, indicating that the sites associated with the grinding equipment were occupied during the winter.

Numerous well-preserved, carbonized (but not burned) plant remains were recovered from two of the Kubbaniya

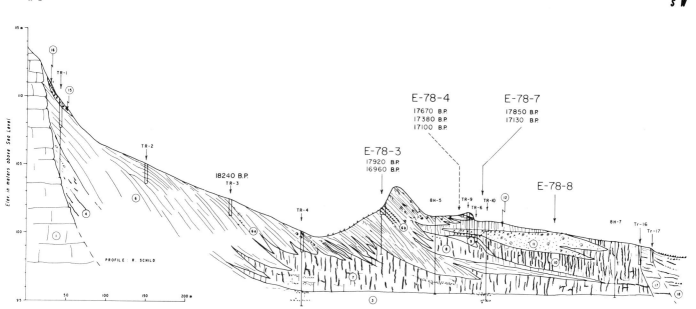

FIGURE 8.1. *Cross-section through Wadi Kubbaniya. Key: 1, Nubia sandstone; 3, wadi sand, gravels, and silts under clastic series in left section of wadi; 4, sandy slope wash, laminated, with eolian sand, pebbles, and angular fragments of Nubia sandstone; 6, eolian sand dune, progressing from northern scarp toward south and contemporaneous with Nile clastic series (7); very deflated, reduced in height, showing almost uniquely foreset beds and foreset slopes interfingering with silt layers invading the dune; contains lenses of charcoal (6a) and numerous cultural layers at Sites E-78-3 (6b) and E-78-4; snails (mostly* Bulinus truncatus) *on foreset, washed slopes; 7, undifferentiated silt and sandy silt bed interfingering with earlier dune; 8, sandy silt and silty sand with clear eolian sand admixture; 9, coarse to fine, cemented, eolian sand in slightly silty matrix; 10, lower vertisol clay bed with angular, medium to small, blocky structure, slickensides, isolated sand grains, and rare, crushed bone; cultural material throughout Trenches 9 and 10 at Site E-78-7; 11, fine, cemented, silty sand with large, blocky structure, crushed and unidentifiable snails, bone fragments and rich cultural material (Sites E-78-7 and E-78-8); 12, upper vertisol clay with large, blocky structure and large, pronounced slickensides; 15, light, diatomaceous, snail breccia with small, crumbly structure; snails mostly* Bulinus truncatus; *16, thin, consolidated, brown silt containing numerous* Corbicula *shells; 17, wadi sands and gravels, laminated pea gravel with occasional pebbles and sand mostly of eolian character; 18, loose, laminated wadi sands and gravels; lithologically similar to (17) but separated from it by a cut.*

sites, buried within the cultural layers. They include fibrous roots of two kinds of unidentified grasses, root fragments of a palm, wood fragments of the common shrubs *Salsola baryosma* and *Tamarix,* pieces of acacia, as well as several carbonized seeds and glumes of barley and einkorn wheat (Wendorf *et al.* 1979; Wendorf *et al.* in press). The seeds were well preserved with intact cellular structure and were evidently not significantly distorted. The evidence, both paleoenvironmental and botanical, seemed overwhelmingly to support the hypothesis that cultivated barley was present in the Nile Valley more than 18,000 years ago.

The case, however, cannot be accepted without some reservations. According to N. Hadidi, who identified the plant remains at Wadi Kubbaniya, the seeds of wild and domestic wheat and barley can in fact be identical in size and structure, and can be certainly distinguished only by inspection of the rachis, which in the wild form would be brittle and have an accompanying smooth base to facilitate the release and natural dispersal of the spikelet. The domestic forms should have a rough and torn base, since no abscission zone forms to assist in grain dispersal. One of the Wadi Kubbaniya grains (einkorn wheat) was still attached to the rachilla. Stemler and Falk (in Wendorf *et al.* in press) used a scanning electron microscope to compare this grain with examples of wild and domestic wheat. These photographs indicate that the base on the Kubbaniya example does not have a smooth abscission zone, but has a protruding rough fracture surface as in the domestic variety. Unfortunately, however, the abscission zone in wild wheat is not complete until the grain is mature, so that wild wheat harvested green and domesticated wheat would have the same rough fracture as has the Kubbaniya specimen.

There is also the question of whether the environment at Wadi Kubbaniya would permit extensive permanent stands of wild wheat and barley. Harlan (*in litt.*) has noted that wild barley might well have grown in the Nile Valley during the late Pleistocene if there had been lower summer temperatures and some retention of moisture in lighter, noncontracting soils beyond the floodplain. Wild einkorn wheat, however, has a much narrower range of ecological tolerance. It occurs today in a broad band from northwestern Iran and northern Iraq, westward across Turkey to eastern Greece, southern Yugoslavia and Bulgaria. It requires more moisture and is more tolerant of cold than wild barley. An almost inconceivable climatic change would have to occur to permit extensive stands of these wild cereals to grow in Southern Egypt. Some of these conditions may have been met. The diatom assemblage in the pond episode at Isna lacked tropical elements, possibly suggesting the necessary lower summer temperatures than today. However, Kassas (*in litt.*), the preeminent specialist on Egyptian flora, has pointed out still another factor unfavorable to the growth of wild wheat and barley in the Nile Valley. According to Kassas, the fluctuating nature of Nile floods, characterized by uneven annual levels, would prevent the development of luxuriant stands. Kassas noted, for instance, that even barley does not grow in the seasonally flooded dune areas

adjacent to the Nile in the Delta or northern Egypt (a modern analog to the Wadi Kubbaniya situation), even though temperatures are low enough here for barley, as evidenced by its occurrence in wadis west of the Delta. Wild cereals may indeed have been occasionally growing in the Nile Valley, but the conditions would not have been very favorable.

For these reasons we believe that the environmental setting required human cultivation of the cereals at Wadi Kubbaniya. The large size of the grains, the morphological change indicated in the rachis, the fact that the grains evidently were harvested in the winter, the obvious dependence of the prehistoric groups on this locality through a period of around a thousand years, the repetition of this phenomenon at several other localities in the Nile Valley, and the sudden florescence of barley pollen at Isna coinciding with the appearance of a nearby settlement where grain was extensively harvested and utilized all combine to form a firm circumstantial and botanical basis for the assumption that Late Paleolithic inhabitants of the Nile Valley used primitive agriculture as one of their important food resources.

It is not yet possible to evaluate the proportion of this dependence on grain within the total economic spectrum. There was still a heavy reliance on the hunting of large animals and on fishing as is indicated by the numerous fish and mammal remains at these sites. The barley "agriculture" certainly took place just after the maximum stage of flooding, and the crop was harvested in early winter.

The close sociocultural relationship indicated between the Kubbaniya sites and Site E71K13 near Isna is a further example of this seasonal variability in the exploitation of local resources. Site E71K13 is an extensive site, certainly representing numerous reoccupations, yet it yielded no grinding equipment. Grain processing was evidently not important when that site was occupied. Clearly, these groups used a very large section of the Nile Valley in their seasonal selection of major food resources. It is therefore extremely difficult to visualize a forced confinement to a single area caused by population pressure.

Certainly, the presence of barley by 18,000 BP at Wadi Kubbaniya reinforces the pollen data from both Tushka and Isna for the presence and use of this grain throughout this area for at least 10,000 years and in a wide variety of cultural units.

A perplexing problem in the pattern of grain dependence along the Nile is its apparent disappearance after the end of the Sahaba–Darau aggradation. F. A. Hassan (1972) attributes this to the exceptionally high floods recorded at the very end of the aggradation, which, he suggests, caused a catastrophic decline in population and culture. Butzer sees the successful hunting and gathering adaptation to the Nilotic microenvironment as the main cause of the decline (Butzer 1976:9). The real problem, however, is the absence of data. After the Sahaba–Darau aggradation there was a sharp drop in the level of the Nile to below the modern floodplain. Few sites are known from this period, primarily because the living areas seem now to be buried. The earliest securely dated site is that of E71P5, near El Kilh, associated with the beginning of the post–Sahaba–Darau, and dated to 11,560 BP ± 80 years (I-3760) (Wendorf and Schild 1976b:40). This is followed by the site of Dibeira West 1, in Sudanese Nubia, which is geologically associated with the Arkin aggradation and has recently been redated to 10,570 BP ± 150 years (SMU-600) and 10,670 BP ± 110 years (SMU-581). After Dibeira West 1, there are no sites known until the series of Terminal Paleolithic localities at El Kab, Dibeira West 51, Catfish Cave, and the Fayum, all of which date after 8800 BP (Wendorf and Schild 1976b:312–313). Sickle sheen and grinding stones, although rare, are present at the two earliest sites (E71P5 and Dibeira West 1), but they are absent from all other Terminal Paleolithic assemblages. The apparent economic stress in all of these Terminal Paleolithic sites was on heavy seasonal fishing (in the Fayum and Catfish Cave) and on the hunting of gazelle and an occasional larger animal. Gathering was presumably important, but this has not been demonstrated and in no instance were identifiable botanical remains recovered.

It seems, then, that the use of ground grains did not cease after the Sahaba–Darau aggradation, but it is almost certain that the specific microenvironment that favored grain did disappear when the Nile fell and the floodwaters could no longer reach the interdunal ponds. At the beginning of this recession, the Nile must have flowed in a narrow valley with a very reduced floodplain, presumably composed mostly of contracting clays. Beyond the valley, the conditions of hyperaridity were being replaced by increasing monsoonal rainfall signaling the onset of the Holocene wet period. Although the floodplain was expanding during the succeeding Arkin aggradation, the surrounding desert was by then stabilized by vegetation, and dunes were not migrating into the floodplain. This could well explain the decline in emphasis on grain as one of the important subsistence elements in the Nile Valley. The technology then available was not adequate to cope with the changes in the environment.

Slightly before 9000 BP large areas of the Western Desert opened for new human colonization for the first time in many thousands of years. The limited summer rains that began then sustained a semiarid environment with small ruminants and lagomorphs, as well as grasses and some trees, the last particularly near basins that collected and held the moisture. The available data indicate that human expansion into these newly opened areas was almost immediate. From the beginning, Terminal Paleolithic sites in the desert contain evidence of domestic cattle and numerous signs of some dependence on ground grain, presumably domestic, but the actual grains or other botanical remains have not yet been recovered. They are undoubtedly present a thousand years later at the earliest site with pottery. Although the extent of dependence on these sources of produced food cannot be determined, it seems clear that the first occupants came with preexistent knowledge and technology, and were already adapted to this new environment, where a combination of grain utilization, animal husbandry, and small mammal hunting was, perhaps, the most efficient exploitative strategy.

The earliest sites are slightly later than the Arkinian settlement of Dibeira West 1, which contains pieces with lustrous edges and grinding stones. It cannot be demonstrated that the first occupants in the Western Desert came directly from the Nile Valley, but there are close similarities in typology and in general tool structure (E-77-7). Subsequent occurrences in this area show considerable differences from the slightly later assemblages in the Nile Valley and seem to be closer in their structure and typology to Northwest Africa and the central Sahara. This could be due to similarities in adaptations to the environment, or to the growing communication and contacts within this general, semiarid area, or both.

One obvious conclusion that can be drawn from these observations is that the beginning of dependence on food production in the Sahara was during a period when the territory available for human use was rapidly expanding, not contracting as is postulated by the advocates of both the Oasis Theory and the demographic pressure hypotheses. It also seems obvious that preadaptation in the form of existing technology and knowledge were prerequisites for this expansion. Resemblances in tool typology, subsistence pattern, settlement location, raw-material economy, and technology strongly suggest a continuity between the non-pottery, "Terminal Paleolithic" societies in the Western Desert and "Neolithic" in the same area. It is not possible to state that the same ethnic groups are represented in each, even though strong stylistic similarities are evident (Close, this volume), but all do fall within the same technocultural complex.

Although data concerning the social structuring of the Terminal Paleolithic are not adequate for comparison, the Neolithic appears to be more highly developed. The earliest Neolithic site, E-75-6, indicates large social groups apparently composed of several families, presumably linked by social or kinship ties. This in turn implies larger production and a more efficient division of labor that may have transcended family units.

Two important phenomena are associated with these early sites. The first concerns the grain. The earliest Neolithic site with pottery (E-75-6) has yielded two grains of six-row barley and several kinds of weeds that usually accompany Mediterranean grain cultigens. Six-row barley and emmer wheat also occur in a slightly later Neolithic site (E-75-8, lower layer), and we believe both wheat and barley were present in the earlier Terminal Paleolithic sites as well, although no traces of grain have been recovered thus far.

The second important phenomenon in both the Terminal Paleolithic and Neolithic sites is the presence of rare *Bos* bones. These are believed to represent domestic cattle, both because the bones are smaller than those of known wild *Bos* and because the environment was probably beyond the ecological tolerance of *Bos primigenius* (Gautier, this volume). There are isolated bones of *Bos* in the Terminal

Paleolithic sites, and in some instances, such as Site E-75-6, lower layer, it is not possible to eliminate contamination from the overlying Neolithic. In other sites (e.g., Site E-77-7), however, such an explanation is unlikely. If Gautier's identification of the *Bos* remains as domestic is correct, then we must conclude that the Terminal Paleolithic colonists took domestic or semidomestic cattle with them when they first went into the Western Desert. It is useful here, however, to remind ourselves that only *Bos primigenius* was found at the Arkinian site of Dibeira West 1 (Gautier 1968; information rechecked by Gautier 1978; *in litt.*), dating only 1000 years earlier than Site E-77-7.

It must be recognized that the problem of domestic cattle in the Sahara is one of the most difficult and controversial questions pertaining to the origin of domestication. In large part this is due to the scarcity of *Bos* remains in archaeological sites and the fragmentary nature of the few that are found, so proper anatomical observations are generally not feasible. Only two localities have yielded truly adequate remains of what could be domestic *Bos:* Adrar Bous, Site 3 (Clark *et al.* 1973), and Uan Muhuggiag (Mori 1965a). Both of these date rather late (about 6000 BP) and yielded a short-horned variety of cattle.

The rarity of *Bos* remains contrasts with the representations of cattle in the rock art found in the central Sahara and in the Gilf el Kebir–Uweinat areas. There are numerous long-horned and undoubtedly domesticated cattle depicted on these panels, so many in fact that this is known as the Bovidian period of rock art. The cattle are often shown with tricolored skins, and are sometimes in association with people, who are occasionally tending them. The dating of this Bovidian art still presents problems, with some maintaining that it belongs with the Ténérian Neolithic and dates in the fourth millennium BC (Camps 1974a); others (Mori 1965a,b) have assigned dates ranging from the sixth to the third millennia BC. McHugh (1971), on the other hand, relates the Gilf el Kebir art to the Neolithic settlements in the same area, which according to our dates should be placed in the second half of the sixth millennium BC. The important point, however, is that the domestic cattle are frequently depicted in the central and eastern Sahara, and thus cattle may be assumed to have been important in those areas.

Cattle pastoralism is also important today throughout large areas of sub-Saharan Africa, from the Sahel to the uplands of East Africa. The cattle are rarely kept for meat; instead, they are used as producers of milk and blood, in which situation one would expect cattle bones to be extremely rare in the food refuse. Such a pattern of cattle-herding and use could well explain the scarcity of cattle bones in all Terminal Paleolithic and early Neolithic sites in the eastern and central Sahara, even in the new localities north of the Tibesti (Gabriel 1977b).

Data on small domestic animals (sheep/goat and dog) are equally scarce in the Western Desert, but these animals were apparently already present in the sixth millennium BC (Site E-75-8 and Gilf el Kebir). This is slightly earlier than the first records from Cyrenaica (McBurney 1967) indicate, but is at about the same time as their occurrence in the Mediterranean Neolithic on the Maghreb coast (Camps 1974a). The rarity of their bones in the Western Desert cannot be explained in the same way as can the rarity of cattle bones, and we must assume instead that these animals were not common and certainly were not kept in large herds.

These speculations aside, there does exist a firm body of data on the beginnings of food production in the Western Desert, which we will now recapitulate. The first Holocene settlers in the Western Desert came there immediately after the area became habitable. They brought with them the basic knowledge and technology appropriate for this very specific, semiarid environment, where animal resources were scarce but quite large areas were suitable for growing grain. They probably brought with them domestic or semidomestic cattle, and knowledge of houses and storage facilities (Site E-77-3).

The point of origin of the Terminal Paleolithic migrants is not known, but the adjacent Nile Valley, from the Second Cataracts northward into Egypt, is a likely source, since contemporary industries from south of there along the Nile are technologically and typologically very different (Qadan industry). On the other hand, nothing is known about the southeastern margins of the Sahara during this period.

The earliest Neolithic is seen as a more complex society, possibly placing greater stress on food production and storage, and certainly using domestic grains. It was perhaps more sedentary, as could be suggested by the presence of pottery and villages. This is seen not as a basic difference in kind, but rather as an intensification of the previous economic pattern. Nor should the development of this particular Neolithic be seen as the result of one cause or as limited to one area. Instead, we see it as spreading over a very broad area where the environmental situation favored trends toward increased dependence on grain and domesticates. The development of the Saharan Neolithic should, in fact, be viewed in the context of the total area of the Levant, Sinai, and the Nile Valley; this entire area shared a common, early dependence on ground grain, although the intensity of the dependence varied from area to area and from time to time.

One of the most interesting aspects of the early Neolithic in the Western Desert is its confinement to the semiarid desert and its absence from the nearby Nile Valley, which would appear to be the better environment. The simplistic explanation that the Nilotic adaptation of the Terminal Paleolithic hunters and gatherers was so successful as to exclude the domestic grains and animals is not adequate; it is hard to imagine a complex and more advanced society living close to this "better" Nile Valley environment more than 2000 years and failing to utilize it. Instead, we must look for other reasons to explain the absence of the Neolithic from the valley. It seems far more likely that the Nilotic environment was seen as less suitable for the kind of agriculture that developed in the Western Desert: the relatively narrow Nile Valley of that time had a limited floodplain, composed mostly of contracting silts, and major seasonal variations in water level, and would have required a more advanced technology than that applied in the Western Desert.

A few very small sites containing Khartoum pottery do occur in the Nile Valley at the Second Cataracts and southward from there (Marks *et al.* 1968; Shiner 1968b). Some of these are quite old, dating 6540 BP ± 110 years (Tx-1155; Shiner, personal communication), but their limited size and thin occupational debris indicate an ephemeral character totally different from those in the Western Desert. Large sites with Khartoum pottery occur along the Nile in central Sudan (Arkell 1949), but these show a subsistence pattern based on intensive fishing and hunting, and there are no traces of domestic animals or of the use of grain. Only later, in the fourth millennium BC, do domestic animals and agriculture seem to appear at sites such as Shaheinab and Kadero, which contain late "Khartoum pottery" (Arkell 1953; Krzyzaniak 1978). At roughly the same time in Nubia, three other apparently fully developed Neolithic groups also occur: the Abkan, A-Group, and a third known from the site of Dibeira West 50. All are slightly different in their pottery and lithics, and date to the beginning of the fourth millennium BC and slightly later.

In the lower Nile Valley, the fully developed Neolithic of Merimda and Fayum A, with both domestic grain and animals, appears suddenly and without any local predecessors near the end of the fifth or early fourth millennium BC. It seems that food production in the lower Nile Valley did not appear until the technology was available that made it possible to overcome the enormous problems of floodplain agriculture. It is possible that the critical element here was the introduction of the techniques for basin irrigation.

Moving farther to the east, and at a time comparable with the first appearance of grain utilization in the Nile Valley or perhaps slightly later, we find complex villagelike, Kebaran settlements in the Levant. Grinding equipment is present, indicating a dependence on grain utilization among some of these Late Paleolithic groups (Bar-Yosef 1975; Ronen *et al.* 1975). The discovery of emmer wheat grains in the Kebaran level of Nahal Oren (Noy *et al.* 1973; Van Zeist 1976) may provide identification of the grain in question, but this needs further confirmation. After the Kebaran, dependence on grain appears to have increased in this area during the Natufian, which dates to the tenth millennium BC.

In the Sinai and the western Negev, the Harifian, dating between 8500 and 8000 BC, had villages with structures, and the associated grinding equipment indicates some dependence on grain. There are also reports of discoveries of pre-pottery Neolithic sites in the southern Sinai (Bar-Yosef and Phillips 1977; Gilead 1973). Clearly, knowledge of grain utilization was present early in this area and persisted for a long time. It was, therefore, available for application to the best advantage wherever and whenever an opportunity arose.

It is in this general context that the emergence of food production in the Western Desert must be viewed. There are still several features of this Neolithic that cannot be satisfactorily explained with the data at hand, among them the history of the domestication of cattle, which is generally believed to be an African domesticate, and the early appearance of well-made, highly decorated, and well-fired pottery, undoubtedly reflecting a considerable history of development. These problems may need reexamination when data are available from the southern and southeastern fringes of the Sahara. Nevertheless, the apparently sudden appearance of food production in the Sahara is no longer a mystery. We can see it as part of an adaptive process, in which societies reacted swiftly to the changed environment and opening opportunities, and this reaction would not have been possible had the basic technology not already been available. This view of the prehistoric societies of northeastern Africa as complex, adaptive systems, successfully reacting to climatic and physiographic changes, provides a better perspective for understanding prehistoric changes than do simplistic, single-cause, demographic explanations. It is also in closer accord with basic biological theory concerning colonization and adjustment in nonhuman societies (compare Diamond 1977; Simon 1969; Terell 1977).

These discoveries, particularly the highly likely presence of food production as early as 18,000 years ago in band societies evidently no different in their structure from those of the same age not utilizing domesticates, force a considerable rethinking of some basic assumptions. The very term *Neolithic,* understood to mean food-producing societies, becomes practically meaningless in terms of implied social changes. It now seems likely that food production is an extremely old skill, well entrenched in simple societies long before the so-called Neolithic Revolution. The social and demographic changes that were associated with the Neolithic Revolution of the early Holocene are obviously a result of factors other than food production itself. These factors are undoubtedly complex and evidently result in a new and better level of adaptation to the environment.

Considerable thought was given to the abandonment of the terms *Terminal Paleolithic* and *Neolithic* as they applied to the Western Desert, but they were retained because satisfactory substitutes could not be found. If food production, as is often believed, were the only diagnostic feature of the Neolithic, then the Wadi Kubbaniya sites would have to be so classified. Undoubtedly, many of the Late Paleolithic and Epipaleolithic groups of Northeast Africa and the Near East had access to food production and might also be classified as Neolithic. Such a use of the term, however, would dilute much of its value as an indicator of a new kind of social, economic, and adaptive structure.

We share with Braidwood and Vavilov the belief that the first domestication of cereals must have occurred in areas where the wild predecessors of those cereals grew in their natural environment. Wild barley requires either winter rainfall or exceptional environmental conditions, which, according to Harlan, include cool summers and retention of sufficient moisture in favorable soils. Harlan believes that the present stands of barley along the Mediterranean coast of Cyrenaica and northern Egypt are relics of a once more widespread distribution of wild barley in the late Pleistocene. This distribution could have included occasional stands in the Nile Valley.

Our paleoenvironmental evidence from the Western Desert and the Nile Valley clearly indicates hyperarid conditions in those areas during this period. The Nile floods, the only available source of moisture in the valley itself, would not provide suitable winter moisture for wild barley, except very occasionally. Whether the first domestication occurred in the Nile Valley or somewhere along the southeastern shores of the Mediterranean, in the Sinai, or in the Near East is not known, but it evidently occurred before 18,000 years ago.

These assumptions lead us further to infer that domestic cereals could have been in use in the Near East at a similar or earlier time. The Upper Paleolithic societies of these areas could well have utilized domestic cereals as one of their food sources. The emergence of seemingly more complex societies in the subsequent Kebaran and Natufian is a logical consequence of an increased dependence on domestic grains, and is not, as some have postulated, the social and demographic cause leading to the later "invention" of food production.

APPENDIX

1

The Quaternary Sediments of the Southern Western Desert of Egypt: An Overview

RUSHDI SAID

This appendix describes the Quaternary sediments of the southern Western Desert of Egypt and gives a brief description of the geomorphology of the desert. The work is the result of an extended program of research that began in the 1960s and culminated in the preparation of the accompanying map of the Quaternary geology of this part of Egypt (Figure A1.1). During these two decades this part of the Egyptian desert, which was almost *terra incognita* and where only a few scientific explorers dared to wander, has become the site of great activity. Several scientific expeditions and active oil and mineral exploration programs have studied this area, and a detailed geologic map for most of the area now exists (Klitzsch *et al.* 1979).

The southern reaches of the Western Desert of Egypt are covered almost exclusively by sandstones belonging to the Nubia Formation. These sandstones extend for several degrees of latitude and longitude beyond the boundaries of Egypt into Libya and the Sudan. They are interrupted by several basement outcrops, which have now been quite well delimited and described (El-Ramly 1972; Issawi 1969). To the east, the sandstone plains of the desert lie in the shadow of a great limestone plateau whose scarps extend from west Dakhla to the Nile Valley, passing by Kharga and the Sinn el Kaddab cliffs. To the west, the sandstone plains rise gradually to the footslopes of the rugged Gilf el Kebir plateau, which forms a dominant mountain of dark-colored sandstones.

STRATIGRAPHY

The stratigraphy of the southern Western Desert has been dealt with by several workers. Among the more recent of these, mention may be made of Said (1969), Issawi (1969, 1971), and Klitzsch *et al.* (1979).

Above the Precambrian lies the Nubia sandstone, which has recently been subjected to intensive studies (Klitzsch *et*

al. 1979) and is now divisible into the following units from bottom to top: the lower clastics, the *Lingula* shales, the desert rose beds, the plant beds, the Taref sandstone, and the variegated shales.

The lower clastics unit is sandstone, with a few shale interbeds. It is of lowermost Cretaceous or uppermost

281

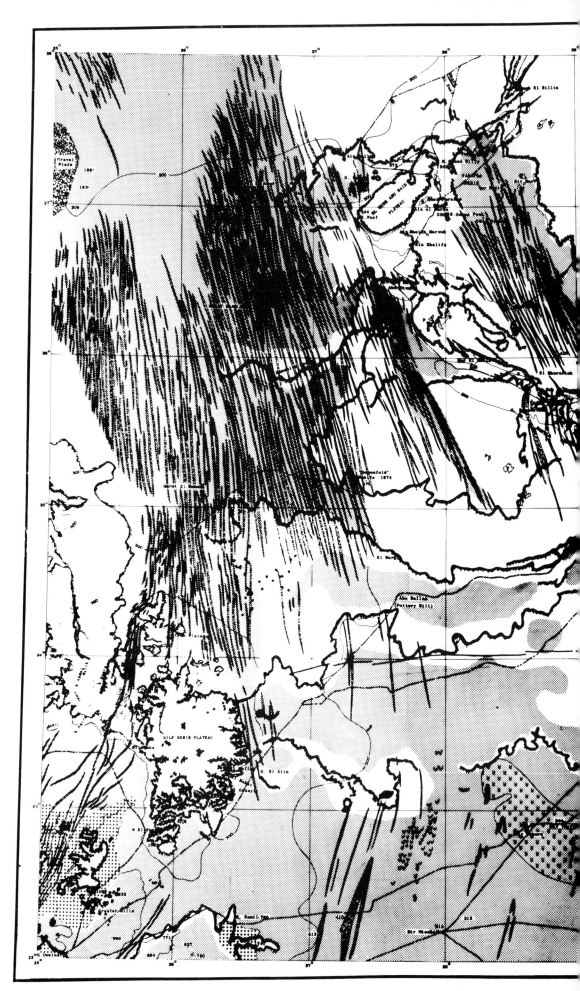

FIGURE A1.1. *Map of southwestern Egypt showing surficial geology.*

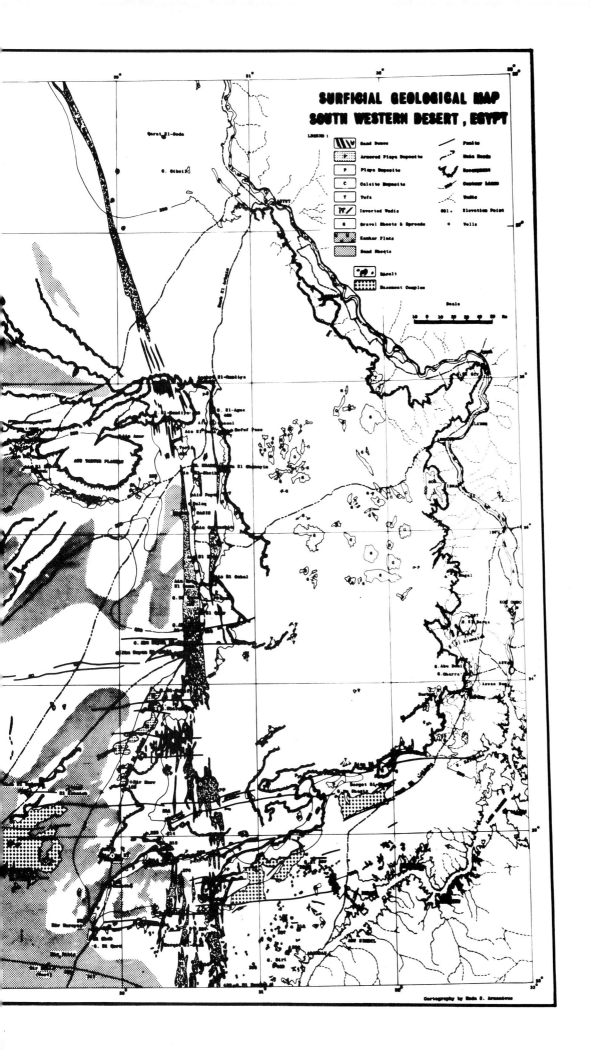

SURFICIAL GEOLOGICAL MAP
SOUTH WESTERN DESERT, EGYPT

Jurassic age. The lower clastics and the overlying *Lingula* shales form the Gilf el Kebir plateau. The lower clastics, the *Lingula* shales, the desert rose beds, the plant beds, and the Taref sandstone form aerially extensive units that can be traced for long distances, but in some areas they are difficult to separate. Thus, in the Baris area, all the units between the *Lingula* shales and the Taref sandstone, inclusive, form one continuous unit, the Baris Formation. The scanty fossils found in the different units indicate a Cretaceous age for the entire formation, although the lowermost part could be Jurassic (Soliman 1977).

Above the Taref sandstone lie the variegated shales, which were subjected to a detailed study by Gindy (1965). They are composed of shales and siltstones of various colors, interbedded with bone beds and flaggy sandstones. Most of the beds are not fossiliferous, but some carry poorly preserved prints of terrestrial plants and a few include marine vertebrate fossils. It is likely, therefore, that the variegated shales were deposited in mud flats at the edge of the Late Cretaceous sea, and the fossils indicate that marine incursions over these flats were not uncommon. The variegated shales outcrop at the footslopes of the limestone plateau.

The thickness of the variegated shales and the Nubia sandstone is difficult to measure, but in the Dungul area where the basement outcrops at Um Shagir hill, the thickness does not exceed 120 m; in many other areas the thickness exceeds 2000 m (e.g., Dakhla, where recent drilling did not reach basement at this depth).

In the north, the variegated shales are overlain by the Phosphate Formation, Dakhla shales, Tarawan chalk, Esna shales, and the Thebes limestones. In the south, however, the Phosphate Formation disappears and is replaced by bone beds; the Dakhla Formation is replaced by the Kurkur Formation, a unit of coquinal limestone and marls. The Tarawan and Esna formations change toward the south into alternating beds of limestone and calcareous shales rich in *Operculina* and small *Nummulites* species: The Garra Formation. The whole succession above the variegated shales ranges in age from Cretaceous (Maastrichtian) to early Eocene.

STRUCTURE

Structurally, the southern Western Desert of Egypt represents a consolidated part of the Stable Shelf, rejuvenated by recent faulting and block dislocations. Principal features of this region are its clear-cut fringing by the limestone scarp, the steplike structure of the slopes formed as recently as late Pleistocene, and the nongrading of the poorly delineated hydrographic system to the underlying structure. The Nile runs along the hinge between the great Red Sea rift (where vertical movements clearly predominate this linear graben) and the east–west faulted southern Western Desert. The latter runs perpendicular to the structural grain of the main Red Sea zone and represents a slowly rising, uparched fold.

The major topographic and geologic features are fault-conditioned. Prominent among them are the rift system of the Nubian Nile, the Kharga high, and the Sinn el Kaddab structure. The last two seem to have developed along east–west trending basement highs that represent spurs or interbasin arches in the original formation of the Stable Shelf. The basement highs (clearly shown on the gravity map of southwestern Egypt) caused major successive east–west strike faults that cut across the entire country,

and also brought about the development of hundreds of small (.5–1 km wide), shallow, circular centroclinal folds along their entire length. The uplifting of these basement highs was continuous, but in places there is evidence that the major uplift occurred in the late Paleocene, since, in some of the folds, both the Paleocene and early Eocene are more or less horizontal. In other folds, both the Paleocene and the lower Eocene strata are mildly affected. Basement rocks outcrop in the center of some of these folds. Beadnell described some of the centroclinal folds in Kharga (1909), and Issawi (1971) has elaborated on some of these structures.

The major uplift of these highs is linked to the plutonic activity of the margins of the Stable Shelf in Late Cretaceous and early Paleocene times, when a large number of ring complexes were developed. There is evidence in the area that faulting movements have continued with less intensity up to recent times. Pleistocene deposits are affected in many areas, and recent earthquakes have affected sediments as late as Neolithic in the Dungul area (Said 1969).

THE QUATERNARY SEDIMENTS

The Quaternary sediments are varied and complex. They may be described as follows.

SAND SHEETS

Sand sheets cover large stretches of the southern Western Desert of Egypt. They form flat areas made up of medium- to coarse-grained sand with a top that is veneered by a thin layer of lag, coarse sand, or small pebbles equidistantly distributed over the surface. The sand sheets form remarkably flat plains with hard and compact surfaces that make car travel easy and fast. The thickness of the sand sheets is difficult to measure, but drilling in the Bir Sahara area by the General Petroleum Company showed a depth of 22 m for the loose sand overlying the Nubia sandstone. To the west, the sand sheet is usually rather thin, according to the interpretation of the seismic lines carried out by the Conoco Oil Company. However, in many other areas, such as Abu Ballas, the sand sheet attains a thickness of 30 m and is underlain by a gravel bed about 8 m thick.

All the sand sheets have a red-brown soil that seems to be of pre-Acheulian age, to judge from the artifacts found in that soil in the Bir Sahara area. In other areas the soils are of Neolithic age. All the sand sheets, especially those covering the western stretches of the desert, are unconformably overlain by eolian dunes that have been forming over them since at least the Neolithic. In the western Sand Sea, the dunes are remarkably parallel, and the interdunal areas consist of well-paved "avenues" made up of flat and more compact sand sheets.

The origin of the sand sheets is intriguing. All authorities agree that they are of eolian origin (Bagnold 1941; Sandford 1935). In an earlier paper, the present author (1975b) advocated an eolian origin for these sand sheets, which were beveled by wind action and then stabilized during the last wet period (Terminal Paleolithic–Neolithic). These sheets later became the site of the accumulation of dunes, which are still forming unconformably over them. Recent observations concerning the distribution of these sheets and their stratigraphy, however, lead the author to change this interpretation, and to advance the view that these sheets represent the relics of a complex drainage system that must have been in existence since the elevation of the southern Western Desert in post–early Eocene times. Several fluvial cycles must have developed since then, and the present-day sand sheets must be assumed to be related to one of the later cycles since they are intimately related to the modern landscape. Their absence from the oasis depressions, however, would indicate that they antedate these depressions. It is possible that the modern sheets were formed during the Neogene (Pliocene?), and were subjected to deflation during the Pleistocene. At this time, they were beveled and eroded to their present shapes, which must have existed with little change since Acheulian times. The sheets seem to have formed a series of coalescing, alluvial cones spreading from the highlands to the east and south. All the sheets emanate from these highlands and finally converge into the major trunk channel, which extended from the Gilf el Kebir to Siwa Oasis and beyond. It is along this same stretch that the great eolian sand dunes accumulate today. An important indication that the sheets are of alluvial origin is the presence of coarse pebbles strewn over their surfaces in many parts, and in particular along the Egyptian–Libyan border around latitude 27°. As previously mentioned, the sheets overlie a thick gravel layer that shows in all seismic records passing through these sheets.

Thus far, no fossils have been noted in the sand sheets, but, near their limits to the south of Siwa, Zittel (1883) reported several Neogene (?) localities with freshwater fauna and flora. In Libya, Savage and White (1965) and Selley (1969) reported a locality in the southern escarpment of Dor Marada, in the central Sirte Basin, which consists of several lithofacies including interbedded green and gray laminated shales, sandstones, sandy limestones, and calcarenites, and carries in its lower part a mammalian fauna of Middle Miocene age. The age of the upper part of the Marada Formation is not certain. Although it has not yet been demonstrated in the field that the alternating continental, littoral, and shallow marine deposits of these localities are connected with the extensive sand sheets of the southern Western Desert of Egypt, such a relationship is not unlikely; the ancient drainage systems may have followed a course that terminated around these localities.

Sand sheets and gravel spreads are known in the northern Western Desert of Egypt. They merge into marginal marine and deltaic deposits that are exposed on the slopes of the scarps of the Fayum and Qattara depressions. The Lower Miocene and Oligocene gravel spread and sand sheets cover extensive, flat areas and fossil wood is frequent. Their fluvial origin and age are not contested. The sand sheets of the southern Western Desert are different, as they include no fossils and their relationships with the deltaic deposits of the north are masked by the great accumulations of windblown sands.

KANKAR FLATS

Kankar flats are parts of the great sand sheets, but are differentiated on the map because they are strewn with kankar, root drip, and carbonate. The most extensive of these flats is the Bir Sahara–Bir Tarfawi sheet, which covers an area of almost 4000 km². It is covered by an almost continuous layer of carbonate, which in some places displays large, polygonal cracks. This layer forms a crust over the beveled surface of the underlying sand sheet and is closely related to it. In many places, the carbonate is evidently the result of calcified root-drip and other vegetative casts, which must have covered the entire Bir Sahara area during the Pleistocene pluvials. The oldest deposits of these pluvials in this area belong to the Acheulian, during which time many fossil springs dotted the carbonate plain. Lacustrine deposits of Mousterian and Aterian ages are also known in several basins in the area. It seems, therefore, that the Bir Sahara–Bir Tarfawi area formed a basin with a high water table in Acheulian times, resulting in a large number of springs and in the wetting of the surface, which became covered by a rich vegetative growth. Upon the lowering of the water table, much of the vegetation dried up, many of the roots and other vegetable matter were calcified, and freshwater carbonates were deposited in the lower areas. During Mousterian and Aterian times, the water table again rose to fill parts of the basins deflated within the Bir Sahara–Bir Tarfawi area, producing lacustrine deposits and vegetative growth.

INVERTED WADIS

Inverted wadis are elongate, sinuous, and sometimes branching gravel ridges, which stand out above the rock-cut surfaces. They were first noted by Giegengack (1968) in the Nubian Desert. They represent ancient thalwegs of an old drainage system, which, in the case of the Nubian Desert, seems to have some relationship with the ancient Nile system. The inverted channels are made up of indurated wadi deposits of poorly sorted gravel and coarse sand, and took shape long after the deflation of the wadi sides. Said (1975a) has related inverted wadis of the Nubian Desert to the Armant pluvial.

The inverted wadis shown on the map are large features. Most are more than 10 km long, and they all lie in the vicinity of the Nubian Nile. The gravels are mostly subrounded; they are indurated by a carbonate matrix and all have a red-brown soil. In addition to these, there are many other, smaller features that appear in the interior of the desert. The latter have angular to subangular pebbles of quartzite and silicified sandstones, and some of them include rolled Acheulian artifacts.

GRAVEL SHEETS, SPREADS, AND MOUNDS

Gravel sheets and spreads of the southern Western Desert may be classified as follows:

Gravel Sheets

Gravel sheets are thin spreads of gravel that were formed by sheet wash or by gravity. They are invariably associated with the scarps of the plateau or the wadis that drain them. The sheets form patches of unbedded, nonindurated gravel spreads or indurated conglomerates about 4 m thick. The loose gravel sheets form over wadi terraces and modern thalwegs and these consist of pebbles of local derivation, ranging from 2 to 12 cm in diameter. Said (1969) gives a description of some of these from Wadi Dungul. Caton-Thompson (1952) and Gardner give a description of the gravel sheets of the Kharga area. Issawi (1969) records the presence along the footslopes of the Kurkur–Dungul scarp of some of these sheets, which cover large stretches and include consolidated conglomerates. All recorded instances seem to be related to the wadi system and all the pebbles included are of local derivation. The consolidation of the conglomerates seems to be related to tufa formation associated with the local spring activity.

Gravel sheets are known to occur above the rock-cut pediments that fringe many of the scarps. In most cases, the pebbles range in size from 2 to 15 cm, and are poorly sorted and less rounded than those associated with the gravel sheets fringing the wadis. Gravel sheets of this nature are due to mass wasting.

Certain gravel sheets form spreads that are not associated with wadis or scarps, such as that which occurs in the extreme western part of Egypt near the Libyan border to the north of Wadi Abdel Malek. This is an extensive sheet made up of well-rounded and well-sorted flint pebbles that are strewn over a sand surface. They are lag gravel that became concentrated on the surface of the sand sheets. The presence of these gravels within and below the sand sheets gives further support to the idea that these sheets are of fluvial origin.

Gravel Mounds

Small mounds of angular pebbles and gravels occur above the limestone plateau and seem to represent erosional remnants of an extensive sheet of gravel that must have covered this part of the limestone plateau. In places, remains of this sheet are still preserved, forming a unit that unconformably overlies the lower Eocene Thebes Formation and is comparable to the Nakheil Formation known in the Safaga–Quseir district on the Red Sea coast (Akkad and Dardir 1966). As in the case of Nakheil, the gravel mounds are made up of angular pebbles and cobbles of silicified limestones, chert, and flint cemented in a matrix of red-brown clays. The mode of formation of this unit is difficult to ascertain; its thickness as revealed in one of the bore holes drilled on the plateau exceeds 8 m. The mounds themselves may reach 4 to 6 m in height. Akkad and Dardir (1966) attributed the breccias of the Nakheil Formation to derivation from nearby beds as rock slides along fault scarps. In the limestone plateau of the southern Western Desert, the gravel mounds are restricted to the middle reaches of that plateau between latitudes 24°30′N and 26°N. No significant faults have been reported from this area and it is possible that the mounds are the remains of a once continuous gravel sheet deposited by sheet flood from across the Nile, long before the uncovering of the Red Sea basement. There is no obvious alignment of the mounds.

SPRING DEPOSITS

Spring deposits in the southern Western Desert of Egypt cover a small area. They feature clean marlstones, black soils, peat deposits, tufas, and salt encrustations. There seem to be several generations of spring activity (Butzer 1964; Caton-Thompson 1952; Issawi 1969, 1971; Said 1969). All the preserved spring deposits are found in the vicinity of the present-day wells or oases. There are, however, indications of earlier spring activity in areas outside those of the modern wells or oases, but their deposits have been almost entirely eroded away and the evidence rests solely on geomorphology (see subsequent discussion).

The oldest of the spring deposits are the massive tufas that lie on top of the limestone plateau in the Kharga, Kurkur, and Dungul regions. They are 10 to 20 m thick and are made up of solid to vesicular crystalline stone without bedding. They include pockets, up to 1 m in diameter, containing boulders of local derivation. The tufa mass is composed of hard, crystalline carbonate rock precipitated around various species of plants, of which the stems and internal structure are still preserved. The age of these massive tufas is difficult to ascertain, but they were certainly formed prior to the excavation of the oasis depressions and are, therefore, of pre-Pleistocene age (Said 1975b).

Several other generations of tufas are known over the plateau, along the scarps, or within the depressions. Many overlie or intercalate boulder beds, marlstones, and peat beds. The tufas range in thickness from 1 to 20 m. At least four generations have been recognized in the Kurkur region (Butzer 1964) and in the Dungul region (Said 1969). Tufas associated with the depressions are all connected with boulder beds and fine-grained spring deposits. They seem to have been formed under wetter and most probably colder climatic conditions, in closed basins with a rich mat of vegetation. The youngest tufas are of Mousterian and Neolithic ages, to judge from the implements included within the boulder beds. It is difficult to establish the age of the oldest tufas. A discussion of the depositional environment and the limnological conditions prevailing in the basins is given in Said (1969).

Spring Features

Evidence of old spring activity is inferred in many parts of the southern Western Desert from geomorphological evidence and in areas that have no source of water today. The features that seem to belong to this old activity may be described as follows:

Circular Depressions. Shallow circular to oval depressions are seen all along the sandstone plains of the southern Western Desert. The diameters of these depressions vary from 15 to 100 km, and the difference in height between the lowest and highest points in them never exceeds 40 m. Although the origin of the depressions is problematical, it is highly likely that they resulted from the settlement of the water-bearing sandstone beds after the drying up of the springs that must have been active all over the sandstone plains of the desert. In some of the depressions, deflated playa deposits with Mousterian artifacts have been observed, indicating that many of them are of pre-Mousterian age (see Chapter 5).

Spring Vents. Subrecent spring mounds are found in many parts of the modern oases (for a description of these in Dakhla see Schild and Wendorf 1977; for Kharga, see Caton-Thompson 1952). They appear in the form of small, mostly conical mounds, ranging in height from a few meters to 20 m. Each has a vent that is cylindrical in shape and is surrounded by layers of clay, ocher, sand, or carbonates, depending on the composition of the oozing waters of the spring.

The sandstone plains of the southern Western Desert of Egypt slope toward the scarps of the limestone plateau and form an elongated depression in its shadow. The growth of this plunging pediplain broke down the piedmont slopes of the plateau, which are reduced to small and gently dipping plains at the foot of the scarp. The modern springs lie at the footslopes of the modern scarp, which represent the lowest points in the plain. The historic (Roman) wells lie away from the scarp and are 10 m higher than the modern wells, indicating a lowering of the water table by this amount since Roman times. A similar drop in the water table was also observed by Murray (1952) in Dakhla. The modern artesian wells have various temperatures and various water compositions. Some of the thermal springs have ferruginated waters that, after evaporation, form mounds of clays and ocherous materials. In many other wells, the ferruginated materials fill the interstitial spaces of the bedrock sandstones or of the eolian sands that drift around them, thus forming mounds of hard, ferruginous sandstones. Other springs have waters rich in silica and, during their last phases of activity, these produce quartzite plugs that fill the vent or the fissure through which the water gushed to the surface. Most of the wells, however, have fresh water with minor carbonates, and these form mounds of indurated sandstones cemented by carbonates, root drip, and carbonate crusts, as well as freshwater, porcelaneous limestones.

An examination of the plains beyond the modern oases and away from the scarps shows the presence of fossil spring mounds that seem to have been formed under conditions that could not have been very different from the present. Some of these mounds are easy to recognize, but many of the older spring mounds have lost their original shape and structure and are now represented by conical to tabular hills of bedded, dark-colored sandstone, which have long been known as *Zeugenberge*, or *nasb* in Arabic. The sandstone plain of the southern Western Desert is interrupted by these small hills, which rise above the surrounding plains by elevations varying from a few meters to 70 m. The distribution of the conical to tabular hills shows that they occur in a belt running more or less parallel to the present-day scarp, separated from it by a distance of 50 to 70 km. The most significant of these hills is Gebel Barqat el Shab, which stands up as a tabular hill at an absolute elevation of 371 m or about 170 m above the surrounding plain. This gebel is unique in that it exhibits a succession of the whole section known from the limestone plateau to the north. The gebel is capped by Eocene nummulitic limestone (Issawi 1973).

The majority of the conical to tabular hills of this belt are much lower in elevation and all are made up of ferruginous or silicified sandstones. The fact that these hills are in a belt away from and parallel to the modern scarp indicates that they were probably formed when the scarp was closer, and that they most probably represent the sites of fossil springs. The surrounding parent rocks were cemented by the waters of the springs, thus giving them the hardness to resist erosion.

It is difficult to determine the time during which these springs were active. Some have archaeological materials of Late Acheulian age in their footslopes (Wendorf 1968), indicating that they were more or less in their present form by that time, but many are devoid of any archaeological materials. The presence of the Eocene-capped and archaeologically sterile Barqat el Shab indicates that some of these springs were active prior to the retreat of the scarp from this latitude and that this mound must be very old (Paleogene?). That the hills run parallel to the scarp shows that many were active under conditions that could have been very similar to those of today (that is, they were active when the scarp was not far from this belt). Some, however, must have been activated much later, when the scarp was farther to the north or east but when the water table was much higher.

LAKE DEPOSITS

Playa Deposits

Remnants of Holocene pluvial lakes have long been known in the Western Desert of Egypt (Ball 1927; Beadnell 1909), but their distribution and extent have never been determined. The accompanying map (Figure A1.1) shows about 50 playa sheets, which lie mostly at the footslopes of the great Libyan limestone plateau or of the other subdued escarpments of the sandstone plain. The playas represent the lowest points of the various enclosed drainage basins in the desert. They are vegetation-free surfaces of fine-grained sediments. In Egypt, these clay silt playas are called *hattiya* (in Arabic, "temporary settlement"). Whatever water falls over the desert accumulates in them, making possible temporary settlements for the roving nomads. They usually have no economic potential, although in Selima (the Sudan), Sheb, and other wells nitrate and alum deposits have been recorded in small quantities. All the southern Western Desert playas belong to the clay flat surface type (Krinsley 1970) and they all have a deep water table. Like all total surface-water-discharging playas, the surface is smooth, hard, commonly dry, and composed of fine-grained clastic sediments. The Western Desert playas range in size from a few to several hundred square kilometers. Most of them owe their origin to pluvial conditions and are not related to springs, and most formed during the Terminal Paleolithic–Neolithic pluvial period. However, some of the lakes that are related to spring activity survived until Roman times, such as the Kharga Oasis lakes, which include Roman pottery at their tops. The stratigraphy of most of these playas shows alternating layers of lacustrine and eolian sands and clays. During their formation, they were active sites of human habitation (Chapter 3). In the Nabta playa, one of the best studied, the surface is made up of brown clay with polygonal shrinkage cracks and shows signs of having been lowered at least 4 m by deflation since the Neolithic. Several portions of the ancient dunes underlying the playa clay outcrop as small hillocks about 4 m higher than the level of the playa.

The Kharga playas cover a large area of the depression, extending from north of Mahariq to Baris for a distance of almost 90 km. They were first noted by Beadnell (1909), who advocated a lacustrine origin for them. Caton-Thompson (1952) thought that the playas owed their origin to eolian and spring activity. The Kharga playas are unique in that they were still forming as late as the Roman period, and it is possible that the younger part of the lake is attributable to drifting sands accumulating in lakes caused by springs. The earlier part of the lake seems, like most other lakes of the southern Western Desert of Egypt, to have had a pluvial origin.

The rate of lowering of the floor of the desert is remarkably fast and is of the order of 4 m per millenium, a rate more or less equal to the lowering of the water table in Kharga. The rate of deflation is measured by the height of the yardangs of playa deposits left behind.

Armored Playas

Armored playas are extensive sheets of playa deposits that are veneered by a layer of white nodular chalcedony cobbles up to 15 cm in diameter. Issawi (1971) noted the chalcedony sheets in the Darb el Arbain area. He ascribed to them to doming movements and related them to structural lines. The chalcedony sheets are here considered to be lag gravel from an underlying reddish brown mudstone, which formed in standing bodies of water rich in silica. The source of the silica is not clear but it could be of pedogenic origin (Haynes n.d.). The age of the armored playas is not known, but they are certainly older than the Neolithic playas. Since some include rolled Acheulian artifacts, they are of post-Acheulian age.

REFERENCES

Akkad, S., and A. Dardir
  1966   Geology and phosphate deposits of Wasif, Safaga area. *Papers of the Geological Survey of Egypt,* No. 36.
Bagnold, R. A.
  1941   *The physics of blown sand and desert dunes.* London: Methuen.
Ball, J.
  1927   Problems of the Libyan Desert. *Geographical Journal* 70:209–224.
Beadnell, H. J. L.
  1909   *An Egyptian Oasis.* London: John Murray.

Butzer, K. W.
  1964   Pleistocene paleoclimates of the Kurkur Oasis. *Canadian Geographer* 8:125–140.
Caton-Thompson, G.
  1952   *Kharga Oasis in prehistory.* London: Athlone Press.
Giegengack, R. F.
  1968   Late Pleistocene history of the Nile Valley in Egyptian Nubia. Ph.D. dissertation, Yale University.
Gindy, A. R.
  1965   The Nubian sandstone around Tell El Zouhour, and its

barite veins and sand crystals. *Bulletin de l'Institut d' Egypte* 38:1–70.

Haynes, C. V.
n.d.   Quaternary lakes of the Nubian Desert. Manuscript.

Issawi, B.
1969   The geology of Kurkur–Dungul area. *Papers of the Geological Survey of Egypt,* No. 46.
1971   Geology of Darb el Arbain, Western Desert. *Annals of the Geological Survey of Egypt* 1:53–92.
1973   Nubia sandstone: Type section. *American Association of Petroleum Geologists Bulletin* 57:741–745.

Klitzsch, E., J. C. Harms, A. Lejal-Nicol, and F. K. List
1979   Major subdivisions and depositional environments of Nubia strata, southwest Egypt. *American Association of Petroleum Geologists Bulletin* 63:967–974.

Krinsley, D. B.
1970   A geomorphological and paleoclimatological study of the playas of Iran. *U.S. Geological Survey, Final Scientific Report, Contract PRO CP70-800,* 2 vols.

Murray, G. W.
1952   The water beneath the Egyptian Western Desert. *Geographical Journal* 118:443–452.

Said, R.
1969   Pleistocene geology of Dungul region, southern Libyan Desert, Egypt. In Prehistoric settlement patterns in the Libyan Desert, edited by J. J. Hester and P. M. Hoebler. *University of Utah Anthropology Papers,* No. 92. Pp. 7–18.
1975a The geological evolution of the River Nile. In *Problems in prehistory: North Africa and the Levant,* edited by F. Wendorf and A. E. Marks. Dallas: Southern Methodist University Press, Pp. 7–44.
1975b Some observations on the geomorphological evolution of

the south Western Desert of Egypt and its relation to the origin of ground water. *Annals of the Geological Survey of Egypt* 5:61–70.

Sanford, K. S.
1935   Geological observations on the north-western frontiers of the Anglo-Egyptian Sudan and adjoining parts of the southern Libyan Desert. *Quarterly Journal of the Geological Society of London* 91:323–381.

Savage, R. J. G., and M. E. White
1965   Two mammal faunas from the Early Tertiary of central Libya. *Proceedings of the Geological Society of London,* No. 1623. Pp. 89–91.

Schild, R., and F. Wendorf
1977   *The prehistory of Dakhla Oasis and adjacent desert.* Wroclaw: Ossolineum.

Selley, R. C.
1969   Nearshore marine and continental sediments of the Sirte Basin, Libya. *Quarterly Journal of the Geological Society of London* 124:419–460.

Soliman, H. A.
1977   Foraminifères et microfossiles végétaux provenant du "Nubia Sandstone" de subsurface de l'oasis El Kharga, Désert de l'ouest, Egypte. *Rév. Micropaléontologie* 20:114–124.

Wendorf, F. (Editor)
1968   *The prehistory of Nubia,* 2 vols. and atlas. Dallas: Fort Burgwin Research Center and Southern Methodist University Press.

Zittel, A. K.
1883   Beiträge zur Geologie und Paläontologie der Libyschen Wüste und der angrenzenden Gebiete von Aegypten. *Paläontographica* 30:1–112.

APPENDIX

2

A Study of Stylistic Variability and Continuity in the Nabta Area

ANGELA E. CLOSE

The proximity in time of the Terminal Paleolithic and Neolithic sites in the Gebel Nabta area poses the question of whether or not the change in subsistence pattern between the two groups was accompanied by a change in population. The change in economy probably involved changes in the activities undertaken at the sites, as witnessed, for example, by the numbers of grinding stones associated with the Neolithic, so that simple typological comparison—a somewhat dubious procedure even at the best of times—cannot be expected to provide a reflection of the social affinities of the makers of the assemblages. Instead, the assemblages are to be compared on the basis of demonstrable stylistic traits.

The concept of style, as used here, depends upon the idea that a single end can frequently be achieved by any one of several different, and equally valid, means. Thus there might be more than one method of making a type of tool, the various methods all producing tools that are equally efficient in performing the intended functions. The specific method to be used is, then, independent of functional considerations and is a matter of choice. It is believed that the choice made will be determined, to a large extent, by what has been learned within the sociocultural context—that is, the group's "traditional" methods of making that tool type. Stylistic traits are therefore independent of function, and, in representing the social input of the learning process, should reflect the social context of that process, usually by a concentration upon one or a few preferred options from the much greater range of available or potentially available (and equally valid) options.

The traits to be examined are attributes of individual classes of retouched tools. On comparatively simple tools, such as those with which we are here concerned, attribute

variability was probably largely determined by functional considerations, by stylistic factors, or by a combination of both, plus a certain amount of random variability. Unfortunately, the functions of the retouched stone tools are not known, but it is thought likely that features such as absolute size, shape, and pointedness would not be unrelated to function. Within each assemblage, each attribute in question will be tested against the probable functional aspects of its tool class, in an attempt to prove that its variability was independent of function, and was therefore primarily (although not necessarily exclusively) determined by style. So far as is possible, tests are carried out within each assemblage individually because it has not been assumed that the assemblages are closely related to each other, so neither can it be assumed that the test results from one assemblage are valid for another. This approach also has the advantage of rendering irrelevant possible differences in the function(s) of a tool class between any two assemblages, since stylistic attributes are, by definition, independent of function in both occurrences.

The patterns of variability of the possible stylistic attributes of individual tool classes are also compared with each other, where sample sizes permit. Suppose it were to be found that the state of attribute a was dependent upon the state of attribute b. This would not provide an explanation of the variation in either, but would suggest, since the attributes occur on the same artifacts, the possibility of an artificial division of a single system of attribute-states—that is, the mistaken splitting of one attribute into two.

This analysis rests on the assumption that assemblages will provide representative samples of the stylistic preferences of the groups responsible for their manufacture. Some consideration should be given to the extent to which this assumption can be justified, but the problem has already been treated at length elsewhere (Close 1977; Close *et al.* 1979—in both of which are also much fuller discussions of the underlying theory). Suffice it to say that it would indeed seem justifiable to assume that an archaeological assemblage may provide quite an accurate picture of the stylistic preferences of its makers, and, hence, of their social affiliations. It is not assumed that an assemblage will provide a representative sample of any other aspect of the cultural system.

There are further sampling problems in that some of the assemblages are rather small, although this could not be avoided since most represent the total population of stone artifacts at that site. Also, because of the typological variations, only three tool classes—backed pieces, notches, and continuously retouched pieces—were sufficiently common in most assemblages to permit meaningful examination for stylistic attributes. Because of these factors the results of the

analysis can be regarded only as tentative and should be treated with caution. A potentially more serious difficulty is the small number of assemblages available. It is expected that if a change in population did take place, then the Terminal Paleolithic and Neolithic assemblages should fall into separate stylistic clusters, but if there was no change in population, then some degree of overlap should occur. However, if, as seems very probable, the area was occupied by more than one group during each period, then it is possible for our samples to represent different groups from the two periods whether there was a change in population or not. This means that continuity of population may be demonstrated, but not change of population.

Assemblages from six sites will be compared: E-77-3 (Terminal Paleolithic), E-77-5 (Neolithic), E-77-6 (Terminal Paleolithic), E-77-7 (Terminal Paleolithic), E-75-6 (both Terminal Paleolithic and Neolithic), and E-75-8, lower cultural layer (Neolithic).

BACKED BLADELETS

As well as "true" backed bladelets (Tixier Types 45–72), lunates (Type 82) have also been included in this group since their classification as double arch-backed bladelets or as geometric microliths is something of a moot point (Tixier 1963: 129) and the sample from E-75-8, lower layer, would otherwise have been too small. The attributes of backed bladelets to be examined as potentially stylistic are the side to which backing was applied (sinister or dexter); on pointed types, the end that was pointed (distal or proximal); and the type of backing retouch used (obverse or *sur enclume*).

The absolute sizes (length, width, and thickness) of sinister- and dexter-backed bladelets were compared by means of *t* tests in all seven assemblages, excepting only the lengths in E-77-5, where the sample was too small. No significant ($p = .05$) differences were found. The frequencies of straight-backed and pointed bladelets (Types 45–51), arch-backed and pointed bladelets (Type 56), and shouldered bladelets (Type 64) with sinister or dexter backing were compared in E-77-3 using the X^2 technique, as were also the frequencies of pieces with and without pointed ends in E-77-3 and in the Neolithic assemblage of E-75-6. These tests yielded respective X^2 values of .076, 3.485, and 1.621, which are less than the critical values of 5.991, 3.841, and 3.841, respectively, and indicate that the side backed was independent both of shape and of pointedness. Tests could not be made in E-77-5, E-77-6, E-77-7, and the Terminal Palaeolithic of E-75-6, but the distributions among sinister and dexter pieces are very similar, and there are no pointed-backed bladelets (except lunates) in E-75-8.

Mean lengths, widths, and thicknesses of distally and proximally pointed, backed bladelets were compared in E-77-3 and E-77-7, as were widths and thicknesses in the

two assemblages from E-75-6. There are no significant differences. The frequencies of distal and proximal points on straight-backed and pointed and on arch-backed and pointed bladelets could be compared only in E-77-3, where a X^2 value of 20.455 was obtained (the critical value is 3.841); more of the straight-backed and pointed bladelets than expected are proximal and more of the arch-backed and pointed are distal. Frequencies could not be statistically compared in E-77-7 and E-75-6, but the distributions of distal points are almost identical to those of the proximal points; all points are distal in E-77-6, and pieces with only one pointed end are virtually absent in E-77-5 and E-75-8.

For the obverse and *sur enclume* backed bladelets, mean widths and thicknesses could be compared in all assemblages except E-77-5, and mean lengths could be compared in E-77-3, E-77-7, the Terminal Paleolithic of E-75-6, and in E-75-8. Although there are no differences in length, in three out of six cases the obverse backed bladelets are significantly wider than the *sur enclume,* and in one case (E-75-6, Terminal Paleolithic) the *sur enclume* backed bladelets are significantly thicker than the obverse. Also, X^2 tests show that in E-77-3 more than expected of the *sur enclume* bladelets are pointed ($X^2 = 11.381$, with one degree of freedom), and that more than expected are straight backed and pointed, as opposed to arch backed and pointed or shouldered ($X^2 = 30.676$, with two degrees of freedom). Although not testable because of small samples, this pattern is also repeated in E-77-5, E-77-7, and E-75-8.

The differences between obverse and *sur enclume* backed bladelets in size, shape, and pointedness suggest that the type of backing used may have been of functional significance. However, there are no indications that such significance can be attached to sinister and dexter backing, and in only one test was the occurrence of distal and proximal points found to correlate with a possibly functional attribute. It would seem, then, justifiable to conclude that the side to be backed and the end to be pointed may have been determined primarily by stylistic considerations. The distributions of distal and proximal points on sinister- and dexter-backed bladelets could be statistically compared only in E-77-3, yielding a value for X^2 of .216, which indicates that the two are independent (the critical value is 3.841); the distributions are also closely similar in E-77-7 and in the two assemblages from E-75-6, although no tests could be carried out. (There are almost no pointed pieces in E-77-5; there are no proximally pointed pieces in E-77-6, and no single-pointed pieces in E-75-8.) It is therefore concluded that the side backed and the end pointed are two stylistic, and mutually independent, attributes of backed bladelets.

NOTCHED PIECES

As possible stylistic attributes of notched pieces were considered the general position of the notch on the flake or blade (lateral sinister, lateral dexter, or distal), the specific position of lateral notches (distal, central, or proximal), and the type of retouch used in their manufacture (obverse or inverse). As well as the sizes of the blanks, the sizes (length and depth) of the notches themselves are also deemed to be of probable functional significance, and may, in fact, be of greater importance than the former.

The dimensions of sinister, dexter, and distal notches that could be compared in each assemblage are given in Table A2.1. Of the 61 t tests performed, only 5 showed significant differences ($p = .05$): Sinister notches occur on narrower blanks than dexter notches in E-77-5, on thinner blanks than dexter notches in E-77-5 and E-75-8, and on narrower blanks than distal notches in the Terminal Paleolithic of E-75-6; and, sinister notches are shorter than distal notches in E-75-8. The three differences in E-75-6 and E-75-8 are, in fact, on the very borderline of significance, the difference in thickness between the sinister and dexter pieces resulting largely from the occurrence of a few very large pieces in the latter group, which has an unusually large variance. The differences between sinister and dexter notches in E-77-5 are less easily explained, but it may be noted that two cases out of 60, or 3%, constitute less than the expected error in these tests.

The tests that could be made between lateral distal, central, and proximal notches and between obversely and inversely retouched notches are also given in Table A2.1. No significant differences were observed in the first group, and in the second group only a single difference occurred: that obverse notches occur on longer blanks than inverse notches in E-75-8.

There are, then, a few possible functional differences between the states of the attributes examined. Such differences, are, however, very rare, and would not appear to contradict the suggestion that the principal determinant of variability was style. The distributions of distal, central, and proximal notches on the sinister and dexter sides could be compared only in E-77-3 and E-75-8, giving X^2 values of 3.509 and .733, respectively; the critical value of X^2 in each case is 5.991, indicating independence of the two attributes. Similar tests could not be made in other assemblages, but the distributions strongly suggest independence in each case. The rarity of inversely retouched notches meant that only one actual statistical test could be carried out on their distributions: The occurrence of obverse and inverse retouch on lateral distal, central, and proximal notches in

Table A2.1
Possible t Tests of Notched Pieces with Different States of Stylistic Attributes

Attributes	E-77-3	E-77-5	E-77-6	E-77-7	E-75-6 Terminal Paleolithic	E-75-6 Neolithic	E-75-8
Overall notch position							
Sinister versus dexter	l,w,th,nl,nd	w,th,nl,nd	l,w,th,nl,nd	w,th,nl,nd	l,w,th,nl,nd	l,w,th,nl,nd	l,w,th,nl,nd
Sinister versus distal			l,w,th,nl,nd		w,th,nl,nd		l,w,th,nl,nd
Dexter versus distal			l,w,th,nl,nd		w,th,nl,nd		l,w,th,nl,nd
Position of lateral notches							
Distal versus central	l,w,th,nl,nd	w,th,nl,nd	l,w,th,nl,nd	w,th,nl,nd	l,w,th,nl,nd	l,w,th,nl,nd	l,w,th,nl,nd
Distal versus proximal	l,w,th,nl,nd				w,th,nl,nd		l,w,th,nl,nd
Central versus proximal	l,w,th,nl,nd				w,th,nl,nd		l,w,th,nl,nd
Retouch type							
Obverse versus inverse	l,w,th,nl,nd	w,th,nl,nd	l,w,th,nl,nd				l,w,th,nl,nd

Key: l = length of blank w = width of blank; th = thickness of blank; nl = length of notch; nd = depth of notch.

E-75-8 gave a value for X^2 of .017 (the critical value is 5.991), indicating independence. However, where four or more inverse notches do occur (E-77-3, E-77-6, and E-75-8), both their general locations (sinister, dexter, or dis-tal) and their specific lateral locations (distal, central, or proximal) closely parallel those of the obverse notches. The three presumably stylistic attributes of the notched pieces would therefore appear to be independent of each other.

CONTINUOUSLY RETOUCHED PIECES

The attributes of the continuously retouched pieces (Tixier Type 105) to be examined are essentially the same as those of the notched pieces: the general position of the retouch (sinister, dexter, bilateral, or distal), the specific position of lateral retouch (distal, central, proximal, or along the entire edge), and type of retouch (obverse or inverse).

Table A2.2 gives the tests that could be carried out between sinister, dexter, bilateral, and distal retouched pieces. Of the 94 t tests, 12 showed significant differences. Eleven of these, however, involve comparisons with distally retouched pieces, which prove to be generally shorter, wider, and thicker than those with lateral retouch. The only remaining difference is that the dexter retouched pieces are wider than the bilateral in E-77-5. These results would suggest that the general location of lateral retouch, whether sinister, dexter, or bilateral, may well have been stylistically determined, but that the use of distal as opposed to lateral retouch might have been of functional significance.

In the second part of Table A2.2 are given the tests performed between pieces with lateral distal, central, proximal, or entire edge retouch. The 87 t tests yielded 6 cases of significant difference, 4 of which involve pieces with retouch along the entire edge. These tend to be shorter, narrower, and thinner than those examples with only partial retouch, and may therefore be functionally different. Among the partially retouched pieces, the only two significant differences are that the centrally retouched pieces are wider than the proximally retouched in the Neolithic of E-75-6, and the proximally retouched are longer than the distally retouched in E-75-8; perhaps not too much importance need be attached to the latter difference since there are only three unbroken, proximally retouched pieces in that assemblage. In any case, as was observed earlier for the general locations of notches, the number of significant differences found between partially retouched pieces (2 out of 46 t tests) is approximately equal to the expected error frequency (5%), and it would seem reasonable to conclude that the position of partial retouch was determined primarily by stylistic considerations.

Fourteen tests could be carried out between obversely and inversely retouched pieces (Table A2.2), and four showed significant differences: Inverse retouched pieces are wider than obverse in E-77-3 and E-77-5, and thicker than obverse in E-77-3 and the Terminal Paleolithic of E-75-6. These differences are to some extent illusory, since more of the inverse than of the obverse examples have distal (as opposed to lateral) retouch, and it has been noted that

Table A2.2
Possible t Tests of Continuously Retouched Pieces with Different States of Stylistic Attributes

Attributes	E-77-3	E-77-5	E-77-6	E-77-7	E-75-6 Terminal Paleolithic	E-75-6 Neolithic	E-75-8
Overall retouch position							
Sinister versus dexter	l,w,th	l,w,th	l,w,th		l,w,th	w,th	l,w,th
Sinister versus bilateral	l,w,th	l,w,th	l,w,th		w,th	l,w,th	l,w,th
Sinister versus distal	w,th	l,w,th	w,th		l,w,th	w,th	l,w,th
Dexter versus bilateral	l,w,th	l,w,th	l,w,th		w,th	w,th	l,w,th
Dexter versus distal	w,th	l,w,th	w,th		l,w,th	w,th	l,w,th
Bilateral versus distal	w,th	l,w,th	w,th		w,th	w,th	l,w,th
Position of lateral retouch							
Distal versus central	l,w,th	l,w,th	l,w,th		l,w,th	w,th	l,w,th
Distal versus proximal	l,w,th	l,w,th	l,w,th			w,th	l,w,th
Distal versus entire		l,w,th	l,w,th		l,w,th	w,th	l,w,th
Central versus proximal	l,w,th	l,w,th	l,w,th			l,w,th	l,w,th
Central versus entire		l,w,th	l,w,th		l,w,th	l,w,th	l,w,th
Proximal versus entire		l,w,th	l,w,th			l,w,th	l,w,th
Obverse versus Inverse	l,w,th	l,w,th	w,th		l,w,th		l,w,th

Key: l = length of blank; w = width of blank; th = thickness of blank.

pieces with distal retouch tend to be wider and thicker than those with lateral retouch. There are, in fact, no significant differences between the two types of retouch if the lateral examples only are considered.

The occurrence of distal, central, or proximal retouch on either side of the blank could be compared only in E-77-3, giving a X² value of 2.438 (with two degrees of freedom) and in E-75-8 (for distal and central retouch only), giving a value for X² of .427 (one degree of freedom). Both of these results indicate independence. Although not testable because of sample sizes, almost identical distributions also occur on both sides of the continuously retouched pieces in E-77-5, E-77-6, and the Neolithic of E-75-6. (There were only one sinister, one dexter, and three bilateral pieces in E-77-7, and five sinister, eight dexter, and three bilateral in the E-75-6 Terminal Paleolithic.) It may be further noted that the occurrence of partial or of entire edge retouch is independent of side in E-77-5 (comparing sinister, dexter, and bilateral), E-77-6 and E-75-8 (sinister *versus* dexter),

and E-75-6, Neolithic (unilateral *versus* bilateral). (There was only one example with entire edge retouch in E-77-3.) These tests gave X² values of 3.141, .079, .599, and 1.551, respectively, the critical values being 5.991 for the first test and 3.841 for the remaining three.

Inverse retouch is almost absent in E-77-7 and E-75-6, and very rare in E-77-3. However, the occurrence of obverse and inverse retouch on sinister, dexter, and bilateral pieces could be tested in E-75-8 (X² = 2.087, the critical value being 5.991) and, although not testable, similar distributions are found in E-77-5 and E-77-6. The frequencies with which obverse and inverse retouch are lateral distal, central, or proximal were also tested in E-75-8, giving a value for X² of .218 (with two degrees of freedom). Similar results would have been obtained from E-77-5 and E-77-6 had the samples been larger. The three stylistic attributes of the continuously retouched pieces appear, then, to be independent of each other.

COMPARISONS OF THE ASSEMBLAGES ON THE BASIS OF STYLISTIC VARIABILITY

Among the retouched stone tools of the Nabta area Terminal Paleolithic and Neolithic assemblages, eight attributes have been identified of which the variabilities appear to have been governed principally by style. The frequencies of the various states of these attributes in each assemblage are given in Table A2.3. A pattern of assemblage variability

Table A2.3
Absolute Frequencies of Stylistic Attributes, by Site

Attributes	E-77-3	E-77-5	E-77-6	E-77-7	E-75-6 Terminal Paleolithic	E-75-6 Neolithic	E-75-8
Backed bladelets							
1. Sinister	67	2	29	20	15	29	13
Dexter	58	4	14	19	19	20	7
2. Distal	30	1[a]	20	16	13	15	0[a]
Proximal	20	2[a]	0	8	7	2	0[a]
Notched pieces							
3. Distal	0	0	5	0	4	1	9
Sinister	36	8	8	3	18	8	23
Dexter	43	15	10	8	12	7	26
4. Lateral distal	16	6	3	4	6	6	13
Lateral central	39	17	15	6	16	9	19
Lateral proximal	24	1	1	1	8	1	14
5. Obverse	73	21	20	10	33	17	48
Inverse	6	3	6	1	1	0	14
Continuously retouched							
6. Sinister	20	13	14	1[a]	5	12	31
Dexter	23	17	22	1[a]	8	6	27
Bilateral	6	29	18	3[a]	3	13	24
7. Lateral distal	11	14	11	3[a]	3	4	17
Lateral central	27	12	16	1[a]	6	11	21
Lateral proximal	13	10	9	1[a]	0	7	13
8. Obverse	53	62	50	5[a]	15	35	72
Inverse	4	6	8	1[a]	4	2	27

[a] Mean value for all assemblages used because of small sample size.

that is primarily stylistically determined should reflect, to some extent, the pattern of sociocultural relationships among the groups that manufactured the assemblages, and it therefore remains to group the assemblages on the basis of such variability.

The procedures used for the grouping are as follows. The initial step is the adaptation of the raw data in Table A2.3. The value of each figure is calculated as a percentage of the relevant total (for example, obverse notches as a percentage of obverse plus inverse notches), but since percentages are mutually dependent—they must add up to 100—and the analysis demands that the variables be independent, a transformation is then applied that partially "decorrelates" the values. The transformation used converts the percentages into angles (expressed in radians) of which the sines are the square roots of the probabilities:

$$\phi_i = \sin^{-1}(P_i/100)^{1/2}$$

where P_i is the percentage frequency of variable i (Fisher 1963). Where data are missing or the samples are very small, such as for the continuously retouched pieces in E-77-7, they are assigned the mean value of that variable in all other assemblages. Two types of analysis are then carried out on the transformed data: a hierarchial linkage of the assemblages, and a Principal Components analysis.

For the former, a matrix of distance coefficients (in this case, squared Euclidean distance) between assemblages is first calculated, and hierarchical linkage is then carried out according to Ward's method, which combines those two clusters of which the fusion yields the least increase in the error sum of squares (Ward 1963). (The error sum of squares is the sum of the distances from each assemblage to the centroid of its parent cluster.) Pairs of assemblages or of clusters of assemblages continue to be fused until the whole sample forms a single cluster, and the analysis may then be summarized as a dendrogram (Figure A2.3).

Principal Components analysis attempts to summarize the data in a more economical form. The analysis operates through a matrix of correlation coefficients between the variables and sets up a series of new axes in hyperspace, so that the first axis (the first Principal Component) accounts for as much of the sample variance as possible; the second axis (the second Principal Component), for as much of the remaining variance as possible; and so forth. Each axis is perpendicular to, and therefore independent of, the others and is defined by weighted combinations of all the variables.

These two methods thus provide two different groupings of the assemblages. The dendrogram provides readily identifiable clusters, but is in only one dimension and may therefore involve considerable "strain." The Principal Components scattergram places the assemblages in two dimensions, involving less distortion, but is more difficult to interpret as the Components are composites of different proportions of the original variables. Consideration of the two together, however, may provide a tolerably accurate

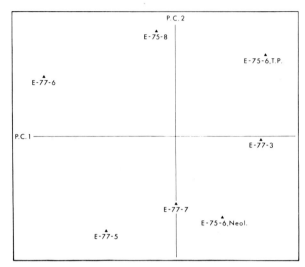

FIGURE A2.1. *Scattergram of seven Terminal Paleolithic and Neolithic assemblages along the axes of the first two Principal Components.*

picture of the "true" interrelationships of the assemblages.

Figure A2.1 gives the scattergram of the Nabta sites along the axes of the first two Principal Components. The first Principal Component accounts for 28.8% of the total sample variance, the weightings of most of the variables are quite high, and no single variable is obviously predominant—indicating quite a large degree of covariation between the variables. The second Principal Component accounts for 25.6% of the total sample variance, and tends to be weighted most heavily for those variables that play a comparatively minor role in the first Component. The first and second Principal Components together account for 54.4% of the sample variance, a fairly high figure that would support the suggestion that a single, predominant factor is responsible for almost all of the variability observed in these attributes. The sites appear to be quite evenly distributed across the scattergram, with no apparent clustering, and this may well be an artifact of the small number of assemblages involved. To test the results further, a second analysis was carried out in which six completely unrelated, Afian assemblages from the Nile Valley (Close *et al.* 1979) were added as background noise. The resultant scattergram along the axes of the first two Principal Components is shown in Figure A2.2, and the separation of the Nabta sites from the Afian would support at least the validity of the method.

Figure A2.3 gives the clustering of the Nabta assemblages in the form of a dendrogram (the scale on the left is the error sum of squares). The nature of hierarchical linkage is such that clusters will always be generated, whether meaningful or not, but the clear separation between some of the clusters in Figure A2.3 suggests that they may not be inappropriate.

The first cluster includes E-77-3, the Terminal Paleolithic of E-75-6, and E-75-8, between which there are

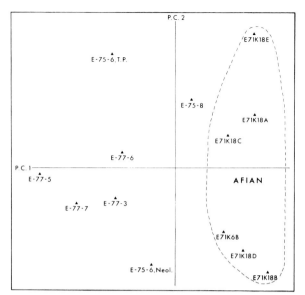

FIGURE A2.2. *Scattergram of seven Terminal Paleolithic and Neolithic and six Afian (Late Paleolithic) assemblages along the axes of the first two Principal Components.*

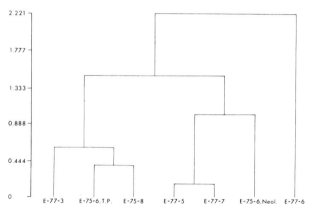

FIGURE A2.3. *Linkage dendrogram of seven Terminal Paleolithic and Neolithic assemblages.*

other similarities in addition to the stylistic. The two Terminal Paleolithic assemblages are almost identical, both in types of raw material utilized and in the types of cores, which are principally of the change-of-orientation and single-platform varieties. E-75-8 is very similar in core typology, but in raw-material selection shows a shift, characteristic of the Neolithic, toward the use of quartz and quartz crystal. Typologically, E-77-3 and the Terminal

Paleolithic of E-75-6 are very close, the only major difference being the relative importance of the microburin technique at E-77-3. In all three assemblages, burins are very rare, endscrapers and perforators are rather less so, and notches and denticulates and continuously retouched pieces are common; all three assemblages include noteworthy frequencies of geometric microliths (although the specific types vary from assemblage to assemblage) and of truncations, and there are no scaled pieces. There are differences in point types in that E-77-3 and E-75-6 have mainly stemmed points, whereas in E-75-8 truncated points predominate, and E-75-8 has a much lower frequency of backed pieces than do the two Terminal Paleolithic assemblages.

Apart from the stylistic similarities, there are no obvious correspondences—technological or typological—between E-77-5 and E-77-7. However, the Neolithic of E-75-6, which is more loosely linked with these two (inspection of the scattergram in Figure A2.1 suggests that this cluster might, nevertheless, be meaningful), shows a number of typological similarities to E-77-5. In both assemblages endscrapers, truncations, and microburins are very rare, although perforators (particularly double-backed perforators) and continuously retouched pieces are numerous. Notches and denticulates are more frequent in E-77-5, whereas backed pieces are more frequent in E-75-6; both show a preference for arch-backed pieces, and both include a few stemmed points.

Site E-77-6 appears to be widely separated from all the other Nabta assemblages in Figures A2.1 and A2.3.

This analysis is bedevilled by the small number of assemblages available. Nevertheless, the results would seem to indicate a mixing of Terminal Paleolithic and Neolithic assemblages within each stylistic cluster. Typological differences within the clusters might, then, be a reflection of the differences in economy between the two periods. Because of sample sizes it is not possible to draw more than very tentative conclusions from the analysis, so that one would not go so far as to suggest that the descendants of the Terminal Paleolithic occupants of E-77-3 and E-75-6 were the Neolithic occupants of E-75-8, or that E-77-5 and E-75-6 were occupied during the Neolithic by descendants of the Terminal Paleolithic group at E-77-7. However, the stylistic linking of Terminal Paleolithic and Neolithic occurrences suggests that the change in economy between the two periods may not have been accompanied by a change in population, although whether the adoption of Neolithic subsistence strategies resulted from some outside stimulus or was a purely local affair cannot at this time be determined.

REFERENCES

Close, A. E.
1977 The identification of style in lithic artefacts from Northeast Africa. *Mémoires de l'Institut d'Egypte* 61.

Close, A. E., F. Wendorf, and R. Schild
1979 *The Afian: A study of stylistic variability in a Nilotic industry.* Dallas: SMU Papers in Anthropology.

Fisher, R. A.
  1963 *Statistical methods for research workers,* 13th ed. New York: Hafner.
Tixier, J.
  1963 Typologie de l'Epipaléolithique du Maghreb. *Mémoires du Centre de Recherches Anthropologiques, Préhistoriques et Ethnographiques, Alger,* No. 2.

Ward, J. H.
  1963 Hierarchical grouping to optimisé an objective function. *Journal of the American Statistical Association* 58:236–244.

3

Ceramics of the Western Desert

K. MORGAN BANKS

Ceramic collections made as part of the Combined Pre-historic Expedition's investigations of Neolithic and later sites in the Western Desert offer an opportunity to identify and define several as yet unreported ceramic traditions. The collections span the period from one of the earliest dated ceramics in North Africa up to and including the historic period; the only periods lacking are Pharaonic and Graeco-Roman, but these have been described in detail elsewhere (Caton-Thompson 1952; Caton-Thompson and Gardner 1934). Sherds dating to these periods have been observed but not collected in the Bir Sahara and Bir Tarfawi regions (Wendorf *et al.* 1977).

Seven areas are represented in the collections: Nabta Playa, Wadi Bakht, Bir Kiseiba–Bir Takhlis, Gebel Uweinat, the Fayum, Kharga Oasis, and Bir Tarfawi. Table A3.1 lists the regions, the sites within each, and the number of sherds recovered.

The associated radiocarbon dates differ from region to region. The earliest dates, ranging from 8000 to 6000 BP, come from Nabta Playa, Wadi Bakht, and, possibly, Kharga Oasis. Dates ranging from 6000 to 3000 BP accompany the Fayum, Kharga Oasis, and one of the Nabta Playa collections. The Gebel Uweinat, Bir Tarfawi, and Bir Kiseiba–Bir Takhlis collections are undated and, with the exception of the Bir Tarfawi collection, come from unsystematically collected surface finds. The Gebel Uweinat collection appears to be an agglomeration of sherds from unrelated occupations covering a long time span. The Bir Kiseiba–Bir Takhlis collection is almost identical to the Khartoum Neolithic ceramics at Nabta Playa and undoubtedly dates to the same period. The Bir Tarfawi collection comes from sites containing historic items, including iron objects and glass, placing these sherds within the historic period (Hays n.d.).

Table A3.1
Ceramic Collections from the Western Desert, by Site and Region[a]

Area collected	Decorated vessel sherds[b]	Rimsherds	Total
Nabta Playa	275	17	476
E-75-6 (Early Neolithic)			7
E-75-7			3
E-75-8 (Middle Neolithic)			239
E-75-8 (Later Neolithic)			172
E-77-1			50
E-77-4			4
E-77-5			1
Bir Kiseiba–Bir Takhlis	8	2	8
Wadi Bakht	48	15	139
Kharga Oasis		3	122
E-76-1			7
E-76-7			30
E-76-8			85
Fayum	1	25	492
E29H2			96
E29G3			333
Gebel Uweinat	8	4	10
Feb-35			7
Feb-40			3
Bir Tarfawi	100	10	112
BT-5			100
BT-21			12

[a] Sherds counted are 1 cm² or larger.
[b] Counts include rimsherds that have fragments of body decorations.

THE COLLECTIONS

Several factors affected the examination of the collections. One problem, seen from Table A3.1, is their small size. No collection from any area exceeds 500 sherds, and no site contains more than 350 sherds, several being represented by 10 sherds or less. A second problem is the lack of whole or reconstructible vessels. Restorations were attempted, but only in one instance could at least 35% of a vessel be reconstructed. This resulted from the generally small size of the sherds (averaging between 9 and 20 cm), the weathered condition of many of them, and the small number of rimsherds, which account for less than 6% of the collections. These factors complicated not only attempts at reconstruction but also determinations of vessel size and shape. A third problem is the small number of decorated sherds, which represent 28% of the collection. This frequency in part reflects the absence of decorated material in the Fayum and Kharga Oasis collections. Decorated sherds are most prevalent in the Bir Tarfawi, Nabta Playa, and Wadi Bakht collections, although decorated material still constitutes less than 50% of the last two.

METHOD OF STUDY

Eight attributes were selected for comparative descriptions and identification: vessel and rim form, construction, hardness, color, firing atmosphere, temper, surface treatment, and vessel and rim decoration. The last three are the most temporally and regionally diagnostic.

Where possible, vessel form was determined by base and body configuration. Overall, the collections lack diversity of form, particularly among the earlier material; straight-walled bowls with rounded bases and globular bowls with incurved rims are the most common forms. Rims are generally indistinguishable from the bodies. This lack of diversity may reflect the small number of sherds from which vessel forms could be identified and the lack of reconstructible vessels.

Coiling, molding, paddle and anvil, and use of the wheel are the only construction methods identified, determination being made by the presence of coil marks, anvil or finger impressions, or parallel striations. Wheel-made wares occur only in the Gebel Uweinat and Bir Tarfawi collections, each containing one such sherd. The other methods have some regional and temporal significance, as coiling appears to be replaced by molding in the Kharga Oasis and Fayum collections.

How the sherd broke—whether with straight or jagged edges—and how well the edges held their integrity are also described. Breakage is related to the quality of construction and firing and the temper used (Shepard 1956).

Hardness determinations are based on the Mohs scale and are also related to the quality of construction and completeness of firing. However, hardness is not regionally or temporally diagnostic; most collections range from 3 to 5.

The Munsell scale was used for color determinations and both the Munsell name and number are given. Three color determinations are quoted: the exterior and interior surfaces and the core, and some indication is given as to how the surface and core colors merge. Colors have some regional and temporal significance.

Firing atmospheres and temperature determinations have been subjectively determined by comparing core and surface colors and the degree of clay isotropism (Colton 1953; Hodges 1963; Shepard 1956). The firing atmosphere has some temporal significance, as vessels fired in reducing atmospheres are prevalent only in the Bir Tarfawi collection.

Temper identification was made through thin-section analysis (Holdaway n.d.) except for the Gebel Uweinat, Bir Tarfawi, and Fayum collections. These groups were examined at a later date and their tempers were determined through comparisons with the other collections.

Nine temper types have been distinguished on the basis of temper origin and constituent mineralogical and/or organic content. Although some tempers occur in several collections, they differ in the frequencies of their components and grain sizes; apparently, tempers were locally derived. Some sands also appear to have been ground prior to use as indicated by the lower limits of the grain sizes and their angularity (Holdaway n.d.). The types of temper identified are as follows:

1. *Intrusive acidic igneous,* composed of microcline, nonpolycrystalline quartz, opaque, biotite, and, occasionally, plagioclase of sodium-rich composition. The microcline is microperthitic. An igneous origin is indicated by the microperthite, biotite as the dominant mica, and the lack of polycrystalline quartz.
2. *Metamorphic gneissic with or without intrusive acidic igneous,* containing microcline, polycrystalline quartz, quartz, plagioclase of sodium-rich composition, biotite, opaque, and granular calcite and hornblende. Metamorphic sources are indicated by the polycrystalline quartz and the granular calcite. The temper also has an igneous origin if the microcline is predominantly microperthitic.
3. *Recycled sandstone,* dominated by quartz and very little feldspar. Fresh and weathered gabbro, either titanaugite or geothite and hematite, is occasionally present.
4. *Intrusive basic and acidic igneous,* containing microcline, quartz, calcic plagioclase, and augite
5. *Calcareous metamorphic,* consisting of granular calcite and epidote, indicating a metamorphosed impure carbonate sediment, probably limestone

6. *Metamorphic mica schist and amphibolite,* characterized by abundant muscovite, with sodic plagioclase and hornblende typical of amphibolite
7. *Fossiliferous shell,* composed of crushed fossil shell fragments
8. *Chaff,* consisting of large and obvious plant fragments, primarily stems
9. *Bone,* containing crushed and burned bone fragments

Tempers are regionally and temporally significant. Sand tempers are most frequent among the earlier collections, whereas organic tempers become more common in the more recent material.

Surface treatment refers to the surface texture and, exclusive of decorations, modification by scraping or hand-smoothing. Surface treatment is especially important on undecorated sherds as a means of identification.

Vessel and rim decorations include any surface modification beyond scraping and hand-smoothing. This includes burnishing, smudging, incision, impression, punctation, or combinations of these. To ensure continuity with other studies of Saharan ceramics (Camps 1969; Camps-Fabrer 1966; Hays 1971b, 1974; Nordström 1972), previously introduced names have been adopted where applicable. Where a motif occurs in unrelated collections, the same name has been retained but with no implication of cultural continuity. Decorations, and the lack of them, are the most sensitive regional and temporal indicators.

The collections are presented by region and in chronological order, beginning with the earliest collection. Where available, radiocarbon dates are included for chronological comparisons.

NABTA PLAYA

The only collection containing more than one identifiable ceramic tradition is that from Nabta Playa. Three Neolithic units have been identified: early, middle, and late (see Chapter 3). The early and middle Neolithic are variants of the Khartoum Neolithic, and the later Neolithic is related to the Abkan tradition along the Nile; these differences are reflected in the ceramics.

EARLY NEOLITHIC

Early Neolithic ceramics come from the upper horizon at E-75-6, and a series of radiocarbon determinations dates this collection to about 8100 BP, one of the earliest dates for ceramics in North Africa. The decorations used, although within the range described for the Khartoum Neolithic (Arkell 1949; Hays 1971b, 1974), are not common and are distinct from those of the succeeding middle Neolithic, suggesting a temporal change in the ceramics that is also matched by changes in the lithics. This suggestion should, however, be viewed with caution since the early Neolithic collection is small.

The decorative techniques and motifs among the E-75-6 ceramics are not matched among early collections from elsewhere in the Sahara. Early Khartoum Neolithic sites such as Ti-n-Torha (Barich 1978), Gabrong (Gabriel 1977, 1978), or Amekni (Camps 1969, 1978) have ceramics more reminiscent of those from the middle Neolithic. If the distinction between the early and middle Neolithic ceramics is valid, a problem arises as to the origin and distribution of these early Neolithic ceramics and their relationship to those of the middle Neolithic.

The collection consists of seven decorated sherds: six vessel sherds and one rimsherd. Although exact determination could not be made, the vessel form was probably that of a bowl with straight walls. The rimsherd is slightly outward flaring but undistinguished from the body. The diameters of the body sherds range from 34 to 38 cm; that of the rimsherd is 38 cm. Sherd thickness ranges from 4 to 6 mm.

Vessels were constructed by coiling; coil marks are faintly evident and there is a tendency to break along the coils. The sherds break with straight edges and little disintegration. Hardness is from 3 to 4. Drill holes for vessel repair are present. The vessels were fired in oxidizing atmospheres, probably at temperatures about 700°C, but for fairly long periods of time. All carbon originally present in the matrix is burned out, but the clay is only slightly isotropic.

Surface and core colors grade into one another with no sharp boundaries. Exterior surfaces vary from dark grayish-brown (10YR 4/2) to dark yellowish-brown (10YR 4/4). Interior surfaces are all light brown (7.5YR 6/4). The core ranges from yellowish brown (10YR 5/4) to strong brown (7.5YR 5/6). Some fire clouds are present on the exterior surfaces.

All tempers are intrusive acidic igneous. The paste includes approximately 40% temper and 5% pore spaces. Temper grains are angular to subangular, ranging in size from .03 to .47 mm.

Scraping striations are apparent on the interior surfaces. Surface textures are smooth. The larger temper grains were submerged below the surface and are thus not readily apparent. Only vessel bodies are decorated, the decoration extending to the base of the lip. The lack of undecorated sherds suggests that vessels were completely decorated except for the rim. Decorative techniques are impression and incision, and no composite decorations were observed. All sherds are decorated with one of two motifs.

Fishnet (Figure A3.1a)

The fishnet motif was found on the rimsherd and consists of two series of incised straight lines, perpendicular to each

FIGURE A3.1. *Early Neolithic sherds from Nabta Playa: (a) fishnet design; (b, c) ripple design. Later Neolithic sherds from Nabta Playa: (d, e) straight line design; (f) atypical chevron design.*

other and at 45° to the rim, which extend to the base of the rim. The design was executed with a fingernail or a pointed wand. The lines are deeply incised, thus bringing the interstices forward. Below this motif is a second unidentifiable decoration. This is the only compositely decorated sherd identified among the Khartoum Neolithic–related wares. A variant of this motif was found at Esh Shaheinab [Arkell 1953: Plate 32(7)], but on a burnished sherd. The motif was also noted on compositely decorated sherds at Guro, Site SE3, in the southwestern Libyan Desert [Arkell 1964: Plate 44(1, 2, 3)]. However, Site SE3 is not a Khartoum Neolithic site. Hays (1971b:43) includes this design among the range for the Khartoum Neolithic, but it is apparently not commonly encountered.

Ripple (Figure A3.1b)

The ripple motif is the more common of the two, having been identified on six sherds. The design consists of columns of raised nodes running down the vessel face, the columns either parallel or at slight angles to one another. The nodes stand out from the surface and are distinct. The design was executed using a split wand, possibly a plant stem, or a fingernail to punctate the vessel surface at an

angle, thus raising the node. The wand or fingernail was then dragged down the vessel face between the columns to accentuate the nodes further. This motif was recorded at Early Khartoum on sherds labeled Atypical Micaceous Ware (Arkell 1949: Plate 82). A similar motif was also recovered from the Khartoum Variant Site 1045, near Wadi Halfa [Shiner 1968: Figure 4(e)]. It has not previously been reported from any Saharan site.

MIDDLE NEOLITHIC

The majority of the Nabta ceramics belong to the middle Neolithic period, which is radiocarbon dated from 7500 to 6300 BP. The ceramics are similar to Khartoum Neolithic ceramics found elsewhere in the Sahara (Camps 1974; Hays 1971b, 1974). This occupation exhibits the most extensive external relationships of any Neolithic unit so far recorded in the Western Desert and is part of a pan-Saharan ceramic tradition (Camps 1974; Hays 1971b).

Some motifs are repeatedly found within all the Nabta sites, whereas others are limited to one or two sites, in part due to the small size of several of the samples. However, the lack of some motifs among the ceramics from the large

E-75-8 collection may indicate further undetected microregional or temporal differences.

The middle Neolithic collection consists of 297 sherds, including 164 decorated sherds and 14 rimsherds. Two vessel forms have been identified. Bowls with straight walls, rounded bases, and undistinguished rims occur in two sizes: The more frequent has a diameter ranging from 35 to 40 cm and a sherd thickness of 4 to 9 mm; the second size has a diameter of 60 cm and a sherd thickness of 7 to 18 mm. The latter also has lugs on the base for added stability (Arkell 1949: Plate 74). For the second form, globular bowls with incurved rims and rounded bases, the body diameter is 25 cm, the rim diameter is 20 cm, and sherds are 7 to 11 mm thick. Both vessel types have indistinguishable rims and wall thicknesses that increase toward the base.

Vessels were constructed by coiling, as coil marks are evident, and there is a tendency to break along the coils. Breakage is variable. Some sherds, particularly those from E-75-8, are extremely friable, with sherd edges that easily disintegrate. Others are not as friable and breakage results in sharp, straight edges that do not easily disintegrate. The hardness varies from 2 to 4. All vessels were fired in oxidiz-

ing atmospheres at temperatures probably about 700°C and not sufficiently high to turn the clay isotropic. Vessels were fired long enough to burn out all carbon streaks.

Exterior surface colors vary from red (2.5YR 5/6) to yellowish red (5YR 5/6 to 5/8) to reddish yellow (5YR 6/8) to dark reddish-gray (5YR 4/2) to strong brown (7.5YR 5/6) to pinkish gray (7.5YR 6/2) to brown to pale brown (10YR 5/3 to 6/3). Interior surfaces range from weak red (2.5YR 5/2) to red (2.5YR 5/8) to yellowish red (5YR 5/8) to reddish yellow (5YR 6/6–7/8 to 7.5YR 6/6) to light brownish-gray (10YR 6/2). Core colors vary from yellowish red (5YR 5/8) to pinkish gray (7.5YR 7/2) to strong brown (7.5YR 5/6) to dark brown (7.5YR 4/4) to very dark gray to grayish brown (10YR 3/1–3/2) to brown (10YR 5/3) to light gray (10YR 7/2). In most cases the surface colors merge with those of the core.

Two types of temper were used. In sherds with metamorphic gneissic temper, with or without intrusive acidic igneous, the paste includes 1.5–5% pore space and 45–49% temper. Grain size varies from .03 to .63 mm. This temper is found among the E-75-8, E-77-1, E-77-4, and E-77-5 ceramics. In sherds with metamorphic mica

FIGURE A3.2. *Middle Neolithic sherds from Nabta Playa: Woven mat design (a, b) with angle-incised rim design; (c) with fern branch rim design; (d) undecorated rim; (e, f) decorated body sherds.*

schist and amphibolite temper, the temper accounts for 40% of the paste and pore spaces are not evident. Grains vary in size from .03 to .31 mm and are angular to subangular. This temper is limited to the Site E-75-7 ceramics.

All surfaces were scraped or hand-smoothed. Large temper grains may be evident on sherd surfaces, depending on the quality of scraping and construction. Site E-75-8 ceramics are more gritty than those from other sites. One undecorated grayware was distinguished, based on several large, undecorated rim and body sherds from the same vessel. Surfaces are rough and granular and large temper grains are evident. Interior and exterior surfaces vary from light brownish-gray (10YR 6/2) to reddish yellow (5YR 6/8). Rims are indistinguishable from the vessel body.

Seven vessel and four rim motifs were distinguished. The decorative techniques include impression, incision, and punctation. The extent of vessel decoration varies by site; a motif may cover an entire vessel at one site but be more restricted at another. There is no evidence for composite decorations.

Woven Mat (Figure A3.2)

The woven mat motif is the most common one, being found on 122 sherds. The design consists of continuously applied and closely spaced comb impressions and resembles a basket weave. The amount of vessel coverage and the orientation relative to the rim vary. On some sherds the design is diagonal to the rim, whereas on others it is parallel; some vessels are only partially covered and others are completely covered. This is one of the most common and widely distributed Khartoum Neolithic motifs. It has been recorded at Early Khartoum (Arkell 1949: Plate 65), in southern Sudan [Hays 1971a: Plate 4 (1, 2, 5, 8, 9)], Amekni (Camps 1969: Plate 15), in the Hoggar (Camps-Fabrer 1966: Plates 43, 44), and at Ti-n-Torha (Barich 1978: Figure 2).

Linear Mat (Figure A3.3a–c)

Recorded on 22 sherds, the linear mat motif consists of short, linear impressions executed by a supple, string-

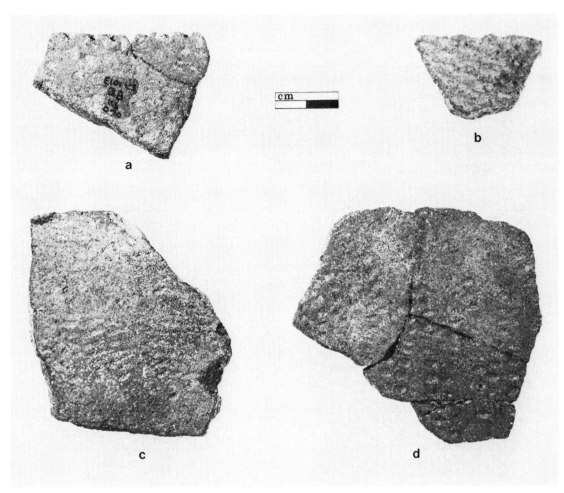

FIGURE A3.3. *Middle Neolithic sherds from Nabta Playa: (a) linear mat design with punctate rim design; (b, c) linear mat design; (d) dotted para-sawtooth.*

wrapped roulette. The impressions are randomly spaced over the vessel surface from rim to base. The roulette is either impressed and then removed, or impressed and slightly dragged. Variants have been recorded in southern Sudan [Hays 1971a: Plate 2 (1, 2, 3, 11), Plate 4 (7, 10, 11)] and at Early Khartoum [Arkell 1949: Plate 75 (3), Plate 76 (2)].

Dotted Para-Sawtooth (Figure A3.3d)

The dotted para-sawtooth design was identified on only one sherd and consists of dotted zigzags executed by pivoting a straight comb across the vessel face. The motif was recorded at Early Khartoum [Arkell 1949: Plate 90(2)] on an "atypical" sherd. It was also part of a composite decoration at Gabrong (Gabriel 1977: Figure 31) and occurs elsewhere in the central Sahara [Camps-Fabrer 1966: Plate 41 (5)].

Atypical Wolftooth (Figure A3.4a)

The major component of the atypical wolftooth motif, identified on four sherds, is a series of raised vertical zigzags running in continuous parallel columns down the vessel face from the rim to the base. The design is executed by inserting a fingernail or curved spatula at an angle to the surface, raising a small node, and then reinserting the implement again at right angles to the first insertion. The design is distantly reminiscent of the ripple motif in the early Neolithic. This design is not a true "wolftooth" as described by Hays (1971b:47–48), since it was not executed by pivoting the implement and the individual elements are more closely spaced than on the classic wolftooth.

Dotted Straight Line (Figure A3.4b)

The dotted straight line motif was identified on eight sherds and consists of a series of repeated comb impressions that create rows of dotted straight lines, each series being at

FIGURE A3.4. *Middle Neolithic sherds from Nabta Playa: (a) atypical wolftooth design; (b) dotted straight line design with punctate rim design; (c) chevron design; (d) straight line design; (e) large punctate sherd with punctate rim design.*

an angle to the next. The pattern is discontinuous and randomly oriented on the vessel surface. The motif is similar to the linear mat motif except that it is executed with a comb. Variations of this motif, usually more systematically oriented, have been recorded at Early Khartoum [Arkell 1949: Plate 63(3)].

Straight Line (Figure A3.4d)

The straight line design was identified on three sherds. A comb was lightly dragged across the vessel face to create a series of parallel lines, with each set at an angle to the next. A similar motif was recorded at Early Khartoum [Arkell 1949: Plate 78(2)].

Punctate (Figure A3.4e)

The punctate motif was found on four sherds and consists of randomly spaced punctations made with a pointed wand. The punctations are most frequent near the rim, decreasing down the vessel face. The base lacks decoration. Occasionally punctations are paired, creating a "fern branch" motif (Hays 1971b:48). No other recorded occurrences of this motif could be found.

Four different rim decorations have been recognized.

Angle Incised (Figure A3.2a–b)

Identified on four sherds, the angle incised design consists of shallow incisions angled into the outer edge of the rim. The incisions may be straight or slightly curved. The design is found on sherds with a woven mat motif.

Fern Branch (Figure A3.2c)

The fern branch decoration, found on one sherd, is composed of two parallel rows of paired punctations that encircle the outer edge of the rim. The associated vessel decoration is the woven mat.

Punctate (Figure A3.3a)

Occurring on four sherds, the punctate motif consists of shallow, vertical punctations on the outer edge of the rim. The motif is associated with the linear mat vessel decoration.

Milled (Figure A3.4b,e)

The milled rim decoration was found on three sherds and consists of shallow impressed lines that cut across the rim, perpendicular to the outer edge. This rim type is associated with the punctate and dotted straight line vessel motifs and was first recorded at Early Khartoum (Arkell 1949: Plate 70).

LATER NEOLITHIC

Later Neolithic material comes from the upper horizon and the surface of E-75-8 and is radiocarbon dated from 6500 BP to after 6300 BP. The collection shows Nilotic affinities and is probably related to the Abkan tradition (Adams and Nordström, personal communication). If so, the Nabta occupation predates the Nilotic Abkan and would suggest a Saharan origin for this tradition (Huard 1973).

The ceramics are completely different from the preceding Khartoum Neolithic ceramics and represent an unrelated tradition. One of the major differences is the appearance of smudging and burnishing.

The only identified vessel shape is that of straight-walled bowls with rounded bases. Rim and vessel diameters vary from 40 to 46 cm and sherd thickness varies from 5 to 8 mm, increasing toward the base. Rims are undifferentiated from the body.

Vessels were constructed by coiling and finished by paddle and anvil; coil and anvil impressions are present, and there is a tendency to break along the coils. Sherds break with straight edges and little disintegration. Hardness ranges from 4 to 5. Both oxidizing and reducing atmospheres were used; smudging indicates that reducing atmospheres were used at least in the final firing. Fairly high temperatures, at least 700°C, were used and vessels were fired long enough to burn out the carbon and allow the clay to become semi-isotropic.

Exterior surface colors include black (7.5YR 2.5/0), browns (7.5YR 3/2 to 6/4), yellowish reds (5YR 5/8 to 6/6), and reds (2.5YR 4/2–6/6 to 10R 5/6). Interior colors vary from black (7.5YR 2.5/0) to pale brown (10YR 6/3) to reddish brown and yellowish red (5YR 6/3 to 5/6) to reds (2.5YR 5/6 to 6/6). Core colors include grayish browns (10YR 3/2 to 6/2), reddish yellows (7.5YR 4/4–6/6 to 3/2–4/2), and reddish browns (5YR 4/4 to 5/8). In most cases, the surface and core colors merge.

Only one temper type, recycled sandstone, was distinguished. The paste includes 3–7% pore spaces and 45–50% temper. Grains are angular to subrounded, varying from .02 to .41 mm.

All interior and unburnished exterior surfaces are scraped. Large temper grains are not visible on the surfaces and textures are smooth to lustrous. One undecorated buffware was defined, represented by 67 sherds. The sherds vary from brown (7.5YR 6/4) to yellowish red (5YR 5/8). Surfaces are smooth, lacking large grains. Rims are also undecorated and undifferentiated from the body. These are included in Nordström's Ware Group M (Nordström 1972, and personal communication). Decorative methods include burnishing, smudging and burnishing, incision, and, on the rims, impression. Five vessel decorations were distinguished and include the following:

Simple Burnishing

Eighty-one sherds are red burnished (2.5YR 4/2–6/6 to 10R 5/6), the color intensity varying. Fire clouds are present. Surfaces are smooth and semilustrous to lustrous.

Smudged and Burnished

The surfaces on 16 sherds are unevenly smudged (6.5YR

2.5/0). Where the smudging is thin, the original color (5YR 6/6) comes through and surfaces are dull. Where the smudging is complete, the surface is lustrous.

Straight Line (Figure A3.1d–e)

Seven sherds are incised with a comb that was dragged around the vessel, creating a series of parallel lines. The decoration does not cover the entire vessel, although which portions of the vessel are undecorated could not be determined. Nordström reported this motif from Abkan sites along the Nile and included them in his Ware Group M [Nordström 1972: Plate 139(3) and personal communication]. The design is not well executed.

Two types of rim decorations were noted (as in the following two sections).

Fern Branch (Figure A3.1e)

A single sherd has two impressed parallel rows of out-ward flaring dots that encircle the base of the rim. The rest of the vessel is undecorated. The design was executed with a blunt wand. Nordström includes this motif in his Ware Family K [Nordström 1972: Plate 121(1), and personal communication], which is from Khartoum Variant sites in Nubia. As this sherd came from the deflated surface of E-75-8, it may be associated with the Khartoum Neolithic occupation, although it was found with other later Neolithic sherds.

Milled

The milled motif, found on one sherd, consists of a series of shallow, impressed, radial lines that cut across the rim top. The associated vessel decoration is unknown. Nordström includes this sherd in his Ware Family K[Nordström 1972: Plate 121(27), and personal communication].

BIR KISEIBA–BIR TAKHLIS

Bir Kiseiba–Bir Takhlis is a series of large playas approximately 100 km west of Nabta Playa. The collection is a grab sample made during a brief reconnaissance of the area by members of the Combined Prehistoric Expedition in 1977. The collection consists of eight decorated sherds, including two with rims, and one undecorated rimsherd. The three motifs present are reminiscent of those from the Nabta middle Neolithic. No radiocarbon dates are yet available from Bir Kiseiba–Bir Takhlis, but the similarities to the Nabta material suggest a comparable age.

No vessel forms could be identified, but they are probably the same as those from Nabta. Vessel diameters range from 44 to 46 cm and sherd thicknesses range from 4 to 11 mm. Two rims have diameters of 41 cm and all are undifferentiated from the vessel body.

Vessels were probably constructed by coiling, although coil impressions are not evident. However, sherds tend to break quadrilaterally, suggesting breakage along coils. Sherds break with straight edges and little disintegration, even on the more weathered sherds. The hardness varies from 4 to 5. Drill holes for repairing the vessels are present. Oxidizing atmospheres were probably used, vessels being fired at temperatures about 700°C but not for long periods of time. The clay was not isotropic, but any carbon originally present has been burned out.

The surface and core colors are uniform, varying from brown (7.5YR 5/2 to 10YR 5/2) to pale brown (10YR 6/3) to red (2.5YR 4/6). In addition, some core and interior surfaces are very dark gray (10YR 3/1). The core and surface colors grade into one another, with no sharp breaks. Fire clouds are also present on the exterior surfaces.

One temper type was identified, intrusive acidic igneous. The paste includes 2–5% pore spaces and 50% temper. Grain size varies from .03 to .47 mm.

Interior surfaces are scraped, but the decorations on the exterior surfaces have destroyed any evidence of external scraping. Large temper grains are visible on the surfaces of some sherds but not on others. Two different decorative techniques, incision and impression, are present. Three vessel motifs have been identified. Woven mat (Figure A3.2) was identified on four sherds and is identical to the motif from Nabta Playa. Atypical wolftooth (Figure A3.4a) was found on two sherds and is also identical to the motif from Nabta. Chevrons (Figure A3.4c) were found on one sherd. This motif consists of rows of short straight lines arranged into a series of overlapping parallel columns. Each column is at an angle to the next, creating a series of vertical, broken zigzags. The design was executed with a pointed wand or spatula. It is almost identical to the chevron motif described by Hays (1971b:48) and was recorded at Early Khartoum [Arkell 1949: Plate 82 (upper left)]. All rims are undecorated.

WADI BAKHT

Wadi Bakht ceramics were first collected and reported by Myers (Bagnold et al. 1939). Subsequently, McHugh (1971, 1975) described part of the original collection in more detail, but his descriptions were primarily limited to undecorated body sherds, as the rimsherds and decorated body sherds were lost during World War II.

The present collection was made during a brief reconnaissance of Wadi Bakht by members of the Combined Prehistoric Expedition. The collection totals 139 sherds, including 21 sherds supplied by McHugh from Myers' original collection, and is composed of 46 decorated and 78 undecorated body sherds and 15 rimsherds. McHugh originally divided Myers' collection into two types on the basis of temper differences and sherd thickness. The present collection shows that McHugh's division encompasses a wide variety of decorative techniques and that his division should be amended.

The associated radiocarbon date, 6930 BP ± 80 years (SMU-273) indicates that the Wadi Bakht ceramics are contemporaneous with those from the Nabta middle Neolithic. However, these ceramics are technologically and stylistically distinct and bear little resemblance to the latter, suggesting an independent origin for the Wadi Bakht material.

Three vessel forms were distinguished. The first are straight-walled and shallow bowls with indistinguishable rims and bases. Rim and vessel diameters vary from 25 to 41 cm and sherd thicknesses vary from 4 to 6 mm, increasing toward the base. Globular bowls with slightly inward curving rims have rim diameters of 20 cm, vessel diameters of 24 cm, and sherd thickness varying from 4 to 6 mm. The rim is distinguished from the vessel body by a slight thickening of the rim base. Finally, globular bowls with short, constricted necks and outward flaring rims have a rim diameter of 15 cm, and the vessel diameter is unknown. Sherd thicknesses range from 4 to 6 mm but increase to 11 mm at the base.

Vessels were constructed by molding, as finger impressions are apparent. Sherds do not break with a particular orientation, although there is little disintegration of sherd edges. Hardnesses vary from 3 to 5. Drill holes are present. Vessels were fired in both oxidizing and reducing atmospheres, the latter being used at least during the final firing stage on the smudged vessels. Firing temperatures were fairly high, probably greater than 700°C, and the vessels were fired for fairly long periods. The clay is semi-isotropic and, in most cases, the carbon is burned out.

Exterior surface colors range from black (7.5YR 2.5/0) to reddish yellow (7.5YR 7/6) to yellowish red (5YR 5/6) to reddish brown (5YR 4/4) to red (10R 4/6). Interior surface colors include reddish yellow (7.5YR 7/6), yellowish red (5YR 5/6), and reddish brown (5YR 4/4 to 5/4). Core colors include gray (10YR 5/1), dark grayish-brown (10YR 4/2), yellowish red (5YR 5/8), and reddish brown (5YR 4/4 to 5/4). Core and surface colors either merge or are sharply distinct.

Two temper types were identified. In the first, intrusive acidic igneous, grain sizes vary from .05 to .33 mm, and grains are rounded to subrounded to subangular. Five percent of the paste is pore spaces and 45% is temper. In the second type, recycled sandstone, grain sizes vary from .03 to .38 mm, and grains are subrounded to round. Two percent of the paste is pore spaces and 40% is temper. Organic material is occasionally present, apparently having been included as temper. Weathered gabbro (geothite and hematite) is also present, possibly being added as a coloring agent (Holdaway n.d.).

Interior and exterior surfaces, except on the burnished sherds, are scraped. Larger temper grains are not present on the majority of sherd surfaces. In addition, plant impressions are very evident on some sherds. Some sherds have a gritty surface texture, the larger temper grains still being identifiable. Four decorative techniques were employed: impression/incision, burnishing and impression, simple burnishing, and smudging and burnishing. Six decorations were distinguished.

Linear (Figure A3.5a,b)

The linear motif, found on 14 unburnished sherds, is composed of incised straight lines made by dragging a comb across the vessel face. Subsequent to application, the surface was lightly scraped to subdue the design. In one instance the comb was first dragged in one direction, rotated through 90°, and dragged again, creating a subdued woven mat motif. On another sherd, each series of lines is offset from the next. This is the only motif reminiscent of the Nabta middle Neolithic motifs.

Ladder (Figure A3.5c)

The two sherds that display the ladder motif are red burnished. The motif consists of short parallel rows of dotted lines running vertically up the vessel face, resembling a ladder. Toward the base and rim, these lines intersect bands of offset, parallel dotted lines that encircle the vessel, setting off the base and rim. The design was executed with a comb and a pointed wand.

Dotted Chevron (Figure A3.5d,e)

On 13 unburnished sherds are horizontal, impressed chevrons that encircle the upper portion of the vessel just below the rim, setting it off. The chevrons are a series of impressed linear dots made by a comb or wand. The dots are less than 1 mm in length but are distinct. The design is sometimes bordered by two parallel rows of linear dots. The entire band is 18 to 28 mm wide.

Brown Burnished (Figure A3.5f)

Twelve brown-burnished sherds have smooth and semilustrous surfaces (color 5YR 4/4). Plant impressions, consisting of stems and stalk fragments, are so apparent, especially toward the rim, that they may have been applied as a decorative technique. These sherds are associated with globular bowls with short, constricted necks and outward flaring rims.

Red Burnished

Four red-burnished sherds also have smooth and semilustrous surfaces. The exterior surface color is 10R 4/6, and

FIGURE A3.5. *Sherds from Wadi Bakht: (a, b) linear design; (c) ladder design; (d, e) dotted chevron design (both rims); (f) brown burnished (note plant impressions on the surface).*

plant impressions are infrequently present. Some exterior surfaces have small, hairline fractures, giving the appearance of a pseudoslip.

Smudged and Burnished

The exterior surface color of the smudged and burnished sherd is 7.5YR 2.5/0. The exterior surface is unevenly smudged and burnished, but where completely executed, it is semilustrous. Where not complete, the original surface color (7.5YR 4/4) comes through, and the surface is dull. No plant impressions are present.

All rims from Wadi Bakht are undecorated.

KHARGA OASIS

Caton-Thompson (1952:38) was the first to describe the early ceramics from Kharga Oasis. Unfortunately, the sherds were so eolized that she could determine only that they lacked decorations, were brown and had organic tempers and gritty surface textures. Investigations by the Combined Prehistoric Expedition have provided a more complete collection, so the original descriptions can be expanded.

The origin and distribution of these ceramics are, at present, unknown. The problem is further complicated by the confusion over the radiocarbon dates (see Chapter 4). If the later date of 4650 BP ± 60 years (SMU-412) is accepted, then ceramics appeared fairly late here, probably during the Old Kingdom. Since these three collections appear to be unrelated, this would imply three independent origins of ceramic technology in the Western Desert.

The present collection includes 122 undecorated sherds, consisting of two distinct types based on temper and color differences. The redware has a pinkish color and fossil shell temper; the brownware is dark brown and has sand temper. Both types occurred at Site E-76-7, indicating their contemporaneity.

Vessel forms could not be determined but probably consisted of shallow bowls with inward sloping sides. Bases and rims are indistinguishable from the body except for a slight thickening toward the base. Sherd thicknesses vary from 4 to 11 mm; however, they are too small to determine vessel diameter. Rim diameters vary from 25 to 28 cm and probably represent the maximum vessel diameter.

Vessels were constructed by molding, as finger impressions are present. Sherds lack orientation in their breakage, although the breakage does vary with the temper. Sherds with fossil shell temper are less friable, and they break with jagged edges and little disintegration. The sand-tempered sherds are extremely friable, and the edges readily disintegrate. The hardness varies from 3 to 4. Vessels were probably fired at about 700°C for short periods of time. The clay is not isotropic and carbon streaks are present.

The sherds can be divided into two distinct color groups depending on the temper. Sherds with fossil shell temper have surface colors of light reddish-brown (2.5YR 6/4 to 5YR 6/4) to very pale brown (10YR 7/3). Core colors range from gray (2.5YR 5/0) to very dark gray (7.5YR 3/0). Sand-tempered sherds have surface colors of reddish brown (5YR 4/4) to brown (10YR 5/3) to pale brown (10YR 6.3). The core color is very dark gray (2.5YR 3/0). In both cases the surface colors are distinct from the core.

Three types of temper, including two varieties of sand temper, were used, and temper is, in part, site specific. Intrusive basic acidic and igneous is limited to the E-76-1 sherds. This temper has subangular to subrounded grains that vary from .05 to .22 mm. The paste includes 5% pore spaces and 33% temper. Calcareous metamorphic was found among the E-76-8 sherds. Grains are angular to rounded to subrounded, with sizes varying from .03 to .47 mm. Forty percent of the paste is temper and 2.5% is pore spaces. Some straw may also have been included. In sherds with fossiliferous shell temper, the shell fragments vary from .08 to .63 mm. Fifty percent of the paste is temper and 2.5% is pore spaces. This temper was found among the E-76-7 and E-76-8 sherds.

Surfaces have a rough texture. Surfaces on the redware are irregular, the shell inclusion being very evident. The brownware surfaces are gritty, and small hairline fractures can be observed. All sherds are undecorated.

THE FAYUM

Fayum Neolithic ceramics were first described by Caton-Thompson (Caton-Thompson and Gardner 1934). They were depicted as being monotonous, consisting of handmade, chaff-tempered wares lacking any decorations beyond simple burnishing. Five vessel forms were distinguished: small bowls and cups, cooking bowls and pots, pedestalled cups, cups with knobbed feet, and rectangular dishes with "peaked" rims (Caton-Thompson and Gardner 1934:36). Except for the last form, all rims were indistinguishable from the body. The first two forms were the most common, but the last three forms were more sophisticated in form and construction and gave the collections a unique flavor.

Four ware types were identified: red polished; black polished; unpolished, slipped, and smoothed; and rough faced. "Red-polished" wares were principally associated with the rectangular dishes, whereas the "black-polished" wares were rare and may have been an accidental by-product of the firing of the "red-polished" wares (Caton-Thompson and Gardner 1934:36). "Unpolished, slipped, and smoothed" wares were also comparatively rare; the smooth finish probably resulted from hand-smoothing rather than from the application of a true slip (Caton-Thompson and Gardner 1934:36). "Rough-faced" wares were the most common and consisted predominantly of small bowls and cups, and cooking bowls and pots.

The Fayum ceramics shared a few formal similarities with the Merimde ceramics, including similar vessel forms (Caton-Thompson and Gardner 1934:91). The major differences were the absence of rectangular dishes at Merimde and the absence of impressed decorations among the Fayum material.

The Combined Prehistoric Expedition located and excavated several of Caton-Thompson's original sites (Wendorf and Schild 1976:155–226). Ceramic collections made at two sites have been radiocarbon dated from 3910 BC ± 115 years to 3210 BC ± 110 years. The new collections are not as extensive as the original ones, consisting of only 497 sherds and lacking any complete or reconstructible vessels. Because the present collection is much smaller and because Caton-Thompson's original descriptions are the most complete, the following discussion should only be considered as an addendum to her work. In general, the new collection conforms with the original, although some differences can be noted.

The only vessel forms identified were cooking bowls and pots. Rim and vessel diameters range from 35 to 45 cm, with one rim diameter measuring 22 cm. Sherd thickness varies from 6 to 17 mm, increasing toward the base. Rims are undifferentiated from the body.

Vessels were molded and sherds lack orientation in their breakage. The constructional quality is variable and is, in part, site specific. The E29G3 ceramics, predominantly chaff tempered, are more coarsely made; the thickness of the same sherd varies; and many sherds are warped and not uniformly curved. These sherds are extremely friable, and the edges readily disintegrate. The E29H2 sherds, predominantly sand tempered, are better constructed. Thicknesses are more uniform, and sherds are not as warped. The material is not so friable, and the edges do not readily disintegrate. The hardness for all sherds varies between 3 and 4.

These ceramics were fired in oxidizing atmospheres at temperatures about 700°C and for short time periods. The clay is not isotropic, carbon is present, and the plant inclusions are still visible.

Exterior surface colors range from reds (7.5R 4/8 to 2/5YR 5/8) to weak red (10R 5/4) to yellowish red (5YR 5/6) to dark red (2.5YR 3/6). Interior surface colors include very dark gray (10YR 3/1), weak red (10YR 5/4), red (2.5YR 3/6), and red (2.5YR 5/8). Core colors vary from black (2.5YR 2.5/0) to very dark gray (10YR 3/1) to dark brown (7.5YR 4/4) to dark red (2.5YR 3/6). The core colors are sharply bounded by the surface colors.

Three temper types were identified, all site specific. Chaff is limited to the E29G3 sherds and consists of plant fragments generally larger than .5 mm. The paste includes 8% pore spaces and 45% temper. Recycled sandstone is found among the E29H2 sherds, and contains subrounded to rounded grains, .03 to .40 mm in diameter. Three percent of the paste is pore spaces, and 40% is temper. Some organic inclusions are occasionally present. Bone is limited to a very few sherds from E29H2. This temper consists of crushed bone fragments that are less than .75 mm in diameter. Pore spaces account for 2–5% of the paste, and temper accounts for 45%.

All surfaces are scraped, scraping marks being particularly evident on the E29G3 sherds. Three of Caton-Thompson's ware types were identified, their distribution, again, being site-specific.

The 332 sherds from E29G3 are "rough-faced" ware. Surfaces have an extremely rough texture caused by deep scraping marks. Plant impressions and pore spaces are readily observed on the surface. The 96 sherds from E29H2 are "unpolished, slipped, and smoothed." These surfaces are hand-smoothed and not truly slipped, although the smoothing is so well executed that no large temper grains are evident. The surface is paler than the immediate subsurface in color, creating the impression of a slip. The single "red-polished" rimsherd from E29G3 has a burnished exterior surface that includes the rim itself. The interior surface is unburnished.

GEBEL UWEINAT

The Gebel Uweinat collection, supplied by C. Vance Haynes, includes 10 weathered sherds recovered during a reconnaissance of Gebel Uweinat in 1978. The sherds come from two undated sites and include 4 rimsherds, 3 of which are decorated, and 4 undecorated and 2 decorated body sherds. One rimsherd also has a sufficient amount of associated body decoration for description.

The collection is diverse. Two sherds are identical to the Fayum "rough-faced" ware and another has a woven mat motif. A fourth sherd resembles material from the Eastern Libyan Desert (Arkell 1964; Vita-Finzi and Kennedy 1965). A fifth undecorated sherd is wheel-made. The remaining sherds do not share any traits identifiable with other ceramic traditions. Because of the diversity, chronological placement is difficult and the collection probably represents a mixture of several temporal units.

No vessel forms could be identified for certain, but probably two types are present: straight-walled vessels with rounded bases, and globular bowls with inward curving rims, the latter type being depicted by de Heinzelin *et al.* (1969: Figure 5). Vessel and rim diameters range from 20 to 45 cm and sherd thickness range from 4 to 15 mm. Rims are either straight, outward flaring, or inward curving. The flared rims have a distinct lip separating the rim from the body.

Three methods of construction were employed: coiling, molding, and use of a wheel. Coil marks and finger impressions are identifiable and there is some tendency to break along the coils. Breakage is variable. The molded and/or chaff-tempered sherds break with jagged edges, whereas the coil and wheel-made sherds or sherds with finer tempers break with straighter edges. In all cases, edges do not readily disintegrate. The hardness varies from 3 to 6.

All sherds appear to have been fired in oxidizing atmospheres, but the temperatures and firing lengths varied. The organic-tempered sherds still have carbon streaks and the clay is not isotropic; on sand-tempered sherds carbon streaks are not as apparent and the clay is more isotropic.

Surface colors include yellowish brown (10YR 5/4), strong brown (7.5YR 5/6), light brown (7.5YR 6/4), yellowish red (5YR 4/6), reddish brown (2.5YR 5/4), dark red (2.5YR 3/6), and red (2.5YR 4/6). Some interior surfaces were also gray (20YR 6/1) and dark gray (7.5YR 4/0). Core colors include very dark gray (10YR 3/1), very dark grayish-brown (10YR 3/2), pale brown (10YR 6/3), and red (2.5YR 4/6).

Two tempers were identified. Chaff fragments may be up to 2 mm in length, consisting of leaves and stalks. Some quartz sands are also present, accounting for 10–15% of the temper. Grains are subangular to subrounded, and .02 to .5 mm in diameter. The paste included 2% pore spaces and 40–50% temper. In sherds with recycled sandstone temper, grains are subangular to subrounded and .03 to .75 mm in diameter. The paste included 2–5% pore spaces and 40–50% temper. Some sherds also have inclusions tentatively identified as shale. The grains are black and lenticular. These inclusions are readily apparent on the surfaces.

Only two sherds lack surface alteration beyond scraping. The decorated sherds have smooth surfaces, although large temper grains are present on some sherds. The decorative techniques are simple burnishing and impression. Six different surface types were identified.

Plain Burnished on Two Surfaces

Three sherds are burnished on both surfaces and lack other decorations. Both surfaces are semilustrous and large temper grains are not apparent. The color is yellowish brown (10YR 5/4) and light brown (7.5YR 6/4). The wheel-made sherd is included in this category.

FIGURE A3.6. *Sherds from Gebel Uweinat: (a) large sherd that is punctated and burnished on one surface; (b) parallel dotted sawtooth design; (c) rough-faced surface.*

Punctated and Burnished on one Surface (Figure A3.6a)

A single rimsherd is burnished on the exterior surface; the color is strong brown (7.5YR 5/6). The burnishing is irregular and the surface is pitted. A series of deep, circular punctations encircles the base of the rim.

Irregularly Burnished

The surfaces of two sherds are incompletely red burnished (2.5YR 3/6) and have a semigranular texture, temper grains being readily apparent. One sherd has a portion of the rim that is decorated by a series of shallow constrictions on both edges, which were executed by impressing a comb. The outer edge is more pronounced as the rim is lipped.

Woven Mat

One sherd displays a woven mat motif almost identical to the Nabta middle Neolithic motif.

Parallel Dotted Sawtooth (Figure A3.6b)

On one large sherd, which includes a portion of the rim, large, parallel, dotted zigzags, one within the other, encircle the vessel body. The design was executed by pivoting a comb at 45° intervals across the vessel face and then repeating the process just below the first line. Impressed inverted V's encircle the base of the rim above the zigzags. This design was made with a pointed spatula. A dotted line separates the V's and the zigzags, and another line is above the V's. Above this second line is a series of smaller inverted V's

that extend onto the rim. Although this motif has not appeared elsewhere in the literature, the use of inverted V's at the rim base to encircle the vessel was one of the more frequently repeated motifs from Wanyanga (Arkell 1964: Plates 45, 47).

Rough Faced (Figure A3.6c)

The two undecorated, rough-faced sherds are almost identical to the Fayum "rough-faced" wares, the surfaces being irregular with deep scraping grooves. Both sherds are chaff tempered, and plant impressions and large pore spaces dot the surfaces. Fire clouds are also evident. A possibly similar sherd has been depicted by de Heinzelin *et al.* [1969: Figure 4 (middle)] and deep scraping marks may have been used as a decorative technique (de Heinzelin *et al.* 1969: Figure 5).

The rim decorations consist of those noted.

BIR TARFAWI

The Bir Tarfawi collection is from two undated sites that contained pieces of iron, bronze, faience, and camel bone (Hays n.d.). The sites are in dune sediments that overlie Old Kingdom sites, one of which has been dated to 4510 BP ± 70 years (SMU-74) (Wendorf *et al.* 1977:217). In addition, sherds from an unspecified site in Bir Tarfawi that are identical to some in the present collection have been radiocarbon dated to 1160 BP ± 95 years (SMU-475).

These ceramics differ from the preceding collections in several ways: There are new vessel forms, vessels have defined necks that offset the rims, rims are well defined, reducing atmospheres were more extensively used, and nipples appear as a decorative technique. The collection also contains a wheel-made sherd. These traits distinguish the Bir Tarfawi ceramics.

The external relationships of these ceramics are difficult to determine, primarily because of the lack of comparative collections. However, some elements are reminiscent of east and central African Iron Age ceramics (LeBeuf 1962; Phillipson 1977; Posnansky 1961). Similarities include the emphasis on constricted necks and outward flaring rims and the use of certain motifs. Although these similarities are suggestive, they are comparatively minor traits and no relationship is implied. If the collection as a whole is considered, the material cannot be assigned to any specific ceramic tradition.

Three vessel forms were distinguished. Globular jars with constricted necks and outward flaring rims are the most common form. Vessel diameters vary from 20 to 34 cm; neck diameters vary from 10 to 20 cm; and rims vary from 10 to 25 cm. Sherd thicknesses range from 5 to 7 mm. The straight-walled bowls with rounded bases and outward flaring rims lack necks. The rim and vessel diameter is 15

cm, with a sherd thickness of 5 mm. The cup resembles a small, straight-walled bowl with rounded base and indistinct rim. The rim and vessel diameter is 7 cm, vessel depth is 8 cm, and sherd thickness is 5 mm.

Three construction methods were employed: coiling, molding, and use of a wheel. Coil and finger impressions are evident. Breakage varies with the method of construction. Coil-made wares tend to break along the coils; the wheel-made and molded sherds break more irregularly. In all cases, the edges exhibit little disintegration. The hardness ranges from 3 to 5. Both oxidizing and reducing atmospheres were used. The reducing atmospheres had fairly high temperatures, at least 700°C, as the clay tends to be isotropic and the carbon is burned out. Vessels fired in oxidizing atmospheres still retain carbon streaks, and the clay is not isotropic. Smudged vessels were fired first in oxidizing and then in reducing atmospheres.

Exterior and interior surface colors include yellowish red (5YR 4/6), reddish yellow (5YR 6/6), light red (2.5YR 6/6), and dark gray (7.5YR 4/0). One exterior surface is light gray (7.5YR 7/0) and one interior surface is very dark gray (2.5YR 3/0). Core colors vary from light gray (7.5YR 7/0) to gray (2.5YR 5/0 to 6/0) to very dark gray (2.5YR 3/0 to 7.5YR 3/0). The core and surface colors are distinct from one another on vessels fired in oxidizing atmospheres but merge on those fired in reducing atmospheres.

Three temper types were distinguished. Chaff fragments vary from .2 to 1 mm in length. Some subrounded to rounded quartz sands are present, grain sizes varying from .03 to .35 mm. The paste includes 5–7% pore spaces and 40–45% temper. This is the most frequent temper type. In the recycled sandstone temper, grains are subrounded to subangular and .03 to .35 mm in diameter. The paste included 45% temper and 3% pore spaces. Fossiliferous shell fragments vary from .02 to .5 mm in diameter and are apparent on the sherd surfaces.

Surface texture is variable. Decorated sherds generally have smooth surfaces, although large temper grains are occasionally present. The undecorated sherds are generally rougher and large temper grains are apparent.

Three undecorated wares were identified.

Rough faced

The eight rough-faced sherds are similar to the Fayum "rough faced." Plant impressions are readily apparent on the surfaces. This category includes the cup.

Grayware

The three grayware sherds are shell tempered and are reminiscent of the Kharga shell-tempered wares. Surfaces are irregular because of the presence of the shell.

The third undecorated ware is represented by the wheel-made sherd.

Four decorative techniques were employed: smudging, burnishing, and impression; impression; incision; and the application of nipples.

Smudged and Burnished Woven Mat

There are four sherds that have a semilustrous, dark gray (2.5YR 3/0) exterior surface. The central portion of the body has been continuously comb impressed, creating a motif similar to the middle Neolithic woven mat. Plant impressions are also present on the exterior surface.

Cord Impressed

The cord-impressed motif was identified on 43 sherds. The lower two-thirds of the vessel body has been impressed by rolling a cord-wrapped roulette across the surface, creating a rippled effect. The design was executed while the clay was still plastic, which dulled the design features. The design runs diagonal to the rim.

Composite Wavy Line

On 54 sherds, one part of the design consists of a set of parallel, zigzag lines that encircle the body at the neck. This motif was executed by incision with a pointed wand and is slightly reminiscent of some of the East African dimple-based ware motifs (Posnansky 1961: Figure 2). The second portion of the design consists of faint wavy lines that are intermittently found over the vessel surface. This motif was executed by dragging a comb across the vessel surface and is reminiscent of the Khartoum Neolithic "wavy-line" motif.

Nipples

One vessel body is undecorated except for four pairs of raised nipples, perpendicular to each other, on the vessel body at the base of the neck. The associated rim is decorated with a series of incised cross-hatches on the rim top. This type of rim decoration is also reminiscent of some East African Iron Age rim decorations [Posnansky 1961: Figure 5(6)].

All rims, except for those noted, are undecorated.

DISCUSSION

These collections exhibit a wide variety of decorative techniques and styles, vessel and rim construction and form, and temper usage. Each collection is unique, and only the Nabta middle Neolithic and the Bir Kiseiba–Bir Takhlis collections exhibit any similarities. The lack of continuity from region to region or through time indicates that the ceramic technology of each region was subjected to influences not repeated elsewhere and that each region of the Western Desert may have had its own, distinctive tradition.

The external relationships of these collections appear to have changed through time, probably reflecting the increasing desiccation that followed the Neolithic wet phase. Only the earliest collections, those from Nabta Playa and Bir Kiseiba–Bir Takhlis, were part of the larger, pan-Saharan Khartoum Neolithic. It appears that as desertification progressed, the various traditions became increasingly localized and individually less varied. Any external relationships, such as those shown by the Fayum and the Nabta later Neolithic, extended toward the Nile.

Some technological changes through time can also be noted. Sand tempers are replaced by organics. The use of smudging and burnishing increases as the use of impression, incision, and punctation decreases, and there is a general decline in the variety of decorative styles. Construction by molding increases although, except for the Bir Tarfawi collection, the quality of vessel construction and the variety of forms decrease. Again, these changes probably reflect increasing regional isolation accompanied by a general decline in ceramic technology.

The origin and interrelationships of these traditions are, at present, unsolved problems that cannot be answered from these collections. However, the lack of continuity from collection to collection does suggest that ceramic technology may have been separately introduced into each region from widely divergent sources. In this regard, the earliest collections, those from Nabta Playa and Wadi Bakht, do not appear to have been an autochthonous development. The quality of construction and the variety of decorative styles and motifs argue against an indigenous development. Instead, ceramic technology appears to have been introduced from outside the Western Desert, but, unfortunately, the problem of from where cannot yet be answered.

REFERENCES

Arkell, A. J.
1949 *Early Khartoum.* London: Oxford University Press.
1953 *Shaheinab.* London: Oxford University Press.
1964 *Wanyanga.* London: Oxford University Press.

Bagnold, R. A., O. H. Myers, R. F. Peel, and H. A. Winkler
1939 An expedition to the Gilf Kebir and Uweinat, 1938. *Geographical Journal 93* (4):281–313.

Barich, B.
1978 Neue Ausgrabungen im Acacus-Gebirge. In *Sahara: 10000 Jahre zwischen Weide und Wüste.* Köln: Museen der Stadt Köln. Pp. 222–245.

Camps, G.
1969 Amekni. Néolithique ancien du Hoggar. *Mémoires du C.R.A.P.E., No. 10.* Paris: Arts et Métiers Graphiques.
1974 *Les civilisations préhistoriques de l'Afrique du Nord et du Sahara.* Paris: Doin.
1978 Amekni und die neolithische Sahara. In *Sahara: 10000 Jahre zwischen Weide und Wüste.* Köln: Museen der Stadt Köln. Pp. 182–188.

Camps-Fabrer, H.
1966 Matière et art mobilier dans la préhistoire nord-africaine et saharienne. *Mémoires du C.R.A.P.E., No. 5.* Paris: Arts et Métiers Graphiques.

Caton-Thompson, G.
1952 *Kharga Oasis in prehistory.* London: Athlone Press.

Caton-Thompson, G., and E. W. Gardner
1934 *The desert Fayum.* London: Royal Anthropological Institute.

Colton, H. S.
1953 *Potsherds. An introduction to the study of prehistoric southwestern ceramics and their use in historic reconstruction.* Museum of Northern Arizona, Bulletin 25.

de Heinzelin, J., P. Haesaerts, and F. van Noten
1969 Géologie récente et préhistoire au Jebel Uweinat. *Africa-Tervuren 15* (4):120–126.

Gabriel, B.
1977 Zum ökologischen Wandel im Neolithikum der östlichen Zentralsahara. *Berliner Geographische Abhandlungen 27.*
1978 Gabrong—achttausendjährige Keramik im Tibesti-Gebirge. In *Sahara: 10000 Jahre zwischen Weide und Wüste.* Köln: Museen der Stadt Köln. Pp. 189–196.

Hays, T. R.
1971a The Karmakol industry: Part of the "Khartoum horizon-style." In *The prehistory and geology of northern Sudan, Part I,* edited by J. L. Shiner. Report submitted to the National Science Foundation. Pp. 89–153.
1971b The Sudanese Neolithic: A critical analysis. Ph.D. dissertation, Southern Methodist University.
1974 "Wavy line" pottery: An element of Nilotic diffusion. *South African Archaeological Bulletin 29:*27–32.
n.d. Late prehistoric occupation of the Egyptian desert: A preliminary report. Report submitted to the Graduate School of the University of Texas at Arlington.

Hodges, H.
1963 The examination of ceramic materials in thin section. In *The scientist and archaeology,* edited by E. Pyddocke. London: Phoenix House. Pp. 101–110.

Holdaway, M. J.
n.d. Report on the petrography of 15 pot sherds from Egypt. Ms.

Huard, P.
1973 Influences culturelles transmises au Sahara tchadien par le Groupe C de Nubie. *Kush 15:*84–124.

LeBeuf, J.-P.
1962 *Archéologie Tchadienne.* Paris: Hermann.

McHugh, W. P.
1971 Late prehistoric cultural adaptation in the southeastern Libyan Desert. Ph.D. dissertation, University of Wisconsin, Madison.
1975 Some archaeological results from the Bagnold–Mond expedition to the Gilf Kebir and Gebel Uweinat, southern Libyan Desert. *Journal of Near Eastern Studies 34* (1):31–62.

Nordström, H.-A.
1972 Neolithic and A-Group sites. *The Scandinavian Joint Expedition to Sudanese Nubia,* Vol. 3, Parts 1 and 2. Stockholm: Scandinavian University Press.

Phillipson, D. W.
1977 *The later prehistory of eastern and southern Africa.* London: Heinemann.

Posnansky, M.
1961 Pottery types from archaeological sites in East Africa. *Journal of African History 2* (2):177–198.

Shepard, A. O.
1956 *Ceramics for the archaeologist.* Carnegie Institution of Washington, Publication 609.

Shiner, J. L.
1968 The Khartoum Variant tradition. In *The prehistory of Nubia,* Vol. 2, edited by F. Wendorf. Dallas: Fort Burgwin Research Center and Southern Methodist University Press. Pp. 768–790.

Vita-Finzi, C., and R. A. Kennedy
1965 Seven Saharan sites. *Journal of the Royal Anthropological Institute 95* (2):195–213.

Wendorf, F., and R. Schild
1976 *Prehistory of the Nile Valley.* New York: Academic Press.

Wendorf, F., R. Schild, R. Said, C. V. Haynes, M. Kobusiewicz, A. Gautier, N. El Hadidi, H. Wieckowska, and A. E. Close
1977 Late Pleistocene and Recent climatic changes in the Egyptian Sahara. *Geographical Journal 143* (2):211–234.

4

Contributions to the Archaeozoology of Egypt

ACHILLES GAUTIER

This appendix contains four sections, each of which describes the faunal remains recovered from one area in the Western Desert of Egypt. The first of these considers the materials from several Early and Middle Paleolithic localities near Bir Sahara; the remaining sections are all on the fauna from several widely scattered localities occupied during the Terminal Paleolithic and Neolithic. Each section contains a description of the materials recovered from that area followed by a discussion. Measurements are always given in millimeters; those for mammals were taken following the techniques outlined in von den Driesch (1977).

NONMARINE MOLLUSCS AND VERTEBRATE REMAINS FROM BIR SAHARA AND BIR TARFAWI

The material discussed in this section was collected from deposits and archaeological middens at Bir Sahara and Bir Tarfawi, two localities some 300 km west of Abu Simbel in the Western Desert of Egypt. Today, at both localities, drinkable water is reached at a shallow depth, and extensive fields of phytogenic dunes with tamarisks occur. The surrounding country is absolutely barren, and almost no traces of life were observed. At the *abyar*, however, birds and their tracks as well as those of lizards, a small carnivore (fox?), and gazelle were noted.

The Bir Sahara collection was made by the Combined Prehistoric Expedition in the winters of 1973 and 1974. The author was present in the 1974 season and thus was able to collect personally most of the faunal samples from Bir Tarfawi and to familiarize himself with the geographical, geological, and archaeological context of the Quaternary deposits at both Bir Sahara and Bir Tarfawi. The geology and archaeology are described elsewhere in this volume (Chapter 2). The fossiliferous freshwater deposits and the associated Middle Paleolithic sites are thought to date from the lower Upper Pleistocene (i.e., the period encompassing the last interglacial and the first part of the last glacial, or part of these periods).

FRESHWATER AND LAND SNAILS

The molluscan samples from Bir Sahara were taken at Site BS-16, at the base of the limestone grading upward into evaporites. Near BS-13 is a sample in the upper part of the same unit. Samples from BS-15, lower and upper level, were collected from the silt overlying the interfingering dune (cf. Chapter 2).

At Site BT-14 samples were taken in the following areas:

1. Trench 6, 140 cm below the surface in the base of the gray silt with carbonate concretions (Layer 4 of Figure 2.24)
2. Trench 13, between 65 and 90 cm below the surface in beach deposits (Layer 3 in Figure 2.24)
3. Trench 17, subsurface sample in blackish layer

The molluscs were identified mainly with the aid of comparative collections from the Ghent laboratory and descriptions found in Mandahl-Barth (1954, 1957). T. Pain (London) and B. Verdcourt (Maidenhead, England) assisted with the identification of the small snail shells referred to as *Pupoides coenopictus.*

Specimens of the form referred to as *Hydrobia* sp. have been sent to G. Mandahl-Barth (Charlottenlund, Denmark) who kindly provided the following comments (*in litt.*, June 27, 1974):

> There is no doubt that they belong to the *Hydrobia*, but I find it difficult to refer them to any of the species known from Africa or the Middle East, perhaps apart from a species occurring in the coastal area of Egypt. This species seems to have a wide distribution in the Middle East, as I have seen what appears to be the same species from Saudi Arabia, Iraq, and Iran. From this area, several, mostly ill-defined "species" have been described, and the oldest available name for them seems to be *H. lactea* Kuester. However, in my opinion your specimens do not fall within the range of variation of *lactea* (as far as it is known), wherefore I am inclined to regard them as belonging to an undescribed species.

A check through the literature made after reading Mandahl-Barth's comments, revealed to me that *Hydrobia* sp. has been recorded by Clark *et al.* (1973) from deposits associated with the Ténérian (Neolithic) at Adrar Bous (Aïr). *Hydrobia perauderi* has been recorded from late Pleistocene and early Holocene deposits in the Tibesti region (Boettcher *et al.* 1972). From the wadi tufas (mainly Middle Paleolithic) in Kharga Oasis, Gardner (1932) reports the same species, but later (1935) gave the name *Hydrobia stagnalis* var. cornea to it. All the forms cited are very similar, and I find it difficult to distinguish them. Until detailed comparative studies are available, it seems better not to identify this material to the specific level.

The assemblages found in each sample are listed in Table A4.1., which also contains a rough estimate of the frequency of the various species per fossiliferous locality. All the species listed are still found in Egypt and adjacent countries and form part of the normal freshwater or land snail fauna.

The freshwater fauna is mainly composed of pulmonate gastropods (five species), two (or three) prosobranch gastropods (*Melanoides tuberculata*, *Hydrobia* sp., and possibly also *Cleopatra bulimoides*), and one smaller bivalve (*Corbicula consobrina*). All of these forms are hermaphrodites, oviparous or viviparous. Eggs or juveniles are transported over long distances attached to the legs of wading water birds, and they can quite easily colonize very isolated bodies of water. Larger bivalves belonging to the unionids (*Caelatura*) or mutelids (*Mutela, Aspatharia*) usually migrate attached to floating objects or are carried by fishes as parasitic glochidium larvae. The absence of large bivalves may therefore reflect not ecological limitations but rather the lack of suitable hydrographic connections. However, the fact that smaller bivalves such as *Pisidium, Sphaerium,* and *Byssanodonta* have not yet been found, and the rarity of *Corbicula consobrina,* point to restricted bodies of water.

In the Uganda savanna, small bodies of water are characterized by the absence of all bivalves and prosobranch snails. The greatest number of species as well as individuals occur in ponds with rich vegetation (Mandahl-Barth 1954: 180). Apparently the bodies of water at both Bir Sahara and Bir Tarfawi should be characterized as large ponds or small, shallow lakes because of the presence of prosobranch snails and, occasionally, the bivalve *Corbicula consobrina.* Visual inspection in the field indicates that the deposits are rich in shells, which indicates well-developed aquatic vegetation, as do the biogenic carbonates and root casts found in the deposits. One of the maximal extensions of the water at Bir Sahara may be indicated by the presence of *C. consobrina* in the BS-15 sample, lower level in the upper silt.

In the sample from BT-14, Trench 17, blackish layer, a poor assemblage is found in which *Hydrobia* sp. dominates; moreover, the sediment is not very rich in snails. As the deposit has a high content of carbonaceous material, the depositional environment may have been unsuitable for most species (too marshy), although *Hydrobia* may have persisted. *Hydrobia* spp. often show a preference for brackish or pseudobrackish water.

Land snails are generally indicative of near-shore conditions or short periods of subaerial exposure through minor level fluctuations. Thus the beach deposit at Site BT-14 is characterized by the presence of *Pupoides coenopictus.* Water-level fluctuations, when the water at Bir Sahara was standing high and hence was more sensitive to minor hydrogeologic changes, are indicated by the presence of *P. coenopictus* and *Zootecus insularis* in the BS-15 samples. Moreover, *Z. insularis* is very common in the upper sample, indicating more marked subaerial influence, as is to be expected.

Changes in the frequencies of the various freshwater species, as recorded in Table A4.1, may have some meaning but cannot yet be explained, because detailed ecological information on most species is lacking. One striking difference, however, between the fauna from Bir Sahara and that from Bir Tarfawi is the virtual absence at Bir Sahara of *Hydrobia* sp., a very frequent species at Bir Tarfawi. Possibly the difference is due to either ecological or chronological factors.

VERTEBRATE REMAINS

The vertebrate remains of Bir Sahara were collected in 1973 from various sites. Those from Bir Tarfawi were collected at one site only (Site BT-14), mostly by the author. Most of the specimens of Site BT-14 were found on the surface or immediately below it in Area A, in Concentration C, and in Concentration N. All other finds are from stratigraphic trenches (see also Table A4.2).

Most of the material from both Bir Tarfawi and Bir Sahara is very poorly preserved. At both localities, remains of animals were exposed to weathering before burial, in the deposits, and were finally cemented by carbonates. Their color is generally yellowish white with brown-yellow ex-

Table A4.1
Distribution of Molluscs in Various Samples from Bir Sahara and Bir Tarfawi[a]

Provenance	Melanoides tuberculata	Lymnaea natalensis	Biomphalaria alexandrina	Gyraulus costulatus	Bulinus truncatus	B. forskalii	Hydrobia sp.	Corbicula consobrina	Zootecus insularia (land snail)	Pupoides coenopictus (land snail)
BS-15, upper level	F	+	F	F	+	+				+
BS-15, lower level[b]	F	+	F	F	+	F			F	+
Near BS-13	F	F	+	F	+		+	+		
BS-16, base of limestone	F	F	+	F	+	+				
BT-14, Trench 6, silt	F	F	+	F	+	+	F			
BT-14, Trench 13, beach	F	+	+	F	+		F			+
BT-14, Trench 17, blackish layer			+	+	+		F			

[a] F = frequent; + = present.
[b] Also contains a juvenile gastropod with two carinas, possibly referrable to *Cleopatra bulimoides*.

Table A4.2
Distribution of Faunal Remains at the Sites of Bir Sahara and Bir Tarfawi[a]

Provenance[b]	Canis (aureus) lupaster?	Vulpes rüppellii ?	Equus asinus	Ceratotherium simum	Phacochoerus aethiopicus?	Camelus thomasi	Homoioceras antiquus ?	Gazella rufifrons	Gazella dama	Large antelope	Medium-sized antelope	Turtle
BS-11 (just below black layer)			1									
BS-11, Surface 1 (just below black layer)					1	1?						
BS-11, Trench 3 (just below black layer)							2					
BS-12, black layer										1?		
BS-13				1								
BS-13, surface			1	4		2	2					
BS-13, lower cultural layer				5		1						
BS-13, D/3, middle cultural layer				3								
BT-14, Area A, surface	1?		6	18		5	8	8	15		5	
BT-14, Concentration C, subsurface				+		2		1	1	3	5	
BT-14, Trench 7, silt (4)									5			
BT-14, Trench 16, beach (3b)												
BT-14, Trench 9, beach (3b)								1				
BT-14, Trench 8, beach (3b)								2	F			
BT-14, Trench 7, silt (3)	1	1										
BT-14, Area N, subsurface[c]						3	2?	2	18			1?
BT-14, Trench 15, blackish layer (2)								F			1	F
BT-14, Trench 5, base of black layer (2/3)				3						7		5
Weight (kg)[d]	10	2	175	1250	85	800	850	27	60	600	160	

[a] F = frequent; + = present.
[b] Numbers in parentheses indicate number of layer in general geological section of Site BT-14 in Figure 2.24.
[c] Many remains of small and medium-sized birds and an intrusive rodent also present.
[d] Derived from Malbrant (1952) and the author's estimates.

terior surfaces (iron oxide staining?). Present-day eolian erosion of these fossilized remains as they become exposed again can be studied very well at Bir Tarfawi. They undergo a third phase of weathering, become bleached, severely fragmented, and eolized. In fact, cancellous bone with much carbonate precipitated in its pores is often better preserved than compact bone and may form ventifacts. In general, bones are ground down by these destructive processes in a plane parallel to the eolian erosion surface of the deposits. A comparable phenomenon is seen in recent camel bones buried in the phytogenic and shifting recent dunes. The material from the trenches has not suffered from the third phase of weathering and is much better preserved.

In the following paragraphs, the vertebrate species encountered are described.

Turtle

The turtle is represented by quite numerous remains at Site BT-14, Concentration N. Some remains were also collected in Trench 7 and Trench 15 of the same site. Probably these remains can be ascribed to *Testudo*, but I am unable to give a definite identification.

From Early Khartoum, *Trionyx* sp. and *Testudo* spp. were recorded by Swinton (in Arkell 1949: 17). *Trionyx* sp. and *Testudo hermanni* were recorded from Esh Shaheinab (Arkell 1953). *Trionyx triunguis* (Nile soft-shelled turtle) was found at Kom Ombo by Churcher (1972). *Testudo* sp. was recorded from the Neolithic at Méniet (Hugot 1963). There is no doubt that our material does not represent *Trionyx*, as the carapace fragment exhibits no vermiculated pattern.

Birds

Remains of birds (probably of one species) occur only at Site BT-14, Concentration N, together with those of turtle. It is hoped that a specialist will be found to deal with these remains.

Jackal (*Canis aureus lupaster?*)

At Site BT-14 a canid jaw fragment with roots of M2 and alveole for M3 was collected from the beach deposits in Trench 7. A second mandible fragment was collected at the same site from the surface, Concentration A, but it is very poorly preserved, and even the identification as canid is tentative.

The anterioposterior diameter across the M2 alveoli of the excavated specimen is 96 mm and is comparable with measurements of fossil canids described by Gautier (1968) from late Quaternary sites in the northern Sudan and identified as *C. aureus soudanicus* or *C. aureus lupaster* (A-P.D. of M$\overline{2}$ alveole: ± 10 mm) and *C. mesomelas* (A-P.D. of M$\overline{2}$ alveole: 7.5 mm). The specimen could be ascribed to *C. aureus*, were it not that in Egypt a related form exists, known as the Egyptian or wolf jackal. This form is either

assigned specific status as *C. lupaster* or considered as a large subspecies of the golden jackal and then labeled *C.a. lupaster* (Zeuner 1967: 71). Measurements of length of M$\overline{2}$ for *C. aureus* and *C. a. lupaster* are given by Knetsch *et al.* (1965). According to these data, our specimen can be reasonably included in *C.a. lupaster* as a small form. Possibly the material formerly ascribed to *C.a. soudanicus* should also be referred to as *C.a. lupaster*.

As already stated, fossil jackals have been described from late Quaternary sites along the Nile by Gautier (1968). At Early Khartoum, *Canis? lupaster* was recorded, and Shaheinab yielded *C. ? cf. aureus soudanicus* (Bate 1949a, 1953).

Small Fox (*Vulpes rüppellii?*)

At Site BT-14, a second carnivore was collected from the beach deposits in Trench 7. It is represented by an incomplete proximal moiety of a tibia, which agrees quite well in morphology and overall size with the same bone in European red fox (*Vulpes vulpes*). That the specimen does not pertain to a juvenile jackal, an adult specimen of which came from the same stratigraphic level, is borne out by the fact that the bone has a well-marked *foramen nutritiva* and longitudinal crests. The transverse diameter of the shaft is about 7.5 mm. The same measurement in a small European fox is about 8.5 mm. Hence the Bir Tarfawi specimen can be ascribed to a very small fox and probably represents the species commonly found in the Egyptian desert and known as *Vulpes rüppellii*.

Small rodent

An incomplete humerus of a rodent was found in the subsurface bone sample at Site BT-14, Concentration N. According to size, it belonged to an animal about 1.5 times as large as the common house mouse (*Mus musculus*). No doubt rodents were attracted by the soft blackish silt at Concentration N and made their holes in it. The specimen is therefore probably intrusive.

Wild Ass [*Equus (Asinus) asinus*[

The Bir Tarfawi collection (Site BT-14) contains only small remains of four fragmentary molariform teeth, and in one case we are not even certain if the fragments really do pertain to an equid. This uninteresting collection is completed by a fragmentary right astragalus and a doubtful fragmentary distal humerus. Remains of equids from Bir Sahara are better preserved. Site BS-13 yielded two fragments of one jaw, with possibly preserved molariform teeth. A fragmentary right upper molariform tooth was recovered from Site BS-14. All of these remains can probably be referred to one equid species. Some approximate measurements* are as follows:

---

*As mentioned previously, all measurements are given in millimeters.

Lower molariform teeth, L.	± 35
Humerus, TR.D., dist.	± 70
Astragalus,	
max. H.	± 58
max. TR.D.	± 62

The distinction of the various equids is a difficult matter, especially when only fragmentary specimens are available. Arambourg (1938) has summarized some general odontological characteristics that can be used to separate asinids and zebras. According to these, the metastylid in zebras is more flattened and angular than the metastylid in asinids, and the lingual sinus penetrates very deep in the double sling of metaconid and metastylid (Arambourg 1938: 27–28, Figure 7). The characteristics of the metastylid on our material are not clear, although the metastylids are certainly not pronouncedly angular. The lingual sinuses, however, are not very deep and are comparable with those of *E. (A.) somaliensis* and *E. (A.) africanus* figured in Stehlin and Graziosi (1935: 8, Figures 5 and 6).

On morphological grounds, then, the material should probably be considered asinid. In size the astragalus agrees well with a specimen attributed to a female *E. (A.) somaliensis* by the same authors (Stehlin and Graziosi 1935: 18, Figure 10; max. H: 57 mm; TR.D: 57 mm). We should not forget, however, that our measurements are approximate. The fossil teeth are certainly larger than those figured in the same publication, in which approximate variation of the molariform teeth (except P2 and M3) attributed to a male *E. (A.) somaliensis* and a female *E. (A.) africanus* is about 23 to 26 mm. However, teeth of *E. (A.) africanus* from late Quaternary sites in Nubia measure between 26 and 28 mm (Gautier 1968). The Western Desert dental material is still larger and may have come from an exceptionally large stallion, or the entire population may have been characterized by greater size. Indeed, our knowledge of size variation in the various forms of wild ass is limited, and it is not even known whether the Somali or Nubian ass is the larger of the two (Bourdelle 1935; Frechkop 1955: 1073; Lydekker 1907). The Nubian wild ass is said to stand on average at about 117 cm at the withers (Lydekker 1907). Epstein (1971) gives a size variation of 120–130 cm; Harper (1945) says males are about 115 cm high but adds that a male of the Atbara River was about 139 cm! Moreover, the sizes of wild asses may have declined considerably during the Holocene as an indirect result of human overpredation and the evacuation of the animals to less suitable biotopes.

Until Roman times at least, three subspecies of wild ass were found in Africa: *E. (A.) asinus atlanticus* in the Maghreb, *E. (A.) a. africanus* in Nubia, and *E. (A.) a. somaliensis*. Of these only the Somali ass, and possibly the Nubian ass, survive. According to some sources, however, wild asses are also still found in the central Sahara in the Tibesti Mountains. They would be related to the Nubian ass (Harper 1945; Malbrant 1952; Zeuner 1967). According to Ducos (1968, 1970), a wild ass was formerly also found in the Near East; it has been called *E. (a.) palestinae* (Ducos 1968). Apparently, wild asses ranged over an extensive ter-ritory, which included the region of Bir Sahara and Bir Tarfawi, and there are no "paleobiogeographical" difficulties in relating the fossils to the wild ass. In view of the various difficulties cited, it would be unwise to identify the specimens down to the subspecific level, but it is very likely that the Western Desert fossil asses will eventually be found to be related to the Nubian wild ass.

White Rhinoceros (*Ceratotherium simum*)

The rhinoceros remains of Bir Sahara are very poorly preserved and have been identified in the light of osteological evidence from Bir Tarfawi. These remains include some mandible fragments (Site BS-13), two fragments of metapodials (Site BS-13), and some eolized tooth fragments (Site BS-13, surface). Other postcranial fragments are characterized by thick bone and may eventually be found to pertain to camel, since the size of camelid specimens at both Bir Sahara and Bir Tarfawi is remarkable. Material from Bir Tarfawi (Site BT-14) includes clearly identified tooth fragments, jaw fragments with teeth, and some postcranial remains, including a femoral shaft fragment with heavy third trochanter, which is diagnostic for rhinocerotids. None of the foregoing specimens could be measured.

There are only two species of rhinoceros in the Late Quarternary of Africa: the black rhinoceros (*Diceros bicornis*) and the white rhinoceros (*Ceratotherium simum*). The former is a browser, the latter a grazer, and their teeth are quite distinct. Identifications are most easily made on the permanent upper dentition. *C. simum* is a hypsodont form with much cement on the teeth and with the transverse lophs in the upper molars (protoloph and metaloph) obliquely placed and recurved backward. This does not show in *D. bicornis*, which also has less-high-crowned teeth (Hooijer 1969; see also Arambourg 1947: 141, Figure 23; 144, Figure 26). The upper molariform teeth of Bir Tarfawi, although fragmented, show retrocurrent curved lophs and are comparable with specimens of white rhinoceros figured in both Arambourg (1947) and Hooijer (1969). They are hence ascribed to *Ceratotherium simum*.

Both the black rhinoceros and the white rhinoceros occurred, at least until recently, in the southern Sudan (Setzer 1956). Bate (1949a, 1953) lists rhinoceros at the Early Khartoum site and at Shaheinab, which she refers to as the *D. bicornis* group (black rhinoceros). Although both species may occur together, the browsing form (black rhinoceros) will more often occur in biotopes with a lusher vegetation. This may account for the presence of the black rhinoceros along the Nile, and the white rhinoceros in the Western Desert.

The species was also found at the Acheulian site in the Tihodaine basin of the central Sahara (Arambourg and Balout 1955).

Warthog (*Phacochoerus aethiopicus?*)

Warthog is represented at Bir Sahara (Site BS-14, surface) by a small piece of mandible with fragments of the adjacent tooth adhering to the alveolar side. In a preliminary report, it was identified as a doubtful equid, but the finding of a fragmentary warthog molar on a playa near Barqat el Sheb during the 1974 season (Haynes, this volume) made me realize that the BS-14 specimen is undoubtedly a suid with strongly hypsodont teeth characterized by high columellar tubes of thick enamel. Nothing more can be said about the specimen.

The late Quaternary warthogs can be referred to as *Phacochoerus africanus* (Gmelin), found in most parts of sub-Saharan Africa, and *P. aethiopicus* (Pallas), which would be the recently extinct Cape warthog. Many authors, however, call the extant species *P. aethiopicus* (Pallas) (cf. Ewer 1956: 528m; Frechkop 1955: 531). No doubt our material is very near to and should probably refer to the warthog species that is still found alive some 1000 km to the south in the Sudan and specifically described as *P. aethiopicus* in Setzer (1956). Bate (1949a, 1953) recorded *Phacochoerus* sp. at Early Khartoum and at Shaheinab. *Phacochoerus* sp. is known from the Acheulian site in the Tihodaine Basin of the central Sahara (Arambourg and Balout 1955). It was also encountered in the Neolithic of Amekni in the Hoggar (Bouchud 1969). Our material is here put on record as *P. aethiopicus?*, the specific name *aethiopicus* being used to denote the still living warthog.

Wild Camel (*Camelus thomasi*)

Remains of large camels were found at Bir Sahara, Site BS-13, and at Bir Tarfawi, Site BT-14, where these remains occur in the beach deposits of Trench 7 and on the surface of the main artifact concentration. Remains were also found scattered over an area of approximately 30 m² about 60 m northeast of Site BT-14, Concentration N. A fragmentary mandible with m³ and some unidentifiable remains were also recorded some 120 m northwest of Concentration N. It is very probable that both clusters represent remains of animals butchered by primitive man, but they are not clearly associated with artifacts. Both lie in green calcareous silt, which covers the blackish silt of Concentration N.

Measurements taken in the field and in the laboratory are as follows:

M3, L.	46.4	
M2, L.	±46	
M3, L.	±50	±10
Radius		
Tot. L.	±580*	
TR.D. diaph.	82	
TR.D. dist.	123	
Cubitus, TR.D. olecranon	48	
Tibia, TR.D., dist.	97	
mt		
Tot. L.	±420*	
TR.D. prox.	±90*	
TR.D. diaph.	±50*	
TR.D. dist.	±95*	

*Measurements taken in the field; specimen not or only incompletely collected.

These measurements can be compared with those for the fossil camel of the northern Sudan studied by Gautier (1966) and identified as *Camelus thomasi* Pomel, 1893. The fossils from the Western Desert are only slightly older and certainly belong to the same form as those found in the northern Sudan. The Western Desert specimens vary quite markedly in size. Some are larger than their Sudanese analogs; others are much smaller and approach in size recent paleoarctic camelids. In my opinion, the size variation is probably due to pronounced sexual dimorphism.

Remains of *Camelus* sp. have been reported from the "Earlier Villafranchian" at Garret Ichkeul, Tunisia (Arambourg and Arnould 1949, cited by Howell *et al.* 1969). Younger sites in the Maghreb yielded various remains including the type specimens of *C. thomasi*. A camelid metacarpal of unknown but probably substantial age was also recorded from the Wadi Derdemy area, Chad (Bochianga locality 2 in Gautier 1966). Camelid remains are also known from the lower Omo Beds in the Omo Valley, southern Ethiopia (Howell *et al.* 1969). Camelid material was also collected by the French in the Omo and is now being studied by Grattard (personal communication). Material from the Marsabit Road Site (Kenya) and Olduvai Gorge, Bed II (Tanzania) may possibly be related to *Camelus thomasi* (Gentry and Gentry 1969). The foregoing records show clearly that camelids entered Africa at the end of the Tertiary and penetrated quite far in that continent.

According to Gautier, *C. thomasi* appears to be much more related to *C. bacterianus* than to *C. dromedarius* because of certain craniological and postcranial details. The extant Bactrian camel differs from the dromedary in its range, its greater size, and its greater sturdiness. *C. thomasi* can be described as a camelid about 1.2 times larger than the extant Bactrian camel but of comparable sturdiness. The fossil metatarsal of the Western Desert has a length–transverse diameter index of 8.2, which agrees with the lowest indices found in metatarsals of the Bactrian camel (cf. Gautier 1968: 1369, Table 1). Clutton-Brock (1970), however, insists that the biogeographical and ecological data do not allow the relation of *C. thomasi* to *C. bacterianus*. This argument has validity, but the fact that *C. thomasi* is osteologically closer to *C. bacterianus* than to *C. dromedarius* remains unexplained. This applies also to other camelid material from East Africa, as pointed out by Gentry and Gentry (1969) and Grattard (personal communication). A detailed study of osteological differences and a careful assessment of the phylogenetic relationship of both recent forms may help to solve this problem. It has indeed been suggested that the two extant forms may have separated only quite recently (Robinson 1936).

Large Bovid (*Homoioceras antiquus?* or *Bos primigenius*)

A large bovid is represented at Bir Sahara, Site BS-13, by an upper molar. Bir Tarfawi, Site BT-14, yielded incomplete remains of lower and upper molars, a cannon-bone fragment and a large but poorly preserved astragalus. Measurements on some of the foregoing specimens follow.

M1/2,
L.	±30	±30
TR.D.	25.5	
M1/2, L.	±32	
Astragalus		
H.	111	
TR.D.	89	

Dental characteristics of upper molars in *Syncerus, Bos,* and *Homoioceras* have been reviewed by Gentry (1964) and Churcher (1972). Both upper molars from the Western Desert have interfossettes that are placed quite lingually. The fossettes are not distorted, and the endostyles are broad and deltoid in cross section. Other characteristics are much less visible, because one of the teeth is only slightly worn, whereas the other is very much damaged. The available evidence, however, suggests that the material should be assigned to *Homoioceras.*

Homoioceras antiquus is said to be larger and more robust than *Bos primigenius* (cf. Higgs 1967). The Bir Tarfawi astragalus exceeds in size the largest specimens collected from upper Quaternary sites in the Sudan (Gautier 1968) and Upper Egypt (Churcher 1972), and is ascribed to *Bos primigenius.* Moreover, it appears to be relatively broader. Its attribution to the extinct *Homoioceras antiquus* is hence acceptable.

Homoioceras antiquus has been recorded from the Neolithic at Amekni and from Meniet, where it occurs together with *Bos* sp. (Bouchud 1969; Hugot 1963). The Acheulian of the Tihodaine Basin yielded both *H. antiquus* and *B. primigenius* (Arambourg and Balout 1955). As already noted, upper Quaternary sites along the Nile in the northern Sudan and Upper Egypt yielded *B. primigenius* and some doubtful remains ascribed to *Homoioceras vignardi* (Churcher 1972; Gaillard 1934; Gautier 1968). From Shaheinab *Syncerus* or *Homoioceras* sp. is recorded (Bate 1953). The absence of buffalo along the Nile may well reflect differences in ecological requirements, the buffalo being possibly adapted to drier conditions than the aurochs. However, from Abu Hugar and Singa, about 200 miles south of Khartoum along the Blue Nile, *Homoioceras singae* was described from deposits that may be lower Upper Pleistocene (Bate 1952). *H. singae* is smaller than *H. antiquus,* but as the size variations in the different *Homoioceras* spp. are not known, it is impossible to decide whether our material should be ascribed to *H. singae* or *H. antiquus.* In my opinion, it is more likely referrable to *H. antiquus.*

Red-fronted Gazelle
(*Gazella rufifrons*)

Gazelle is represented at Bir Tarfawi by a pair of horn cores, a mandible fragment, and some postcranial remains, including an incomplete metacarpus and metatarsus. Some measurements follow:

Horn core
A-P.D.	±34
TR.D.	±27.5
Index	±7.1
L.	±205
M3, L.	±14
M1/2, L.	±11.4
mt, TR.D. prox.	18.4
mc/mt, TR.D. dist.	±19
Ph.II, TR.D. diaph.	8.3
Ph.III, max. L.	±31

According to these measurements, the material belongs to a gazelle within the size range of *G. rufifrons* and the somewhat smaller *G. dorcas* or related forms (cf. measurements in Gautier 1968).

The horn cores are not very compressed, which is characteristic for *G. rufifrons* and *G. dorcas.* However, the fact that they are straight and show no sign of twisting indicates that the material can be assigned to *G. rufifrons,* since *G. dorcas* has lyrate horns. The material has also been compared successfully with fossil *G. rufifrons* (Upper Paleolithic) from the northern Sudan and southern Egypt (Gautier 1968).

Gazelle has also been recorded from the Acheulian level in the Tihodaine Basin (Arambourg and Balout 1955). At Meniet and Amekni *G. dorcas* was identified (Bouchud 1969; Hugot 1963).

Gazella dama

A medium-sized gazelle is represented at Site BT-14 by a pair of fragmented horn cores, some skull fragments with teeth, isolated teeth, and several postcranial fragments. According to the simple morphology of the teeth and the slenderness of the postcranial remains, this material should be ascribed to a larger gazelle-type herbivore. Measurements are as follows:

Horn core
A-P.D. (1)	40
TR.D. (2)	31
Index (2):(1)	0.78
P4	11.4
M1, L.	13–14.5
M2, L.	16.2
M3, L.	20.0
M2, L.	17.4
M3, L.	±23
P2-P3	
L.	±92
Cuboid, TR.D.	±28
Humerus, TR.D. dist.	±39
mc/mt, TR.D. dist.	32
Ph. I	
L.	64.6
TR.D. prox.	13.0
TR.D. diaph.	10.8
TR.D. dist.	11.5

According to the foregoing measurements, the material can be assigned to a gazelle, about 1.5 times larger than the species in this collection identified as *Gazella rufifrons.* No doubt it can be referred to one of the following species: *G. dama, G. soemeringi,* or *G. granti.* The horn-core index points to *G. dama,* for both of the other species have lower indices (Gentry 1964: 358). A comparison of the horn-core fragments and teeth with *Gazella dama* in the Institut Royale des Sciences Naturelles de Belgique—henceforth I.R.S.N.B.—(Brussels) confirmed the foregoing identification.

Large Antelope

A large antelope is represented by articulating remains from the beach deposits in Trench 5 at Site BT-14. Here fragments of a tibia, a calcaneum, an astragalus, and a proximal metatarsus were collected. Some poorly preserved and isolated specimens from the surface (astragalus, distal fragment mt/mc, etc.) are referred to the same species because of comparable size. Measurements are as follows:

Astragalus	
H.	±80
TR.D.	±52
mt,	
TR.D. prox.	±54
TR.D. diaph.	±30
mt/mc, TR.D. dist.	±51*

The astragalus and proximal metatarsal fragments have been compared at the I.R.S.N.B. (Brussels) with their respective homologs in a specimen of *Taurotragus oryx,* which appears to be slightly smaller (astragalus, H.: 74; mt, TR.D. prox.: 52). Possibly the material can be referred to *Taurotragus,* of which two species are known: *T. oryx,* or the lesser eland, and the larger *T. derbyanus,* or giant eland. Both occur today only in farthest southern Sudan; in the Chad *T. derbyanus* is found only south of 11°N latitude (MacKenzie 1954; Malbrant 1952). As far as I could ascertain, both species overlap in size. Moreover, I have not enough comparative material or fossil specimens to ascertain which species is present at Bir Tarfawi. In my opinion, *T. derbyanus* is the most reasonable guess based on the present-day distribution of both species and the relatively large size of the fossils. *T. derbyanus* is a game animal of the Lower and Middle Paleolithic in the Maghreb (Vaufrey 1955).

Medium-sized Antelope

At Site BT-14, Area A, a poorly preserved proximal moiety of what seems to be a radius and a proximal fragment of a metacarpal in a comparable state of preservation represent a medium-sized antelope. Measurements for these specimens are as follows:

Radius, TR.D. prox.	±60
mc, TR.D. prox.	±43

---

*Calculated estimate based on half immature metapodial.

According to these measurements, the specimens may well pertain to hartebeest (cf. Churcher 1972; Gautier 1968). *Alcelaphus buselaphus* is a common species in upper Quaternary sites along the Nile, and it was also recorded at the Neolithic site of Amekni (Bouchud 1969). The Acheulian in the Tihodaine Basin yielded the same species, which was recorded as *Alcelaphus bubalis* (Arambourg and Balout 1955).

This medium-sized antelope may also be represented by a mandibular condyle, an atlas fragment, a sesamoid from the same area at BT-14, and a not fully grown and incomplete vertebra together with some splinters of a hypsodont bovid molar, collected in the beach deposits of Trench 15 at the same site.

No definite identification of these fossils can be given.

DISCUSSION AND COMMENTS

The density and location of bone fragments at Site BT-14, Area A, were mapped and have been reported elsewhere (Chapter 2). Differences in frequencies of fragments per surface unit are due to several factors. In some areas eolian deposits cover and partially mask the archaeological layer. Elsewhere, deflation and weathering have apparently progressed too far, destroying most of the layer. At some points, however, bone clusters seem to correspond to remains of a single animal or a few butchered animals. Moreover, during mapping we gained the impression that certain bones such as fragments of metapodials, jaws, vertebrae, and ribs are somewhat more frequent than others. Whether this results from differential weathering or reflects butchering techniques may be impossible to determine. In most prehistoric sites, however, skulls and long bones such as humerus, radius, femur, and tibia are smashed to extract their contents (brain, marrow), and some splinters found in Area A do show the typical morphology of bones broken by man. The absence of long bones surrounded by much edible tissue may also be due in part to the carrying off of choice pieces of meat.

As noted, the lacustrine deposits overlying the archaeological layer of Site BT-14, Area A, contain a cluster of 11 bone elements pertaining in all probability to one camel, scattered over a triangular area of some 30 m². The recovered bones include fragmentary ribs, jaws, tarsals, and metatarsals and may represent the residue from a kill. This cluster provides us with an estimate of the surface that may be covered by the remains of a single animal. In Area A many identifiable specimens are separated by greater distances and therefore may represent the remains of one consumed animal. Moreover, scatters of different animals appear to overlap. These observations and the size of the ossiferous zone (±6000 m²) suggest that Area A contained a large number of remains and that for an appreciable length of time it was a preferred hunting spot for the Aterian. No doubt the location of the site, near what must have been regular watering places for game, played a role in the continued use of the site and presumably the same applies to all the other sites at Bir Sahara and at Bir Tarfawi.

In Table A4.2, the vertebrate species and the approximate absolute frequencies of specimens per unit are listed. The number of identified specimens per site or feature is too low to illustrate clear changes in time and space, but the Bir Sahara and Bir Tarfawi assemblages differ strikingly. At Bir Sahara only the larger species are represented. This is certainly due in part to differences in preservation, but may result from the fact that the collecting at Bir Tarfawi was done by a specialist, in casu, myself, who can locate poorly preserved and inconspicuous specimens in the field, give an immediate identification replacing a possibly tedious and unsuccessful curating job either on the spot or in the laboratory and who generally collects with an eye for those bone scraps that are identifiable. In either case, the Site BT-14 fauna gives a more complete picture of the fauna hunted by Middle Paleolithic man in the Western Desert than the fauna from Bir Sahara.

The game animal recovered most frequently is *Gazella dama*. Other typical game animals are all less well represented, but distortion of frequencies through differential preservation is difficult to gauge, and smaller species (e.g., *Gazella rufifrons*) may be underrepresented, whereas large species (*Ceratotherium simum, Camelus thomasi, Homoioceras*) may be relatively overrepresented.

If we consider their respective weights, the relative importance of the different game animals changes. Providers of much meat or animal protein are white rhinoceros (*C. simum*), giant buffalo (*Homoioceras*), wild camel (*C. thomasi*), and the large antelope (possibly *Taurotragus derbyanus*); the smaller herbivores are of much less importance. Hunting the larger game may have been a more difficult task for primitive man, but the effort was certainly worthwhile. In this connection, special attention should be paid to the assemblage collected at Site BT-14, Area N. It contains only birds and turtle remains and apparently indicates that the Aterians also practiced specialized gathering and hunting, which yielded much less food than big-game hunting or trapping.

As a whole the fauna of both the Mousterian and the Aterian is characterized mainly by herbivorous species living in herds or small bands in open biotopes of savanna or steppe type. The presence of camel and red-fronted gazelle points rather to generalized dry steppic conditions. Biogeographically, the fauna is basically Ethiopian with the exception of the extinct *C. thomasi*. Camelids entered Africa several million years ago and descended as far south as Tanzania. *Homoioceras* is certainly an extinct African buffalo genus.

The other species recorded at Bir Tarfawi or Bir Sahara are still found today in the Sudan or Chad at distances at least 1000 km southwest, south, or southeast of the Western Desert sites. The contraction of their ranges is due to the combined effect of human activities (hunting, herding, agriculture) and Quaternary climatological changes. Today rains from June to August brought by the Southern Atlantic

monsoons reach approximately as far as 20°N in the Sudan. Under more marked interglacial conditions, the rains may have reached farther north (cf. Van Zinderen-Bakker 1967: 130, Figure 139), thus having a positive effect on the hydrogeology of the areas feeding the springs at the *abyar*, the general water table level, and local precipitation. In early glacial times, furthermore, the area may have profited from stored fossil waters for some time.

As already noted, the white rhinoceros (*Ceratotherium simum*) is a grazer, whereas the other African species (black rhinoceros, *Diceros bicornis*) is a browser. White rhinoceros are said to live in families consisting of a male, a female, their nursing calf, and possibly one or two more fully grown calves. They prefer good grassland and often several families will concentrate on one feeding ground. This phenomenon lies at the root of the erroneous belief that the white rhinoceros, in contrast to other rhinocerotids, is a gregarious species. Solitary females with their young, bands of subadults, and not well understood heterogeneous bands are also recorded. Today the white rhinoceros is a species threatened with extinction, and one can imagine only with difficulty that formerly it occurred in large numbers in many areas (cf. Harper 1945; Heller 1913; Malbrant 1952). The white rhinoceros is quite well represented both at Bir Sahara and Bir Tarfawi, but as already pointed out, the size of its skeletal remains may be responsible for preferential preservation with respect to less sturdily built species. In any case, the presence of white rhinoceros can be seen as a fair indicator that trees, bushes, and shrubs played only a minor role in the landscape. Rhinoceros probably frequented the depression regularly in search of water or good pastures. As the hunting of rhinoceros without firearms is a difficult and dangerous task, it is conceivable that Mousterians and Aterians made pitfalls along the paths regularly used by the animals. This hypothesis has been formulated by Soergel (1922) to explain the high incidence of juvenile rhinoceros in rich and well-preserved assemblages recovered from deposits at Taubach and at Sussenboern in Thuringia (Germany) and probably dating from the last interglacial.

According to Malbrant (1952), the warthog, although not very dependent on ample water supply, prefers to live in well-irrigated terrain, where it feeds on herbs, fruits, roots, tubercles, and aquatic plants. Generally the species occurs in small bands of a few females with their young and a leading boar. The scarcity of warthog may indicate that these animals were much less frequent than typical herd animals such as gazelle, buffao, ass, or camel. However, it may also indicate that general conditions were not exactly those preferred by warthogs: Only the immediate surroundings of the bodies of water provided their most preferred habitat and diet. It is maybe significant that warthog was not found at Bir Tarfawi, although the faunal sample is thought to be much more representative than the small samples of Bir Sahara. The Aterian levels of Site BT-14 are thought to be younger than the Mousterian of Bir Sahara. The absence of warthog may then indicate a vegetation less lush than during the Mousterian occupation and may illustrate the trend toward aridification culminating in the following period in which no freshwater deposits were formed and which apparently coincides with the Upper Paleolithic.

Finally, attention should be drawn to the fact that seasonal variations of climate may have influenced the biomass in the vicinities of the depressions. Indeed, the fauna may have concentrated near the ponds in the dry season. Malbrant (1952) notes that in Chad and Oubangi-Chari (Central African Republic) *Phacochoerus aethiopicus, Alcelaphus* sp., *Gazella rufifrons,* and *G. dama* show more or less marked seasonal migration toward the north relative to the rainy season. It is therefore possible that the Bir Sahara–Bir Tarfawi region was well stocked with game only during the rainy season, and that Middle Paleolithic man hunted in the area only in that period of the year. Seasonal migratory patterns are characteristic of many hunter–gatherers and pastoralists as a result of their symbiotic relations with their prey or their livestock.

—TERMINAL PALEOLITHIC AND NEOLITHIC MATERIALS FROM NABTA—

The animal remains described in this section were collected from sites at Nabta Playa and at several nearby areas. They were excavated in 1975 and 1977. Part of one site (Site E-75-6) was also excavated in 1974, but the lithostratigraphy and chronology were not then well understood, and the collected material cannot be assigned an exact cultural provenience. The zoological remains from this test excavation are, nevertheless, included here. A short visit was paid to Nabta and vicinity in 1976, in order to gauge the potential for further prehistoric research; at that time some additional remains were collected.

Nabta Playa is situated approximately 100 km west of Abu Simbel in an area that today is almost completely barren and lacking any trace of animals. In the past, however, animal life must have been relatively abundant, as indicated by the zoological remains from the sites investigated. The most important sites are on the fringe of Nabta Playa where archaeological remains occur in deposits originally associated with the playa, in dune deposits, in reworked dune deposits, or in fine clastics filling archaeological features (e.g., at E-75-6). Other sites are associated with playas 10 km west of Nabta (E-77-1); 20 km north of Nabta (Kortein Playa: Sites E-77-3, E-77-5, and E-77-6); and 25 km north of Nabta (El Gebal El Beid Playa: Site E-77-7). The environment of these sites is basically the same as that of Nabta itself.

The sites are Terminal Paleolithic (Sites E-75-7, E-77-3, and E-77-7), Terminal Paleolithic followed by an early Neolithic characterized by Early Khartoum pottery (Site E-75-6), Neolithic with Early Khartoum pottery (Sites E-77-4, E-75-1, and E-77-5), and middle Neolithic with Early Khartoum pottery, followed by late Neolithic (Site E-75-8). According to the radiocarbon dates, this sequence covers the period from approximately 9400 BP to 5800 BP. In Table A4.3, the sites have been listed according to the estimated ages.

The faunal material is in very poor and fragmentary condition as is indicated by the low ratio of identified to total numbers of fragments (see Tables A4.3 and A4.4). The poor condition is mainly the result of desert weathering, which apparently involves extreme dehydration and heating. The collection of osseous remains is stored in the Laboratorium voor Paleontologie, University of Ghent, under number P2291.

DESCRIPTION OF THE MATERIAL

Molluscs

Cowrie (Cypraeidae *gen. et spec. indet.*). Fragments of cowrie shells were collected at Site E-75-8 in middle Neolithic context. In all specimens, part of the shell has been removed from the surface opposite the peristome. Apparently, the shells have been used as beads. Necklaces made of similar cowrie shells are still sold in Aswan, the shells for them probably being collected from the Red Sea.

Bulinus truncatus. The freshwater pulmonate *Bulinus truncatus* is frequent in the deposits filling the various pits and features at Site E-75-8, and is contemporaneous with or slightly later than the middle Neolithic occupation there. Fully grown specimens are characterized by a rather prominent spire, an almost straight columella, a truncate lower peristome, a strongly irregularly curved outer peristome margin, and coarse growth lines. Adults measure 10.9, 11.4, and 13.4 mm, but fragments of a larger specimen have been noted. Following Mandahl-Barth (1957), this form can best be included with *B.t. truncatus,* although perhaps an identification to the subspecific level should not be attempted with fossil material. *B.t. truncatus* is the typical bulinid of North Africa and the Nile Valley, the southernmost record being from Buyende, Uganda. It acts as intermediate host of *Schistosoma haematobium,* which causes bilharzia or schistosomiasis.

Zootecus insularis. The land snail *Zootecus insularis* is typical of semiarid regions in India, Arabia, Eritrea, Sudan, Senegal, the Cape Verde Islands, and elsewhere, but its present distribution is artifical and a product of human activity (Verdcourt 1960). Specimens were collected in 1974 and in 1975 in the same context as *Bulinus truncatus,* but the species occurs also at other sites (e.g., E-77-4). The species has already been recorded from late Quaternary deposits along the Nile in the northern Sudan (Martin 1968) and in Middle Paleolithic deposits at Bir Sahara (see the preceding section), indicating that it was already present in Nubia and the Western Desert in upper Pleistocene times.

Freshwater Bivalves (Aspatharia rubens?). Bivalve fragments collected from the Neolithic layer at Site E-76-6 in 1974 and 1975 cannot be identified specifically. However, at Site E-75-8 (in a pit feature in the Connecting Trench) a fragmentary shell could be identified as *Aspatharia,* and very probably as *A. rubens,* a common bivalve of the Nile (cf. Mandahl-Barth 1954). It is likely that all the unidentifiable finds can be referred to the same species. No other deposits in the area yielded freshwater molluscs, with the exception of the sediments at E-75-6, which contained only the gastropods already described. This implies that bivalve shells were imported from the Nile Valley. *Aspatharia* shells can be used as spoons or small bowls.

Vertebrates

Fish. Fish remains include one fragment each of a small and of a large vertebra collected at Site E-75-6, but not labeled precisely. P. H. Greenwood (*in litt.*) suggests that the larger vertebral fragment may pertain to *Lates* sp. As far as I understand, the presence of *Lates* at Nabta would be indicative of a well-oxygenated—that is a fairly large—body of water. *Lates* sp. has been recorded from various Upper Paleolithic sites along the Nile (Churcher 1972; Greenwood 1968). It was also found at Amekni (Camps 1969: 179) and in the Ténérian of Adrar Bous (Clark *et al.* 1973).

Turtle. One fragment of a carapace was collected at E-75-6 in a culturally mixed context. *Trionyx* and *Testudo* have been variously recorded from Early Khartoum, Esh Shaheinab, Kom Ombo, Meniet, and Bir Tarfawi (Arkell 1953; Churcher 1972; Hugot 1963; Swinton, in Arkell 1949). The material from Nabta represents *Testudo* sp., since it does not show the vermiculate pattern found in the soft-shelled Nile turtle (*Trionyx triunguis*).

Birds. Bird remains, generally very fragmentary and hence not easily identifiable, were collected at Sites E-75-6 and E-75-8. As far as can be deduced from the size of these remains several species are present. The material will be studied by P. Ballmann (Munich).

Remains of ostrich eggs are frequent in most sites, and several of these fragments show evidence of working to make beads. There is no conclusive evidence that ostrich eggs were consumed; the absence of ostrich bones could also indicate that this bird was not on the menu and may have been tabu (cf. Morel 1975).

Hedgehog (Erinaceidae *gen. et spec. indet.*). A relatively large insectivore is represented at Sites E-75-6 and E-75-8 by several mandibular fragments and a fragmentary cubitus. In two cases, the alveolar length of the jugal teeth series is 14.6 mm. The morphology and position of the teeth is as in several *Erinaceus* spp. *sensu lato* seen in the I.R.S.N.B. (Brussels), and no doubt the material represents a hedgehog.

Several hedgehogs are known from Egypt and listed as *Erinaceus auritus, E. aethiopicus,* and *E. albiventris* by Anderson (1902); these seem to correspond to *Hemiechinus libycus, Paraechinus aethiopicus,* and *Atelerix pruneri* in Allen (1939). From the Sudan, Setzer (1956) records *A. pruneri* and *Paraechinus aethiopicus.* However, with only fragmentary specimens and without access to good comparative material, it can be said only that the fossils pertain to a hedgehog, of which the mandibles are about seven-tenths as large as those of the common European hedgehog (*Erinaceus europaeus*). All the African forms mentioned appear to be much smaller than the European hedgehog.

*Hare (*Lepus capensis*).* Lagomorph remains are rather frequent in most of the sites, but are generally very fragmentary. Most common and well preserved are the articular ends of scapulae and distal fragments of tibiae, apparently because these compact bones preserve well or escape destruction during butchering, preparation for consumption, and consumption itself. An incomplete mandible contains P3, M1, and M2, which can be compared with their homologs in *Lepus capensis* as figured by MacInnes (1953). Measurements for some of the better fragments are as follows:

$\overline{P2}$-$\overline{M3}$, L.	±16.5
Scapula, max. D. articular end	8.4–10.5
Humerus, TR.D. dist.	8.6–9.9
Radius, TR.D. prox.	6.5–7.0
Femur, TR.D. dist.	7.1
Tibia, TR.D. prox.	15.2
Tibia, TR.D. dist.	10.9–11.9
Calcaneum, tot. L.	23.2–26.0
Astragalus, tot. L.	12.0

The measurements point to a lagomorph that is smaller than the European hare (formerly called *Lepus europaeus,* but now included in *Lepus capensis*) and approaches in size European wild rabbit. Malbrant (1952) records that *L. chadensis* (=*L. capensis*) in Chad and Ubangi is generally considered as a rabbit by the Europeans and others because of its comparatively small size.

Lepus sp. and *Lepus capensis* were recorded from Esh Shaheinab (Bate 1953), from Late Paleolithic sites in the northern Sudan (Gautier 1968), from Kom Ombo (Churcher 1972), and from comparable sites in southern Egypt (Gautier 1976c).

*Porcupine (*Hystrix cristata?*).* A porcupine is represented by isolated, fragmentary teeth at several sites. At Site E-75-8 were a cubitus fragment and a metacarpal, which are definitely larger (1.4 to 1.6 times) than their analogs in

Table A4.3
Absolute Frequencies of Invertebrates and Vertebrates (Fragment Counts) at Nabta and Related Sites[a,b,c]

Provenance	Unidentified	Bulinus truncatus	Zootecus insularis	Aspatharia rubens	Reptiles	Birds	Ostrich eggshell	Hedgehog	Hare
Site E-75-8									
Surface	1500		2			?1	1		2
Connecting Trench, Unit 5[c]	800		1			3		1	8
Unit 5[c]	2000		18		1	1	2		10
Unit 5[c]	800		3		1	1	1		2
Connecting Trench, B12	750		3	1	2				7
South Trench	300	2					1		3
Pit 1	400								12
Pit 2	1000				2	2	2		11
Pit 3	600								2
Units 3 and 4[c]	800	2	16		3		4		8
Unit 2 (0–20 cm)[c]	4800		5	1	3	11	7	1	15
Unit 2 (20–40 cm)[c]	1000		1		7		10		13
Unit 2 (40–60 cm)[c]	1200	1	1	1	2	1	3	6	12
Unit 2 (60–80 cm)[c]	300		1		6	2	3	1	17
Surface, Hearth E, Unit 2[c]	125		1						4
West Trench, Unit 2[c]	500	1					3		2
East Trench	75		7						2
Unit 2[c]	F			1	5	5	4		16
Unit 2? (1975)[c]	F					3	+		18
Site E-77-5	±1000		3	1					11
Site E-77-1									
Surface	2								
Locus 2	0								
Locus 3	0								
Locus 4	0								
Locus 5	120								2
Locus 6	0								
Site E-75-6									
Feature 1	75								5
Pit 1	250						2		1
Feature 2	120						3		5
Pit 2	150						2		10
Pit 3	200					1			16
Posthole 4	10								
Pit 4	400					1		2	22
Feature 4	55		1	1	1			3	5
Pit 5	15								
Feature 6	±1000		4		2	4	F	1	40
Pit 6	49								
Feature 7	F					2			8
Pit 7	140								2
Feature 1 (1975)	R			+					1
Feature 3 (1975)	R		+						9
Feature 4 (1975)	R					2			13
Feature 5 (1975)	R		+						6
Feature 15 (1975)	0								
Early Khartoum (1975)	F	F	F	+		3			32
Site E-77-4									
Surface	0								
Hearth 4	29		6				9		
Near Hearth 4	300								
Site E-75-6									
Mixed (1975)	F				1				5
Mixed (1974)	F	F				13		2	
Terminal Paleolithic (1975)	F					7			27
Site E-77-7									
Surface	0								
Site E-77-3									
Surface	0								
Pit 1	±10						1		3

[a] F = frequent.
[b] All collections made in 1977 unless otherwise indicated.
[c] Unit numbers refer to sedimentary units as shown in Figs. 3.19 and 3.20, pp. 94–95.

Porcupine	Murid	Mongoose	Wild cat	Jackal	Dog	Red-fronted gazelle	Small gazelle	Large bovid/ cattle	Caprovid	Remarks
				3	5	3		4	5	
						7		6	6	
2	13				6	17	1	11	21	
3	2			1		7	2	3	14	
2	3					23	8	1		
	1			1		21		11	20	
	1					11		1		
	1					4			16	
	1					3			7	
	4			4		12		3	24	
5	4			4		9		1	46	Cowrie: 3
	8	1		3		26		2	1	
	4			1		14		16	3	
1	2					4			?1	
	1			1		?2	?1			
	5					4	1		3	
							1			
	3					19	13	1		Cowrie: 1
	7			4		40	4	3	1	Smaller rodent: 1
	2					49		1		
						7		1		
								2		
						1				
						11		1		
						50	2			
								1		
	1									
				1		2				Large rodent ?
						1				
						4				
						8				
						6				
						±55				
						1	1			
						1				
	1					25				Larger rodent: 2?
1						1				
						28				
1						5				
						3				
						22		1		Small carnivore
						17	2			
						1				
	5					35				
								1		
						2				
						4				
						42	1	1		Reptile is turtle Fish: 2
		2	1			127	126			
						80	30	1		
						2	2	2		
								1		
1						13	11			

Table A4.4
Identification Rates and Frequencies of the Most Common Game Animals at Nabta and Related Sites[a]

Site	NF	NI	NI/NF	Hare		Small gazelle		Large gazelle	
				No.	%	No.	%	No.	%
E-75-8 LN	5000	173	.03	22	37.3	34	57.6	3	5.1
E-75-8 mixed	3000	190	.06	35	33.3	62	59.0	8	7.7
E-75-8 MN	1000	481	.05	107	41.6	130	50.6	20	7.2
E-77-5 MN	1000	63	.06	11	18.3	49	81.7	0	0.0
E-77-1 EN(?)	200	78	.39	2	2.7	69	94.5	2	2.7
E-75-6 EN	5000	441	.08	187	45.7	215	52.6	3	1.7
E-77-4 EN/TP	329	7	.02	0	0.0	6	100.0	0	0.0
E-75-6 EN/TP	high	321	low	5	1.7	169	56.1	127	42.2
E-75-6 TP	high	145	low	27	19.7	80	58.4	30	21.9

[a] NF = approximate number of vertebrate fragments.
NI = number of identified vertebrate fragments.
LN = Late Neolithic.
MN = Middle Neolithic.
EN = Early Neolithic.
TP = Terminal Paleolithic.

Atherurus africanus is our collections (origin: Antwerp Zoo). The cubitus also agrees well in form with that of *Hystrix hirsutirostris* figured by Gromova (1950), but is only about three-quarters the size of this specimen. The teeth compare very well with drawings in Grassé (1955) and are definitely too large for *Atherurus*. It would therefore appear that the Nabta fossils should be ascribed to a small *Hystrix* form. The common *Hystrix* form of northern Africa is *Hystrix cristata*.

Large Rodent. A large rodent is represented at Site E-75-6 by a proximal moiety of a humerus and two distal tibial ends. In morphology they are similar to their homologs in Norwegian and black rats (*Rattus norvegicus, R. rattus*), but they are about 1.5 times as large. In the absence of cranial material and extensive comparative collections, identification of this rodent is not possible.

Small Rodent (Murid). A small rodent is well represented at Site E-75-8 by some postcranial bones, several mandibles, some skull fragments, and loose incisors. Some material was also collected at Sites E-75-6 and E-77-5. According to Misonne (*in litt.*), this rodent is a murid and may be a new species or even a new genus, related to the *Arvicanthis–Aethomys–Lemniscomys* group. A detailed study of this species will be published separately as soon as possible.

Small Rodent. A skull fragment and a fragmentary femur at E-75-8 represent a second rodent species, which is distinctly smaller than the murid already described.

Mongoose (Herpestes ichneumon). A small carnivore is represented at Site E-75-6 (1974 collection, context unknown) by a skull fragment with alveoli for the left incisors and an incomplete right mandible with fragmentary P1–M2. In size and morphology these specimens agree very

well with a specimen of *Herpestes ichneumon* in the I.R.S.N.B. (Brussels), of which the lower P1–M2 row measures 31.4 mm; the measurement in the fossil is approximately 32 mm.

Herpestes ichneumon is a common, small carnivore in Egypt and has been reported from the Neolithic at Amekni in the Hoggar (Bouchud 1969).

Wild Cat (Felis libyca?). A proximal moiety of a radius (Site E-75-6, context unknown) represents a small felid and agrees in morphology with its homolog in the European domestic cat (*Felis libyca* f. cattus). Its transverse diameter at the epiphysis is 9.2 mm, and the shaft is about 5.8 mm wide. In *Felis libyca* the shaft has a width varying between 5.5 and 5.7 mm (Requate 1960), and the fossil can very probably be ascribed to this species.

A fragment of a cubitus from E-75-8 can also be ascribed to a small felid, about 1.1–1.2 times larger than an average modern domestic cat.

Felis cf. *libyca* was recorded from Esh Shaheinab by Bate (1953), and Gautier (1976c) described a small felid from an Upper Paleolithic site in southern Egypt as *Felis libyca?*.

Jackal? (Canis aureus?) or Small Dog? (Canis lupus f. familiaris?). Remains of a small canid are rather well represented at Site E-75-8; they include a skull fragment with M1–M2, some isolated teeth, three articulating metatarsals, phalanges, and a calcaneum. An incomplete scapula was found at E-75-6. Some of the measurements are as follows:

Upper P4, L.	16.1
id. M1, L.	10.5
Scapula, TR.D.	±21
Calcaneum, L.	±40
mt 3, L.	64.5
mt 4, L.	65.3
mt 5, L.	59.4

The canid represented by this material is somewhat bigger (1.1 to 1.2 times) than the European red fox (*Vulpes vulpes*), so that an identification as *Vulpes rüppellii*, the small fox found in the Egyptian desert, seems unlikely. The material should very probably be ascribed to the golden jackal (*Canis aureus*), although the presence of the small *Canis mesomelas,* a species today found toward the south in the Sudan, cannot be ruled out *a priori.* Jackals have been described from various sites including Early Khartoum (Bate 1949a), Esh Shaheinab (Bate 1953), late Quaternary sites along the Nile (Gautier 1968), and Bir Tarfawi in the Western Desert (see preceding section).

As dogs are said to have been domesticated at an early date, it is not impossible that the canid remains from Nabta are those of domestic dogs. However, the writer has observed in several post-Neolithic bone assemblages from Western Europe that dogs normally play an important role in the selective removal of smaller bones, so that the high frequency of small bones (e.g., phalanges) at the Nabta sites would indicate that dogs were certainly not common animals at these sites.

One proximal radius fragment collected at Site E-75-8 (late Neolithic) could also represent a carnivore. It falls within the size range of the remains described but shows some morphological differences, and its identification is therefore tentative.

Dog (Canis lupus f. familiaris). A larger canid is represented in the upper strata (late Neolithic) at Site E-75-8 by a lower jaw fragment; a tooth fragment; six metapodials, some of which articulate together; and several phalanges. It is likely that all these remains represent one animal. Some measurements follow.

Humerus, TR.D. d.	33.5
mt 3, L.	76.2
mt 4, L.	74.2
mt 5, L.	66.5

The jaw fragment can be matched with the heavily built jaw of a Belgian prehistoric dog with lower teeth-row lengths (P1–M3) of approximately 67 mm. The remains are about 1.1–1.2 times larger than those attributed to the jackal and would hence represent animals with a shoulder height of 55–60 cm. As the deposits in which these finds occur are late Neolithic, we can probably identify the remains as derived from larger domestic dogs within the size range of German shepherds (or Alsatians). Large dog remains from a late Neolithic site on Wadi Bakht in the Gilf el Kebir (about 7300 BP) will be described later.

The finds were associated with a tubular concretion, which looks like a dehydrated canid coprolite. Chemical investigation of its phosphorus content revealed the presence of a high percentage of P_2O_5 (E. Van Ranst, Ghent, personal communication). Carnivore coprolites generally contain dissolved bone (apatite) as well as bone fragments, so it is likely that the object found is indeed a coprolite. Canid coprolites in human habitation sites are generally derived from domesticates, which would corroborate the identification of the bones as dog.

Small Carnivore. A fragment of a mandible without teeth seems to represent a small carnivore with slender jaws (Site E-75-6, early Neolithic). The fragmentary nature of the specimen and the lack of good comparative collections or studies prevent a more precise identification of the material. The mongoose mandible (described earlier) is approximately twice as large as the specimen discussed here.

Gazelle (red-fronted Gazelle?; Gazella rufifrons?). Gazelle remains are frequent in most of the sites. Cranial remains, mandibles, and specimens of most of the postcranial bones are present, but only compact or sturdily built bones are more or less completely preserved. Some measurements follow:

Male horn core, D.	±(28 × 19)
	±(28 × 12)
	±(29 × 19)
Female horn core, D.	±(12 × 11)
	±(11.5 × 11)
	(13.5 × 12.2)
	(13.6 × 11)
	(16.6 × 11.4)
	(17.9 × 14)
Lower M3, L.	15.0
	15.5
	17.2
	18.9
Lower M3, L.	13.7
	14.0
Lower P2–M3, L.	59.6
Lower P2–P4, L.	18.3
Lower M1–M3, L.	40.5
	41.4
	±42
Scapula, max. D. articular surface	27.5
	28.3
	29.5
Tibia, TR.D. dist.	±19
	21.0
	22.0
Astragalus, H.	24.5
	24.8
	25.0
	25.5
	27.0
Navicocuboid, TR.D	±17
Ph. I, L.	35.0–42.3
Ph. II, L.	20.5–26.5
Ph. III, L.	23.5–25.3

As the horn cores in the collections are very poorly preserved, we can only rely on size for specific identification. The Nabta gazelle appears to be somewhat larger than *G. dorcas* as identified by Gautier (1968) in Holocene sites along the Nile in the northern Sudan, but it does compare in size with *G. rufifrons,* from Late Paleolithic sites from the same region and southern Egypt (Gautier 1968). *G. rufifrons* has also been found in a Middle Paleolithic context at Bir Tarfawi (see preceding section). Hence, the material can, in all probability, be ascribed to *Gazella rufifrons*.

Large gazelle (Gazella dama?) At most sites, a large gazelle-like herbivore is represented by a few remains. Some measurements follow:

Upper M3, L.			19.4
			19.4
Lower M3, L.			26.4
Tibia, TR.D. dist.			28.3
			27.0
mc, TR.D. prox.			±27
mt, TR.D. prox.			±27
Navicocuboid, TR.D.			26.4
Ph. I, L.	±60	—	11.2
	57.0*	15.9	13.9
	57.0	—	11.0
	31.9	—	11.4
	51.0	13.2	11.9
	—	12.2	—
	—	12.5	11.0
	—	12.2	10.9
Ph. II, L.			32.0
			31.0
			29.2
			29.2
Ph. III, L.			30.0
			±30.0
			29.8
			±28.0

The measurements indicate a gazelle about 1.5 times larger than the material assigned to *Gazella rufifrons*?. A gazelle of this size at Bir Tarfawi was identified as *Gazella dama* (see preceding section) and the Nabta material probably represents the same species.

It should be noted that one first phalanx (from a culturally mixed context at Site E-75-6) appears to be relatively broad in comparison with the others. This may be a teratological specimen, of which the great width is due to a healed and now almost invisible fracture. If not, it may represent a large male or a different species.

Large Bovid (Mainly Domestic Cattle? Bos primigenius f. taurus?)   Remains of large bovids were collected at Sites E-77-3 (Terminal Paleolithic), E-77-7 (Terminal Paleolithic), E-77-4 (Early Khartoum), E-75-6 (Terminal Paleolithic; Early Khartoum), E-75-2 (Early Khartoum), and E-75-8 (Early Khartoum and younger).

A site typologically comparable to E-75-6 (early Neolithic), near a new well ("Bir Ayed") at about 25 km north of Bir Kiseiba, yielded an almost complete lower molar of a big bovid, and, during a visit to the region in 1976, I was able to ascertain that other, comparable sites along the Kiseiba scarp also have evidence of the presence of a large bovid.

---

*Possible teratological specimen.

Measurements on some of these remains are as follows:

Upper M1, L.	±26	(E-75-8, surface)		
Lower M1/2, L.	32.5	(E-75-8, find 1975)	±32	(Bir Ayed)
Lower M3, L.	45.0	(E-77-1)	41.5	(E-77-4)
Humerus, TR.D. dist.	±100	(E-77-1)	±85	(E-75-8, find 1975)
mc, TR.D. prox.	±65	(E-77-7)		
mc, TR.D. dist.	75	(E-77-1)	±51	(E-75-8, Layer 4)
mt, TR.D. prox.	57	(E-75-8, Layer 5)		
mc/mt, TR.D. dist.	±60	(E-77-3)		
Ph. II, TR.D. dist.	±38.5	(E-75-8, Layer 5)	±32	(E-77-5)
Ph. III, L.	±70	(E-75-8, Layer 2)		

Some measurements fall within the lowermost range of aurochs from Paleolithic sites along the Nile (Gautier 1968, 1976c). Most measurements, however, are smaller and fall partially within the upper range of the Manching cattle (Latene, Bavaria; Boessneck *et al.* 1964). It must be stressed that the remains from the Terminal Paleolithic sites (E-77-3 and E-77-7) fall fully within the range of the Manching cattle. In principle, the collection could be a mixture of several bovids, perhaps including small *Bos primigenius,* African buffalo (*Syncerus caffer*), and large domestic cattle, but the most frequent mammals at Nabta are hare and smaller gazelle, indicating a very low carrying capacity of the region. It would therefore seem unlikely that it was inhabited by larger, wild ungulates, and one is tempted to consider all the material as derived from large domestic cattle, introduced into the region by man. Some of the remains are from "Terminal Paleolithic" sites, and careful appraisal of the archaeological and taphonomic contexts seems to indicate that there is little chance that these remains could be intrusive from early Neolithic settlements. Therefore, if the identifications are correct, the "Terminal Paleolithic" at Nabta is associated with domestic cattle— but this incongruity may be more apparent than real and may reflect only problems in nomenclature.

The evidence for domestic cattle at Nabta is incomplete, being based only on osteometric data (the relatively small size of the remains) and the accepted paleoenvironmental setting of the area (low game biomass). A question mark is therefore appended to the proposed identification: large bovid, probably domestic cattle (*Bos primigenius* f. taurus?).

Caprovid (Goat, Sheep; Capra aegragus f. hircus; Ovis ammon f. aries).   Remains ascribable to caprovids occur at Site E-75-8, in both the middle Neolithic and the late Neolithic levels. The remains consist of mandibular fragments, isolated teeth, and various postcranial fragments including distal humerus moieties, distal metapodial ends, and phalanges.

The remains attributed to caprovids can generally be distinguished easily from those attributed to larger gazelle because of clear odontological differences (more hypsodont and complicated teeth) and the sturdier build. In some cases, a distinction between sheep and goat according to the criteria given by Boessneck *et al.* (1964) and in Boessneck (1969) could be made. Sheep seem to predominate markedly (ratio: 3:1; 12 identified specimens) in the early Neolithic and the late Neolithic contexts. A comparison of some specimens with *Ammotragus lervia* (Barbary sheep) gave negative results, and the flat region around Nabta does not appear to be suitable for the Barbary sheep, which is said to prefer mountainous regions. Some measurements follow. Those measurements followed by *S* or *G* are attributed to sheep or goat; the others could not be assigned definitely.

Lower P2–P4	±28		
Lower M3	27.6		
Humerus, TR.D. dist.	34.2 (S)	35.0 (S)	27.8 (G?)
Astragalus	31.8 (S?)		
Tibia, TR.D. dist.	29.0		
Ph. I, TR.D. dist.	14.2	14.0	

Most measurements can be attributed to sheep. These animals have sizes within the uppermost range of the ovine breed found at Manching (Boessneck *et al.* 1964). One small humerus is possibly derived from a goat smaller than the goats found at Manching; it suggests that goats of diminutive size may have been present at Nabta. The sheep may have had a height at the withers of about 70 cm (cf. Boessneck *et al.* 1964). In the absence of horn cores little more can be said about the caprovid breeds of Nabta.

Special Characteristics of the Collection

Pathological Specimens. A first phalanx (Site E-75-6, mixed cultural context), possibly thickened as a result of fracture healing, was described with the material on the larger gazelle. Undeniable and marked pathological traces are present on a cubitus of the small gazelle and are probably due to a fracture. The specimen can be compared with a pathological cubitus of a roe deer (*Capreolus capreolus*) collected in Belgium; both suggest that these slenderly built artiodactyls were subject to comparable traumatic experiences.

Articulated Specimens. At Site E-75-7 large bovid bones (a scaphoid and a lunate), which had been cemented together in articulated position, were collected on the surface. At E-75-6, a comparable collection includes articulated second and third phalanges (Terminal Paleolithic; mixed context); a distal radius and carpals (Terminal Paleolithic); a sesamoid and second phalanx (Terminal Paleolithic), all of small gazelle. Among the hare remains, articulated proximal halves of both radius and cubitus were found at the same site (mixed context). At E-75-8, a distal tibia moiety is cemented together with the articulating astragalus and calcaneum, and a proximal metatarsus is comparably associated with tarsals. No doubt the specimens described were discarded in an articulated condition, the bones still being held together by subcutaneous tissue or

by hide. It should also be noted that the position of the third phalanges with respect to the second phalanges in the gazelle sample indicates distortion of the corresponding leg sections. Such distortion can be best explained as a result of a mummification process and shrinkage of the soft tissues. Mummification is a normal step in the postmortem disintegration sequence of subaerially exposed animals, especially in dry climates. The articulated and distorted bone groups encountered indicate that they were incorporated in the archaeological deposits before the connecting tissues were destroyed and before the effects of mummification. This implies rapid burial after they had been discarded (i.e., within a few years at the most).

The materials ascribed to a jackal, which articulate together and which were collected at Site E-75-8, were probably also incorporated together but were not cemented together, perhaps because the soft tissue was already too decomposed. Some of the larger canid tarsals ascribed to dog in the late Neolithic of the same site also are derived from one leg and apparently underwent the same fate.

Animal Traces. A hare tibia shaft at Site E-75-8 (Hearth E) exhibits a few transverse, short grooves and other less well-defined traces at the central break. These traces are tentatively attributed to a small wild carnivore, scavenging on the garbage left by the site occupants.

Human Traces. The poor preservation and matrix-coating of most of the material has obliterated or covered all evidence of butchering and most other human activities. Only some traces of fire (resulting in brown, black, and white coloring) should be mentioned.

Age and Sex of the Hunted Animals. The fragmentary nature of most remains makes determining age and sex impossible. The presence among the small gazelle jaws of two specimens with only lower M3 and M1 should, however, be noted. The other jaws seem to be mainly derived from fully grown animals, and, among the postcranial fragments of the same species, only one first phalanx is not yet proximally fused. Among the caprovid remains, an immature jaw fragment and various, ill-defined remains seem to represent juvenile animals.

The 15 fragmentary horn cores of gazelle are derived from female as well as male animals, and the ratio of females to males according to these remains is 9:6, which could indicate that female animals were killed more often than were males, especially if it is taken into account that horn cores of females are more easily destroyed. It is possible that females were easier prey, as, for example, when they were gravid. In any case, the observed sex ratios certainly do not indicate selective hunting with a conservationist approach, but an opportunistic catch-as-catch-can attitude.

The absence of caprovid horn cores, with the exception of a doubtful caprine horn core fragment at Site E-75-8 (surface) contrasts markedly with the several gazelle horn-core finds. Their absence is probably not due to selective removal, since it would then be expected that gazelle horn cores also would be missing; it appears more likely that the herds were mainly composed of hornless caprovids (i.e., ewes). The caprine horn-core fragment could belong to a female animal with slender (twisted?) scimitar horn cores.

PALEOCOLOGICAL AND PALEOECONOMICAL EVALUATION

The absolute frequencies of the various animals are summarized by site, level, and year of excavation in Table A4.3.

Molluscs

The nonmarine gastropods indicate clearly that the deposits were laid down on the fringe of Nabta Playa, as was also indicated by field observations. The land snail *Zootecus insularis* suggests subarid subaerial conditions at short distances from the localities in which it is present, or repeated temporary emergence of the freshwater deposits containing this snail. The monospecific assemblages of the pulmonate snail, *Bulinus truncatus*, point to ephemeral bodies of water or, as is more likely in this case, to shallow ponds on the playa fringe during the latter's higher stands. The absence of other freshwater gastropods in the sites or in the playa deposits (personal observations, 1974) indicates that the playa lake supported only a poor vegetation and, therefore, an impoverished fauna at the most.

The bivalve remains can probably all be ascribed to *Aspatharia rubens*. As indicated, this bivalve was probably not living in the playa, but it could have been imported from the Nile. The presence of some cowries used as beads at Site E-75-8 corroborates this suggestion, since these marine shells were probably imported from the Red Sea Coast.

Vertebrates

As a whole the game fauna from Nabta and adjacent regions differs strikingly from the assemblages collected from a Middle Paleolithic context at Bir Sahara and Bir Tarfawi (see previous section). Apart from some remains ascribed to large bovids at the Terminal Paleolithic sites and tentatively referred to domestic cattle, remains of larger herbivores, such as camel and rhinoceros, are lacking. This absence suggests much less favorable ecological conditions and a much lower biomass (especially of larger ungulates) at Nabta and in adjacent areas. Undoubtedly, the probably rather poor vegetation was concentrated around the playa lakes, whereas the surrounding country formed an arid and patchy steppe at best, so that only a slight shift toward drier conditions was needed to reduce Nabta and adjacent areas to the barren waste seen now. At Bir Sahara and Bir Tarfawi, water is still found at a shallow depth, and tamarisks

crown the phytogenic dunes. The unfavorable environment of Nabta and the adjacent areas has been invoked as one of the arguments against the wild status of the large bovid remains collected at the various sites. It would indeed seem that only man can be responsible for the introduction of larger herd animals in the environment described.

In most of the sites and levels game is the major source of animal protein, the most important game animals being hare and small and larger gazelle. Other vertebrates are much less frequent, and the rodents may represent intrusive elements, since these animals are attracted by organic matter left behind by man and like to make their burrows in soft, anthropogenic deposits. Rodents are especially frequent at Site E-75-8, which consists of eolian sands with organic admixture and apparently provided a very favorable habitat for these micromammals.

The number of carnivores in the assemblages also is rather impressive (four species). Competition between these predators and man may have been severe because of the low biomass and its probable concentration around the playa. The carnivores, as well as the hedgehog and hare, may have been caught mainly with traps and snares. Birds and fish were also eaten but left few remains, either because they were unimportant food items or because most of the hard parts were destroyed in the process of food preparation and/or consumption. In view of the considerations given earlier on the nature of the playa lakes, it seems likely, however, that the fish fauna was poor, and that fishing represented only a minor food-procuring activity.

The frequencies of the most important game animals change from the Terminal Paleolithic to the Neolithic. Domesticates appear to be already present in the Terminal Paleolithic, but become more frequent in later sites. Changes of the relative frequencies of the major game species based on the number of specimens per site or archaeological level are given in Table A4.4.

Table A4.4 also gives the approximate number of fragments (NF), the number of identified vertebrate fragments (NI) and their ratio (NI/NF). Assuming that all the samples were collected in the same fashion, the estimated ratios provide us with an indication of the fragmentation of the material, since the more the material is fragmented the more unidentified specimens will be found. The degree of fragmentation does, however, bias the relative frequencies of the animals recorded; with increasing fragmentation, the relative number of identified specimens of smaller species (in this case, mainly hare) will increase. Furthermore, it can be assumed that small samples are less likely to reflect the "true" quantitative composition of the fauna, so that it appears desirable to assess changes in the faunal assemblages on the basis only of the larger samples with comparable identification rates (NI/NF). The results are listed in Table A4.5.

In the post-Paleolithic sites, the frequency of hare increases markedly, and that of larger gazelle decreases correspondingly. This faunal break could reflect the increased reliance on domesticates in the region, and the frequencies

Table A4.5
Relative Frequencies of Major Game Species at Selected Sites[a]

Site[b]	Percentage of hare	Percentage of small gazelle	Percentage of larger gazelle
E-75-8 LN	37.3 (4.1)	57.6 (79.1)	5.1 (16.8)
E-75-8 MN	41.6 (4.6)	50.6 (69.7)	7.2 (25.7)
E-75-6 EN	45.7 (6.3)	52.6 (90.7)	1.7 (3.0)
E-75-6 TP	19.7 (1.4)	58.4 (51.9)	21.9 (46.7)

[a] Figures in parentheses are dietary ratios.
[b] LN = Late Neolithic.
 MN = Middle Neolithic.
 EN = Early Neolithic.
 TP = Terminal Paleolithic.

of the major game species (hare, gazelle) and domesticates at E-75-6 and later sites are therefore summarized in Table A4.6.

Table A4.6 shows that the decline in the relative number of larger gazelle and the increase in the relative number of hare are probably not caused by the introduction of domesticates. The samples from Site E-75-6 can, on the basis of their low NI/NF, be considered as reliable as those obtained at E-75-8, but only a few specimens of cattle are present at E-75-6. Sites E-77-5 and E-77-1 are also characterized by low percentages of cattle, although here a presumably slight negative bias with regard to caprovids may exist. We should also bear in mind that domesticated cattle may be very rare in the faunal records of the earlier sites if they were not exploited for their meat. However, the Terminal Paleolithic of Site E-75-6 accumulated at the end of the moist phase associated with Playa I at Nabta (see Chapter 3), whereas the early Neolithic assemblages at the same site seem to date from the end of the ensuing dry phase. It therefore appears likely that the faunal break reflects a change in biotopes and a more arid climate.

The climatic fluctuations connected with Playa II and Playa III seem not to be reflected in the fauna. Indeed greater reliance on domesticates may have rendered the hunting of larger game unnecessary when the climate

ameliorated. Moreover, the combined effect of overgrazing and cultivation (domestic barley) may have induced the destruction of the very delicately balanced biotopes around the playa at Nabta and hence may have furthered anthropogenic desertification. If it is assumed that the shift toward intense exploitation of domesticates in the Sahara was somehow related to the climatic deterioration, then, in general agreement with some of the current ideas on the causes and results of domestication, the introduction of domesticates at Nabta might be considered as a minor example of the so-called second cybernetics, rapidly furthering in this case the irreversible destruction of the local ecosystem.

The introduction of domestic animals appears to have been a gradual process. If the evidence from E-75-6 and the earlier sites is accepted, domestic cattle were introduced first, but apparently were not regularly consumed for meat. Later (Site E-75-8), domesticates became more important as meat providers (29.1% of the major animals), both cattle and caprovids being present in the ratio of 1:3. In the later Neolithic of E-75-8, domesticates become slightly predominant (54.2%) with a cattle-to-caprovid ratio of 1:2. This change in ratio may be significant, indicating a decrease in the importance of small livestock. However, such a shift is difficult to explain and may be due to sampling bias (surface and subsurface collections with low caprovid frequencies included in later Neolithic).

From the paleoeconomical viewpoint the distinction between specific and dietary ratios proves useful. Dietary ratios can be tentatively estimated by multiplying the number of fragments per species by the average life weight of the species. The average weights used are based on data found in Malbrant (1952) and Nobis (1965; primitive demesticates): hare, 2 kg; small gazelle, 25 kg; large gazelle, 60 kg; cattle, 200 kg; and caprovids, 25 kg. The dietary ratios for the major game species and for game and domesticates are given in Table A4.5 and Table A4.6. The tables illustrate that as a result of the low weight of hare, the post-Paleolithic shift toward a greater reliance on hare in the game fauna is much less obvious than when it is calcu-

Table A4.6
Frequencies of Major Game Animals and Domesticates at Nabta and Related Sites[a]

Site[b]	Game		Domesticates		Cattle		Caprovids	
	No.	%	No.	%	No.	%	No.	%
E-75-8 LN	59	45.8 (15.3)	70	54.2 (84.7)	24	34.3 (68.3)	46	65.7 (16.4)
E-75-8 MN	257	70.9 (39.3)	105	29.1 (60.6)	26	24.8 (43.9)	79	75.2 (16.7)
E-77-5 MN	60	98.4	?1	1.6	?1	100.0		
E-77-1 EN (?)	73	93.6	5	6.4	5	100.0		
E-75-6 EN	405	99.8 (96.7)	?1	0.2 (3.3)	?1	100.0		
E-75-6 TP	137	99.9 (97.5)	1	0.1 (2.5)	1	100.0		

[a] Figures in parentheses are dietary ratios.
[b] LN = Late Neolithic.
 MN = Middle Neolithic.
 EN = Early Neolithic.
 TP = Terminal Paleolithic.

lated in terms of specific ratios (numbers of fragments). Moreover, at Site E-75-8, the domesticates become clearly the major meat providers because of the high weight of cattle with respect to all the other major sources of animal protein.

Domestication and cattle pastoralism in the Sahara

The remains from Sites E-75-6, E-77-3, and E-77-7 identified as cattle, and those from E-75-8 identified as sheep and goat are among the oldest known for Africa. They are dated to about 9300 BP, about 8100 BP, and about 7000 BP, respectively. Sheep was found in Neolithic Fayum A and dated to about 5800 BP (Gautier 1976a); older references to sheep or other domesticates in the Fayum Neolithic are not substantiated by osteological or osteometric reports. At the Haua Fteah in Cyrenaica, sheep or goat were present at about 6800 BP (Higgs 1967). At Esh Shaheinab (late Khartoum Neolithic) in the northern Sudan, wild fauna is accompanied by some remains identified as goat and sheep (Bate 1953). The site is dated to about 5300 BP but the date had been questioned (6500 BP? cf. Mauny 1957). At the site of Kadero near Khartoum, also referred to the late Khartoum Neolithic and dated about 6000–5800 BP, cattle and small livestock (goat, sheep) predominate (Sobocinski 1977; L. Krzyzaniak, personal communication). An older site in the northern Sudan known as "Early Khartoum" did not yield evidence of domestic stock (Bate 1949b), but in the Sahara, Hoggar, Ténéré, and Ennedi, sites with pottery comparable to that found at Early Khartoum are dated between 8000 and 6000 BP; domestic cattle could be present at some of these (Uan Muhuggiag, about 6000 BP; Adrar Bous, about 5800 BP; cf. Clark 1971). At Adrar Bous, a complete bovid skeleton was recovered; this skeleton appears to represent a small, short-horned breed (size at the withers estimated at 104 cm; Carter and Clark 1976). The Uan Muhuggiag material may be comparable, and the presence of small, short-horned forms suggests that domestication of wild cattle could have taken place at an appreciably earlier date. Outside Africa, domestic cattle seem to be already present at Haçilar, Turkey, at about 9000 BP; at Çatal Hüyük, Turkey, at about 8400 BP; and at Bougras, Syria, at about 8000 BP; (Bökönyi 1976; Clason 1977). The caprovids were probably domesticated even earlier in the Near East; domesticated sheep may occur at Zawi Chemi Shanidar, Iraq, at about 11,000 BP and domesticated goat at Tell Asiab, Iran, at about 10,000 BP (Bökönyi 1976). This early domestication of caprovids leaves ample time for the spread of these animals outside the range of their wild ancestors, which do not occur in Africa. Cattle, on the other hand, were probably domesticated in Africa (cf. Hays 1975), since aurochs were living in North Africa and in the Nile Valley as far south as Wadi Halfa (Gautier 1968). This could explain why domestic cattle precede the domestic caprovids in Africa, as seems to be the case at Nabta and adjacent areas (cf. Tables A4.3 and A4.5).

Evaluating the significance of the Nabta sites involves problems discussed by Gabriel (1972, 1973; personal communication) and by McHugh (1974), among others. Gabriel studied surface features in the eastern part of the central Sahara and interpreted these as hearths left by Neolithic cattle pastoralists. Radiocarbon dates range from about 7500 to about 3200 BP, but most dates cluster in the period between about 5700 and about 5400 BP. Ceramics, ostrich-egg fragments, backed blades, scrapers, arrowheads, and grinding-stones are associated with these hearths. They occur in serir areas (sand flats) or small depressions. Faunal remains were identified by various workers as elephant, giraffe, buffalo, cattle, antelope (Hippotragus?), gazelle, sheep, and ostrich, and radiocarbon dates for the fauna are between about 7500 and about 5500 BP. In the Tibesti mountains and adjacent areas faunal remains dated between about 8000 and about 4700 BP contain a felid, gazelle, buffalo, some other bovids of different size, and ostrich. A few elephant bones both from the serir areas and the highlands, however, are much younger and have been dated, respectively, to about 2400 BP and about 2700 BP. The remains are generally eolized and in poor condition, and they were identified by workers not well acquainted with eolized materials; V. Eisenmann (personal communication) insists on the provisional character of some of the identifications. They may, therefore, provide us with no more than general indications, and it is possible that buffalo and cattle should be grouped together as large bovid. The term sheep (German: Schaf) may refer to domestic sheep or to goat, and possibly also to Barbary sheep (Ammortragus lervia). In any case, the faunal remains left by the central Saharan pastoralists seem to include several game animals, possible domestic cattle, and maybe domestic caprovid. Furthermore, if it is accepted that these people obtained their animal proteins from the dairy products of their domestic stock and from game animals, their kitchen middens should be composed mainly of game animal remains. This appears also to be the case at the older sites at Nabta.

McHugh (1974) discussed the introduction of domestic cattle in the Sahara on the basis of the rock art found in various areas, including Gebel Uweinat. In early Holocene times the Saharan highlands received substantial annual rains (200–600 mm, as deduced from pre-pastoralist rock drawings), allowing the development in these areas of extensive Neolithic cattle pastoralism. McHugh has estimated the transhumant movements of the human groups involved, between dry season refuges in and near the highlands and the wet season pastures, at about 320 km (200 miles). Special efforts to secure water during the dry season would result in the digging of water holes.

It is tempting to regard at least some of the older Neolithic sites found at Nabta and adjacent areas, and the many as yet undescribed but presumably contemporary sites west of the Kiseiba scarp, as the remains of early nomadic pastoralists, comparable to those of the central Sahara, and, indeed, they do share many features with the sites described by Gabriel (hearths, grinding-stones, ostrich-egg fragments, predominance of game, but domestic cattle probably present). The Libyan sites, defined by Hoebler and Hester (1969) in the Dungul area (one radiocarbon date of about 8000 BP) and at one locality in Kurkur, may also represent cattle pastoralist remains. The evidence at Nabta further suggests that after a certain moment in time these putative pastoralists may have begun to rely more heavily on their livestock for meat, and that they became at least semisedentary (house remains, domestic plants).

McHugh (1974) has argued that the spread of cattle pastoralism from Gebel Uweinat toward the Nile was precluded by the absence of suitable dry season refuges. Apparently he was not aware that the area west of the Kiseiba scarp is marked by several *abyar* (Bir Sheb, Domaat Abu Hamed, Bir Kiseiba, and Bir Ayed, for example), some of which are associated with quite extensive phytogenic dune fields and palm groves, as well as playa deposits. Farther east is the extensive playa of Nabta. There is no obvious reason why nomadic pastoralists should have been unable to pass from the plains east of Gebel Uweinat to the region west of Bir Kiseiba (400 km), where they probably found another dry season refuge. From the area east of the Kiseiba scarp, cattle pastoralists passing through or near Nabta could easily reach the Nile Valley about 180 km to the east. As already noted, evidence for contact with the Nile is provided by, among others, the bivalve remains that probably represent *Aspatharia rubens,* a species commonly found in the Nile.) (Cowrie beads from Nabta that probably originated from the Red Sea are also indicative of relations with the Nile and beyond.

DISCUSSION AND COMMENTS

The archaeozoological assemblages collected at Nabta and adjacent areas reflect a semiarid environment with a relatively low biomass, especially of larger herbivorous animals. Changes in the assemblages seem to illustrate the transition of a hunter–gatherer economy (hare, gazelle) in the Terminal Paleolithic toward a mixed subsistence base including hunting as well as herding of livestock (cattle, goat, sheep). The major game animals in the Terminal Paleolithic were hare, small gazelle, and larger gazelle, but other smaller vertebrates are also found (porcupine, birds), as were some large bovids. Remains of the large bovids are rare and fall within the size range of larger domestic cattle. It would appear that only man could have introduced large bovids in the area, so the remains have tentatively been identified as domestic cattle.

During the early Neolithic phase, the number of large gazelle falls, whereas that of hare increases. This faunal change probably reflects a climatic deterioration (dry phase after the formation of Playa I). The older early Neolithic sites contain only a few specimens of domestic cattle; later (Site E-75-8) both domestic cattle and caprovids (sheep, goat) are found (29.1% of major animals). In the late Neolithic at E-75-8, domestic livestock become slightly more important than game (54.2%).

Cattle were probably introduced in the Nabta region through the agency of Saharan cattle pastoralists. From Nabta or comparable "stepping-stones" within the Western Desert, they may have reached the Nile Valley. Contact of the Early Khartoum inhabitants of Nabta with the Nile Valley is evidenced by freshwater and marine mollusc shells.

After the arid phase thought to be documented by the Terminal Paleolithic–early Neolithic faunal break, the climatic vicissitudes (Playas II and III) are not reflected in the faunal record of the later middle Neolithic and late Neolithic occupations. The deleterious effects of overgrazing and possibly of certain agricultural practices may have counterbalanced the increase in humidity. Hence, an anthropogenic aridification process may have preceded the climatic deterioration that finally forced the Neolithic population to abandon Nabta and adjacent areas.

FAUNAL REMAINS FROM THE KHARGA DEPRESSION

This section describes some animal remains collected in the Kharga depression in February and March of 1976 by the author and other members of the Combined Prehistoric Expedition; it also provides a critical appraisal of finds described and evaluated by other workers.

REMAINS FROM THE WADI TUFA

Limestone tufas associated with silts were described by Gardner (1935) and by Caton-Thompson (1952) under two headings: *(a)* plateau tufa and *(b)* wadi tufa. The plateau tufas contain no fossils except reed stems. They occur typically in horizontal sheets on Eocene limestone just below the edge of the scarp bounding the Kharga depression to the east (mainly at Bulaq Pass and at Rizeikat Pass). The wadi tufa rests on gravels, silts, and breccias at a lower level than the plateau tufa in wadi cuts postdating the formation of the latter. Wadi tufa deposits contain plant remains and molds (leaves, stems, nuts) and gastropod shells. They would be contemporaneous with late Lower Paleolithic and Middle Paleolithic industries, excluding the "Khargan," the Aterian, and the "Epi-Levalloisian." The plant species present are *Ficus ingens* (fig), *F.* cf. *salicifolia* (fig), *F. sycomorus* (fig), *Phoenix* sp. (*reclinata?*; date), *Celtis* sp. (*integrifolia?*; hackberry), *Arundo* sp. (reed), and

Pteris vittata (fern). Date seeds (*Phoenix reclinata*) were also collected in the Aterian spring mound of Site KO6E. The flora is predominantly African and requires the presence of standing water but not much direct rainfall. Indeed, Caton-Thompson and Gardner (1939) described small oases with palms, figs (*F. salicifolia, F. sycomorus*), maidenhair fern, and other vegetation in Hadhramaut, nourished almost entirely by groundwater, since direct rainfall is virtually unknown there.

The gastropods associated with the wadi tufa deposits are listed next. Some changes in nomenclature, based on Mandahl-Barth (1954) and on Brown and Mandahl Barth (1973), have been added.

1. Land Snails (12 forms):

> *Gulella gwendolinae*
> *Euconulus fulvus*
> *Vitrina* sp.
> *Zonitoides nitidens*
> *Helicella conspurcata*
> *Vallonia excentrica*
> *V. pulchella, V. pulchella* var. *enniensis*
> *Gastrocopta insula*
> *Pepoides sennaariensis*
> *Vertigo antivertigo*
> *Pseudopeas saxatile*
> *Zootecus insularis*

2. Hygrophylic (1 form):

> *Succinea cleopatrae*

3. Freshwater snails (10 forms):

> *Lymnaea caillaudi, L. natalensis, L.n.* var. *excula* = *L. natalensis*
> *Planorbis alexandrinus* = *Biomphalaria alexandrina*
> *Pl. gibbonsi* = *Ceratophyllus natalensis*
> *Pl. mareoticus* = *Gyraulus ehrenbergi*
> *Segmentina angusta* = *Segmentorbis angustus*
> *Bulinus forskalii*
> *Bulinus truncatus*
> *Ferrissia clessiana*
> *Melanoides tuberculata*
> *Hydrobia stagnalis* var. *cornea*

The most common species are the land snail *Zootecus insularis*, and *Melanoides tuberculata*. The ecological requirements of *M. tuberculata* will be discussed later, but there is no doubt that its high frequencies indicate poor living conditions for freshwater molluscs. The number of terrestrial snails also is very high and suggests that the tufas and related deposits were formed in small bodies of water. The aquatic species are still found in Egypt today. The terrestrial fauna contains approximately as many paleoarctic as sub-Saharan species. The Kharga depression was undoubtedly colonized through the intermediary of water birds carrying snails or snail eggs attached to their legs, the most effective carriers in this case probably being migratory birds that cross the depression twice a year.

Among the land snails, many species do not occur today in Egypt. This is probably due to the filter effect of passive migration. Indeed, land snails can stand prolonged transport much better than aquatic snails; therefore, land snails can be brought in from farther away than water snails.

Taking into account the modern distribution of *Ficus* spp., *Celtis integrifolia*, and *Zootecus insularis*, Caton-Thompson (1952) suggested that the wadi tufas were probably deposited during periods having between 200 and 400 mm annual rainfall. In my opinion, neither the tufa nor the paleontological evidence warrants this conclusion, as indicated by the Hadhramaut example referred to by Caton-Thompson herself. The crucial point is that springs relieve desert conditions for a small area, and that the groundwater released by the springs may be fossil; therefore, the remains from springs do not tell much about the prevailing conditions from the area around the springs. According to Caton-Thompson, most of the wadi tufa deposits are separated by erosional phases indicating increased precipitation. These pluvial periods may have replenished groundwater reservoirs, so that the spring deposits may not indicate contemporaneous rainfall conditions. The presence of paleoarctic land snails also does not necessarily imply a cooler and moister period. These forms may be relics of an earlier, less dry period in suitable environment, or such suitable niches may have persisted in various locations enabling passive migration of paleoarctic as well as southern molluscs. On the other hand, the occurrence of sub-Saharan and paleoarctic forms together could suggest an environment with less extreme temperatures than prevail today: cooler summers and warmer winters.

Butzer and Hansen (1968) refer to radiometric dating and geochemical studies of present-day artesian waters at Kharga Oasis. Radiocarbon dates give ages between 19,000 and 25,000 years BP (Münnich and Vogel 1963). Ratios of ^{14}C to ^{13}C suggest a surface accumulation environment with about 100–200 mm precipitation. Ratios of ^{18}O to ^{16}O in the water would suggest that it was derived from rainwater collected in subaerial drainage systems during a former "pluvial" period (Degens 1962). Butzer and Hansen (1968) advocate these findings to substantiate Caton-Thompson's claim that the wadi tufas were deposited during a wetter period. However, if correctly dated, the wadi tufas are certainly older than the fossil water now being used in Kharga. Also, no good evidence for pluvial conditions has been found in the Kharga depression that can be dated to the Late Weichselian, and Upper Paleolithic artifacts are virtually absent. This suggests that the dates for the fossil water are either incorrect or that this water was collected in a distant region or regions subject to pluvial conditions during the Late Weichselian.

Remains other than those of plants or snails are virtually absent. Gardner (1935: 480) records only an insect larva, and, at Refuf Pass, a ruminant tooth so fragile that it crumbled at a touch. The deposits may contain more bone remains, but they would be coated with lime and hence extremely difficult to detect in the cellular tufa. Caton-Thompson (1952: 146n) also records gazelle horn cores "unearthed in the Scarp deposits"; it is likely that these were also collected in the wadi tufa, but the available provenience data are incomplete.

As a conclusion, we may say that a paleoclimatological evaluation of the wadi tufa and its fossils is not really possible. Moreover, the claim by Butzer and Hansen (1968) that a snail sample from the wadi tufa has been analysed by Degens (1962), who deduced an annual paleotemperature average for it based on the $^{18}O-^{16}O$ content, is open to question; the available evidence suggests that this sample is Graeco-Roman. It will, therefore, be discussed with the other remains of the historical deposits.

REMAINS ASSOCIATED WITH THE PALEOLITHIC SPRING MOUNDS

Almost no fauna has been found associated with the Paleolithic spring-mound deposits. Caton-Thompson (1952: 72, 79) only records a fragmentary bovine cheek tooth from the Levalloisian spring mound at Site KO10 associated with a handaxe, and a fragmentary equine tooth from another Levalloisian spring mound at Site KO8A. It has so far not been possible to locate this material for reexamination. According to Caton-Thompson, the absence of shells and bones in the spring-mound deposits is probably due to the acidity of the springs. Shell and bone fragments from younger deposits in the Kharga depression are associated not directly with springs but with bodies of standing water, apparently derived from springs comparable to the Paleolithic ones but with altered chemistry.

REMAINS FROM THE NEOLITHIC DEPOSITS

Deposits in which Neolithic sites are intercalated (e.g., E-76-7) can be, at least in part, equated with those described by Caton-Thompson and Gardner (1932) as loess-like deposits and later by Caton-Thompson (1952) as eolian silt. These deposits can be characterized generally as silty sands with very marked mudcracks; the presence of calcium carbonate is revealed by calcareous root casts and effervescence with acid. Caton-Thompson and Gardner discussed at length whether these deposits could be playa sediments, but rejected this hypothesis because of the absence of lateral facies changes, evaporite bands, carbonaceous horizons, and molluscs. Facies changes in playa sediments may, however, be very subtle and difficult to trace in very eroded terrain; evaporites do not necessarily precipitate in bands; and the absence of carbonaceous horizons and of molluscan fauna may both have the same cause: poor ecological conditions in the lake, inhibiting plant growth

and molluscan life. As demonstrated by Beadle (1975), highly alkaline lakes (those with many CO_3 ions) and saline lakes may not support any molluscan life. It therefore seems possible that the Neolithic sites are associated with deposits laid down in a lake with a high carbonate content, although eolian activity probably also contributed in the sedimentation process. Playa deposits at Nabta are also devoid of molluscan life with the exception of *Lymnaea natalensis* in some freshwater pools on their fringes (see preceding text).

Very few animal remains are associated with the Neolithic. Caton-Thompson (1952: 168) describes a hearth (number 3) at spring mound KO8A with some artifacts and fragmentary animal remains, which were identified by Bate as a gazelle mandible fragment (in my opinion probably *Gazella dorcas*) and teeth of *Hyaena* cf. *striata*. Unfortunately, I have been unable to locate this material for restudy. The excavations in 1976 also produced only a few very poorly preserved faunal remains of Neolithic age, which are discussed in the following paragraphs.

The Neolithic site E-76-2 yielded very few, poorly preserved tooth-enamel and bone fragments. The bigger tooth fragments are derived from a large bovid species, the smaller ones from gazelle (*Gazelle dorcas?*) or a caprovid (sheep/goat; *Ovis ammon* f. aries, *Capra aegragus* f. hircus). The postcranial remains fall also into these categories.

At Site E-76-7 dispersed bone fragments were seen, which can probably be referred to the large bovid recorded at E-76-2. About 50 m south-southwest of the site, fragmentary remains of the upper jaws of a large bovid were collected. Measurements for this material are as follows:

L, M1–M3	87.5
L, M1	26.5
L, M2	29.8
L, M3	31.2

Morphologically the teeth correspond to those of *Bos primigenius,* but they are smaller than specimens of that species collected along the Nile (Gautier 1968); they may represent a large breed of domestic cattle.

REMAINS FROM THE GRAECO-ROMAN DEPOSITS

Silty sand deposits characterized by numerous red clay bands, ferruginous root-markings, mammalian remains, Graeco-Roman potsherds, and segments of clay water pipes were described by Caton-Thompson and Gardner (1932) and Caton-Thompson (1952) as (historic) well deposits. They are thought to be the combined result of sedimentation in the overflow of irrigation water and the trapping of eolian sediments by vegetation associated with overflow pools. This mechanism accounts for the observed grain size, stratification, and great thickness of these deposits. This has also been accepted by Beadnell (1933), who gave the first description of these deposits, but who thought that they represented remnants of an extensive lake.

According to Beadnell (1909), both *Melanoides tuberculata* and *Lymnaea* sp. are associated with these deposits. My own investigations demonstrate clearly that the species most commonly found in the deposits is *Melanoides tuberculata*. Much less common, but sometimes occuring in small clusters of several individuals (e.g., near Site E-76-7) is a bulinid snail. Following Mandahl-Barth (1954), this pulmonate can be identified as *Bulinus truncatus truncatus,* which is the typical *Bulinus* form of Egypt.

Melanoides tuberculata is a hardy viviparous and parthenogenetic species, widely distributed in Africa and parts of Asia. It is found in almost all imaginable habitats, including brackish and hot water, and propagates very rapidly, as juvenile animals may participate in reproduction. *M. tuberculata* is hence a species frequently found in unfavorable environments, where it may be very numerous. It is very common in the wadi tufas. *Bulinus truncatus* is capable of prolonged aestivation periods and can survive several months of desiccation. Therefore, it is a typical pulmonate snail of temporary pools (cf. Beadle 1975). The clusters found undoubtedly represent monospecific assemblages that lived in small overflow pools or in interdunal ponds.

As mentioned earlier, Butzer and Hansen (1968) refer to an $^{18}O-^{16}O$ isotopic temperature determination of snails from spring-mound deposits at Kharga. However, the original report (Degens 1962) only says that snails were collected from the lacustrine deposits at Kharga, and Butzer and Hansen do not specify that they have received detailed information concerning the origin of the snail sample. As far as I was able to determine, the team to which Degens belongs (Knetsch *et al.* 1965) refers to (*a*) Pleistocene lacustrine deposits with many "*Melania tuberculata*" and to (*b*) spring tufa ("Quellsinter and Tuffe") on the scarp, containing gastropods and plant remains. This suggests that the snails investigated are probably *Melanoides tuberculata* from the Graeco-Roman deposits. The $^{18}O-^{16}O$ isotopic temperature for the snail sample would indicate a former annual temperature about 6°C (11°F) lower than the modern mean of 22.5°C (73°F). The Roman deposits were probably formed mainly as a result of overflow of artesian water and under climatic conditions comparable with the present-day ones. It would therefore seem that the

paleotemperature estimate has little meaning, possibly because the basic geochemical assumptions and those concerning the isotope uptake of organisms are questionable. At least this illustrates the dangers of geochemical studies unrelated to detailed field studies.

Not only snails have been found in association with the Graeco-Roman deposits. Beadnell (1909, 1933) also records the presence of a small, slightly built ox and a small equid in Graeco-Roman context. My own observations near the 1976 expedition camp northwest of Kharga revealed the presence of cattle (*Bos primigenius* f. taurus), dromedary (*C. dromedarius* f. domestica), donkey (*Equus africanus* f. asinus), and caprovids goat (*Capra aegragus* f. hircus) and/or sheep (*Ovis ammon* f. aries). The cattle seem to be quite large; the donkey is a small form. Both animals were usually found as complete articulated skeletons or parts of such skeletons, probably because they had been buried. The dromedary was much less frequent, and only a distal metacarpus fragment was collected. Caprovid remains were collected mainly from a kitchen midden associated with charcoal near Site E-76-7 (Neolithic); among the various postcranial fragments, several could be assigned to goat, as they exhibit features typical of that species (Boessneck 1969).

Moustafa (1963) described human remains associated with large bovid teeth from Gabal el Qalaa southeast of Bulaq and postulated a Pleistocene age for these remains. The large bovid remains are described as those of a buffalo but are given the specific name *Bos africanus,* which, according to modern usage of nomenclature, would be a breed of domestic cattle. The coordinates given for the site are incorrect, for all Quaternary deposits have been deflated, and the Nubia Formation is exposed at the locality indicated. However, on the southeastern slope of Gabal el Qalaa, important remnants of eolian deposits reworked by water and containing *Melanoides tuberculata,* Graeco-Roman potsherds, and the remnants of a stone building, as well as fragmentary teeth of cattle and donkey, were found. Scattered Neolithic artifacts ("Peasant Neolithic" *sensu* Caton-Thompson) can also be found on the slopes of the hillock. It seems likely, however, that the material described by Moustafa was derived from a Graeco-Roman settlement now being destroyed by deflation, and I have little doubt that none of the remains recorded by Moustafa are of Pleistocene age.

FAUNAL REMAINS FROM THE NEOLITHIC SITE AT WADI BAKHT, GILF EL KEBIR

The few remains described in this section were collected in 1975 by the Combined Prehistoric Expedition from a site in Wadi Bakht, a dry valley cut into the eastern scarp of the Gilf el Kebir plateau. The site yielded lithic artifacts and pottery, as well as some fragmentary faunal remains. These faunal remains are now included in the collections of the

Laboratorium voor Paleontologie, University of Ghent, Belgium, under number P2356. The site is the same as the one worked by Myers for 3 weeks in 1938 (Bagnold *et al.* 1939). The geology and archaeology of the site are discussed in Chapter 5.

INVENTORY

Dog (*Canis lupus* f. familiaris)

Various fragments of a mandible can be referred to a large carnivore. They are accompanied by a fragment of a femur pertaining to a large canid. Measurements on the teeth in the mandible are as follows:

P2, L.   ±12.5
P3, L.   ±19
P4, L.   ±19

The position of the foramina on the outer side of the mandible and odontomorphologic details, as far as they can be seen, indicate that the specimen is a large canid. The teeth are crowded together and the first molar apparently did not develop (absence of alveole for the first premolar or traces of such alveole). The length of the complete jugal teeth row has been estimated at 100 mm. The Wadi Bakht canid therefore falls within the range of larger wolves. These features suggest that the mandible is derived from a very large domestic dog. Such dogs (e.g., mastiffs) were known already during the Old Kingdon (Zeuner 1967), but their origin may go back to prehistoric times.

Dorcas Gazelle *(Gazella dorcas)*

Gazelle is represented by two mandible fragments and a horn core. The horn core is much eolized but seems to belong to a male gazelle with rather small horn cores. The molariform teeth have been measured:

M$\overline{1}$, L.   11.0   —
M$\overline{2}$, L.   12.1   11.5
M$\overline{3}$, L.   —   17.9
M$\overline{1}$–M$\overline{2}$, L.   —   ±39

Because of the small size of the material, it can probably be assigned to the dorcas gazelle, the extant species of the Egyptian deserts and semideserts. This species or comparable forms have been recorded from various prehistoric sites in Egypt and the northern Sudan (Churcher 1972; Gautier 1968).

Sheep and/or Goat (*Ovis ammon* f. aries and/or *Capra aegragus* f. hircus).

Sheep or goat (or both) is represented by a few tooth fragments and a lower first or second molar (L.:16.2 mm). This material compares very well with recent and prehistoric material from various places.

Cattle (*Bos primigenius* f. taurus)

Molariform tooth fragments of a large bovid are comparable with analogous fragments of cattle from various sites and ages. Some postcranial fragments have also been referred to cattle, mainly because of their size.

PALEOECOLOGICAL EVALUATION

The collection is poorly preserved and very small. Therefore the frequencies of the various animals encountered, given here, probably have little meaning.

Dog	2 (one animal?)
Dorcas gazelle	3
Goat/sheep	8 (mainly tooth fragments)
Cattle	25 (mainly tooth fragments)

The assemblage is dominated by domestic animals, which was to be expected in view of the age of the site. The presence of large dogs and of dorcas gazelle brings to mind the many scenes of gazelle hunting and capture with the use of large hunting dogs that are depicted in Egyptian paintings and illustrated by Clark (1971). It suggests that hunting was regularly practiced near the site.

The present-day wild fauna of the Gilf el Kebir is very poor and may include Barbary sheep (*Ammotragus lervia*) and gazelle (*Gazella dorcas, G. leptoceros*), which are recorded from Gebel Uweinat by Misonne (in Van Noten n.d.). The environmental deterioration since prehistoric times is also illustrated by the rich faunal remains collected by Myers during the Mond–Bagnold Expedition (Bagnold *et al.* 1939) and the rock drawings from both Gebel Uweinat and the Gilf el Kebir.

According to the latest field studies, the rock art of Gebel Uweinat can be classified tentatively in five phases (Van Noten n.d.):

1. Engravings of wild herbivores and ostriches
2. Engravings of game and domestic cattle (hypothetical and not well documented)
3. Engravings of long-horned cattle
4. Paintings of short-horned cattle and, later, goats
5. Engravings of dromedaries and other domesticates (protohistoric)

Neolithic surface material including ostrich eggshell, grinding stones, and sickle blades found in the plain to the north of Karkur Talh (southern edge of Gebel Uweinat) is dated approximately between 3300 and 6100 BP. At one site, skull fragments of a gazelle were found, which Misonne identified as *Gazella soemmeringi*. An elephant molar fragment (*Elephas africanus*) was also found associated with pottery at the entrance of Karkur Ibrahim. The sites are probably contemporaneous with the main pastoralist period represented by the paintings of short-horned cattle. The Wadi Bakht Assemblage seems to fit in the same time bracket, more precisely in the second part of phase 4 (presence of small livestock).

The faunal remains collected by Myers and now housed in the British Museum, Natural History, include ?*Elephas* sp. (elephant), *Bos* sp. (bovid), *Addax* cf. *nasosulcatus* (addax), *Damaliscus* sp., *Gazella* sp., ?*Capra* sp. (goat?), *Canis* cf. *anthus* (jackal?), *Struthio camelus* (ostrich), and *Equus asinus* (ass), according to preliminary identifications by Bate and Jackson (personal communication, Clutton-Brock). Unfortunately the exact provenience of these remains is not known, although it is likely that most of them were found associated with "Neolithic" artifacts. Moreover, some of the bone remains may be derived from the site discussed here, for it seems that Myers worked this same site in 1938.

Today Gebel Uweinat and the Gilf el Kebir lie within the zone of less than 50 mm annual rainfall (Hoebler and Hester 1969). The wild animals predominantly illustrated in the pre-pastoralist rock art are giraffe, ostrich, and scimitar oryx (*Oryx dammah*). These animals suggest a rainfall of at least 200 mm and a dry savanna landscape with isolated stands of thorny *Acacia* (McHugh 1974). The absence of elephants in the rock pictures, although twice recorded among the faunal remains, should not unduly concern us. These animals may have been very uncommon visitors to the region. In fact, their remains may even be manuports.

The Neolithic pastoralists may have lived under conditions similar to those prevailing during the previous hunger–gatherer stage, at least initially, and they may be responsible for the aridification of the region. Indeed, some of the later rock paintings depict herds of goats accompanied by men busily tearing off branches to feed animals. The presence of goat or sheep at the Wadi Bakht site suggests that it was occupied when the aridification was already forcing people to abandon cattle for the much less demanding small livestock. In 1968–1969, one Tubu family was living at Gebel Uweinat with about 60 goats, 12 dromedaries, and a dozen or so semiwild donkeys, but 50 years ago Uweinat was still inhabited regularly by small numbers of Tubu shepherds. Apparently the environmental deterioration continues, probably mainly as a result of human overexploitation.

REFERENCES

Allen, G. A.
  1939 A checklist of African mammals. *Bulletin of The Museum of Comparative Zoology 83.*
Anderson, J.
  1902 *Zoology of Egypt. Mammalia.* London.
Arambourg, C.
  1938 Mammifères fossiles du Maroc. *Memories de la Société de Sciences Naturelles du Maroc,* No. XLVI.
  1947 Contribution à l'étude géologique et paléontologique du bassin du lac Rodolphe et de basse vallée de l'Omo. Deuxième partie. Paléontologie *Mission Scientifique Omo 1932–1933,* Vol. 1. Paris: Muséum National d'Histoire Naturelle.
Arambourg, C., and L. Balout
  1955 L'ancien lac de Tihodaine et ses gisements préhistoires. *Actes de la IIe session, Congrès Panafricain de Préhistoire, Alger 1952.* Pp. 281–292.
Arkell, A. J.
  1949 *Early Khartoum.* London: Oxford University Press.
  1953 *Esh Shaheinab.* London: Oxford University Press.
Bagnold, R. A., O. H. Myers, R. F. Peel, and M. A. Winkler
  1939 An expedition to the Gilf Kebir and Uweinat, 1938. *Geographical Journal 93:* 287–313.
Bate, D. M. A.
  1949a Mammals. In *Early Khartoum,* by A. J. Arkell. London: Oxford University Press. Pp. 16–30.
  1949b A new fossil long-horned buffalo. *Annals and Magazine of Natural History,* Series 12; No. 17. Pp. 396–398.
  1952 The mammals from Singa and Abu Hugar. *Fossil Mammals of Africa,* No. 2. Pp. 1–28.
  1953 Mammals. In *Esh Shaheinab,* by A. J. Arkell. London: Oxford University Press. Pp. 11–19.
Beadle, L. C.
  1975 *The inland waters of tropical Africa.* New York: Longman.
Beadnell, H. J. L.
  1909 *An Egyptian oasis: An account of the Oasis of Kharga in the Libyan Desert.* London: John Murray.
  1933 Remarks on the prehistoric geography and underground waters of Kharga Oasis. *Geographical Journal 81* (2): 128–134.
Boessneck, J.
  1969 Osteological differences between sheep (*Ovis aries* Linné) and goat (*Capra hircus* Linné). In *Science in archaeology,* edited by D. A. Brothwell and E. S. Higgs. London: Thames and Hudson. Pp. 331–358.
Boessneck, J., H. H. Mueller, and M. Teichert
  1964 Osteologische Unterscheidungsmerkmale zwischen Schaf (*Ovis aries* Linné) und Ziege (*Capra hircus* Linné). *Kühn-Archiv 78:* 1–126.
Boettcher, U., P. J. Erzinger, S. H. Jaeckel, and K. Kaiser
  1972 Quartäre Seebildungen und ihre Mollusken - Inhalte in Tibesti-Gebirge und seinen Rahmenbereichen der zentralen Ostsahara. *Zeitschrift für Geomorphologie, 16* (2): 182–234.
Bökönyi, S.
  1976 Development of early stock rearing in the Near East. *Nature 264 (5581):* 19–23.
Bouchud, J.
  1969 Etudes des Mammiferes et des oiseaux d'Amekni. In Amekni. Néolithique ancien du Hoggar. *Mémoires du Centre de Recherches Anthropologiqaes, Préhistoriques et Ethnographiques,* No. 10, by G. Camps. Paris: Arts et Métiers Graphiques. Pp. 173–177.
Bourdelle, E.
  1935 Notes ostéologiques et ostéométriques sur les ânes sauvages d'Afrique. *Bulletin du Musée d'Histoire Naturelle 7:* 304–315.
Brown, D. S., and G. Mandahl-Barth
  1973 Two new genera of Planorbidae from Africa and Madagascar. *Proceedings of The Malacological Society of London 40:* 287–301.
Butzer, K. W., and C. L. Hansen
  1968 *Desert and river in Nubia.* Madison: University of Wisconsin Press.
Camps, G.
  1969 Amekni. Néolithique ancien de Hoggar. *Mémoires du Centre de Recherches Anthropologiques, Préhistoriques et Ethnographiques,* No. 10. Paris: Arts et Métiers Graphiques.
Carter, P. L., and J. D. Clark
  1976 Adrar Bous and African cattle. *Panafrican Congress, 7th Session, 1971.* Pp. 487–493.
Canton-Thompson, G.
  1952 *Kharga Oasis in prehistory.* London: Athlone Press.
Caton-Thompson, G., and E. W. Gardner
  1932 The prehistoric geography of Kharga Oasis. *Geographical Journal 80* (5): 309–406.

1939 Climate, irrigation and early man in Hadhramaut. *Geographical Journal 93:* 18–38.

Churcher, C. S.
1972 Late Pleistocene vertebrates from archaeological sites in the Plain of Kom Ombo, Upper Egypt. *Life Sciences Contributions Royal Ontario Museum 82.*

Clark, J. D.
1971 A Re-examination of the evidence for agricultural origins in the Nile Valley. *Proceedings of the Prehistoric Society 37:* 34–79.

Clark, J. D., M. A. J. Williams, and A. B. Smith
1973 The geomorphology and archaeology of Adrar Bous, central Sahara: A preliminary report. *Quaternaria 17:* 245–297.

Clason, A. T.
1977 Bouqras, Gomolova en Molenaarsgraaf, drie stadia in de ontwikkeling van de veeteelt. *Museologia 7:* 54–64.

Clutton-Brock, J.
1970 The fossil fauna from an upper Pleistocene site in Jordan. *Journal of Zoology 162:* 19–29.

Degens, E. T.
1962 Geochemische Untersuchungen von Wässern aus der ägyptischen Sahara. *Geologische Rundschau 52:* 625–639.

Ducos, P.
1968 L'Origine des Animaux domestiques en Palestine. *Publications de l'Institut de Préhistoire de l'Université de Bordeaux,* Mémoire No. 6.
1970 The Oriental Institute excavations at Mureybit, Syria: Preliminary report on the 1965 campaign. Part IV: Les restes d'Equidés. *Journal of Near Eastern Studies 29* (4): 273–289.

Epstein, H.
1971 *The origin of domestic animals of Africa,* Vol. II. New York, London, Munich: Africana.

Ewer, F.
1956 The fossil suids of the Transvaal Caves. *Proceedings of the Zoological Society of London 127* (4): 527–544.

Frechkop, S.
1955 Sous-ordre des Suiformes. In *Traité de Zoologie,* edited by P. P. Grassé. Paris: Masson.

Gabriel, B.
1972 Neuere Ergebnisse der Vorgeschichtsforschung in der östlichen Zentral Sahara. *Berliner Geographische Abhandlungen 16:* 153–158.
1973 Steinplätze: Feuerstellen neolithischer Nomaden in der Sahara. *Libyca 21:* 151–168.

Gaillard, C.
1934 Contribution à l'étude de la faune préhistorique de l'Egypte (3). *Archives du Musée de l'Histoire Naturelle de Lyon 14:* 1–126.

Gardner, E. W.
1932 Some problems of the Pleistocene hydrography of Kharga Oasis. *Geological Magazine 69:* 386–421.
1935 The Pleistocene fauna and flora of Kharga Oasis, Egypt. *Quarterly Journal of the Geological Society 91:* 479–518.

Gautier, A.
1966 Camelus thomasi from the northern Sudan and its bearing on the relationship C. thomasi–C. bacterianus. *Journal of Palaeontology 40* (6):1368–1372.
1968 Mammalian remains of the northern Sudan and southern Egypt. In *The prehistory of Nubia,* Vol. 1, edited by F. Wendorf. Dallas: Fort Burgwin Research Center and Southern Methodist University Press. Pp. 80–99.
1976a Animal remains from archaeological sites of Terminal Paleolithic to Old Kingdom Age of the Fayum. In *Prehistory of the Nile Valley,* by F. Wendorf and R. Schild. New York: Academic Press. Pp. 339–381.
1976b Animal remains from localities near Dishna. In *Prehistory of the Nile Valley,* by F. Wendorf and R. Schild. New York: Academic Press. Pp. 365–367.
1976c Freshwater mollusks and mammals from Upper Paleolithic sites near Idfu and Isna. In *Prehistory of the Nile Valley,* by F. Wendorf and R. Schild. New York: Academic Press. Pp. 349–363.

Gentry, A. W.
1964 Skull characters of African gazelles. *Annals and Magazine of Natural History 7:* 353–382.

Gentry, A. W., and A. Gentry
1969 Fossil camels in Kenya and Tanzania. *Nature 221* (5196): 898.

Grassé, P. P. (Editor)
1955 *Traité de zoologie: anatomie, systématique, biologie.* Paris: Masson.

Greenwood, P. H.
1968 Fish remains. In *The prehistory of Nubia,* Vol. 1, edited by F. Wendorf. Dallas: Fort Burgwin Research Center and Southern Methodist University Press. Pp. 100–109.
1976 Fish remains from Upper Paleolithic sites near Idfu and Isna. In *Prehistory of the Nile Valley,* by F. Wendorf and R. Schild. New York: Academic Press. Pp. 383–388.

Gromova, V.
1950 Opredelitel mlekopitayuchtchich SSSR po kostiam skeleta. Bipusk l. Opredelitel po krupnim trubtsatim kostiam. B. Albom risunkov. Moskva: Izdatelstvo Akademii Nauk SSSR.

Harper, F.
1945 *Extinct and vanishing mammals of the Old World.* American Committee for International Wild Life Protection, Special Publication No. 12.

Hays, T. R.
1975 Neolithic settlement of the Sahara as it relates to the Nile Valley. In *Problems in prehisotry: North Africa and the Levant,* edited by F. Wendorf and A. E. Marks. Dallas: Southern Methodist University Press. Pp. 193–204.

Heller, E.
1913 The white rhinoceros. *Smithsonian Miscellaneous Collections 61* (1): 1–77.

Higgs, E.
1967 Environment and chronology—The evidence from mammalian fauna. In *The Haua Fteah (Cyrenaica) and the Stone Age of the Southeast Mediterranean,* by C. B. M. McBurney. London: Cambridge University Press. Pp. 16–44.

Hoebler, P. M., and J. J. Hester
1969 Prehistory and environment in the Libyan Desert. *South African Archaeological Bulletin 23* (4): 120–130.

Hooijer, D. A.
1969 Pleistocene East African rhinocerosses. In *Fossil vertebrates of Africa,* Vol. 1. London: Academic Press. Pp. 71–98.

Howell, C., L. S. Fichter, and R. Wolff
1969 Fossil camels in the Omo Beds, southern Ethiopia. *Nature 223* (5196): 150–152.

Hugot, H. J.
1963 Recherches préhistoriques dans l'Ahaggar nord-occidental. *Mémoires du Centre de Recherches Anthropologiques, Préhistoriques et Ethnographiques,* No. 1. Paris: Arts et Métiers Graphiques.

Kurtèn, B.
1965 The carnivora of the Palestine Caves. *Acta Zoologica Fennica 107.*

Lydekker, R.
1907 Guide to the specimens of the Horse Family (Equidae) exhibited in the Department of Zoology. London: Trustees of the British Museum.

MacInnes, D. G.
1953 The Miocene and Pleistocene Lagomorpha of East Africa. *Fossil Mammals of Africa 6.*

MacKenzie, P. Z.
1954 *Catalogue of wild mammals of the Sudan occurring in the natural orders Artiodactyla and Perissodactyla.* Sudan Museum Natural History Publication, No. 4.

Malbrant, R.
1952 Faune du Centre Africain Français. Paris: P. Lechevalier.

Mandahl-Barth, G.
1954 The freshwater mollusks of Uganda and adjacent territories. *Annales du Musée Royale de Congo Belge, Sci. Zool. 32.*

1957 Intermediate hosts of Schistosoma. African *Biomphalaria* and *Bulinus:* I & II. *Bulletin of the World Health Organization 16:* 1103–1163; *17:* 1–65.

Martin, F.
1968 Pleistocene mollusks from Sudanese Nubia. In *The prehisotry of Nubia,* Vol. 1, edited by F. Wendorf. Dallas: Fort Burgwin Research Center and Southern Methodist University Press. Pp. 56–79.

Mauny, R. A.
1957 Répartition de la grande faune éthiopienne du Nord-Ouest africain du Paléolithique à nos jours. *Actes 3e Pan-Afr. Congr. Préhist.,* Livingstone 1955. Pp. 102–105.

McHugh, W. P.
1974 Cattle pastoralism in Africa—A model for interpreting archaeological evidence from the Eastern Sahara Desert. *Arctic Anthropology 11* (Suppl.): 236–244.

Morel, J.
1974 La faune de l'escargotière de Dra-Mta-El-Ma-El-Abiod (Sud Algérien). *Anthropologie 78:* 299–232.

Moustafa, Y. S.
1963 On some Pleistocene human remains from the Kharga Oasis. *Proceedings of the Zoological Society of the United Arab Republic 1:* 219–222.

Münnich, K. O., and J. C. Vogel
1963 Untersuchungen an pluvialen Wassern der Ost-Sahara. *Geologische Rundschau 52:* 611–624.

Nobis, G.
1965 Haustiere im mittelalterlichen Bremer. *Bremer Archäologische Blätter 4:* 39–48.

Requate, H.
1960 Die Hauskatze. In *Die Haustiere von Haithabu,* by W.

Herre, G. Nobis, H. Requate, and G. Siewing. Neumünster: K. Walholtz Verlag. Pp. 131–155.

Robinson, A. E.
1936 The camel in antiquity. *Sudan Notes 19* (Part 1): 47–69.

Setzer, H. W.
1956 Mammals of the Anglo-Egyptian Sudan. *Proceedings of the U.S. National Museum 106* (3377): 447–587.

Sobocinski, M.
1977 Animal remains from the Neolithic settlement at Kadero (Sudan). *Roczniki Akademii Rolniczej w Poznaniu 93,* Archeozoologia, 3. Pp. 49–60.

Soergel, W.
1922 *Die Jagd des Vorzeit.* Jena. Fischer (Verlag)

Stehlin, H. G., and P. Graziosi
1935 Ricerche sugli Asinidi fossili d'Europa. *Mémoires Societé Paléontologique Suisse,* Vol. LVI.

Van Noten, F.
1978 *Rock art of the Gebel Uweinat.* Graz: Akademische Druck- und Verlagsanstalt.

Vaufrey, R.
1955 *La Préhistoire de l'Afrique. Tome I: Le Maghreb.* Paris: Masson.

Verdcourt, B.
1960 Some further records of Mollusca from N. Kenya, Ethiopia, Somaliland and Arabia, mostly from arid areas. *Revue de Zoologie et de Botanie Africaines 61:* 221–265.

von den Driesch, A.
1977 *A guide to the measurement of animal bones from archaeological sites.* Peabody Museum Bulletin 4.

Wendorf, F., R. Schild, R. Said, C. V. Haynes, M. Kobusiewicz, A. Gautier, N. el Hadidi, H. Wieckowska, and A. E. Close
1977 Late Pleistocene and Recent climatic changes in the Egyptian Sahara. *Geographical Journal 143:* 210–234.

Wermuth, H., and R. Mertens
1961 Schildkröten. Krokodile. *In Brückenechsen,* Vol. 9. Jena: Fischer

Zeuner, F. A.
1967 *Geschichte der Haustiere.* Munich: Bayerische Landwirtschaftsverlag.

5

Vegetation of the Nubian Desert (Nabta Region)

M. NABIL EL HADIDI

VEGETATION DURING THE LATE PLEISTOCENE AND HOLOCENE

We owe our knowledge of the vegetation in the Nubian Desert during the late Pleistocene and Holocene to the results of the Combined Prehistoric Expedition's work in the Western Desert since 1972. According to Wendorf *et al.* (1976), the Paleolithic material recovered from the Nubian Desert represents seven distinct episodes of occupation ranging from Upper Acheulian to Old Kingdom. Each of these episodes (except for the Terminal Paleolithic and the Neolithic) appears to be separated from the others by periods of aridity, a lower water table, and deflation.

The lithostratigraphic sequences at Bir Sahara–Bir Tarfawi (350 km west and slightly north of Abu Simbel) demonstrate probably the earliest wet events in this region, dating back to the Final Acheulian. The environmental reconstructions based on records of fauna suggest the existence of a woodland or grassland type of vegetation. Although no plant remains or pollen samples are available for identification, the types of sediments (soil factor) indicate the species that may once have existed.

At Bir Sahara, the carbonate bed dating to the Mousterian (32,000–41,000 BP) and rich in thick mats of carbonized root casts with high CaCO$_3$ content may be indicative of the existence of a *Tamarix* woodland rather than the *Acacia* of the savanna vegetation. The Arabic word *tarfa* in Tarfawi is the vernacular name of *Tamarix amplexicaulis* Ehrenb., which today is common in the Bir Sahara–Bir Tarfawi area. The present growth of this species in the area seems to be a continuation of a previous occurrence during the Mousterian age or even earlier.

The evidence of another wet episode dating 8000–7000

BC is best preserved at Nabta Playa, a huge (more than 100 km²), irregular, shallow, internally drained deflation basin located about 250 km southeast of Bir Sahara and 100 km west of Abu Simbel. The beginning of the moist episode is recorded by the stabilization of the underlying dunes supporting the growth of vegetation. Dense mats of silicified root casts and unidentified plant remains are characteristic of this substratum. At higher horizons, the ash deposits contained abundant well-preserved and identifiable plant remains. Pollen grains were not recorded in the playa sediments despite extensive testing.

Sites E-75-6 and E-75-8 yielded most of our information about the vegetation in Nabta Playa during the Terminal Paleolithic and Neolithic periods.

At Site E-75-6 the basal dunal layer was stabilized, thus enabling the growth of plants while pond sediments were accumulating and the first known Terminal Paleolithic occupation occurred (9360–8580 BP). Among the plant remains identified at this level are pieces of *Salsola baryosma* (Schult.) Dandy, and some empty glumes of *Phragmites australis* (Cav.) Trin. ex Steud., as well as numerous fibrous roots of grasses. *Salsola baryosma (kharit)* is a desert shrub that bursts forth after local rain or grows rapidly in soil with low moisture content. It is also a good sand binder, and a dunal layer in the early stages of stabilization is a favorable habitat for the growth of this species. The enrichment of the sediments with dense mats of fibrous roots of grasses indicates that the soil was apparently saturated with water, which permitted the reed grasses among which *Phragmites* was identified (Figure A5.1d).

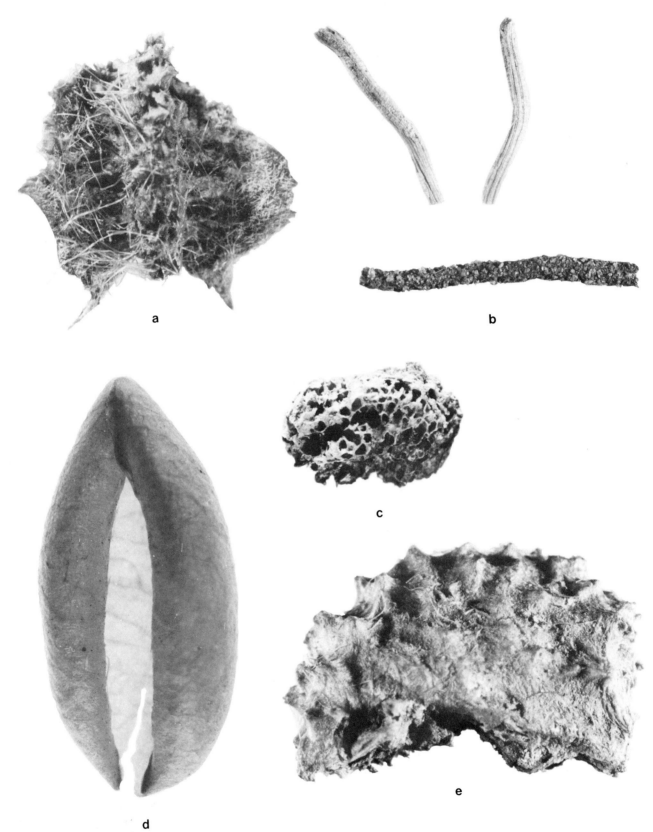

FIGURE A5.1. *Botanical remains from Nabta Neolithic sites: (a) mericarp of* Tribulus pentandrus *(× 15) (Site E-75-8, layer 3); (b) rootlet of a palm and two rootlets of a grass (× 5) (Site E-75-8, Layer 2); (c) fragment of dom palm pericarp (× 20) (Site E-75-6); (d) empty glume of* Phragmites australis *(× 200) (Site E-75-6); (e) fruit of* Calendula *sp. (× 20 (Site E-75-8, Layer 3).*

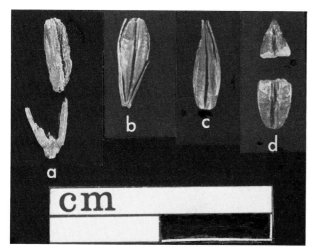

FIGURE A5.2. *Spikelets and seeds of small-sized barley from Nabta sites: (a) Site E-75-8, Layer 2, 0–20 cm; (b) Site E-75-8, Layer 2; (c) Site E-75-6, Feature 4; (d) Site E-75-6, Feature 1. The rachis and grain shown in (a) may not have been associated with each other. Further study of these specimens is in progress.*

The first Neolithic occupation yielded many charcoal pieces (unidentified); numerous fragments of *Tamarix* branchlets; fibrous roots of a grass; reticulated vascular strands of a palm; numerous wood fragments of *Acacia ehrenbergiana* Hayne; bark and wood fragments of *Salsola*

baryosma (Schult.) Dandy; a fragment of the pericarp of *Hyphaene thebaica* (L.) Mart. (dom palm); a fragment of a fruit of a *Medicago* sp. (an annual weed); and two well-preserved grains of barley (Figure A5.2c, d). The grains are small and within the size range of some barley cultivated by the Bedouin in Mariut (Egypt). A panicle rachis of a grass, at first tentatively identified as *Sorghum* sp., is now thought to belong to the closely allied *Phragmites*.

The occurrence of walk-in wells gives evidence of a water table about 2 m below the surface of occupation. The climate must have been quite dry, favoring the growth of tamarisks and palms, which could extend their root systems to the shallow water table, and of other plants with xeromorphic characters, such as *Salsola baryosma*. The water table must, however, have been well replenished to permit the growth of acacias and dom palms (Figure A5.1c). Seasonal precipitation would be necessary for the successful germination of the seeds of these plants, and to support the growth of the young plants until they became able to tap the water table.

Site E-75-8 is about 3 km west of Site E-75-6 and is located at the top of a hill that is 6 m higher than that site. The surface of the hill is mantled with artifacts and other relics of an enormous settlement area, differing in nature from Site E-75-6, which seems to represent an early food-producing society with hunting in the woodlands still important. Site E-75-8 housed social units, of unknown size

FIGURE A5.3. *Seed of date palm,* Phoenix dactylifera, *prototype, Site E-75-8, Layer 2. Stratigraphic unit refers to Figure 3.19.*

that repeatedly reoccupied the same locality. This locality may have contained houses, deep walk-in wells, and domesticated animals; there may have been extensive use of ground grains. The identified plant material reflects this situation. No remains of woody plants such as *Acacia* or *Tamarix* were recorded, and fruits or seeds of weeds of cultivation as well as hulled grains or empty glumes of a cereal have been identified.

The playa sediments of the early Neolithic age (Layer 2, 25–30 cm) revealed the presence of numerous fibrous roots (several thousand per cubic foot) of a grass and a few spikelets of a small-sized variety of barley (Figure A5.2a, b). A higher level of the same horizon (0–20 cm) also showed extensive fibrous roots of a grass and larger and broader spikelets of barley (about 8 mm long and 4 mm wide). The presence of extensive mats of fibrous grass roots suggests extensive growth or cultivation of a grass, and the discovery of barley spikelets at the same levels supports the hypothesis that this growth or cultivation was of barley. A slightly higher level (Layer 3) in Site E-75-8 yielded a fruit of a *Calendula* sp. (Figure A5.1e), seeds and a fruit fragment of a *Solanum* sp., and mericarps of *Tribulus pentandrus* Forssk. (= *T. longipetalus* Viv.) (Figure A5.1a). These species are weeds of cultivated land or similar disturbed, moist areas.

The same level (Layer 2, 40–60 cm), dating between 7000 and 6500 BP, yielded a palm seed that is about 20 mm long and 6 mm wide and is rounded at both ends (Figure A5.3). These characteristics are not known for any of the cultivated varieties of date palm (*Phoenix dactylifera* L.). Täckholm (1951) reported the occurrence of seeds of *Phoenix silvestris* from the Pleistocene of Kharga Oasis. These seeds have the dimensions of a coffee bean; that is, they are about half the size of the Nabta seed. The latter is similar in size to seeds of *Phoenix reclinata,* which is a small, tropical African palm, 1–2m high. It occurs in Gebel Elba, Darfour, Gebel Marra, and southern Sudan. No living specimens of this species have yet been recorded in the Nubian Desert.

On the other hand, a dwarf date palm has been recorded at Bir Kiseiba and Baharia Oasis. It has seeds that are small (similar to the Nabta seed) and less fleshy, inedible fruits, known to the natives as *sees.* It may be regarded as one of the prototypes of date palm, which grows wild, producing its seeds without the influence of man. The occurrence of this prototype in prehistoric sites is rather significant, since it was probably at an early stage of domestication. The cultivars of date palm are first recorded during the Middle Empire (about 1500 BC), when artificial pollination was practiced.

VEGETATION IN MODERN TIMES

Botanically, the Nubian Desert is one of the least known parts of Egypt. With the exception of the massif of Uweinat, most of the area has seldom been visited by botanists. The earliest records on the vegetation of the Uweinat area are those of Hassanein Bey (1924), Kemal El Din (1928), and Newbold (1928). Shaw and Hutchinson (1931, 1934) published the first detailed account on the flora of this area, including some ecological observations. They listed about 22 species belonging to 12 families of angiosperms. During April 1967, the United States Naval Medical Research Unit Number Three Expedition (NAMRU-3) visited the Uweinat region. Osborn and Krombein (1969) published an account of the botanical results of this expedition, including a list of 55 species belonging to 22 families of angiosperms. Among these, 33 species and 4 varieties were new records for the Uweinat region. Later in 1968 and early in 1969, the area was visited by the members of the Belgian Scientific Expedition, and an account of the ecology and the vegetation of this area published by Léonard (1969) included new records for 5 species of angiosperms. Accordingly, the Uweinat region is the best known part of the Nubian Desert, and 60 species belonging to 25 families of angiosperms are known to occur.

Most of the Nubian Desert was not explored by botanists until quite recently because of its extreme aridity and the lack of means of transport. The visits carried out by the author and the members of the Combined Prehistoric Expedition to the Western Desert are probably the first during modern times. They provide the following preliminary information, but future studies are still required for a better understanding of the vegetation and the flora of this area.

Altogether, 21 species of angiosperms, belonging to 9 families, are now known from the Nubian Desert. These are mainly confined to the sand or clay accumulations in the vicinity of widely scattered wells (*abyar*) and the lowermost portions of large, internally drained basins. They are found particularly after the very rare rain showers.

VEGETATION AROUND THE *ABYAR*

Wells, or *abyar,* are generally located in depressions in the Nubian Desert where the water table is not far from the surface. It is, for instance, 25–35 cm deep at Bir Safsaf. The vegetation around the *abyar* follows the same general pattern. Usually one or more palm groves grow near the water source, which is clearly marked by the growth of the tall reed, *Phragmites australis.* A grass community is usually present, effectively extending over vast areas of the depression. The *bir* area is delimited in various directions by low, phytogenic sand dunes that support the growth of acacias or tamarisks.

Bir Takhlis represents probably the basic, rather primitive pattern with the lowest number of species. Two dom palm groves occur in the middle of a vast area dominated by the *takhlis* grass, *Stipagrostis pungens* (Desf.) De Winter, an efficient sand binder. The individual plants reach the considerable size of 2 m high and 5 m wide. At the northern limit, a phytogenic *Acacia ehrenbergiana (selim)* mound grows.

A similar pattern is seen at Bir Safsaf where two palm groves, a date palm and a dom palm, grow in the vicinity of the water source. Remains of a third date palm grove lie not far from the living ones (Figure A5.4). The grass community is dominated by *safsaf* grass, *Pharagmites australis* (Cav.) Trin. ex Steud. This can be attributed to the apparently shallow and richly fed water table impregnating the soil with sufficient moisture to favor the growth of this reed plant. A thick superficial salt crust inhibits the expansion of this plant in several directions. The *bir* area is encircled by several *Acacia ehrenbergiana* mounds (Figure A5.5).

An advanced stage is met with at Bir Nakhlai where a single date palm grove exists, with one remaining palm. The water source is lined by the reed, *Phragmites australis*, and the grass community is rather complex. It is codominated by the *halfa* plant, *Imperata cylindrica*, and the *takhlis* grass *Stipagrostis pungens*. The phytogenic dunes are covered by *tarfa* plants, *Tamarix amplexicaulis* which delimit the area in southerly and westerly directions.

At Bir Kiseiba, the grass community is absent because of the development of a superficial salt crust, which is concealed by a thin sand sheet. The palm groves are outstanding and represent three different species. The date palm groves are either tall and robust (cultivated by man) and yield edible dates, or are dwarf and wild (prototypes), producing inedible dates (*sees*). Besides the forked, slender-trunked dom palm, *Hyphaene thebaica*, there are a few palms with stout, nonforked trunks that belong to a species not previously known from Egypt. The latter, called by the Bedouin *delib*, is presumably a *Borassus* sp. (Figure A5.6). The palms at Bir Kiesiba are subject to severe human destruction, since the area is a stopping point on the Darb el Arbain camel caravan route. A grass, *Sorghum sudanese* (Piper) Stapf, was collected recently at Bir Kiseiba (March 2, 1978, Mehringer 2, CAI). The seeds of this grass were probably introduced to this locality via the camel route.

FIGURE A5.5. *"Terbal" of* Acacia ehrenbergiana, *located southeast of Bir Safsaf. Photograph by C. V. Haynes.*

FIGURE A5.6. *View of Bir Kiseiba.* Borassus *sp. are the two palms to the right and the three palms in the left background. Photograph by C. V. Haynes.*

VEGETATION OF THE DESERT PLAIN

The greater part of the Nubian Desert is a plain of sandy desert with low elevations. The underlying rock is Nubia sandstone, which has been eroded, leaving numerous remnants standing as hills. Vast flat areas are armored with

FIGURE A5.4. *Bir Safsaf, view toward date and dom palm groves, with safsaf grass,* Phragmites australis, *in front. Photograph by C. V. Haynes.*

pebbles and frequently veneered with thin sheets of sand. Here and there, the sand has accumulated into sterile dunes and, in certain areas, into extensive sand sheets, some covering several hundred square kilometers. The vegetation of these plains is very scarce and is restricted to the lowermost portions of large internally drained basins, particularly after short and sudden rain showers, which may happen once every 20–50 years.

Among the annual desert plants confined to moistened, thin, sand sheets are *Stipagrostis ciliata* (Desf.) De Winter and *Astragalus vogelii* (Webb) Bornm. These have been observed on a sheet 31 km southwest of Bir Nakhlai.

Several desert perennial shrublets are widespread on shallow sand accumulations mixed with pebbles; for example, 15 km west of Gebel Nabta. These include three species of *Zygophyllaceae* (*Fagonia arabica* L., *F. indica* Burm. f., and *Tribulus pentandrus* Forssk.) as well as *Euphorbia granulata* Forssk. In the lowermost portions of the inter-

nally drained basins are comparatively thick layers (25–30 cm) of sand and silt, which are the habitats of other desert perennials, including the grass *Panicum turgidum* Forssk., the ground gourd *Citrullus colocynthis* (L.) Schrad., and the shrublets *Aerva persica* (Burm.) Merrill, *Crotalaria thebaica* (Del.) DC., and *Francoeuria crispa* (Forssk.) Cass. The highly tolerant desert shrub *Salsola baryosma* (Schult.) Dandy is commonly met with in diverse habitats and under the most arid conditions. A radiocarbon analysis of a skeleton of intermediate age, from a pan in Nabta Playa, showed it to contain 102.7% modern atmospheric ^{14}C. This indicates that the plant probably started its growth in the early part of the atomic era, about 1960–1961 (communication from C. V. Haynes), presumably after sudden showers fell in this area. The plant can grow rapidly whenever moisture is available and can resist drought for as long as 20–30 years.

DISCUSSION

The number of species recorded in the Nubian Desert is strikingly low, and does not exceed 21 species of angiosperms. Further exploration of the area is not expected to increase this number significantly. As might be expected of such an arid region, all plants belong to phylogenetically advanced families or genera and are especially adapted to extreme conditions. For example, the most successful and advanced family of the angiosperms *(Gramineae)* is represented by 6 species. Two other advanced families, the *Palmae* and *Leguminosae*, are represented by 3 species each. *Compositae, Cucurbitaceae,* and *Amaranthaceae* are among the advanced families each represented with 1 species. Such species are characterized by xeromorphic features as adaptations to the arid conditions. *Zygophyllaceae* (3 species), *Chenopodiaceae* (1 species), and *Tamaricaceae* (1 species) are confined to the dry and arid regions of the world; the large genus *Euphorbia (Euphorbiaceae)* is represented by a typical desert species, *E. granulata.* This low number of living species is probably only a small fraction of what would grow if the environmental conditions were similar to those during the wet episodes.

Among the species identified in the deposits of Nabta Playa were species of moist areas (*Medicago* sp., *Calendula* sp., and *Solanum* sp.). Nowadays these are common weeds of cultivation. With the decline of seasonal rainfall, arid conditions prevailed, resulting in the disappearance or shifting of the human settlement and the accompanying

cultivation (barley) eastward toward the Nile Valley.

An intermediate stage between the previous and present-day vegetation in the Nubian Desert exists at Uweinat. Here are recorded at least 60 species of angiosperms showing characters of the Indo-Saharan element and traces of Mediterranean and Sudano-Deccanian influence.

This raises the question of what the vegetation of the Nubian Desert would have been during the Paleolithic and Neolithic periods. There is evidence that it was similar to that existing today in the Kharga–Dakhla area, with the exception of neophytes introduced to these areas at various intervals.

Detailed studies of the vegetation around the *abyar*, including analysis of archaeological remains, can provide useful information concerning the changes in plant cover in relation to climate. The vegetation at Bir Nakhlai is apparently well stabilized when compared with that at Bir Takhlis, which is at an early stage of stabilization. Also worthy of note are the phytogenic sand dunes supporting the growth of acacias and tamarisks. Those inhabited by *Acacia ehrenbergiana* are referred to by the author (El Hadidi n.d.) as "acacia islets" and are recognized by Comyn (1911) as "tarabele" (Figure A5.5). Some of these acacias must be 500–700 years old, and others have near their bases considerable amounts of artifacts and traces of earlier human settlements. These "tarabele" deserve special study.

ACKNOWLEDGMENTS

The author is greatly indebted to the members of the Combined Prehistoric Expedition in the Western Desert, in particular Fred Wendorf, for the facilities provided during the 1975 and 1977 seasons. Thanks are also due to the National Geographic Society for grants extended to C. V. Haynes, who photographed the *abyar*. Professor Haynes kindly provided me with useful information about the *abyar* and the carbon dating for a skeleton of *Salsola baryosma*. M. Kassas, Cairo, read the manuscript and made useful comments, for which I am grateful.

REFERENCES

Comyn, D. C. G.
1911 *Service and Sport in the Sudan.* London: John Lane.

El Hadidi, M. N.
n.d. A synopsis of Vivi Täckholm Biological Symposium, Lund, August 1978. *Bot. Notiser 131* (in press).

Hassanein Bey, A. M.
1924 Crossing the untraversed Libyan Desert. *National Geographic Magazine 46:* 233–277.

Kemal el Din, H.
1928 L'exploration du Désert Libyque. *La Géographie 50:* 171–183, 320–336.

Léonard, J.
1969 Expedition Scientifique Belge dans le Désert de Libye. Jebel Uweinat 1968–1969; La Flore. *Africa-Tervuren 15* (4): 110–116.

Newbold, D.
1928 Rock pictures and archaeology in the Libyan Desert. *Antiquity 2:* 261–288.

Osborn, D. J., and K. V. Krombein
1969 Habitats, flora, mammals, and wasps of Gebel Uweinat, Libyan Desert. *Smithsonian Contributions 11:* 4–11.

Shaw, W. B. K., and J. Hutchinson
1931 The flora of the Libyan Desert. *Bull. Misc. Inf. Roy. Bot. Gardens Kew 4:* 161–166.
1934 The flora of the Libyan Desert, botanical notes, *Bull. Misc. Inf. Roy. Bot. Gardens Kew 7:* 281–289.

Täckholm, V.
1951 Faraos blomster: 201. *Natur och Kultur.*

Wendorf, F., R. Schild, R. Said, C. V. Haynes, A. Gautier, and M. Kobusiewicz
1976 The prehistory of the Egyptian Sahara. *Science 193:* 103–114.

6

Geological Evidence of Pluvial Climates in the Nabta Area of the Western Desert, Egypt

C. VANCE HAYNES

Gebel Nabta, a 346-m-high limestone-capped mountain in the Western Desert approximately 100 km west of the Nile Valley at Abu Simbel, is a conspicuous landmark (Figure A6.1a). It lies isolated within a shallow depression, below 200 m, that extends southwestward from Dungul Oasis almost to Bir Sheb, then northward to Bir Kiseiba (Figure A6.2). This, the Dungul–Kiseiba depression, is bounded by cliffs of the limestone plateau on the north and by the Kiseiba escarpment of the Atmur el Kibeish (Sheep Plain) on the west. South and east the borders of the depression are not conspicuous because of the gentle rise of the ground. The only watering places are the half-dozen or so *abyar* (wells) widely scattered over the southern Western Desert, wherever deflation has lowered the desert surface to within a meter or two of the local water table. At Dungul, Dineigl, Bir Nakhlai, Bir Sheb, Bir Kiseiba, Bir Abu el Hus-

sein, and Bir Murr, the wells have to be reexcavated with each visit. The vegetation varies from one *bir* to another, but generally includes one or more plant species such as date palm, dom palm, tamarisk, acacia, and various shrubs and grasses.

The importance of the Gebel Nabta area is that there are several buried archaeological sites, ranging in age from Terminal Paleolithic (about 9500–8500 BP) to Neolithic (about 8300–6000 BP), interstratified with ancient sand dunes and playa lake deposits. In addition, there are geomorphic features of different ages attributed to past climates considerably different from the hyperarid climate prevailing today.

Bedrock in the region is dominated by sandstones and variegated shales of the Cretaceous to lower Paleocene Nubia Formation (Said 1962), and Precambrian granite

353

FIGURE A6.1. *Geomorphic features of the Gebel Nabta area: (a) view of Gebel Nabta from Nabta Playa; ripple dunes in foreground and Site E-75-7 in middle ground on the floor of northwest arm of Nabta Playa; (b) inverted wadi gravels east of Black Hill (south) reveal former existence of a meandering streambed; (c) wind-faceted remnants of a limestone cap on Black Hill (south); (d) limestone cap of Gebel Nabta has been sandblasted into a series of yardangs, separated by relatively evenly spaced megaflutes.*

and granite gneiss (Issawi 1971). The sandstones are commonly silicified and ferruginized to various degrees. Outliers of Paleocene limestone occur on top of Gebel Nabta and Barqat el Shab 30 km to the southwest, and basalt of post-Paleocene and pre-Pleistocene age occurs as small cupola-like intrusions into the Nubia sandstone, resulting in reddening and further silicification. Some sandstone hills display a pronounced columnar jointing, which is believed to reflect a core of basalt (Sandford 1935).

Landforms of the area can be generally subdivided into *(a)* hills and small mountains or *gebels, (b)* broken-ground areas of differentially eroded bedrock, *(c)* stony deserts or hamadas, *(d)* deflated playas, and *(e)* sand dunes and sand sheets (Figure A6.3). Today the dominant geologic process is the action of wind, but runnels and shallow, dry washes indicate that running water has played a significant role in the past. How far in the past, 10 years or 100, is a difficult question to answer. In this, one of the driest regions on earth, a human lifetime is too short for adequate observation. Rainfall, averaging less than 1 mm per year, comes as very infrequent and very localized thunderstorms. How far apart these may be in any particular spot is unknown. In fact, the meteorological facility of the agricultural research farm at Abu Simbel has no rain gauge; at Kharga Oasis, 340 km to the north-northwest, the average precipitation is .9 mm per year (Ezzat and el Atta 1974).

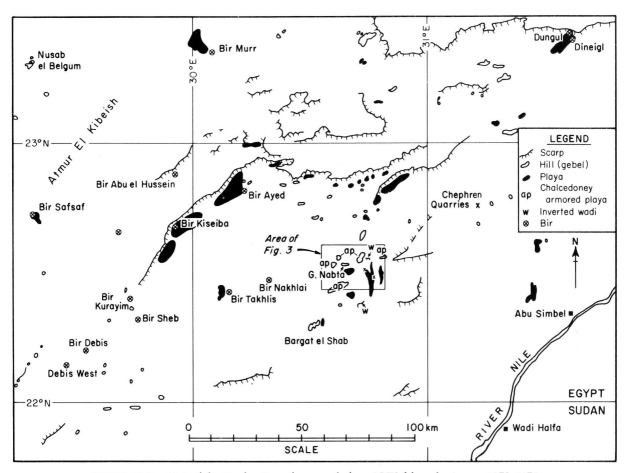

FIGURE A6.2. *Map of the Kiseiba–Dungul area made from ERTS false-color images, 1973–1975.*

HILLS AND BASINS

Differential resistance to sandblasting is at present the main factor determining the shape of bedrock outcrops. Most of the pronounced positive features of the land are due to protective caps of hardened Nubia sandstone, and a few features are held up by ancient stream or wadi gravels resulting in inverted topography. These commonly meandering ridges, or *inverted wadis* as they are termed, stand above 200 m and have well-developed, red, salty soils in them (Figure A6.1b).

The limestone caps on Gebel Nabta and Barqat el Shab are underlain by hard, silicified, ferruginous sandstone and interbedded shale. On Gebel Nabta, the limestone is so faceted and fluted by sandblasting that the whole cap can be considered as one giant ventifact. This accounts for its rounded shape, as compared with the flatter top of Barqat el Shab, which has only small remnants of limestone on top of a cap of silicified, manganiferous, Nubia sandstone. On a conspicuous black hill northeast of Barqat el Shab, vestiges of a limestone cap are in the form of isolated ventifacts (Figure A6.1c).

As seen from the north, the crest of Gebel Nabta is serrated by what can reasonably be described as megaflutes cut into the Kurkur limestone by wind-driven sand (Figure A6.1d). The north–south oriented flutes are about 10–30 m wide, up to 70 m long, and about 6 m deep; they are floored by eolian sand to an unknown depth, but probably not over 3 m. The limestone divides between the flutes are relatively flat areas, 20 to 40 m across, that display pronounced solution pits and hollows subsequently faceted by sandblasting (Figure A6.4a).

Rounded hills are rare and due primarily to spheroidally weathered and exfoliated granite outcrops (Figure A6.4b). Parallel slope retreat is predominant, and many mesa caps are being undercut by sandblasting. The peripheral fragments, upon breaking away from the main cap, commonly lie tilted on edge. Upon weathering, flaggy sandstone breaks up into relatively thin, flat slabs that accumulate on the slopes as a shingle-like colluvium intermixed with eolian sand (Figure A6.5a). The shingle forms an effective armor against deflation, and the degree of soil develop-

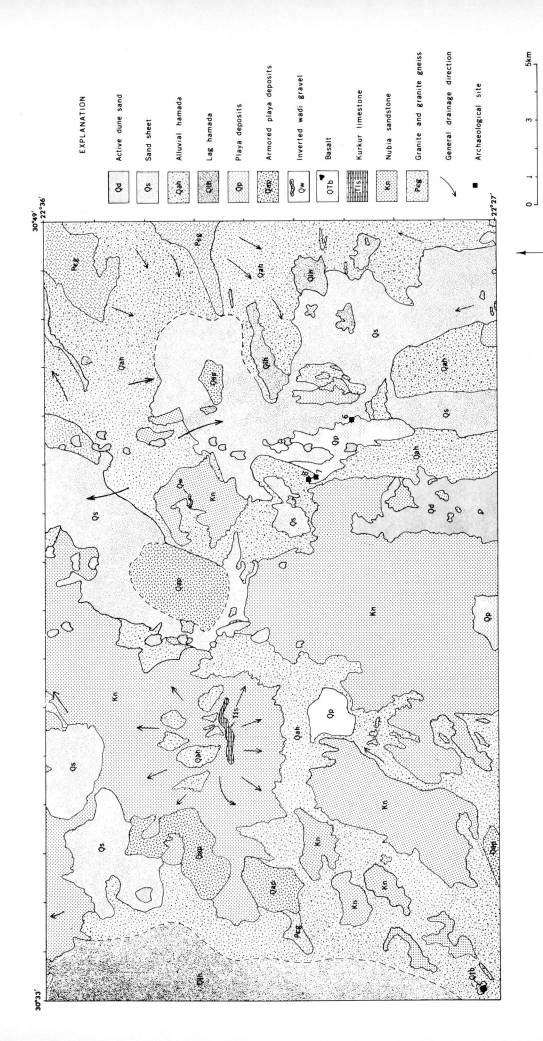

FIGURE A6.3. *Surficial geologic map of the Gebel Nabta area from 1 : 100,000 scale controlled photo-mosaics of the Geological Survey of Egypt (Aero Service Corp., Contract ICAc-1755, USAID).*

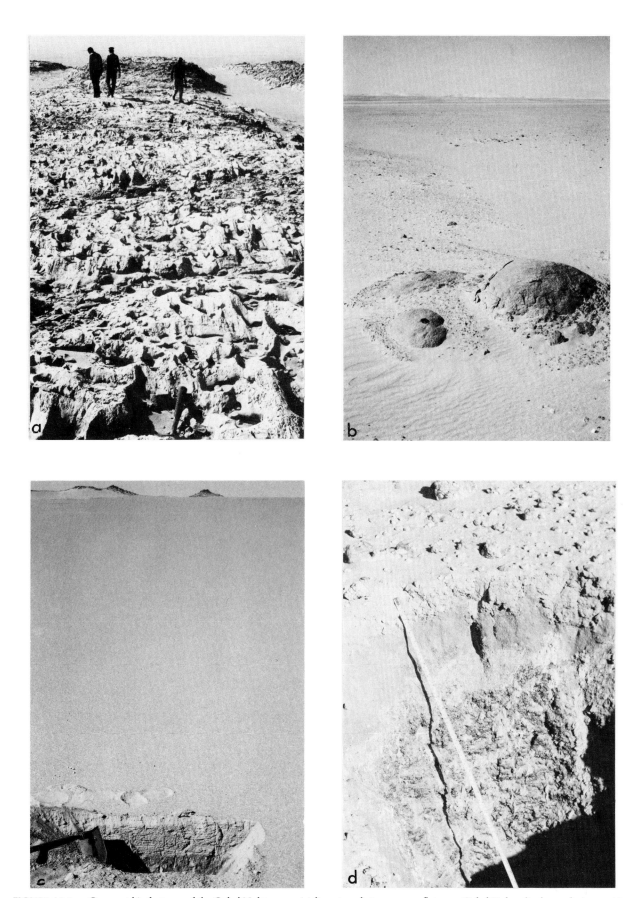

FIGURE A6.4. *Geomorphic features of the Gebel Nabta area: (a) limestone between megaflutes on Gebel Nabta displays solution cavities truncated by wind facets; (b) last vestige of spheroidally weathered granite tor projects above a flat, wind-scoured surface of nodular caliche; sand-blasted Acheulian artifacts occur on this surface, as well as active barchan dunes visible in the distance; (c) test pit in sand sheet at north end of Nabta Playa reveals medium and coarse, laminated sand over truncated playa clay; hills are upheld by ferruginized and silicified sandstone of the Nubia Formation; (d) test pit in northern part of Nabta Playa area exposes dispersed chalcedony–quartz nodules in maroon mudstone, overlain by expanded salts horizon under a vesicular horizon covered by active sand and lagged nodules.*

FIGURE A6.5. *Geomorphic features of the Gebel Nabta area: (a) wind-eroded remnant of ferruginized and silicified, flaggy sandstone (Nubia Formation) produces shingle-armored hamada in area of broken ground south of Gebel Nabta (in distance); (b) alluvial hamada between northeastern edge of Nabta Playa and granitic uplands about .5 km away; older alluvial surface at foot of the hills stands about 2 m above the younger surface; (c) isolated remnants of Pleistocene alluvial fan extend northward from the upper slope of Gebel Nabta; two younger surfaces are visible in middle ground; (d) sandblasted surface of highest alluvial fan on Gebel Nabta reveals truncated limestone cobbles and boulders of a petrocalcic horizon. Prevailing wind is from the north (right).*

ment, buried in many cases, on these slopes suggests that the type of weathering that produced most of the shingle is a condition of the past.

Shales are most commonly the sites of deflationary basins, but there are a few steep-sided hills of fissile shale that assume various odd shapes due to sandblasting. These do not appear to have had protective caps recently so their existence may be due to subtle differences in degree of induration or to peculiarities of the local airflow. Most of the basins appear to be the result of abrasion and deflation of less resistant portions of the Nubia Formation, and drainages occur only on a very local scale in association with closed basins, so most of the region is one of essentially no integrated drainage.

HAMADAS

Between the bedrock outcrops and the lower parts of the basins are surfaces of low to intermediate slope that are covered by surficial deposits of various mixtures of sand and rock fragments. These stony deserts or surfaces dominated by gravel-size particles are known as hamadas. I have subdivided hamadas on the basis of origin and composition into two types: alluvial and lag. Around the base of higher masses of bedrock there are low to intermediate slopes covered by poorly sorted angular rock debris derived from outcrops at the heads of the slopes and intermixed with reworked eolian sand, which occurs on the north and south slopes of practically all hills. There are numerous pronounced but shallow washes and runnels (wadi) separated by stone-covered interfluves (Figure A6.5b) bearing weak to very strong soils indicating significant differences in relative age. The lithology clearly indicates that the alluvial hamada deposits are derived from the uplands by alluvial processes, mainly slope wash, but no fresh evidence of discharge was seen anywhere in the region. Even the wadi floors show at least weak soil development.

From 260 to 290 m on the north slopes of Gebel Nabta there are remnants (segments) of ancient alluvial fans with slopes of 1 to 1½° (Figures A6.1d and A6.5c) composed almost entirely of angular to subangular limestone fragments derived from the Paleocene Kurkur limestone capping the mountain. The inactive alluvial surface is a desert pavement with more exposed rock surfaces than interstitial sand, and every rock surface is faceted or fluted by windblown sand (Figure A6.5d). A strong red soil on this deposit is unusual in that it displays clear evidence of intense solution and redeposition of calcium carbonate. For at least a .5 m depth each stone has a solution-etched top and a caliche-jacketed bottom showing stalagtitic pendants. On some, the volume of the pendant exceeds that of the remainder of the clast. None of the lower-elevation alluvial hamadas containing limestone clasts bear soils of this type or any evidence of solution, such as *rillensteine*, indicating that the climatic regime under which they formed was considerably different from what it has been since. Increased rainfall must be a dominant factor. These may be the oldest alluvial deposits in the area and are a marked contrast to the intermediate Holocene fans and small modern (?) fans on the upper slopes of Gebel Nabta (Figure A6.6a).

Extending directly from the base of low outcrops of bedrock are the alluvial hamadas of low-gradient slopes composed of windblown sand intermixed with coarser grained

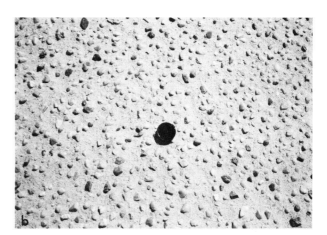

FIGURE A6.6. *Geomorphic features of the Gebel Nabta area: (a) Holocene alluvial fan on the north slope of Gebel Nabta displays debris-flow channel and levees; boulders in middle ground are about 20 cm in maximum dimension; (b) evenly spaced pebbles of a lag hamada near Barqat el Shab appear to be derived from eolian destruction of an inverted wadi; (c) test pit in sand sheet on the Atmur el Kibeish reveals laminated, medium and coarse sand over a truncated, light-brown paleosol, developed on an earlier sand sheet; prismatic soil structure on upper sand sheet indicates incipient pedogenesis; (d) view to southeast from top of basalt-colored hill southwest of Gebel Nabta shows a large, light area of chalcedony-armored mudstone in background.*

alluvium and/or colluvium derived from higher ground by slope washing. In some areas, shallow test pits revealed interbedded sand and mixed sand and gravel. Weak to very strong soil development was observed with hard caliche nodules occurring in some of the more strongly developed soils. On these low-gradient hamadas, shallow drainages or runnels are either very few or absent.

The second type of stony desert surface recognized in the area, here called a lag hamada, consists of relatively flat to low rounded surfaces formed by an armor of pebbles or shingle over either windblown sand or underlying rock. Usually the pebbles are evenly spaced (Figure A6.6b) and in places they are roughly aligned with the dominant wind direction. They may be angular to well rounded, depending on whether the source is the underlying deposit or lagged stream-rounded gravels from sources no longer evident. In the case of bedrock fragments or shingle, the lag is composed of the last vestige of a bedrock high, which is reflected by the concentration of angular or platy fragments

of identical lithology, commonly silicified and ferruginized (Figure A6.5a). Excavation commonly reveals bedrock a few centimeters below. The bedrock is overlain by a mixture of windblown sand and rock fragments. Soil development is again weak to strong, and in the western edge of the mapped area a lag hamada of caliche nodules from the underlying soil (Figure A6.4b) contains local concentrations of wind-faceted, Late Acheulian artifacts.

In some areas, particularly to the west between Bir Kiseiba and Bir Nakhlai, the surface lag of black, silicified, manganiferous (?) shingle is underlain by very soft, powdery, prismatic salt (presumably calcium sulfate) soil, developed in shale and in which moving vehicles can sink to the axle without warning. It is not known whether this natric horizon is derived from weathering of evaporites within bedrock, or whether it is the result of the evaporation of a former lake over the shale. Because such evaporites are not common in the Nubia Formation, the latter is more likely to be true.

SAND SHEETS

Another type of surficial deposit of the area is the sand sheet. These essentially eolian deposits occur on flat, nearly level surfaces such as the large area of lag hamada in the western part of the mapped area, on playa floors, and in flat areas of Nubia sandstone. Around Nabta Playa, alluvial hamadas to the north and east grade into sand sheets covering the playa floor (Figure A6.4c), suggesting alluvial transport for some of the sand. Lithologically, the sand sheets are composed of medium to coarse sand interbedded with fine pebble layers and armored by fine pebbles, in some places evenly spaced apart. Soils observed on sand sheets are weak to moderately developed red desert soils (Figure A6.6c). Sand sheets provide the best surface for motoring in the desert, but under certain, little understood conditions, they can grade into sand ripples with amplitudes of up to .5 m, rendering the ground hazardous for traverse by motor vehicle. In areas near the Gilf el Kebir, some large ripples were seen to be truncated without the intervening troughs being filled.

A relatively large area (about 500 km²) of sand sheet in

the triangle formed by Bir Kiseiba, Bir Ayed, and Bir Nakhlai is over 1 m thick and contains a weak to moderately developed, coarse prismatic paleosol, under a fine pebble to coarse sand armor. The section consists of interbedded silty, medium to fine sand and fine pebble to coarse sand layers. Farther west, on the Atmur el Kibeish, extensive areas of sand sheet coalesce between Bir Tarfawi and Bir Misaha, thus forming the northern extension of the Great Selima sand sheet in northern Sudan (Bagnold 1931). A test pit between Bir Kiseiba and Bir Tarfawi revealed fine pebble armor, over 15 cm of pale yellow, soft, laminated, fine pebbles and medium to fine sand with prismatic structure, and over 30 cm of the same without pedogenic structure (Figure A6.6c). A smooth, sharp contact separated this from at least 20 cm of firm, yellowish brown, clayey, medium to coarse sand with dispersed 1 mm flecks of calcium carbonate. This sequence clearly indicates a buried paleosol within the sand sheet. The "old mud surface" under the sand sheet described by Bagnold (1941: 244) was probably a truncated paleosol.

CHALCEDONY-ARMORED MUDSTONES

Several basins in the Nabta area contain mudstones armored with nodules of drusy quartz and chalcedony that, by means of delation, have become concentrated on the surface, forming a lag deposit protecting the underlying mudstone from further erosion. In most places these deposits form rounded surfaces of positive but low relief and are thus topographically inverted (Figure A6.6d).

The nodules range from a few millimeters to, in extreme

cases, as much as 20 cm in diameter and occur in a matrix of maroon kaolinite (?) and mixed layer clays high in soluble noncarbonate calcium and sodium salts (Table A6.1) with a strong sodium chloride taste. The upper few decimeters are invariably soft and powdery due to the high content of efflorescent salts constituting a strong natric horizon (Figure A6.4d).

The character and occurrence of these sedimentary silica

Table A6.1
Chemical Analyses of Sediments from the Nabta Area, Western Desert, Egypt[a]

Sample number	Provenance[b]	Distilled water wash (mg/g sample)				1M HCl wash (mg/g sample)				Combined H₂O and HCl washes (mg/g sample)					pH	Mineralogy[c]	Remarks
		Ca	Mg	Na	K	Ca	Mg	Na	K	Ca	Mg	Na	K	% CO₃²⁻ by Weight			
5 Eg G77	Salts in green clay on alluvial hamada	4.836	0.445	5.641	0.330	28.604	2.000	2,470 / 0.173	1.139	33.440	2.445	8.111 / 5.814	1.469	2.24	7.33	Carbonate, halite (?), anhydrite (?), mixed-layer clay > kaolinite	Bedrock clay with salts from evaporation of Nabta Playa
6 Eg G77	Green clay under alluvial hamada	4.516	0.351	4.085	0.203 / 0.136	27.430	1.570	0.233 / 0.366	0.782	31.946	1.921	4.318 / 4.415	0.985 / 0.918	0.690	7.75	Smectite > kaolinite, trace carbonate	Bedrock clay with salts from evaporation of Nabta Playa
13 Eg G77	Soil on Granitic alluvial hamada	6.153	0.879 / 0.160	20.698	0.005	45.152	5.174	0.207	1.155	51.305	6.053 / 5.334	20.905	1.160	8.49	7.34	Smectite > kaolinite, anhydrite, carbonates and quartz	Salts derived from evaporation of Nabta Playa
14 Eg G77	Salts in beach gravel at Beid Playa	5.838	0.579	12.69	0.218	3.004	0.768	0.154	0.150	8.842	1.347	12.84	0.368		8.23	Kaolinite > smectite, carbonate	Salts derived from evaporation of Beid Playa
16 Eg G77	Beid Playa sediment	0.945	0.111	2.704	0.0493	3.911	0.529	0.0438	0.211	4.856	0.640	2.748	0.260		8.08	Kaolinite > smectite mixed layer clay carbonate	Salts derived from evaporation of Beid Playa
18 Eg G77	Kortein Playa sediment	1.06	0.157	2.986	0.0257	5.907	1.09	1.27	0.163	6.97	1.25	4.26	0.189	0.637	7.68	Kaolinite > smectite mixed layer clay carbonate	Salts derived from evaporation of Kortein Playa
19 Eg G77	Nabta Playa clay	0.0824	0.0186	4.037	0.0371 / 0.0284	5.301	2.091	1.945	0.903	5.383	2.110	5.982	0.940 / 0.931		8.30	Kaolinite > smectite anhydrite	Salts derived from evaporation of Nabta Playa
21 Eg G77	Nabta chalcedony deposit, surface sand	0.250	0.0233	1.282	0.127	16.183	1.201	0.107	0.591	16.433	1.224	1.389	0.718	3.93	8.04	Medium-grained quartz sand	Salts derived from evaporation of Nabta Playa
22 Eg G77	Nabta chalcedony deposit, A-Horizon	3.588	0.258	2.712	0.152	17.462	1.996	0.345	1.478	21.050	2.254	3.057	1.630	0.428	7.97	Kaolinite (?) mixed-layer clay carbonate, amorphous	Part of salts may be indigenous
23 Eg G77	Nabta chalcedony deposit, salt horizon	3.882	0.607	13.138	0.362	17.433	3.402	0.680	1.575	21.315	4.009	13.818	1.937		7.28	Kaolinite (?) mixed-layer clay amorphous	Parts of salts may be indigenous
24 Eg G77	Nabta chalcedony deposit, mudstone matrix	5.494	1.883	16.803	0.182	28.481	1.859	0.614	0.894	33.975	3.742	17.417	1.076		7.43	Quartz[a], anhydrite[a], amorphous[a]	Salts derived from evaporation of older lake
25 Eg G77	Dune sand on top of gebel nabta	0.0666	0.0085	0.338	0.0072	5.441	0.296	0.0324	0.0554	5.508	0.305	0.370	0.0626	4.45	8.26	Medium-grained quartz sand	Salts presumed to be of eolian origin

[a] Determinations by Thomas Taylor, Department of Chemistry, University of Arizona.
[b] All samples from Nabta Playa unless stated otherwise.
[c] X-Ray mineral determination by Kenneth Bladh, Department of Geosciences, University of Arizona, except 24 Eg G77 by Donna Prestel, Lockheed.

nodules are similar those of chert nodules described from the Pliocene Rome beds in Oregon (Sheppard and Gude 1974) and from Lake Magadi, Kenya (Eugster 1967). It is likely that they have similar origins and formed in water high in sodium carbonate and silica with a pH of 9.5 or higher. Similar deposits have been mapped along the ancient caravan route (Darb el Arbain) north of Bir Murr (Issawi 1971) and the question arises whether they are a facies of the Nubia Formation or of much younger (Quaternary) age. A variegated, dark reddish-brown and olive-green shale is known to occur at the top of the Nubia Formation in the Kharga–Dakhla area (Hermina *et al.* 1961) and 5 m of similar shale occurs in a similar stratigraphic position in exposures around Bir Abu el Hussein (Issawi 1971). High concentrations of salts and chalcedony are not reported from these occurrences, but the

chalcedony-armored mudstones along the Darb el Arbain and those in the Nabta area could be vestiges of Nubia variegated shale protected by the lag concentrate. Another possibility is that the salt and silica formed later as evaporites in a basin developed within the shale during post-Pliocene time (after destruction of the limestone plateau in this area), or possibly both mudstone and nodules formed in lakes of Quaternary age. The fact that the nodules have not been observed in place under the Dakhla Formation and the lack of concentrated evaporites in the variegated shale suggest the last two hypotheses to be the more plausible, in which case the nodules constitute a special type of lag hamada and would represent inverted playas. The high clay content of the Nabta Playa deposits is likely derived from the chalcedony-armored claystone that occurs in the northern part of the basin (Figure A6.3).

HOLOCENE PLAYAS

Many basins of the Nabta area contain playa deposits of Terminal Paleolithic and Neolithic age ranging in composition from clay to sand; others contain mixtures of alluvium and eolian sand that very likely overlie lacustrine beds.

The youngest playa deposit observed in any detail is that of a shallow basin 10 km southeast of Gebel Nabta (Figure A6.3). This, Nabta Playa, consists of a brown (7.5YR 5/4) expanding clay (kaolinite < smectite < mixed layer) with soft white irregular nodules of powdery anhydrite (?) and shrinkage cracks producing a polygonal pattern (1 m or so in diameter) on the basin floor (Figure A6.7a) in which the clay is exposed over an area of approximately 10 km². In the absence of shore features and adequate topographic maps for the area, the limits of the basin and its depth cannot be accurately determined, but we would estimate the catchment area to be at least 20 times that of the exposed clay floor, which varies from 172 to 178 m in elevation. How much playa clay lies hidden by slope wash and eolian sand is unknown, but test trenches and auger holes reveal as much as 2 m or more of playa clay over either ancient dune sand or greenish gray shale of the Nubia Formation. Relief on the deflated surface of playa clay is in excess of 6 m and in places thicknesses of this order may have been removed by deflation, which continues at the present time. During sandstorms, sand-size particles of playa clay were observed in motion and accumulated in sand ripples and in barchan dunes on the playa floor, thus forming clay dunes (Figure A6.7b).

At Nabta Playa Site E-75-6 the lacustrine clay overlies dune sand (Figure A6.7a) that is mottled orange and brown to black by hydrated iron and manganese oxides and is weakly cemented by silica deposited upon evaporation of the lake waters. Today the clay floor of the playa is relatively flat, but it slopes upward toward higher ground and contains low mounds of playa clay armored by stones of ancient camp fires. A local relief of as much as 4 m is

evident and is partly due to deflation. Further evidence of deflation is the fact that the ancient dunes underlying the clay are now exposed as geologic windows (Figure A6.7c). One of the ancient dunes stands 3 m above the playa floor yet has remnants of playa clay near the top, clearly indicating that the lake waters once inundated the sand dune, which must have been an island part of the time. Several areas around the base of the exposed dunes are now deflated to a depth of as much as 1 m below the clay floor, but test pits and auger holes excavated through the clay a few meters away from where it thins out against the exposed dune revealed as much as 2 m of clay. This suggests that the ancient slopes of the old dunes are preserved in at least some places, but proof of this is the fact that archaeological features, including hearths and pits with numerous artifacts of Terminal Paleolithic aspect, are remarkably well preserved below the playa clay and on the contact with the cemented dune sand (Wendorf *et al.* 1976, 1977). The iron and manganese that stain the sand also stain fragments of bone and ostrich eggshell associated with the human occupation.

In addition to the microlithic artifacts of the Terminal Paleolithic occupation, exposed portions of the old dune are littered with Neolithic artifacts that are found below the playa clay in features that were dug through the earlier occupation surface (Wendorf *et al.* 1976, 1977). Many Neolithic artifacts occur on the exposed surface of the old dune, but are somewhat dispersed by wind action. Some are remarkably evenly spaced (Figure A6.7d). Some concentrations, especially of hearthstones or *salats*, are sufficiently tight to act as armor, thus inhibiting deflation. These concentrations appear as low mounds in which test pits reveal a weakly to moderately developed red desert soil.

Three kilometers east of the eastern edge of Barqat el Shab, a small basin of 1 km² or less in catchment contains remnants of a playa deposit composed of silty sand, dis-

FIGURE A6.7. *Geomorphic features of the Gebel Nabta area: (a) deflated clay floor of Nabta Playa shows polygonal cracks; Terminal Paleolithic and Neolithic artifacts occur on ancient dune under the playa clay and exposed by deflation at Site E-75-6 (where figures are mapping); (b) barchan dune on Nabta Playa is accumulating sand-size clay aggregates derived from deflation of the playa and forming dark streaks on the slip slope; (c) floor of Nabta Playa with a procession of active barchans on top and ancient dune-sand below where exposed by deflation; broken ground in distance defines the western margin of the playa clay; (d) a completely deflated archaeological site near Barqat el Shab displays hearthstones and artifacts evenly dispersed by wind. The degree of abrasion shown on Neolithic artifacts from deflated sites is less than that shown on Middle Paleolithic artifacts, and considerably less than that on Late Acheulian artifacts.*

playing numerous casts of plant roots, which suggests deposition of eolian sand in a vegetated, wet depression or marsh (Figure A6.8a). Today, less than 20% of the fill remains as deflational remnants adhering to the periphery of the basin, which will be referred to as Barqat el Shab Playa.

Playa deposits similar to both the Nabta Playa mudstone and the Barqat el Shab Playa sand occur at about 190 m in a small basin 4 km south of Gebel Nabta at the toe of the alluvial slope extending radially away from the mountains.

Playa sands with numerous root casts occur around the southern periphery of this basin, which we shall call Nusub ("monolith") Playa because of a prominent blocky outcrop farther south, and mudstone similar to that of Nabta Playa occurs in the central portion. Although continuity between the two could not be established, it is likely that the sand is a littoral facies of the mudstone.

Recent mudcracks and dead tamarisk mounds in the lowest parts of this basin are clear evidence that runoff accumulated here in the recent past (Figure A6.8b). Today the nearest living vegetation is at Bir Nakhlai and Bir Takhlis, 40 and 60 km respectively to the west (Figure A6.2). An auger hole in the lowest part of Nusub Playa encountered dry Nubian shale at 2 m, indicating that the water table there had been perched and not part of the static water table.

Even smaller remnants of playa sediments were observed in another depression approximately 8 km southeast of Gebel Nabta, giving one the impression that other depressions may have completely lost their playa deposits due to abrasion and deflation. Measurement of rates are much needed, but an estimate can be made from the situation at Nabta Playa.

One of the larger drainages from the granite highlands

FIGURE A6.8. *Geomorphic features of the Gebel Nabta area: (a) playa, clayey-sand remnants with casts of plant roots occur around the periphery of Barqat el Shab Playa; southwestern edge of Barqat el Shab visible in right background; (b) phytogenic mounds of dead Tamarix sp. and dune sand indicate shallow groundwater in recent past; (c) distinct strand is visible against a hill on the western edge of El Beid Playa; erosional remnants of playa sediments in foreground contain Terminal Paleolithic artifacts; (d) beach gravels exposed in bench on east side of El Kortein Playa display rounding by wave action and salt aggregate from evaporation.*

northeast of Nabta Playa contains two terraces that may correlate with two main Neolithic stands of the lake. This wadi is graded to the present deflated floor of the playa where a recent mudflat deposit is presently being removed by deflation. The sandblasted remnants of *kharit* bushes (cf. *Salsola baryosma*) are rooted in this clayey silt and sand and were probably germinated in response to a single storm that washed the sediment into the sub-basin and created a perched water table for a brief time.

A radiocarbon analysis of the *kharit* wood revealed 102.7 ± .5% (SMU-212) of the ^{14}C content of the modern atmosphere, indicating growth during the early part of the atomic era, about 1960–1961. The exposed roots indicate about 15 cm of deflation since then, or a rate of approximately 1 cm per year. Because of the less consolidated nature of this recent sediment compared to the Neolithic playa sediments, this can be taken as a maximum rate. A minimum rate of .07 cm per year can be estimated if we assume that 4 m of playa clay have been removed since latest Neolithic or earliest Old Kingdom time, about 5800

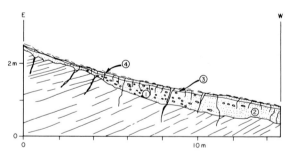

FIGURE A6.9. *Stratigraphic trench in beach along eastern strand of Kortein Playa showing (1) pale brown, silty, sandy, fine to medium, subrounded, pebble gravel with crystalline aggregates of Na and Ca salts and interbedded with (2) pale brown, clayey, sandy, soft-fine sand with dispersed pebbles; (3) pale brown, laminated, pebbley, soft-fine to medium sand with coarse prismatic to platey structure and white salt films on clasts and overlain by (4) shingle lag of dark brown to black angular fragments of flaggy sandstone. Bedrock is made up of brown, white, and gray, flaggy, soft, friable sandstone gradational up slope to fissile, very soft to powdery shale with numerous white crystalline aggregates of Na and Ca salts. Beach deposits are truncated by a recessional scarp a few meters west of the section.*

BP. The actual rate for Nabta Playa is probably between these values.

To the north–northeast of Gebel Nabta, 18 and 27 km, are two playas, Kortein and Beid respectively, where beach features were first recognized as strand lines at the base of some hills (Figure A6.8c). Trenching reveals subrounded to subangular pebble gravels with platy clasts lying parallel to the beach surface and overlying rotten, salt-impregnated, Nubia Sandstone (Figures A6.8d and A6.9). Crystalline aggregates of calcium and sodium salts occur in the beach deposits. Elevations can only be estimated from the 10-m contour maps available, but the Beid beach appears to be at least about 160 m, and Kortein, about 175 m, with neither elevation closing around the respective playa deposits. Either the enclosures have been breached by erosion or much larger bodies of water existed than the present extent of playa deposits would indicate. A major part of subsequent research in the Kiseiba–Dungul depression will have to be directed to this critical question.

EOLIAN FEATURES

Moving from north to south across the Nabta area today are several processions of barchan dunes (Figure A6.7c). Those that have crossed to the southern part of Nabta Playa were seen in 1975 to acquire sand-size clay aggregates particularly prevalent on the slip face (Figure A6.7b). Comparison of their positions on the playa floor in 1974 with aerial photographs taken in 1962 indicated remarkably little change during 12 years. However, the 1974 positions were based not upon aerial photography but upon measurement from reference outcrops using an automobile and speedometer. It is possible, therefore, that a whole new procession of barchans has displaced earlier ones, and that we could not distinguish the difference on the ground. Between March 1975 and March 1977 one dune had moved

FIGURE A6.10. *Geomorphic features of the Gebel Nabta area: (a) test pit on shingle-armored slope reveals interbedded eolian sand, sandy shingle, and buried soil; (b) outcrop of sandblasted sandstone (Nubia Formation) at El Kortein Playa reveals protuberances protected by more resistant, concretionary masses; (c) Neolithic wells at Nabta Playa Site E-75-7 were filled with backdirt, eolian sand, and mud of the second playa phase; (d) soil exposed in spoil pile at the 3000–2000 B.C. Chephren quarry reveals significant pedogenesis.*

at least 30 m. Sand drifts against some hills and scarps are common, and a few sief dunes occur on the lee side of hills. Sand sheets, as mentioned previously, cover parts of Nabta Playa floor and grade into alluvial hamadas. particularly to the northwest.

Eolian sand is ubiquitous, and all colluvial slopes upon excavation reveal layers of colluvium, commonly shingle-like, interbedded with pure eolian sand (Figure A6.10a). Buried red desert soils are common and the sequences indicate cycles of colluvial and eolian deposition during presumably hyperarid climates separated by more stable conditions, presumably during periods of greater rainfall (pluvials).

The coherence of buried dunes, Neolithic to pre-Neolithic in age, ranges from loose, unconsolidated sand to firm sand, weakly cemented with various combinations of hydrated iron and manganese oxides, silica, and calcium carbonate, but some patches of sand near the top of an exposed pre-Neolithic dune near Site E-75-6 are firmly cemented by silica and small amounts of $CaCO_3$. The silicification is probably derived from highly alkaline lake water during Neolithic time, and an apparent radiocarbon age of $21,590 \pm 180$ BP (SMU-207) for the carbonate is attributed to wind-borne limestone dust, as the Chephren quarry (described later).

Practically all hard rock surfaces and exposed artifacts show some degree of eolian abrasion, but scoured, fluted, or faceted surfaces are restricted to certain areas, apparently where sources of sand and aerodynamic factors are more conducive than others (Figure A6.10b). Many artifacts have become ventifacts, with the oldest ones (Acheulian and Mousterian) being the most strongly faceted. Neolithic artifacts are commonly wind polished but few, if any, show wind faceting.

Remarkable features are areas where pebbles occur essentially equally spaced upon a surface of windblown sand (Figure A6.6b). This phenomenon has been in part explained by Bagnold (1941), but in the Nabta area the spacing between pebbles appears to be a function of diameter, with cobble-size particles being spaced as much as 30 cm apart (Figure A6.7d).

On top of Gebel Nabta the fluting of the limestone mentioned previously may be a product of the past, because cairns of limestone boulders constructed at least 40 years

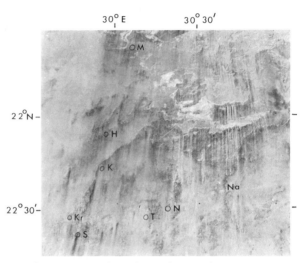

FIGURE A6.11. *LANDSAT photograph (E-1110-07570, November 10, 1972) of the Kiseiba–Dungul depression showing Gebel Nabta (Na), Bir Nakhlai (N), Bir Takhlis (T), Bir Sheb (S), Bir Kurayim (Kr), Bir Kiseiba (K), Bir Abu el Hussein (H), and Bir Murr (M). The Kiseiba escarpment extending northeast–southwest from Bir Kiseiba is plainly visible, with the Atmur el Kibeish to the west. The possible maximum outline of Nabta Playa is outlined, with a broken line indicating the more uncertain boundary. Wind streaks are best defined in areas of alternating sand accumulation and denudation.*

ago show no detectable sandblasting. (One was reconstructed by Issawi in 1965; personal communication.) One wonders if the top of a hill may be removed from more active sandblasting by isolation and the increase in relief as erosion lowers the ground around it. Only relatively minor scouring occurs on the stone-and-mortar block houses at Bir Nakhlai, which were apparently constructed in 1894 to guard the water source from the dervishes. Mortar on the northern corners has receded about 5 cm.

Throughout the area, the more obvious wind effects seem to be confined to relatively long, narrow zones or streaks aligned with the prevailing north wind. These streaks are quite apparent on LANDSAT photographs and appear to be uniformly spaced (Figure A6.11). It may be instructive in future work to determine how wind velocities are related to them.

GEOCHRONOLOGY

The absolute age of the playa deposit in the Nabta area can now be assessed on the basis of radiocarbon dates on charcoal and ostrich eggshell, but the relative ages of older deposits can only be estimated on the basis of soil development, stratigraphy, and archaeology. A proposed sequence is shown in Figure A6.12, in which the earlier part of the record is in part determined from previous work (Wendorf *et al.* 1976, 1977).

Charcoal and ostrich eggshell are the two most common materials from archaeological sites suitable for radiocarbon dating, and ^{14}C analysis of several pairs of these samples demonstrated that the eggshell is as reliable as charcoal provided it comes from a buried context and is carefully pretreated to remove altered or exchanged layers. Samples from the surface lag, on the other hand, commonly yield radiocarbon dates that are consistently too young by 300 to

DEPOSIT	CONDITION	OCCUPATION	^{14}C AGE IN YEARS B.P.
Wetted dunes	Perched water table (?)	Neolithic III	5000 – 5500
Interbedded Clay and sand	Playa edge	Neolithic II	6700 – 7200 (8 dates)
Dune sand	Deflation	None	
Sheet-wash sand Under clay	Dug wells filled first with sand and then with playa clay	Neolithic I	
Interbedded Sheet-wash Sand and clay	Playa edge		8000 – 8300 (11 dates)
Interbedded Dune sand and clay	Dune stabilization & Rising playa	Terminal Paleolithic	8800 – 9400 (6 dates)
Dune sand	Deflation	None	
Marl & Silt	Pond or Marsh	Aterian	30,870±1000 (SMU-75) >44,700 (SMU-79)
Dune sand	Deflation	?	
Marl	Pond or Marsh	Mousterian	32,780±900 (SMU-80) 40,710±3270 (SMU-82) >41,500 (SMU-81)
Soil	Stability		28,000±1250 (SMU-108)
Oxidized peat	Marsh		37,740±1980 (SMU-95)
Dune sand	Deflation	None	
Calcrete & Feeder sand	Spring Discharge	Late & Final Acheulian	≧ 200,000 (estimate)
Dune sand	Deflation	None	

FIGURE A6.12. *Chart of the succession of climatic events inferred from stratigraphy, archaeology, and radiocarbon dating.*

500 years, which indicates exchange with atmospheric CO_2, probably during the few times that the shell fragments have been wetted by past rains.

Analyses of pedogenic carbonate in a spoil pile at the 4000–5000-year-old Chephren diorite quarry, discussed later, indicate eolian derivation from ancient limestone to the north. This and uncertainties regarding subsequent exchange with atmospheric CO_2 make secondary carbonates useless for radiocarbon-dating purposes.

At Nabta Playa Site E-75-6, the earliest occupation (Terminal Paleolithic) has one radiocarbon date of 9360 ± 70 BP (SMU-200) on charcoal from a concentration in dune sand that underlies playa mud. It is assumed that this dates an early stage of playa lake formation, when people were living on dunes where interdunal ponds were forming (Figure A6.13). Subsequent work in the Kiseiba area has revealed numerous hearths of Terminal Paleolithic occupations dating from 9100 to 8700 BP associated with playa lake

deposits. These, and similar dates from Kortein and El Beid playas, clearly indicate the Terminal Paleolithic period of this part of the Western Desert to be between 9400 and 8700 BP.

The first Neolithic (I) occupation at Nabta Playa, during a rising lake phase, occurred between 8300 and 8000 radiocarbon years ago, on the basis of analyses on charcoal and shell (Figures A6.12 and A6.13).

At Nabta Site E-75-8, on a low sandy ridge 2.8 km northwest of Site E-75-6, a middle Neolithic (II) occupation was found in dune deposits overlying eroded playa mud of the earlier pluvial phase and related to a younger one (Wendorf *et al.* 1976, 1977). Here eight radiocarbon analyses date the second Neolithic (II) occupation at between 7000 and 6300 BP. Approximately 200 m east of Site E-75-8, at Site E-75-7, prehistoric wells were found that had been dug through the earlier playa muds in order to obtain water during a period when the playa had dried up.

FIGURE A6.13. *Generalized, composite cross section of Nabta Playa archaeological sites showing (1) ancient dune with Terminal Paleolithic (TP) and first Neolithic (N I) occupations, interbedded with playa clay (2), unconformably overlain by dune sand with second Neolithic (N II) occupation interbedded with younger playa clay (4), unconformably overlain by dune sand (5). The prehistoric well at the left was dug sometime during the hiatus between (2) and (3), and was filled first by eolian sand of deposition (3) and then by clay of deposition (4). A third Neolithic occupation occurred in association with playa silt (Figure A6.12).*

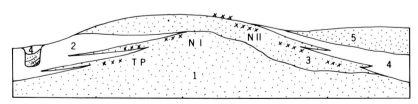

GENERALIZED GEOLOGIC CROSS SECTION OF NABTA PLAYA

NUBIAN DESERT, EGYPT

(No Scale)

The wells were subsequently filled with windblown sand followed by muds of the second playa phase (Figure A6.10). Since the end of the Neolithic I occupation, deflation of at least 2 m of playa clay has occurred, and it is apparent that the cycle occurred again during the Neolithic II occupation. During the arid interim, people at Site E-75-7 were making use of wells as much as 3 m deep, presumably trying to extend their stay in the area after the first lake had dried up. Subsequent work at E-75-8 has produced evidence of a third Neolithic (III) phase dating between 6300 and 5800 BP (see Chapter 3).

The age of Barqat el Shab Playa relative to Nabta Playa is not certain. It may antedate the Neolithic, since artifact concentrations of this period occur over the deflational floor. The fact that the playa sands are more blown out than the Nabta clay may not be temporally significant because of the differences between the two lithologies (friable sand is more easily eroded than clay), but tooth fragments of African warthog (*Phacochoerus* sp.) and a very large rodent from the top of the Barqat el Shab Playa sand suggest that it may be older. These forms do not occur at Nabta Playa, and *Phacochoerus* sp. is not found even on the fringes of the desert today, as the elements of the fauna from the Nabta Playa sites are (A. Gautier, personal communication).

The relative ages of the other Quaternary deposits can only be estimated, but it is apparent that a detailed investigation of soils in relation to geomorphic surfaces would help to establish a relative chronology. In order better to assess the relative age of paleosols a special trip was made to a Second to Twelfth Dynasty site where metadiorite for statues found in the tomb of Chephren was quarried 4000–5000 years ago. The Chephren quarry, rediscovered in 1936 (Murray 1939), is located 70 km northeast of Gebel Nabta and about 70 km west of the Nile. Soils developed on a spoil pile provided a useful index of what pedogenesis under the climate of the past 4000 years should look like (Figure A6.10d). Beneath a veneer of windblown sand was a layer of soft vesicular silty sand 1–2 cm thick, over 6 cm of mixed, pale, reddish brown, weak platy, soft, silty sand and rock fragments, over 18 cm of very pale brown (white), calcareous, coarse prismatic, soft, silty sand with more rock fragments, over light brown, laminated, eolian sand.

The nearest carbonate rocks are on the Eocene plateau 50 km to the north and the metadiorite is practically unweathered. A sample of the soil was hydrolyzed in HCl, and the released CO_2 was analyzed for radiocarbon to determine if the source for the calcium carbonate was limestone dust. The apparent age for the Ca-horizon of 24,680 BP ± 330 years (SMU-210) clearly indicates the plateau as the source, with subsequent exchange with atmospheric CO_2 brought in by the infrequent rains of the past 4000 years.

Late Holocene soils of the Nabta area show very weak to moderate development of calcic red desert soils commonly with weak, platy, vesicular horizons over a coarse, prismatic horizon and with small, dispersed, crystalline aggregates of salts. The Chephren quarry soil is intermediate in this qualitative range. Similar but more strongly developed soils on hamadas are undoubtedly older and therefore of early Holocene age and older. Older still are the truncated red soils with strong calcic horizons of nodular caliche. The strongest of these wind-scoured petrocalcic horizons forms the surface upon which wind-faceted Acheulian and Middle Stone Age artifacts were found in a lag hamada of rounded gravels. In field jargon, we refer to this as the "Acheulian" surface. Similar petrocalcic horizons occur above the Kiseiba scarp on the Atmur el Kibeish and for tens of kilometers around Bir Tarfawi–Bir Sahara, 100 km west of Bir Kiseiba. All of these truncated exposures appear to be parts of an ancient land surface that extended from below the Gilf el Kebir to the Nile Valley in Late Acheulian times. By Mousterian times, significant deflational basins had formed in it as revealed at Bir Tarfawi and Bir Sahara (Wendorf *et al.* 1976, and 1977), and by Terminal Paleolithic times most of this surface east of the Kiseiba scarp had been destroyed. The ancient calcic soils in the limestone alluvial fans of Gebel Nabta (described earlier) may be the same age as the "Acheulian" surface or older, and both may be correlated in a general way with the upper and lower sheet gravels of the Kharga escarpment (Caton-Thompson 1952: 5).

Older still are the red soils on inverted wadi gravels that occur on ridges (Figure A6.1b) standing at or above the elevations of the chalcedony-armored mudstones, but chert nodules in the gravel are apparently reworked from them. The stream gravels and the relatively strong red soil developed on them are, therefore, younger than the armored playas. Despite careful searching, no Middle or Early Paleolithic artifacts were found in the gravels, which are composed mostly of subrounded to well-rounded medium pebbles to medium cobbles of quartzite and white quartz, but several quartz pebbles show edges formed by three or more scars where flakes were removed from alternate edges (Figure A6.14). Without more evidence it is not possible to

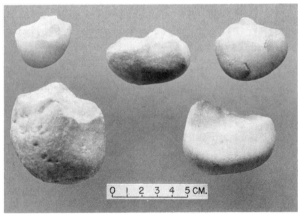

FIGURE A6.14. *Possible pebble tools from inverted wadi gravels east of Gebel Nabta (see Figure A6.3).*

tell if these are pebble tools, but it is likely that the inverted wadis are older than the calcified Acheulian surface west of Gebel Nabta, because the rounded gravels let down on that surface are probably derived from the destruction of the inverted wadis. In any case, the inverted wadis indicate the former existence of a drainage system that included meandering streams similar to those observed by Giegengack (1968) near the Nile. Since that time, presumably no later than middle Pleistocene, drainages were never again integrated, and the present geomorphic configuration of the Western Desert had formed. Climatic oscillations since the Late Acheulian have been from arid conditions, when deflation and sandblasting scoured out depressions and formed dune fields, to pluvial conditions when internally drained basins filled with playa lakes and other lakes developed from a rising water table. Because of the abundance of clay in playa sediments, implying some degree of filtering of slope wash, and the weak to moderate soils, the latest pluvial conditions undoubtedly were attended by more extensive vegetation and by stabilized dunes, much as in semiarid central Sudan today. However, there was insufficient time and precipitation in late Quaternary pluvial cycles to reestablish an integrated drainage system.

The chalcedony-armored clays, many of which were under the water of the Neolithic lakes, display very strong postdeflational soil development (Figure A6.4d) in all cases, and the geochemical conditions under which sufficient silica was carried in solution to develop quartz and chert nodules required climatic conditions in the past that have not affected later playas to the same degree. Because there is no obvious volcanic or hydrothermal source, the movement of silica in solution indicated by the chalcedony–quartz nodules may be related to conditions under which silica enters solution via pedogenesis such as occurs with lateritic soils. No relicts of this type of soil are observed in the area, but red ferrocretes and pisolitic deposits have been observed on top of the Gilf el Kebir plateau and elsewhere in the higher regions to the west and south and have been interpreted as relicts of very old lateritic soils (Sandford 1935). If such a relationship existed it must have been very early relative to the inverted wadis, the deflated petrocalcic horizons, and the higher alluvial fans with petrocalcic horizons, on Gebel Nabta. Even though there is no direct stratigraphic evidence, the sum of the geomorphic and pedogenic evidence suggests that the chalcedony-armored claystones are the oldest Pleistocene (?) deposits of the Nabta area. As mentioned previously, it is also possible that the chalcedony resulted from the action of a highly saline lake on bedrock shale, and the possibility of a purely bedrock origin, though unlikely, cannot be ruled out.

SUMMARY OF QUATERNARY EVENTS AND LANDFORM DEVELOPMENT

What is probably the oldest Quaternary event in the Western Desert can only be inferred, but it appears to have been the destruction of the limestones over the depressions by alternating solution and eolian abrasion in earliest Pleistocene, or even Pliocene, times. Recent observations on the Eocene plateau between Kharga and the Nile Valley reveal the presence of remnants of *terra rosa* soils, some in excess of 2 m thick, in solution pipes and cavities (Haynes n.d.). Much of this soil (there may be more than one episode of pedogenesis represented) has been destroyed by eolian abrasion, which has scoured and fluted the limestone on a scale ranging from small flutes and protrusions to megaflutes forming parallel valleys between yardangs of porous limestone. The process is still going on at present, but the evidence for multiple episodes of solution is the occurrences of spring-laid sheets of tufa reported by Caton-Thompson and Gardner (1932) at various elevations up to 40 m below the scarp in the Kharga depression. No artifacts were found in the highest plateau tufa, and "Acheulio-Levalloisan" artifacts occur in the tufa terraces formed by seepage from the limestone. It is clear, therefore, that the Kharga depression had begun to form well before Acheulian times and had been deepened to very near its present depth by Late Acheulian time as indicated by archaeological sites in ancient spring vents on the floor of the depression (Caton-Thompson and Gardner 1932). Similar sites occurred in the Dakhla depression (Schild and Wendorf 1977). It is likely that isolation of the Gilf el Kebir plateau began at essentially the same time because Late Acheulian sites occur in an alluvial fan deposit considerably below the level of the plateau (Myers n.d.).

The limestone on Gebel Nabta, as mentioned earlier, has eolian abrasion features superimposed over solution features, but no vestige of *terra rosa* soil remains—presumably because of lowering below the extent of pedogenesis. Following what must have been a long period of land lowering, probably including several climatic oscillations, lakes formed in the lowest parts of the depressions, the earliest of which may be the chalcedony-armored mudstones. No artifacts have been found in association with these deposits, and as mentioned previously they appear to be pre-Acheulian.

At a later time of unknown age, meandering streams crossed the area and may have been integrated with the Nile Valley. No definitive artifacts have been found in the inverted wadi gravel unless the chipped pebbles mentioned earlier are tools. Acheulian artifacts have been found in gravels of inverted wadis in the Nile Valley (Giegengack 1968).

Early Acheulian sites are not known from the Western Desert, but Late Acheulian artifacts are relatively common and associated with the calcic horizon on the Atmur el

Kibeish and the "Acheulian" surface near Nabta. At this time, the Kiseiba escarpment may not have existed, at least with its present height, and the general relief may have been less than it is today. The earliest alluvial fans on Gebel Nabta are compatible with this interpretation.

During each of the aforesaid episodes, a climatic regime considerably more moist than that of today is assumed. The chalcedony–mudstone beds imply highly alkaline, lacustrine conditions and, therefore, an arid or semiarid climate with sparse vegetation; otherwise the high pH conditions required for the movement of silica could not be maintained. The well-rounded gravels and meandering pattern of the inverted wadis indicate significant fluvial action, the likes of which have not been seen again in the Western Desert. But the climate need not have been vastly wetter, because meandering wadis with rounded gravels are common in the Eastern Desert today (Murray 1951). The climate there is only arid instead of hyperarid.

During Late Acheulian time the abundance of artesian springs at Kharga, Dakhla, Bir Tarfawi, and Bir Tarfawi West indicates a piezometric surface many meters higher than that of today, implying considerably more recharge to the Nubian aquifer than in late Quaternary times.

Between these implied wet phases, the climate is presumed to have been at least as hyperarid as today, with eolian processes being dominant (Murray 1951), but the only evidence for this interpretation is the occurrence of dune sand stratigraphically below the Acheulian spring sites at Bir Tarfawi and Bir Tarfawi West. For the earlier episodes, there is no evidence, but deflation is most likely to have been the cause of the former basins holding the chalcedony–mudstone deposits, and of the topographic inversion of the wadi gravels.

Post-Acheulian deflation led to the formation of basins at Bir Tarfawi and Bir Tarfawi West, and subsequent wet conditions led to first a marsh and then a pond phase, both of which attracted Mousterian people and game animals of Central Africa to the area. The occurrence of similar Mousterian archaeology with clayey sand deposits at the Dyke site, some 100 km north-northeast of Bir Tarfawi, indicates true pluvial conditions in the area during Mousterian times, and probably Aterian as well, as opposed to simply a higher static water table due to reduced evaporation and/or recharge in the mountainous areas of Chad.

Following the Aterian occupation at Bir Tarfawi, a period of hyperaridity set in, which appears to have lasted for at least 20,000 years. This conclusion is based upon the fact that the area is devoid of any evidence of habitation by man or animals, and that dune sand is the only deposit of this period in the stratigraphic record. During this time, corresponding to late Pleistocene glaciation in northern latitudes, eolian processes were predominant almost to the exclusion of all others, and the Western Desert took on the ultrasandblasted and deflated character that is so manifest today.

The only interruption in the eolian modification of the Western Desert since Aterian time has been the relatively brief pluvial episodes of the Holocene. Beginning with Terminal Paleolithic occupation of the area about 9500 BP, many localized basins and interdunal low areas became vegetated and faunal elements similar to those of northern Sudan appeared. Ephemeral lakes appeared in many areas of the Western Desert (Haynes et al. 1977) between 8000 and 8300 BP, with associated Neolithic occupation and domesticated animals, and again between 6200 and 7000 BP with what appears to be domestic barley. A relatively brief period of about a millennium separates the two Neolithic occupations. Deflation and dune migration during this period are revealed by an erosional contact with considerable relief on the lower playa clays at Nabta, and by eolian sand between the two playa deposits. A third phase of Neolithic occupation indicated at Nabta Playa is associated with very sandy playa deposition between 5800 and 6200 BP and is followed by the hyperarid conditions that persist today.

The pluvial chronology of Nabta Playa and other basins in the area shows fluctuations of Holocene lake levels that are similar to those of East Africa and Chad (Butzer et al. 1972). The Nabta lake starts later and the final phase appears to have been of smaller magnitude and ended sooner than Lake Chad, presumably because the precipitation in the Nabta area was less than in the Chad basin during the pluvial phases as well as today.

In historic times, the only occupation of the Western Desert has been through the use of wells with artesian flow in the main oases, and of walk-in wells at abyar mainly used by caravans. There is some indication of minor, but significant, climatic fluctuations since Neolithic times in the form of scattered small sites of the Old Kingdom and later periods in the desert. The occurrence of dead phytogenic mounds at widely scattered places in the desert indicates that watering places were more abundant at various times in the recent past than they are today (Beadnell 1931). These may have permitted travel in the remote desert before the introduction of camels, presumably by Persians about 525 BC, and the last high stand of the shallow water table may correspond to the final phases of Lake Chad, which existed between 3500 and 1000 years ago.

For the past 5000 years, eolian erosion appears to have removed much more of the playa deposits than remain today, and there is some evidence that, at times, the climate may have been even drier than it is today (Haynes et al. n.d.). Extrapolating backward in time, it is apparent that similar deposits of Mousterian and Aterian age must have been widespread in the Western Desert. It is also apparent that the geomorphic development of the Western Desert is a product of the alternation of drastically different climatic regimens: one pluvial or wet (arid or semiarid) during which lacustrine sedimentation, evaporite formation, weathering, and soil formation took place, and one hyperarid during which wind stripped the land of irregularities and of deposits created or weakened during the pluvial phases (Haynes 1977).

ACKNOWLEDGMENTS

This work was done as part of the Combined Prehistoric Expedition sponsored by Southern Methodist University, the Polish Academy of Science, and the Geological Survey of Egypt. Funds provided by the Smithsonian Institution (Foreign Currency Program grants 2423, SF 3-00101, and FR 4-60094), the National Science Foundation (grants GS-1880 and GS-36959), and the National Geographic Society are gratefully acknowledged. A special word of appreciation is expressed for R. Said, B. Issawi, M. Said, M. El Hennawi, S. Zaghloul, Ayed Marief Salim, Saleh, and other members of the Geological Survey of Egypt who made this work possible.

REFERENCES

Bagnold, R. A.
  1931 Journeys in the Libyan Desert, 1929 and 1930. *Geographical Journal* 78 (1): 13–39.
  1941 *The physics of blown sand and desert dunes.* London: Methuen.
Beadnell, H. J. L.
  1931 Zerzura. *Geographical Journal* 77: 245–250.
Butzer, K. W., G. L. Isaac, J. L. Richardson, and C. Washbourn-Kaman
  1972 Radiocarbon dating of East African lake levels. *Science* 175: 1069–1076.
Caton-Thompson, G.
  1952 *Kharga Oasis in prehistory.* London: Athlone Press.
Caton-Thompson, G., and E. W. Gardner
  1932 The prehistoric geography of Kharga Oasis. *Geographical Journal* 80: 369–409.
Eugster, H. P.
  1967 Hydrous sodium silicates from Lake Madadi, Kenya—Precursors of bedded cherts. *Science* 157: 1177–1180.
Ezzat, M. A., and A. A. A. el Atta
  1974 Groundwater series in the U.A.R., exploration of groundwater in el Wadi el-Gedid (New Valley) Project: Part II hydrologic conditions, Dakhla–Kharga area.
Giegengack, R. F., Jr.
  1968 Late Pleistocene history of the Nile Valley in Egyptian Nubia. Ph.D. dissertation, Yale University.
Haynes, C. V.
  1977 The Nubian Desert: A product of Quaternary climatic cycles. Presented to the *Planetary Geology Field Conference on Aeolian Processes,* N.A.S.A., Palm Desert, California.
  n.d. *Terra rosa* soils and solution phenomena of the Eocene limestone plateaux, Western Desert, Egypt (in preparation).
Haynes, C. V., P. J. Mehringer, Jr., and S. A. Zaghloul
  n.d. Pluvial lakes of northwestern Sudan. *Geographical Journal.*
Haynes, C. V., R. Said, and M. el Hennawi
  1977 Quaternary lakes of the Nubian desert. Presented to the *Tenth Congress, INQUA,* Birmingham.

Hermina, M., M. Ghobrial, and B. Issawi
  1961 The geology of the Dakhla area. *Geological Survey of Egypt 33:* 1–33.
Issawi, B.
  1971 Geology of Darb el Arbain, Western Desert, Egypt. *Annals of the Geological Survey of Egypt 1:* 53–92.
Myers, O. H.
  n.d. Excavations of the Lower Palaeolithic in the Gilf al Kabir region. Manuscript
Murray, G. W.
  1939 The road to Chephren's quarries. *Geographical Journal 94:* 97–114.
  1951 The Egyptian climate: An historical outline. *Geographical Journal 117:* 422–434.
Said, R.
  1962 *The geology of Egypt.* New York: Elsevier.
Sandford, K. S.
  1935 Geological observations on the northwest frontiers of the Anglo-Egyptian Sudan and the adjoining part of the southern Libyan Desert. *Quarterly Journal of the Geological Society of London 91:* 323–381.
Schild, R. and F. Wendorf
  1977 *The prehistory of Dakhla Oasis and adjacent desert.* Wroclaw: Ossolineum.
Sheppard, R. A., and A. J. Gude
  1974 Chert derived from magadiite in a lacustrine deposit near Rome, Malheur County, Oregon. *Journal Research, U.S. Geological Survey 2* (5): 625–630.
Wendorf, F., R. Schild, R. Said, C. V. Haynes, A. Gautier, and M. Kobusiewicz
  1976 The prehistory of the Egyptian Sahara. *Science 193:* 103–114.
Wendorf, F., R. Schild, R. Said, C. V. Haynes, M. Kobusiewicz, A. Gautier, N. el Hadidi, H. Wieckowska, and A. E. Close
  1977 Late Pleistocene and Recent climatic changes in the Egyptian Sahara *Geographical Journal 143* (Part II): 211–234.

7

Discussion of Radiocarbon Dates from the Western Desert

HERBERT HAAS AND C. VANCE HAYNES

All radiocarbon dates referred to in this volume are listed by site in Table A7.1.

The following discussion is an attempt to evaluate the age dates based on laboratory procedures and observations. All samples are pretreated to remove contaminants like humates or secondary carbonate deposits. The carbon content is then extracted from the sample and converted into benzene for liquid scintillation counting. This procedure has been described by Haynes and Haas (1974) and Haas (n.d.). The counting results are statistically screened by a computer program specifically adapted to the SMU ^{14}C lab

procedures that are described in Haas et al. (1978) and Meeks (n.d.).

Different types of sample materials were submitted: charcoal, organic soil (peat), ostrich eggshells, clam and snail shells, carbonaceous sediments (tufa), and potsherds. In the following discussion some of the specific dating problems of each material will be outlined; the peat radiocarbon dates will be analyzed in connection with all dating work done on Site BS-16 (Bir Sahara). Exact site descriptions including stratigraphic sequences are given elsewhere in this volume.

CHARCOAL SAMPLES

Charcoal is considered to be the most reliable material for dating. Its carbon does not exchange with the environment, and absorbed contaminants can in many cases readily be removed with inorganic chemical treatments. The strength of such treatments must be adapted to the condition of the sample.

Every charcoal sample first undergoes a rigorous treatment with hydrochloric acid to remove all carbonate contamination that postdates the origin of the charcoal. Other contaminants we attempt to remove routinely are fulvic and humic acids, which are readily absorbed by charcoal. Humic acids are soluble in base solutions such as diluted NaOH, which also dissolves organic tissue. This can pose a problem when wood used in making a fire is only partly carbonized. Although its appearance is that of charcoal the

structure seems to be made of weakened lignin holding together layers of carbon particles. An NaOH solution will rapidly destroy this lignin and what initially looked like solid pieces of charcoal decays to a very fine powder of carbon that is often very difficult to recover from the solution. Separation of this carbon and humates, if present, is even more difficult.

These difficulties were encountered with most North African charcoal samples. In order to prevent excessive sample loss, very weak NaOH solutions of .01–.05% were used in numerous "washes" through the sample, resting on a glass-fiber filter. The pH of the solution dripping from the filter was monitored and found to be neutral for several washes. The NaOH either reacted with humic acids contained in the charcoal or was retained in the charcoal itself.

Table A7.1
Radiocarbon Dates from the Western Desert

Site	Level	Cultural Association	SMU No.	Date BP[a]	$\delta^{13/12}$C Sample	$\delta^{13/12}$C Standard	Material
Bir Sahara							
15	Trench 20–50 cm	Aterian (?)	79	>44,700			*Melanoides*
15	Trench 20–50 cm	Aterian (?)	75	30,870 ± 1000			Clamshells
16	Base of diatomite	Mousterian	81	>41,450			Large shells
16	Base of diatomite	Mousterian	82	40,710 ± 3270			Smaller shells
16	Peat	Mousterian	218	33,080 ± 1120			Peat
16	Peat (top)	Mousterian	95	37,740 ± 1980			Humates
16	Peat (top)	Mousterian	108	28,000 ± 1250			Humates (?)
16	Marl found with peat	Mousterian	215	34,600 ± 970			Carbonate
13	Surface of diatomite	Mousterian	80	32,780 ± 900			*Melanoides*
Bir Tarfawi							
14	Trench 6	Aterian	177	44,190 ± 1380			*Melanoides*
14	Area N	Aterian	205	26,530 ± 470			Carbonaceous rock
14	Trench 16	Aterian	214	21,950 ± 490			Organic residue
20		Neolithic	74	4,510 ± 70			Ostrich eggshell
5		Historic	475	160 ± 100			Potsherds
5		Historic	469	440 ± 80			Potsherds
Kharga							
Trench 1	Top of mound		395	12,360 ± 120	−3		Carbonate
Trench 1	Top of mound		393	12,300 ± 100	−3		Carbonate
E-76-1,4	1 m below top of spring mound between Sites E-76-1 and E-76-4		376	5,320 ± 70			Carbonized plants
			384	5,300 ± 70			Carbonized plants
E-76-3	Trench 1, 10 cm		378	7,920 ± 90	−5.3		Tufa
E-76-3	Trench 1, 45–50 cm		385	3,600 ± 70			Charcoal
E-76-6		Terminal Paleolithic	734	7,860 ± 90			Ostrich eggshell
E-76-6		Terminal Paleolithic	326	7,850 ± 70	−3.7		Ostrich eggshell
				7,890	−3.7	−6.2	
E-76-7		Late Neolithic	741	5,450 ± 80			Ostrich eggshell
E-76-8	Deflated hearth mound	Late Neolithic	408	4,740 ± 60			Charcoal
E-76-4	Hearth top spring vent	Late Neolithic (?)	412	4,650 ± 60			Charcoal
E-76-7	Graeco-Roman playa	Graeco-Roman	383	18,500 ± 170	−6.3		Snail shells
E-76-7	Graeco-Roman yardang	Graeco-Roman	377	2,890 ± 70			Charcoal
El Beid, E-77-7	Surface/subsurface	Terminal Paleolithic	440	8,960 ± 110			Charcoal
El Kortein, E-77-3	Pit 1, hearths A + B	Terminal Paleolithic	416	8,840 ± 90			Charcoal
Nabta, E-75-6	Trench 2 m NNW of feature 100	Terminal Paleolithic (?)	200	9,360 ± 70			Charcoal
	Terminal Paleolithic cultural layer	Terminal Paleolithic (?)	257	8,290 ± 80	−7.3		Ostrich eggshell
				8,270	−7.3	−6.2	
	Pit 3, 40 cm	Neolithic	255	8,130 ± 60			Charcoal
	Pit 2, 30–40 cm	Neolithic	253	8,070 ± 90			Humates
	Pit 2, 30–40 cm	Neolithic	249	8,040 ± 90			Charcoal
	Pit 1	Neolithic	252	8,080 ± 90			Charcoal
	Pit 1, 40–45 m	Neolithic	240	7,970 ± 70			Charcoal
	Feature 132	Neolithic	208	7,930 ± 40			Charcoal
	Feature 132	Neolithic	219	8,120 ± 80			Humates extracted from SMU-208
	Feature 132	Neolithic	203	8,010 ± 80			Charcoal
	Feature 117	Neolithic	199	8,120 ± 100			Charcoal
	Feature 117	Neolithic	191	7,710 ± 70			Ostrich eggshell
	Surface	Neolithic	202	8,000 ± 110	−4.6		Ostrich eggshell
				8,020	−4.6	−6.2	
	Surface	Neolithic	189	7,910 ± 100	−7.2		Ostrich eggshell
				7,890	−7.2	−6.2	(same as SMU-202)
	Dune surface west of E-75-6		207	21,530 ± 220			Carbonate cemented sand
Nabta, E-75-8	Connecting Trench, A, B 18, Unit 2	Middle Neolithic	487	6,550 ± 80			Charcoal
	Connecting Trench, Layer 2	Middle Neolithic	452	6,570 ± 70			Charcoal
	Connecting Trench, Layer 2	Middle Neolithic	424	6,690 ± 80			Charcoal
	Connecting Trench, A 14, Layer 2	Middle Neolithic	436	14,940 ± 160			Charcoal

(continued)

Table A7.1—*Continued*

Site	Level	Cultural Association	SMU No.	Date BP[a]	$\delta^{13/12}C$ Sample	$\delta^{13/12}C$ Standard	Material
Nabta, E-75-8							
	Connecting Trench, A, B 15, 20 cm BS	Middle Neolithic	441	6,310 ± 90			Charcoal
	East Trench, 50–80 cm BS	Middle Neolithic	472	8,900 ± 80	−3.9		Snail shell
	Pit 3, 90 cm BS	Middle Neolithic	421	6,960 ± 150			Charcoal
	Pit 2, 98 cm BS	Middle Neolithic	435	6,500 ± 80			Charcoal
	Hearth 3	Middle Neolithic	373	6,880 ± 70			Charcoal
	Hearth 2 at surface	Middle Neolithic	261	6,700 ± 50			Charcoal
	Hearth 2	Middle Neolithic	368	6,500 ± 90			Charcoal
	Hearth 1	Middle Neolithic	361	6,240 ± 70			Charcoal (strong base pretreatment)
	Hearth 1	Middle Neolithic	366	6,130 ± 80			Charcoal (weak base pretreatment)
	Vertical Metate, 30–40 cm	Middle Neolithic	242	7,120 ± 150			Charcoal
	Vertical Metate, 30–40 cm	Middle Neolithic	352	6,600 ± 90 6,630	−4.6 −4.6	−6.2	Ostrich eggshell
	South Trench, 10–15 cm BS	Late Neolithic	473	5,810 ± 80			Charcoal
El Kortein							
E-77-5	0–15 cm (surface)	Late Neolithic	462	7,530 ± 180			Charcoal
E-77-5A	Upper playa silts	Late Neolithic	470	7,230 ± 100			Charcoal
Wadi Bakht		Neolithic	273	6,980 ± 80 6,970	−7.3 −7.3	−6.2	Ostrich eggshell
Chephren Quarry	in spoil-heap, below soil B-horizon		210	24,590 ± 330			Carbonaceous sand
Abu Ballas (Pottery Hill)			490	7,790 ± 350			Potsherds

[a] Ages given are not corrected for fractionation, except ostrich eggshell samples where second date is corrected to −6.2‰.
[b] Black sand.

An observed rise in pH was taken as a sign that the most soluble fractions of the humic acids had been removed. The physical appearance of the charcoal helped in deciding whether additional and stronger NaOH treatments could be performed. After this treatment the charcoals were rinsed with distilled water until neutral and then acidified to pH 1 to prevent absorption of atmospheric CO_2.

Incomplete humate removal resulting from so cautious a treatment could result in incorrect age dates. We evaluated this possibility by extracting humates from the large charcoal sample, Feature 132 from Nabta Playa, E-75-6. Age date SMU-208 on the charcoal is 7930 ± 40 BP; SMU-219 on the humates is 8120 ± 80 BP. The error ranges overlap on the 2σ level. The humates are older and thus show the same trend as observed with the peat sample, discussed subsequently.

It can be concluded that incomplete removal of humate contamination from the charcoals is not a serious problem. This fact is not surprising since the Western Desert has not recently been covered by vegetation; most of the reported sites have been extremely arid since deposition of the features that provided the samples. The charcoal dates listed in Table A7.1 therefore provide a reliable framework for the chronology of the area.

The dates SMU-436 and SMU-491, Nabta Site E-75-8, Connecting Trench, are the only dramatic exceptions, with 14,940 ± 160 and 9310 ± 550 BP, respectively, instead of an expected age of approximately 6700 BP. The SMU-436 sample consisted of 10 g of good charcoal collected from a hearth. The standard pretreatment was performed, including a relatively strong wash with 1% NaOH. The possibility was considered that some carbonate may have remained within the charcoal. After combustion this carbonate could be detected in the form of calcium oxide in the ash. Calculations show that the weight of the ash should contain 45.4% CaO if it is assumed that the carbonate was devoid of any ^{14}C, that is, of > 40,000 BP age. Any younger carbonate would result in even larger amounts of CaO present in the ash to explain the age discrepancy. An x-ray diffraction pattern run on the ash did not show any trace of CaO; neither was $CaCO_3$ detected. There is no reasonable explanation for the improbably high age, and the possibility that some much older piece of wood was collected and utilized at the site in one particular hearth may be considered.

Sample SMU-491 was collected on the same horizon over several squares and very close to sample SMU-436. The size of the sample, 0.7g, was too small to provide a reliable date. It could be a mixture of charcoal of the expected age range with one or two small pieces from the hearth dated with SMU-436.

OSTRICH-EGGSHELL SAMPLES

In addition to the usual statistical error of ^{14}C counting, two kinds of processes affecting the shell carbonate contribute to the uncertainty of the eggshell dates: first, isotope fractionation (distortion of the natural ratio of abundance between the carbon isotopes with masses 12, 13, and 14) during formation of the shell, and second, alteration of the shell through aging or contamination during burial or surface exposure.

Contamination is normally easy to recognize as a surficial deposition or filling of shell pores made of secondary carbonate and silt. Most of this contamination can easily be removed by filing, scraping, and acid leaching. Only an insignificant amount of pore filling may remain. Alteration of the shell carbonate can occur as recrystallization. Hereby some carbon from the shell could exchange with carbon from a surrounding source, such as CO_2 in the atmosphere, carbonate dust in an arid environment, or calcium bicarbonate in solution in a groundwater-saturated soil or sediment layer. The second of the three possibilities is most likely to apply to the samples discussed here, resulting in older age dates. Samples SMU-207 (21,530 ± 220 BP) and SMU-210 (24,590 ± 330 BP) are from weak, calcic horizons of Holocene soils, and clearly demonstrate the contaminating effect of wind-transported, carbonate dust from the Eocene limestone plateau to the north (cf. Appendix 6).

Alteration is difficult to detect, even in thin sections of the shell. An indication of possible alteration is dark staining of shells, mostly seen in samples on or close to the surface. The magnitude of the carbon exchange is not known and therefore the reliability of ostrich-eggshell dates must be demonstrated by dating several samples from sites of known age. The effect of fractionation can be corrected arithmetically during age calculations. The computations have been described in numerous publications, most recently by Stuiver and Polach (1977). The ratio of ^{13}C to ^{12}C in the sample is measured and a correction is made to adjust it to the value of an appropriate standard. Twice the adjustment is then applied to the measured ^{14}C activity. The standard is the shell of a modern ostrich egg laid by an animal living in a similar climatic environment to that postulated for most archaeological sites in North Africa and feeding on a similar diet. Such an eggshell was purchased in 1974 at a local farmers' market in Addis Ababa. It was dated as SMU-124 and showed 163% modern activity. The $\delta^{13/12}$C is −6.2‰ relative to the PDB standard.

Three dates for checking the reliability of ostrich eggshells are available:

1. From Nabta E-75-6, charcoal and eggshells found in the same early Neolithic association, where seven charcoal dates range from 7930 to 8130 BP and two eggshell dates are as follows:
   a. SMU-191 7680 ± 70 BP (not corrected for fractionation, $\delta^{13/12}$C not measured)
   b. SMU-202 8000 ± 110 BP (uncorrected; corrected for fractionation 8020 ± 110 BP)
2. From Bir Kiseiba in an assemblage tentatively assigned to the Terminal Paleolithic:
   a. charcoal, SMU-489 8740 ± 95 BP
   b. eggshells, SMU-494 8730 ± 70 (uncorrected; corrected for fractionation 8740 ± 70 BP)

Two eggshell dates present a perfect match with the assumed correct age and one date is slightly too young.

From the foregoing data and from Table A7.1 one can also conclude that the correction for fractionation does not have a substantial influence on the final age date, the largest correction being 35 years for SMU-326. More research and more measurements on recent shells suitable as standards are needed to ascertain reliability of fractionation corrections. For this reason the uncorrected eggshell dates are used in the main section of this volume.

BIR SAHARA SITE BS-16 AGE DATES

A silty peatlike layer was sampled from a trench and four independent dates were obtained from different components within this layer:

1. The whole organic portion of the peat (secondary carbonate or marl removed): SMU-218, 33,080 ± 1120 BP
2. Residue of peat after three subsequent humate extractions: SMU-108, 28,000 ± 1250 BP
3. Humates from peat: SMU-95, 37,740 ± 1980 BP
4. Pieces of marl found within peat: SMU-215, 34,600 ± 970 BP

An additional theoretical date was obtained by calculating a combined age of the residue and humate fractions: 33,160 ± 1000 BP (standard deviation estimated). This calculated age is nearly identical with the whole peat age and indicates the reliability of the dating procedures on the organic fractions.

The organic material in the residue fraction is the chemically most stable and physically least mobile fraction that was dated. Since the peat is overlain by a diatomaceous sediment that protects the peat from downward infiltration of fine organic particles, there is, from the point of view of radiometric chronology, no reason to doubt the reliability of the SMU-108 residue date. There is no simple explanation for the much older humate date. It is possible that remobilized humates from a much older deposit were carried in by groundwater and became fixed in the peat during its immature state while its pH was low.

The overlying diatomite contains numerous snail shells (Melanoides), which were also dated. These shells were collected from the wall of the same trench where the underlying peat was sampled. The shells were separated into a "large shells" sample and a "small shells" sample. The age dates are > 41,450 BP (SMU-81, based on 2σ minimum age criterion) and 40,710 ± 3270 BP (SMU-82), respectively. Aquatic snails build their shells in part from bicarbonate molecules dissolved in the water. The bicarbonate in turn can be partially derived from ^{14}C−free limestone or windblown carbonate silt with which the well water had come in contact. Thus the shell carbonate may be diluted in ^{14}C, in which case a too old age is measured. Rubin et al. (1963) exposed aquatic snails to ^{14}C-labeled carbonate water for 24 days. His study shows that the error of age dates may be limited to approximately 1000 years.

This result is contradicted by an age date on aquatic snail shells collected from Graeco-Roman agricultural deposits (semi-playa deposits; Embabi 1972) near Kharga. The shells were found in close association with Graeco-Roman pottery, and were collected to test the hypothesis that the semi-playa deposits were derived from the agricultural use of ancient ground-water, instead of precipitation, during a period believed to have been nearly as arid as today. The apparent age of 18,500 ± 170 BP (SMU-383) instead of what should be approximately 2200 BP, shows the ^{14}C in the growing shells was diluted by a factor of approximately 7.7 from atmospheric concentration. If the Bir Sahara snail shell date, SMU-82, is corrected with this same dilution factor, a corrected age of 24,500 BP is obtained. Since we do not know if the Bir Sahara snails grew in a fossil water environment, the Kharga shell correction cannot be applied in the same magnitude. However, it shows that an age correction by several thousand years toward a younger date may be in order.

In the preceding discussion it was assumed that no post-depositional alteration of the shell material occurred. This assumption is probably correct for the snail shells discussed (SMU-81 and SMU-82). These Melanoides shells did not have the chalky appearance typical for recrystallized shell samples. Breaking the shells, removing the tips, ultrasonic cleaning and extensive etching (about 30% sample weight loss) resulted in a clean sample material. Even so these shells provide dates that could be several millenia in error in either direction, since post-mortem carbon exchange cannot be excluded.

Close to the collection site of the buried Melanoides shells dated in SMU-81 and SMU-82 the diatomite layer was exposed to the surface by deflation (Bir Sahara Site 13). The same type of shells was collected there from the surface and dated as SMU-80: 32,780 ± 900 BP. This much younger shell date indicates that surface exposure, even in an arid environment, can cause contamination of the shell carbonate, in this case probably by atmospheric CO_2 or from infrequent rains, especially since the beginning of the atomic era.

Finally, there is a date on marl-like nodules collected from within the peat. The carbonate age (SMU-215) of 34,600 ± 970 BP dates an event where the peat was submerged in water or groundwater that was supersaturated in calcium carbonate. Again, a strong possibility exists that the carbonate is diluted with respect to ^{14}C by solution of ancient sediments. The date therefore represents a maximum age for the event, which in turn is either more recent than or contemporaneous with the peat formation.

Considering all uncertainties and probabilities, the best age estimate for the Bir Sahara 16 peat is 28,000 to 38,000 BP although an even greater error is not precluded. The radiocarbon dating results gained from this site are leading to one of the most difficult interpretations the senior author has faced to date and more dating work is advised.

CARBONATE SEDIMENT AGE DATES

Carbonate dates are rarely used in archaeological chronology. Frequently these sediments are derived from more than one carbon source and therefore yield mixed ages. The usefulness of these dates lies in answers provided to geological and geochemical problems.

At the Kharga site of Trench 1, klinkerey $CaCO_3$ cemented sand and concretions on top of a spring mound yielded apparent dates of 12,295 BP ± 100 BP (SMU-393) and 12,360 BP ± 120 BP (SMU-395). Charcoal collected in the same trench at 45 to 50 cm depth was dated 3600 BP ± 70 BP (SMU-385). The formation of this carbonate was controlled by the presence of fossil water and the influx of carbonate dust derived from ancient limestones which encompass the site. Dilution of its ^{14}C content is responsible for the much-too-old, apparent age date. The same comments apply to a nearby spring tufa dated 7920 BP ± 90 BP (SMU-378), although ancient spring-water was probably the main source of contamination, since discharge would have prevented the inclusion of carbonate dust at the site of tufa formation.

The $\delta^{13/12}$C fractionation data are indicated in Table A7.1. No attempt was made to define a suitable standard for a fractionation correction and therefore no corrected ages are given.

POTSHERD DATES SMU-469 AND SMU-475

Potsherds can rarely be dated with the radiocarbon method. Contemporary plant fibers were used as temper in the two sherd samples and the kiln used to fire the pottery was of inefficient design, resulting in a low firing temperature that allowed the fibrous material inside the pottery walls to survive as carbon, instead of being converted to carbon dioxide. Furthermore, age dates on potsherds are only accurate if no other organic material of different age was present in the raw materials—specifically, there should be no ancient, organic carbon in the clay, as was clearly the case with the sample from Abu Ballas (SMU-490; 7790 ± 350 BP) which should not be older than 4000 years ago.

The potsherds were collected in February 1977 near Bir Tarfawi by the junior author, who submitted the sample to test the above assumptions.

The sherds were crushed in a mortar and hydrolyzed in 5% HCl for 3 days. During the following combustion process, we noticed a larger than expected CO_2 yield. The combustion, only 25% complete, was stopped. The sample was reground and hydrolyzed in 10% HCl for 2 additional days. The following second combustion yielded date SMU-475, 160 BP ± 95, which appears to be a reliable date. The CO_2 collected from the first and interrupted combustion was dated as SMU-469, 440 BP ± 75. Obviously some carbonate matrix was still present, resulting in dilution of the CO_2 derived by the organic material with 3.5% of "dead" CO_2 from ancient carbonates.

REFERENCES

Embabi, N. S.
  1972 The semi-playa deposits of Kharga depression, the Western Desert, Egypt. *Bulletin de la Société Géologique d'Egypte 41–42:* 73–87.
Haas, H.
  n.d. Specific problems with liquid scintillation counting of small benzene volumes and background count rate estimation. In *Proceedings of the Ninth International Radiocarbon Conference* (in press).
Haas, H., H. J. Hietala, S. L. Meeks, C. Campbell, and N. Neubert
  1978 Investigation into the adequacy of C^{14} counting procedures. Report submitted to the Institute for the Study of Earth and Man, Southern Methodist University.

Haynes, C. V., and H. Haas
  1974 Southern Methodist University radiocarbon date list, I. *Radiocarbon 16* (3): 368–380.
Meeks, S. L.
  n.d. A comparison of two estimators of the standard deviation for age estimates. In *Proceedings of the Ninth International Radiocarbon Conference* (in press).
Rubin, M., R. C. Likins, and E. G. Berry
  1963 On the validity of radiocarbon dates from snail shells. *Journal of Geology 71:* 84–89.
Stuiver, M., and H. A. Polach
  1977 Discussion, reporting of C^{14} data. *Radiocarbon 19* (3): 355–363.

8

Intrasite and Intersite Spatial Analyses at Bir Tarfawi

HAROLD J. HIETALA AND RICHARD E. LARSON

Intrasite and intersite spatial analyses have seldom been simultaneously applied to a series of sites in order to gauge, measure, or test the scope of inferences drawn from the two complementary approaches. Fortunately, the sites at Bir Tarfawi (BT-14) offer such a possibility.

The purpose of this analysis is to evaluate statistically selected aspects of the lithic and faunal information from BT-14 within intersite and intrasite frameworks. The intersite comparisons, to be presented first, are designed to evaluate some behavioral interpretations for several areas

of BT-14 by expanding some common approaches to the study of intersite variability. The intrasite analyses, on the other hand, are constructed to complement the intersite approach. It is our belief that variability and patterns suggested by an intersite analysis should have some behavioral implications at the intrasite level. Conversely, patterns detected at an intrasite level should have some structural, normative implications at the intersite level. We shall find that the two approaches are only partially isomorphic.

BACKGROUND

Lithic and faunal variability have been discussed elsewhere in this volume for the distinct areas of BT-14, which are spatially portrayed in Figure 2.46. Differences and similarities in several technological and typological indices coupled with variable faunal densities are interpreted, for the secure data bases, on a functional level. For example, A-surface is considered to be a kill site because of a relatively small number of cores and core-preparation debitage elements, a high proportion of retouched tools, and relatively high faunal densities. Likewise, C-surface, which overlies C-excavated, is considered to be a kill site because it is generally similar to A-surface. On the other hand, C-excavated is interpreted as a habitation site. The interpretation is based on high percentages of cores and core-preparation debitage elements, different faunal elements from those found in A-surface and C-surface, and different tool-class proportions. B-surface is also considered to be a habitation site. This designation is related to

relatively high percentages of cores and core-preparation-debitage elements and a low proportion of retouched tools. There were few faunal elements recovered from B-surface, probably because of poor preservation conditions. The B-surface area showed the existence of some fragmentary faunal material. Finally, D-surface is considered different from the other areas on lithostratigraphic evidence. Core and core-preparation elements are low and tools are scarce. Denticulate pieces are numerous, as they are for all areas of BT-14 with the exception of C-excavated. Faunal elements are also scarce at D-surface. A functional placement of D-surface was not attempted because the recovered sample was not large.

Intersite and intrasite analyses of the sites at Bir Tarfawi follow in the next two sections. Hereafter, the letters A_S, B_S, C_S, D_S, and C_E denote surface areas A, B, C, and D, and the excavated portion of Area C, respectively.

INTERSITE ANALYSES

The statistical methods employed in this section are based on partitioning the log-likelihood chi-square statistic for contingency table data into homogeneous subsets of units and/or variables with significant heterogeneity between the subsets. Such partitioning schemes are statistically discussed in Bishop *et al.* (1975) and are applied in Butler *et al.* (1977) and Hietala and Close (1979). These schemes are philosophically similar to analysis of variance procedures for partitioning variance into within-group and between-group components.

The intersite analyses are based on the data portrayed in Figures 7.7 and 7.8. Since the Levallois Index data, discussed earlier in this volume, suggest significant technological variability between the five assemblage units, we begin our analysis with the technological material.

Table A8.1a presents the core information data for the five areas. Cores are categorized as Levallois cores, non-Levallois cores (single-platform flake, etc., as defined in Figure 7.7), and undetermined cores. The last category is included for the sake of completeness. It is clear that Area D_S has a very low percentage, 12.5%, of known Levallois

cores, whereas Area C_E has a very high percentage, 93.3%, of known Levallois cores. The other areas, A_S, C_S, and B_S, have known Levallois core percentages varying from 35.4 to 50.0%. Testing for equality of Areas A_S, C_S, and B_S relative to the core category data in this table, we find the log-likelihood chi-square statistic for testing the null hypothesis of homogeneity possesses a value of $G^2 = 5.75$ with four degrees of freedom, which is clearly nonsignificant. On the other hand, using Area D_S as one group, Areas A_S, C_S, and B_S as a second group, and Area C_E as a third group, the log-likelihood chi-square statistic for testing equality of the three groups, through a null hypothesis of homogeneity, possesses a value of $G^2 = 28.73$ with four degrees of freedom, which is highly significant. The results of these tests are given in Table A8.4. Thus, partitioning the data into the three groups allows us to conclude that the areas of the second group are alike whereas the three groups themselves are highly different. This is partially indicated by the percentages of Levallois cores just discussed (shown in Table A8.1a).

Table A8.1b presents the debitage variability produced

Table A8.1
Intersite Technological Data

	D_S	A_S	C_S	B_S	C_E
a. Core variability					
Levallois	2	17	8	36	14
Non-Levallois	4	19	6	18	0
Undetermined	10	12	2	23	1
Total	16	48	16	77	15
Percentage Levallois	12.5	35.4	50.0	46.7	93.3
b. Levallois core and debitage variability					
Preparation flakes	12	50	40	675	365
Production pieces	11	59	16	164	56
Cores	2	17	8	36	14
Preparation/core	6.0	2.9	5.0	18.8	26.1
Production/core	5.5	3.5	2.0	4.6	4.0
Total debitage/core	11.5	6.4	7.0	23.3	30.1
c. Non-Levallois variability					
Early core preparation	1	22	2	100	55
Flakes, blades	95	684	269	784	231
Cores	14	31	8	41	1
Preparation flakes/core	.07	.71	.25	2.44	55.0
Preparation/production	.01	.03	.01	.13	.24
Total debitage/core	6.9	22.8	33.9	21.6	286.0
d. Overall core to debitage variability					
Primary flakes	5	96	28	267	58
Preparatory debitage	13	72	42	775	420
Production debitage	106	743	285	948	287
Cores	16	48	16	77	15
Preparation/production	.12	.10	.15	.82	1.46
Preparatory debitage/core	.81	1.5	2.63	10.06	28.0
Primary flakes/core	.31	2.0	1.75	3.47	3.87

from Levallois cores for the five areas where the variables are Levallois preparation flakes (class 4 of Figure 7.7), Levallois pieces, and Levallois cores. The preparation-flake-to-core ratio in this table suggests that Areas B_S and C_E have very high values, 18.8 and 26.1, whereas the other areas have values that range from 2.9 to 6.0. If we let the two areas with large values form one group and let the three areas with small values form a second group and then compare the total debitage (preparatory flakes and production pieces) frequencies with core frequencies, we obtain the results given in Table A8.4, which suggest that the two groups are internally homogeneous but are quite different from each other. On the other hand, if we look at the proportion of Levallois production elements per Levallois core we have the percentages given in Table A8.1. A test of the homogeneity hypothesis is given in Table A8.4. It is clear that there are no differences between all areas, relative to the production of Levallois elements and the corresponding percentage of Levallois cores.

These results suggest that although there are substan-tially more Levallois core-preparation pieces (per core) for Areas B_S and C_E, the proportion of Levallois production elements per core is seemingly constant. This is consistent with a greater degree of core preparation at Areas B_S and C_E, with some transference or curation of partially reduced cores from Areas B_S and C_E to the other areas.

It is also consistent with a transference of partially reduced cores to the other areas (A_S, C_S, and D_S?) with a consequent return of unexhausted cores. Curation studies might help in this regard. We hope to unravel some of these problems in the near future.

The non-Levallois core variability portrays a different pattern where Areas A_S, C_S, and B_S are similar. The data are given in Table A8.1c with the analysis results given in Table A8.4. For the non-Levallois cores, the debitage-to-core ratio has a low value of 6.9 for Area D_S, ranges from 21.6 to 33.9 for Areas A_S, C_S, and B_S, and has a maximum value of 286.0 for Area C_E. The last high value is the result of C_E possessing only one non-Levallois core. Nevertheless, it is clear that a seemingly consistent pattern is emerging

Table A8.2
Intersite Technological and Typological Data

a. Non-preparatory debitage and total tool variability

	D_S	A_S	C_S	B_S	C_E
Levallois production (L)	11	59	16	164	56
Non-Levallois production (NL)	95	684	269	784	231
Tools (T)	50	340	65	237	71
L/NL	.12	.09	.06	.21	.24
T/L	4.5	5.8	4.1	1.4	1.3
T/NL	.53	.50	.24	.30	.31
Tool/total production	.47	.46	.23	.25	.25

b. Variability for selected tool classes

	C_E	A_S	C_S	B_S	D_S
Levallois pieces (L)	56	59	16	164	11
Mousterian points (P)	13	25	7	6	0
Scrapers (S)	28	73	12	42	1
Denticulates, notches (ND)	13	173	38	155	46
P/L	.23	.42	.44	.04	.00
P/S	.46	.34	.58	.14	.00
S/ND	2.15	.42	.32	.27	.02
P/ND	1.00	.14	.18	.04	.00

c. Relative proportions for P, S, ND

	C_E	A_S	C_S	B_S	D_S
P	.24	.09	.12	.03	.00
S	.52	.27	.21	.21	.02
ND	.24	64	.67	.76	.98

from these initial analyses. Namely, Area C_E seems to have a very strong component related to Levallois core-reduction processes and potentially a stronger component related to non-Levallois core-reduction processes. Area B_S seems to possess a weaker pattern related to reduction processes in general. Area D_S seems to possess the least amount of reduction, particularly with respect to non-Levallois elements, whereas Areas A_S and C_S seem to be alike with an amount of core reduction between that of D_S and B_S. The relation of production to core elements parallels the total debitage-to-core ratios. To look at this notion more generally we can look at the overall reduction process.

The data given in Table A8.1d present reduction sequence information by categorizing the lithic data set into total cores, primary flakes, preparatory debitage (classes 3 and 4 of Figure 7.7) and production debitage (all Levallois pieces and non-Levallois flakes and blades). It is clear from these data that the previously discussed "emerging" pattern is in fact real. Table A8.4 gives the results of testing for homogeneity between Area A_S and Area C_S. The hypothesis is clearly accepted. It should also be noted that the other areas are different from each other and from the group consisting of A_S and C_S together. In addition, the initial core-removal elements are indicated in Areas B_S and C_E with increased production occurring in Areas D_S, A_S, and

C_S. The second stage of intersite analysis considers gross interaction between the technological and typological information data sets and looks at the typological information at the class level.

Table A8.2a gives the summary data for the categories of total Levallois production elements, total non-Levallois production elements, and total tools. If the non-Levallois cateogry is temporarily ignored, the Levallois production and tool categories lead to two groups. One group consists of Areas B_S and C_E; the other group consists of the other three areas. When only the non-Levallois category is compared with the tools, we also end up with two groups, except that C_S now combines with B_S and C_E. All three variables together lead to a partition into three groups with D_S and A_S forming a single group, C_S remaining by itself, and B_S and C_E combining into the third group. Table A8.4 gives a confirmation of this partition. In addition, Table A8.2 suggests that Mousterian points and Levallois pieces lead to a homogeneous group of Areas C_S and A_S, whereas scrapers, notched and denticulated pieces, and non-Levallois elements lead to a homogeneous group of Areas C_S and B_S. Table A8.2b considers the interrelationship of the Levallois piece category with the foregoing three tool-classes. From these data it is clear that A_S and C_S are homogeneous, as is shown in Table A8.4 with a formal

Table A8.3
Technological and Typological Data for Areas A_S and C_S

a. Reduction elements

	C_S	A_S
Cores	16	48
Primary flakes	28	96
Preparation flakes	42	72
Levallois pieces	16	59
Non-Levallois flakes/blades	269	684
Total	371	959

b. Tools

	C_S	A_S
Mousterian points (P)	7	25
Scrapers (S)	12	73
Notches and Denticulates (ND)	38	173
Other	8	69
Total	65	340

c. Core and debitage to tool variability

	C_S	A_S
Cores and debitage	371	959
Tools	65	340
Total	436	1299

d. Hypotheses tests for C_S, A_S homogeneity

	G^2	d.f.	p
Within lithic reduction	8.13	4	>.08
Within tools	3.61	3	>.30
Between reduction and tools	24.83	1	<.001

hypothesis test. Fortunately, we have a statistical break-down of tools into those made on Levallois blanks and non-Levallois blanks. This information is given in Table A8.7. In this table we see that the proportion of specific tool classes made on Levallois blanks is highest for the B_S and C_E areas in combination with the Mousterian point category. This is consistent with the area of high Levallois production processes.

The results have suggested that Areas A_S and C_S are essentially homogeneous. To test this notion explicity, Table A8.3 was generated to look at the hypothesis within technological reduction categories, within tool categories, and between reduction and tool categories. As expected, the areas are homogeneous within each of the technological and typological systems but are not homogeneous between the category of cores and debitage relative to the category of tools. On the other hand, these two areas are the only ones that consistently change together.

It may well be that the lithic reduction component differences in preparation and production elements may be accounted for by differential curation of Levallois and non-Levallois cores with possible curation of Levallois pieces. Work toward a better understanding of potential differential curation rates is now in progress.

If we now separately consider the restricted typological information given by Mousterian points (P), scrapers (S), and notches and denticulates (ND), a different picture is seen to emerge. Although Areas A_S and C_S are alike, it is noted that a different ordering occurs with respect to the distinct groups. The ratios in Table A8.2b suggest that C_E is more like A_S and C_S whereas B_S is more like D_S. This is a reversal from the technological ordering. To be specific, C_E, A_S, and C_S are alike relative to the scraper and point categories, whereas A_S, C_S, and B_S are alike relative to the scraper and notched categories; D_S is not similar to any other area. It may also be noted that C_E, in addition, is the area with 93.3% Levallois cores, whereas Area D_S possesses only 12.5% Levallois cores. Furthermore, D_S has a very high relative proportion of notches and denticulates, equal to 97.9%, whereas C_E has the lowest percentage (24.1%). This is not so unusual since notches and denticulates are more likely to be produced on non-Levallois production blanks. What is unusual is that the excavated portion of Area C, Area C_E, has a very low restricted notch and denticulate percentage (24.1%) whereas Area D_S has a very high notch and denticulate percentage (97.9%). It should be noted here that Area C_E possesses only fragmentary (unarticulated) skeletal material (as opposed to Areas A_S and C_S) and D_S has only meager, poorly preserved, fragmentary material. However, the areas designated as possessing faunal material elements are not necessarily equivalent to those with high Levallois reduction and non-Levallois reduction components. Table A8.2c gives relative percentage values for the point, scraper, and notched variables relative to each other. The areas with large preserved faunal components have larger point percentages, with one area, C_E, also possessing a low notch and denticulate percentage. This is also the site with very strong Levallois and non-Levallois reduction components. In addition, the areas with light or no faunal elements have

Table A8.4
Summary of Hypothesis Testing for Data in Tables A8.1 and A8.2

Data source	Group	Within group			Between groups		
		G^2	df	p	G^2	df	p
Table A8.1a	A_S,C_S,B_S	5.75	4	> .20			
					28.73	4	< .001
Table A8.1b[a]	D_S,A_S,C_S	.64	2	> .70			
	B_S,C_E	.65	1	> .30			
					22.74	1	< .001
Table A8.1b[b]	All areas	3.29	4	> .50			
Table A8.1c	A_S,C_S,B_S	1.49	2	> .40			
					30.64	2	< .001
Table A8.1d	A_S,C_S	6.40	3	> .08			
					631.54	9	< .001
Table A8.2a	D_S,A_S	.71	2	> .70			
	B_S,C_E	.73	2	> .70			
					115.01	4	< .001
Table A8.2b	A_S,C_S	1.77	3	< .50			
					168.18	9	< .001

[a] Comparisons for cores versus total debitage.
[b] Comparisons for cores versus production pieces.

very low point percentages with one area, D_S, also possessing an incredibly high notch and denticulate percentage. This is also a site with relatively weak reduction components. It would be interesting to attempt to draw a parallel between the existence of strong fauna components and lithic reduction activities but such an argument would not work. First, Area B_S has heavy lithic reduction components but does not possess a single preserved faunal element. Second, Areas A_S and C_S, which are generally alike, have weak lithic reduction components but strong faunal components. Thus, it appears that there are several responses interacting here. There is definitely a body of data to suggest curation, since high preparatory indices seem to be inversely related to high production indices. This holds for both Levallois and non-Levallois reduction processes. Area C_E always possesses the highest preparatory indices but the lowest production indices. Also, the curation effort seems to be unrelated to fauna. Finally, the highest Mousterian point indices occur for the sites with large amounts of preserved fauna, whereas the highest notch and denticulate indices occur for sites with little preserved faunal material.

Based on these intersite data, we would expect in the intrasite analysis of Area C_E that fauna and lithic reduction processes would spatially segregate. We would also expect that tool categories overall would be distributed independently of the faunal categories. However, we would expect certain tool classes to be associated with the faunal material. Specifically, we might quantitatively expect Mousterian points to be positively associated, scrapers to be independently distributed, and maybe even denticulates to be segregated from the fauna. We find in the next section that not all of our expectations are met.

INTRASITE ANALYSES

The data for the intrasite comparisons were obtained from Area C_E. We have derived a general spatial analysis methodology to investigae C_E (Hietala and Larson n.d.). Although our studies of C_E were primarily concerned with methodologies useful in obtaining meaningful nearest-neighbor associations, we observed that C_E represented a locality with several distinct areas of activity that are behaviorally comparable in a local setting to the activity models presented in the intersite portion of this analysis.

The intrasite areas used in this section are portrayed in Figure A8.1. The primary reduction area, R, was subjectively and arbitrarily defined by noting the visual overlap of the spatial distributions for cores and debitage (Levallois flakes and blades, non-Levallois flakes and blades, and debris). The six faunal areas (F_1, F_2, . . ., F_6) were similarly defined using the faunal information specified in Figure 2.43. Although the faunal areas are not used beyond their descriptive potential, note that the faunal and reduction areas seem to be somewhat spatially distinct. The central area of the site, however, contains both lithic reduction and faunal elements. To investigate the interrelationship of artifacts to fauna we begin by looking at the reduction area.

Table A8.5a presents a tabulation of the artifact counts and faunal element counts within and outside the boundary defining the reduction area, R. In this table, C represents cores, L and NL represent Levallois pieces and other elements (non-Levallois debitage, all preparation elements, and all debris), F denotes fauna, and the tool classes of scrapers, Mousterian points, and notched pieces are denoted by the letters S, P, and D respectively. By visual insepction, the reduction area, R, contains the majority of the cores (C), Levallois pieces (L), and non-Levallois piece elements (NL). However, the greater portion of the faunal elements (F), and tool classes (S, P, and D) are found outside the bounds of the reduction area (i.e., are in $\bar{R}$). The ratio of the frequencies given by R/$\bar{R}$ suggests that reduc-

tion elements, given by C, NL, and L, are found in R (as expected) and that the fauna and tools, given by F, S, P, and D, are found in $\bar{R}$. The calculated G^2, given in Table A8.6, clearly demonstrates that the preceding variable groups are internally homogeneous but are strongly heterogeneous externally (between groups). That is, the major source of intrasite variability is probably spatial variability between the lithic reduction component, on one hand, and the faunal and tool component on the other hand.

Our earlier intrasite study concluded that cores and Levallois pieces segregated from the faunal elements and the members of the restricted tool group. The data presented in Tables A8.5a and A8.6 support this conclusion. Furthermore, the fact that scrapers, Mousterian points, and notches/denticulates tend to be located away from Area R fits the model discussed earlier in the intersite section. Although the fauna and tools tend to occur in the nonreduction area ($\bar{R}$) we should ascertain the spatial interrelationship, if any, between the tool classes and faunal material. This is the subject of the following analytical phase.

Since the total number of faunal and restricted tool elements is only equal to 133, it is reasonable to use a form of distance analysis. In the following, an artifact is defined to occur in the proximity of faunal elements if the artifact is within 60 cm of a faunal element. The use of a 60-cm search radius was employed because it is roughly twice the average nearest-neighbor distance of the faunal elements found at the site and because 50% of the piece-plotted artifacts were found in the 60-cm radius.

Table A8.5b gives the frequencies of all artifact categories (excluding NL because of unreasonably high frequencies) by the foregoing proximity definition.

A test of complete homogeneity for the five variables in Table A8.5b is clearly not significant. That is, the likelihood of any artifact class element occurring within 60 cm of a faunal element is equal to the likelihood that it will not.

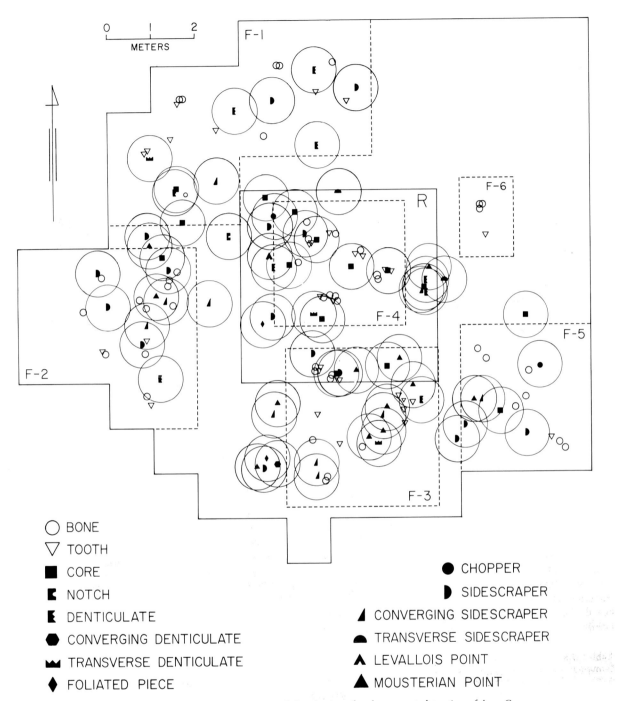

0   1   2
METERS

○ BONE
▽ TOOTH
■ CORE
E NOTCH
E DENTICULATE
⬡ CONVERGING DENTICULATE
⏗ TRANSVERSE DENTICULATE
◆ FOLIATED PIECE

● CHOPPER
◗ SIDESCRAPER
◢ CONVERGING SIDESCRAPER
◠ TRANSVERSE SIDESCRAPER
▲ LEVALLOIS POINT
▲ MOUSTERIAN POINT

FIGURE A8.1. *Fauna and lithic material distributions for the excavated portion of Area C.*

This result is documented by the G^2 statistic given in Table A8.6. On the other hand, Table A8.5b also indicates that Mousterian points and notched pieces tend to occur closer to faunal elements than do scrapers. The sample sizes, unfortunately, are far too small for any reasonable conclusions to be drawn from them. The best that we can say is that the data do not contradict the earlier intersite model. Note that if one partitions the data in Table A8.5b into one group consisting of C, P, and D and a second group consisting of L and S, then the two groups are internally homogeneous. Also, the G^2 value between the groups has a value equal to $G^2 = 4.45$, with one degree of freedom, and is certainly significant at the .05 level. Nonetheless, it is a marginal result at best.

Thus far, the spatial breakdown of the assemblage has studied the horizontal variability at C_E in terms of Area R

Table A8.5
Intrasite Data for Area C$_E$

a. Artifact and faunal frequencies
   for lithic reduction area

	C	NL	L	F	S	P	D
Inside reduction area (R)	10	2321	35	32	9	5	4
Outside reduction area ($\bar{R}$)	5	1180	21	48	18	8	9
Total	15	3501	56	80	27	13	13
R/$\bar{R}$	2.00	1.97	1.67	.67	.67	.63	.44

b. Tool, core, and Levallois piece
   frequencies by faunal proximity

	C	L	S	P	D	Total
Proximal to fauna (P)	9	24	12	8	9	62
Peripheral to fauna ($\bar{P}$)	6	32	15	5	4	62
Total	15	56	27	13	13	124

c. Artifact frequencies across
   reduction and faunal proximity
   groups

	C	L	S	P	D	Total
R and $\bar{P}$	6	15	2	3	2	28
R and $\bar{P}$	4	20	2	5	1	32
$\bar{R}$ and P	3	9	6	9	7	34
$\bar{R}$ and $\bar{P}$	2	12	3	10	3	30
Total	15	56	13	27	13	124

and faunal proximity. However, we feel that another step is necessary to evaluate the activity model presented in the intersite segment. Consequently, we recorded the pieces plotted into the following spatial categories: within Area R in close proximity to faunal elements; within Area R, but not close to faunal elements; outside Area R in close proximity to faunal elements; and outside Area R and not close to faunal elements. The results obtained using this approach are presented in Table A8.5c.

As with the results obtained from the analysis of the reduction area, the cores and Levallois pieces load in Area R and the restricted tools load in the area outside Area R. Furthermore, partitioning the data into a core and Levallois

piece group and a restricted tool group again supports the earlier results. The homogeneity of the partitioned groups and the significant difference between the groups are documented in Table A8.6. Finally, it may be noted that outside Area R there are twice as many Mousterian points and notches/denticulates within 60 cm of faunal elements as there are beyond the 60-cm search radius. The data samples are, however, too small to make valid conclusions.

Our earlier study also investigated the tendency for specific tools to associate with faunal elements. One of the results obtained was that pointed pieces (Mousterian points, converging sidescrapers, and converging denticulates) tended to be more strongly associated with

Table A8.6
Summary of Hypothesis Testing for Data in Table A8.5

Data source	Group	Within group			Between groups		
		G²	df	p	G²	df	p
Table A8.5a	C,NL,L	0.35	2	> .80			
	F,S,P,D	0.68	3	> .80			
					43.59	1	< .001
Table A8.5b	C,L,S,P,D	4.75	4	> .30			
Table A8.5c	C,L,	1.49	3	> .50			
	P,S,D	2.79	6	> .80			
					16.19	3	≅ .001

Table A8.7
Tool-Blank Configurations by Area

Tool[a]	Blank[b]	D_S	A_S	C_S	B_S	C_E	All areas
ND	L.	5	16	4	37	2	64
	NL	42	160	34	116	11	363
	% L.	.106	.091	.105	.242	.154	.150
S	L.	–	16	4	11	8	39
	NL	1	55	8	42	19	125
	% L.	.000	.225	.333	.208	.296	.238
P	L.	–	10	3	3	9	25
	NL	–	16	3	2	4	25
	% L.	–	.385	.500	.600	.692	.500
Total	L.	5	42	11	51	19	128
	NL	43	231	45	160	34	513
	% L.	.104	.154	.196	.243	.358	.200

[a] Restricted tool classes. ND = notches and denticulates, S = scrapers, P = Mousterian points.
[b] L = Levallois, NL = non-Levallois.

faunal elements than were the other artifacts studied in the analysis. Other artifacts either were virtually independent of or segregated from the faunal elements. This is in support of the intersite analysis conclusions from the previous section.

METHODOLOGICAL CONCLUSIONS

The analytical techniques employed for the intrasite analysis have demonstrated that the single excavated *in situ* site in the Bir Tarfawi basin contains recognizable spatial patterns. Our analyses have clearly shown that artifacts are differentially distributed relative to a lithic reduction area. Additionally, the artifact classes segregating from the reduction area are the retouched tools. Although we were unable definitively to isolate which tool-classes were aggregating with the faunal elements, we have been able to note that retouched tools tend to associate with faunal elements outside the bounds of the lithic reduction area.

Also, it is clear that the intrasite analysis supports the intersite predictions when any conclusive statement can be made, and does not in any case contradict them. Conversely, if we make intrasite analysis predictions, we would predict that fauna and tool classes would be independent. This is certainly verified at the intersite level of analysis.

On the other hand, there are some intersite and intrasite characteristics that are not held in common for the two analytical formulations. Specifically, the intersite analysis *might* suggest that Levallois pieces would spatially associate with Mousterian points but not with scrapers and notched pieces. The intrasite analysis suggests, however, that the Levallois pieces *might* spatially associate with the scrapers. Also, the intrasite analysis suggests that tools, in general, would coassociate with faunal material. The intersite analysis suggests, however, that notched pieces might segregate from the faunal material. In addition, some contradictory statements might be inferred from the nature of core, preparatory element, production debitage, and tool relationships (intrasite and intersite).

On a positive note, there are some conclusions that can be garnered from these data sets and analyses.

INTERPRETATIVE CONCLUSIONS

The intrasite and intersite analyses support the following notions:

1. Fauna-related activities are spatially separated from lithic reduction activities.

2. Faunal areas are related to tools.

Most important, the notion of "kill" and "habitation" sites as a dichotomy for typological purposes is potentially too simplistic. Further work is needed for example to ascertain the nature and adaptive value of curation.

SUMMARY

At this time, we feel that only part of the problem is due to small sample sizes. The techniques used were global in nature and did not emphasize a methodology for measuring positive associations between faunal elements and artifacts. In addition, no attempt was made to measure curation rates.

As a result of this analysis, we feel that the surface sites A_S, B_S, C_S, and D_S should be spatially investigated from an intrasite perspective, since visual inspection of the scattergrams indicates some patterning.

Our study, however, could not include the time for such an analysis. We plan to pursue this problem in the near future.

Although the two approaches are not totally isomorphic, we should not have expected a one-to-one correspondence. Intersite patterns only inferentially suggest behavioral patterns, whereas intrasite patterns are only capable of defining general local behavioral patterns that have not been subject to extreme or gross cultural (c-transform) or natural (n-transform) processes. This, however, should not inhibit our efforts to extract the most meager of behavioral conclusions from the worst data base. The challenge is ours.

REFERENCES

Bishop, Y. M. M., S. E. Fienberg, and P. W. Holland
1975 *Discrete multivariate analysis: Theory and practice.* Cambridge: M. I.T. Press.
Butler, B. H., E. Tchernov, H. J. Hietala, and S. Davis
1977 Faunal exploitation during the Late Epipaleolithic in the Har Harif. In *Prehistory and paleoenvironments in the central Negev, Israel,* Vol. 2, edited by A. E. Marks, Dallas: Department of Anthropology, Institute for the Study of Earth and Man, Southern Methodist University. Pp. 327–345.

Hietala, H. J., and A. E. Close
1979 Testing hypotheses of independence on symmetrical artifacts. *Journal of Archaeological Science 6:* 85–92.
Hietala, H. J., and R. E. Larson
n.d. *A general approach for testing multidimensional association for distance, directional or grid unit frequency data* (in preparation).

9

Biometrical Analysis of the Early Neolithic Human Mandible from Nabta Playa (Western Desert of Egypt)

MACIEJ HENNEBERG, JANUSZ PIONTEK, AND JAN STRZAŁKO

Three human skeletons were found during the excavation of the Neolithic site of E-75-8 at Nabta Playa. Only one specimen, a well-preserved mandible, was brought to the authors for preliminary analysis. The remainder of the skeletal material is deposited in the Egyptian Museum (Cairo).

Since the site from which the mandible originates is situated approximately halfway in time and space between the Neolithic centers in the Sahara and those along the Nile, it is of some value to consider the affinities of the people who occupied the site. The most important question is whether the people from Nabta belonged to the so-called "Northwestern African type" (or "Mechta type") described by Briggs and Anderson (Anderson 1968), or showed more similarities to the populations living south of the Sahara often imprecisely labeled "Negroes." We are aware that examination of a single mandible is inadequate for a full solution to this problem, but it is at present the only material at our disposal. Hence, conclusions from the analysis given here should be treated as suggestions only, and will require support from further work on larger and more complete samples of skeletal material.

DESCRIPTION OF THE BONE AND TEETH

The mandible is almost complete; the only parts lacking are the right condylar process and the right canine tooth, which was lost postmortem (most probably during excavation or transportation). The bone is strongly polished by sand, which has given it a rough surface and has led to partial destruction of the compacta. In general, although

389

not uncommonly large, the mandible seems to be that of a strongly built individual with well-developed muscles (Figure A9.1). All morphological features (lines, protuberances, and so forth) are very clearly defined and distinct, and relief on the muscle attachment surfaces is strong. The bone is massive and thick with moderately pronounced gonial eversion. When viewed from below, the outline of the inferior margin shows three eminences: at the angle (gonial eversion), at the level of the molars where the external oblique line joins the body, and at the mental eminences. These eminences are large, extending from the level of the lateral incisor to the first premolar, and are very distinctive. Mental foramina are single and round, approximately 1.5 mm in diameter, and lie exactly in the middle of the body at the level of P_2/M_1. The alveolar process is seriously resorbed, especially in the region of the incisors and canines, where about half of the root is visible above the osseous ridge of the dental sockets.

The teeth are rather large and well developed without any traces of pathological changes. Attrition is at Stage 2–3; that is, islands of dentine are visible, and on some molars more than two islands of dentine have coalesced. The third molars show the same degree and pattern of wear

as other posterior teeth, so it may be concluded that they had been in regular contact with upper M_3. With such a pattern of attrition, it is difficult to determine the number of cusps with certainty. It seems, however, that the first molars had five cusps and the second and third molars had four. It is noteworthy that the frontal teeth (including the premolars) are slightly less worn that the molars. This may suggest a prevalence of chewing over other functions (such as the use of teeth as tools). Moreover, the surface of the worn molars is curved: on M_1 the buccal half of the crown is the more worn, and on M_3 the lingual half is more worn. On this basis, we may suppose that the teeth were predominantly used for grinding hard food (plant seeds and so forth). However, this suggestion needs confirmation from larger and more complete samples that would permit observation of the upper and lower teeth in various stages of wear.

On the basis of the general appearance and the size of the mandible, it may be concluded that the Nabta individual was a male. Since conditions of preservation have changed the dentine of the roots into a soft, chalk-like substance, attrition was the only age indicator we were able to observe. We have also taken resorption of the alveolar process

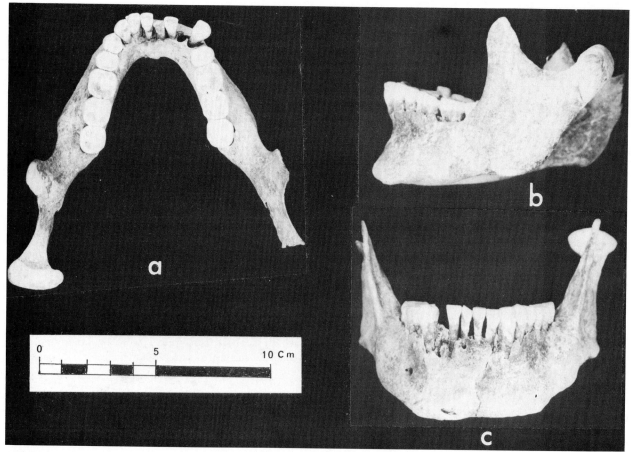

FIGURE A9.1.   *Mandible from Burial 2, Site E-75-8, Nabta: (a) horizontal upper view; (b) lateral aspect; (c) frontal aspect. Photographs by J. and M. Kozak.*

into account, uncertain as this is. Comparing stages of wear in the first and second molars, we can estimate that about one-eighth of the crown was worn out during 7 years of life (using the procedure proposed by Miles 1963). Thus, on the basis of the wear of M_2 and M_3, the age at death of this individual is estimated as about 35 years. Serious resorption of the alveolar process, mentioned earlier, supports such an estimation.

ANALYSIS OF METRICAL CHARACTERISTICS

Measurements of the mandible and teeth were taken in accordance with standard techniques and the results are given in Tables A9.1 and A9.2.

We have used three sets of comparative data in order to answer the following questions:

1. Is the individual from Nabta similar to Paleolithic and Mesolithic finds from northern Africa and the Wadi Halfa region?
2. Did the individual belong to a Negroid or a Caucasoid population, as defined by modern data?

To answer the first question we have used metrical data on mandibles and teeth from the following African collections: Wadi Halfa (Greene and Armelagos 1972); Gebel Sahaba, Taforalt, and northwestern African Mesolithic finds (Anderson 1968); and Izriten (Charon *et al.* 1973). From Europe we have used data from Muge (Lefèvre 1973), Grotte des Hoteaux (Vallois 1972), and l'Abri Vidon (Riquet 1972). To answer the second question, we have used metrical data on mandibles from Uganda (Górny 1957) and teeth of Negroids and Australoids of mixed origin (Corrucini 1973) as a model for Negroids. The model for Caucasoids comprises data on early medieval teeth and mandibles from Poland (Stęślicka 1970; Strzałko 1970) and teeth of a modern French population (Lavergne 1974).

Comparisons were made with the use of Penrose size and shape distances. In Table A9.3 are given the distances be-

Table A9.1
Metrical Data on the Mandible and Teeth (mm)

Bigonial diameter (go–go)[a]	103.5
Body length (go–gn)[a]	96.3
Symphysis height (gn–id)[a]	28.7
Max. ramus breadth	47.2
Min. ramus breadth	36.9
Condylar height	56.4
Temp. height	56.8

Table A9.2
Mesio-distal (M–D) and Bucco-lingual (B–L) Diameters of the Teeth (mm)

Tooth	M–D		B–L	
	Left	Right	Left	Right
I_1[b]	5.0	4.1	6.0	4.8
I_2	5.6	5.6	6.4	6.4
C	6.5	–	7.5	–
P_1	6.9	6.8	8.5	8.3
P_2	7.2	7.0	9.6	9.5
M_1	11.0	11.1	11.7	11.8
M_2	10.0	10.5	11.1	11.6
M_3	10.8	10.7	10.4	11.4

[a] go = gonion; gn = gnathion; id = infradentale.
[b] I_1 = first incisor; I_2 = second incisor; C = canine; P_1 = first premolar; P_2 = second premolar; M_1 = first molar; M_2 = second molar; M_3 = third molar (all mandibular teeth).

Table A9.3
Penrose Distances between the Nabta Site E-75-8 Mandible and Comparative Data.

Comparative sample	N[a]	Size[b] C_Q^2	Shape C_H^2	Linearized distance $\sqrt{C_Q^2 + C_H^2}$
Gebel Sahaba (Late Paleolithic)	10	0.04	5.75	2.40
Wadi Halfa (Mesolithic)	6	(+) 0.42	2.29	1.84
Taforalt (Epipaleolithic)	10	(+) 2.56	4.01	2.56
Northwest African Mesolithic	50	(−) 3.10	3.91	2.64
Izriten (Morocco, about 8100 BP)	1	(+) 1.23	4.85	2.46
Muge (Portugal, about 8000 BP)	40	(+) 0.15	2.73	1.70
Grotte des Hoteaux (Magdalenian)	1	(−) 0.31	2.37	1.63
L'Abri Vidon (Magdalenian)	1	0.02	1.17	1.09
Poland (Early Medieval)	500	(−) 0.25	2.96	1.79
France (Modern)	100	0.00	3.16	1.78
Uganda (eighteenth and nineteenth centuries)	28	0.03	0.70	0.85
Negroid and Australoid (Modern)	100	(−) 0.30	1.61	1.38

[a] Except for those instances where only a single specimen is listed, only approximate numbers are given, because within each series the number of observations made for each characteristic varies.
[b] A plus (+) indicates the Nabta mandible was larger than the comparative material, and a minus (−) indicates that it was smaller.

tween the Nabta mandible and the comparative data. In size distances, although this is against mathematical rules, we have indicated whether the distances are positive or negative in order to give the reader an impression of whether the subject was larger (+) or smaller (−) than the comparative material. From Table A9.3 it may be seen that the largest differences exist between the individual from Nabta and the series from northwestern Africa, Wadi Halfa, and Gebel Sahaba. Although still distinctly different, the mandible is more similar to finds from Europe than to those claimed to belong to the Mechta type. The smallest Penrose distances were found between the Nabta individual and the Negroid model. It is noteworthy that size and shape distances to the Caucasoid model are smaller than are those to the African Paleolithic–Mesolithic series.

It must be taken into account that we are dealing with a single bone and that comparative date are rare, but it may

nevertheless be concluded (with all due reservations) that Site E-75-8 was occupied by people dissimilar to the northwestern African type and much closer to Negroes living south of the Sahara. In this context, it is worth mentioning that, although metrical characteristics were not taken into account, the same conclusion was drawn by Derry (1949) when examining fragmentary skeletal material from Khartoum. Moreover, in the Hoggar region of the southern central Sahara, skeletons of an elderly woman and two children found at the site of Amekni (early Neolithic of Saharo-Sudanese tradition) are also claimed to be Negroids (Camps 1974).

A more soundly based exploration of the possibly Negroid origin of early Neolithic human groups in Egypt must await the collection of sufficient material to permit a thorough analysis in terms of population biology.

ACKNOWLEDGMENT

This work was carried out within Section IA of the Biological History of Human Populations Research Program.

REFERENCES

Anderson, J. E.
1968   Late Paleolithic skeletal remains from Nubia. In *The prehistory of Nubia*, edited by F. Wendorf. Dallas: Fort Burgwin Research Center and Southern Methodist University Press. Pp. 996–1040.

Camps, G.
1974   *Les Civilisations Préhistoriques de l'Afrique du Nord et du Sahara*. Paris: Doin.

Charon, M., L. Ortlieb, and N. Petit-Maire
1973   Occupation humaine holocéne de la région du Cap Juby. *Bulletin et Mémoires de la Société d'Anthropologie de Paris 10:* 379–412.

Corrucini, R. S.
1973   Size and shape similarity coefficients based on metric characters. *American Journal of Physical Anthropology 38:* 743–754.

Derry, D. E.
1949   Report on the human remains. In *Early Khartoum*, by A. J. Arkell. London: Oxford University Press.

Górny, S.
1957   Crania Africana, Uganda. *Materiały i Prace Antropologiczne 14.*

Greene, D. L. and G. Armelagos
1972   *The Wadi Halfa Mesolithic population.* Department of Anthropology Research Report No. 11. Amherst: University of Massachusetts.

Lavergne, J.
1974   Dimensions mésio-distales et vestibulo-linguales de dents humaines permanentes. *Bulletin et Mémoires de la Société d'Anthropologie de Paris 11:* 351–355.

Lefèvre, J.
1973   Etude odontologique des hommes de Muge. *Bulletin et Mémoires de la Société d'Anthropologie de Paris 10:* 301–333.

Miles, A. E. W.
1963   The dentition in the assessment of individual age in skeletal material. In *Dental anthropology*, edited by D. Brothwell. Oxford: Pergamon Press. Pp. 191–209.

Riquet, R.
1972   Quelques documents réputés paléolithiques. *Bulletin et Mémoires de la Société d'Anthropologie de Paris 9:* 135–160.

Stęślicka, W.
1970   Badania morfologiczne uzębienia mlecznego i trwałego mieszkańców Gruczna z XII i XIII wieku. *Zeszyty Naukowe Uniwerysytetu M. Kopernika w Toruniu*, Vol. 22, Biologia XII. Pp. 43–77.

Strzałko, J.
1970   Rda mięśnia skroniowego w morfogenezie szkieletu twarzy. *Przegląd Antropologiczny 38:* 3–24.

Vallois, H. V.
1972   Le crane magdalénien des Hoteaux. *Bulletin et Mémoires de la Société d'Anthropologie de Paris 9:* 7–25.

10

A Scanning Electron Microscope Study of Cereal Grains from Nabta Playa

ANN STEMLER AND RICHARD FALK

Scanning electron microscopy was used to make a more detailed study of cereal grains from Nabta Playa than is possible with conventional light microscopy and photography. The cereal grains studied were found at two sites: the Neolithic of Site E-75-6, with ten radiocarbon dates clustered around 8100 BP, and the lower cultural layer of E-75-8, which is radiocarbon dated to about 7200 BP (Wendorf *et al.* 1976). The preservation of the three cereal grains and one inflorescence fragment is excellent and allows confident assignment of two grains to hulled six-row barley, one grain to naked barley, and the inflorescence fragment to domesticated wheat, most probably tetraploid emmer wheat. Photographs of the archaeological specimens and their modern counterparts, produced with a Stereoscan S4 scanning electron microscope, are presented in the plates and the implications of the evidence will be discussed briefly in this report.

Figure A10.1 shows the two archaeological grains of hulled six-row barley, a grain of modern six-row barley, and a portion of an inflorescence of modern six-row barley. It should be noted that the archaeological specimens are actually only a little over half the size of the modern barley shown. (The photograph of modern barley was magnified less than the photographs of archaeological barley in order to fit in the frame.) It should also be noted that the scan-

ning electron micrographs are composite photographs. This is necessary since the scanning electron microscope, designed as it is for the study of very small structures, cannot take a single photograph of something as large as a cereal grain, even set at its lowest power of magnification. The procedure for photographing the grains was to use the lowest magnification possible on the instrument (20×), to take two or three pictures and to match them as well as possible.

Comparison of specimens in Figure A10.1a and b shows that the ventral crease (CR) curves more in the specimen in Figure A10.1a, and in this regard it is similar to the specimen in Figure A10.1c. This curvature is significant because it indicates that (a) is a lateral floret (L) of six-row barley. Hybridization between domesticated six-row barley and wild barley occasionally produces six-row barley with a brittle rachis. This barley has, in the past, been considered by some authorities to be a genuine species of wild barley, but cytogenetic studies (Zohary 1963) have revealed the hybrid origin of these populations and indicate that they could not have existed before populations of domesticated six-row barley were established. As there is, then, no wild six-row barley, the barley from Nabta Playa must have been a domesticate.

Figure A10.2a shows the inflorescence fragment from Site E-75-8. A comparison of this fragment and fragments

393

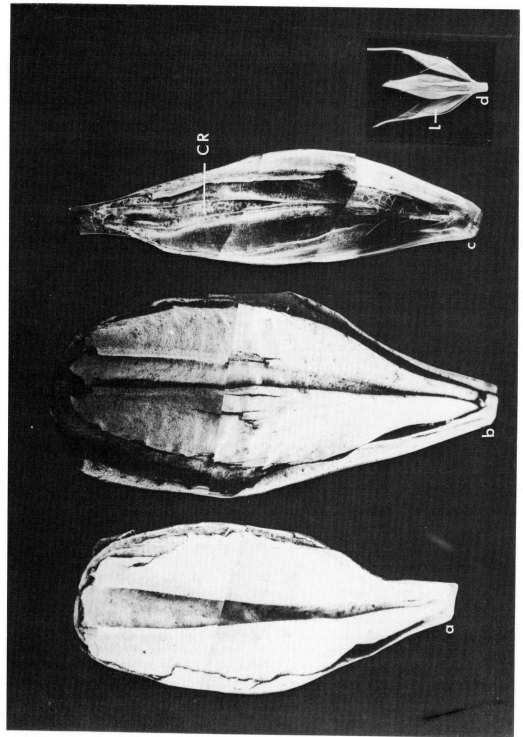

FIGURE A10.1. *Hulled six-row barley from Nabta Playa and modern six-row barley. (a) hulled six-row barley from E-75-6, Feature 4, magnified approximately 19.3×; (b) hulled barley from E-75-8, lower cultural layer, magnified approximately 19.3×; (c) lateral grain of modern six-row barley magnified 9.9×; (d) portion (one node) of an inflorescence of modern six-row barley showing the central and two lateral (L) florets containing grains. The lateral florets, because of their position, develop a curved ventral crease (CR) as shown in (a) and (c). (Note: the apparent difference in length between [a] and [b] is a result of the relatively more vertical orientation of [a] during photography; [a] and [b] are approximately the same size.)*

394

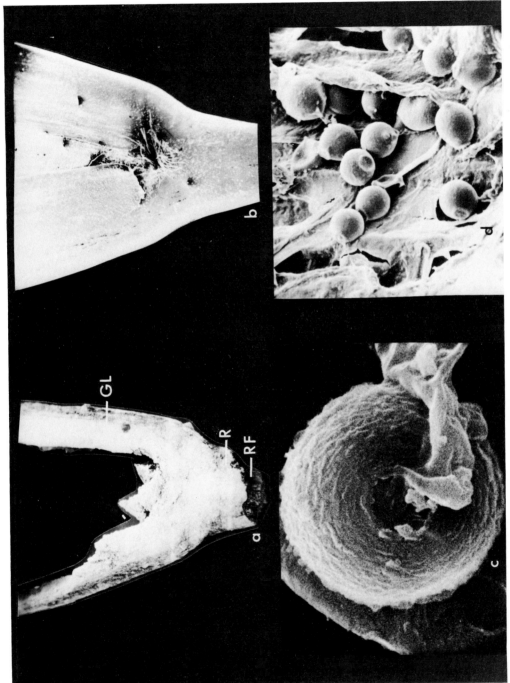

FIGURE A10.2. Wheat from Nabta Playa, modern emmer wheat, and fungal spores from the rachis of the Nabta wheat. (a) inflorescence fragment of emmer wheat from the lower cultural layer of Site E-75-8 (16×); (b) modern emmer wheat, the same view as a (16×); (c) fungal spore on the rachis of the wheat fragment from Nabta Playa (9000×) (spore diameter approximately 6.5 microns); (d) fungal spores on the rachis of the wheat fragment from Nabta Playa (1800×) (spore diameter approximately 5.3 microns).

FIGURE A10.3. *Naked barley from Site E-75-6, Feature 1, and modern naked barley (magnification approximately 12.7× for all views). (a) dorsal view of archaeological grain (the bottom right is the end of the grain that attached to the parent plant; the portion of the grain that surrounded the embryo [EM] is preserved); (b) modern naked barley, same view as (a); (c) dorso-ventral view of archaeological grain showing its thickness; (d) modern naked barley, same view as (c); (e) view of archaeological grain looking down on the distal tip of grain, showing relative width (horizontal) and thickness (vertical), transverse ripples in the seed coat, shallow dorsal (top) groove and the broad ventral crease (CR); (f) modern naked barley, same view as (e).*

of six-row and two-row barley clearly indicates that the archaeological specimen is not barley, but comparison of the archaeological specimen and of modern emmer wheat (Figure A10.2: b) shows very close similarities. The ascending portions of the archaeological specimen are glumes (GL) and the descending portion is the rachis (R). The fact that the rachis ends in a rough fracture (RF) indicates that the wheat is domesticated. If this were wild wheat, the base of the rachis fragment would be smooth, as a result of the formation of the abscission, or separation, zone that facilitates natural fragmentation of the inflorescence and dispersal of grain. (A more complete discussion of the differences between wild and domesticated cereals in archaeological contexts is included in the report on cereals from Wadi Kubbaniya (Stemler and Falk, in press), and discussions of the process of cereal domestication can be found in Harlan *et al.* (1976) and in Stemler (in press).) The similarity in dimensions of the archaeological wheat and its modern counterpart suggests that the wheat grown at the site was not a great deal less in thickness than modern emmer wheat. As only the base of the glumes is preserved, the length of the grain, compared with modern varieties of emmer wheat, cannot be determined.

Figure A10.1c and d show highly magnified views of fungal spores on the rachis of the archaeological wheat. The spores are still under investigation. The initial impression of the plant pathologists who have examined the photographs is that the spores are of decomposers rather than of disease-producing organisms (Wells, Butler personal communication).

Figure A10.3 shows three views of a grain from Site E-75-6 and the same views of modern naked barley. The similarity suggests the archaeological specimen is naked barley. Another possibility considered was that the grain might be emmer wheat, but the Nabta Playa grain is more similar to naked barley than to emmer wheat in several respects. The E-75-6 grain has a prominent lower tip where the grain attached to the parent plant; in emmer wheat this portion of the grain is not so prominent. The Nabta Playa grain has a relatively broad, but shallow, ventral crease (CR) as seen in Figure A10.3e; in emmer wheat the ventral crease is more deep and narrow. The Nabta Playa grain and naked barley are both relatively greater in width and smaller in dorso-ventral thickness than emmer wheat, and the Nabta Playa grain has faintly visible, transverse ripples in the seed coat and a shallow, dorsal groove, which are characteristics of naked barley (Renfrew 1973) (Figure A10.3e and f).

High magnification pictures were also taken of the seed coats of the archaeological grain, of modern naked barley, and of emmer wheat. However, this line of investigation proved fruitless because the pattern of the seed coat in the archaeological specimen was not sufficiently well preserved. Furthermore, the seed coat patterns of modern emmer wheat and of naked barley are remarkably similar, so that it may not be possible confidently to assign a specimen to either of these two species on the basis of seed coat pattern, even if the preservation is very good. Although seed coat patterns were not well preserved in the archaeological grains, the epidermal patterns in the lemmas and paleas of the hulled barley were beautifully preserved; epidermal patterns may, therefore, provide useful data in future palaeoethnobotanical studies.

DISCUSSION

Radiocarbon dates for the cereal grains from Site E-75-6 cluster around 8100 BP. This site yielded the naked barley and one grain of hulled barley. The radiocarbon dates for the lower cultural layer of Site E-75-8 are about 7200 BP. That site contained the wheat inflorescence fragment and one grain of hulled barley. Thus, the Nabta Playa grains predate grain from the Fayum, which have radiocarbon dates ranging from 5810 BP to 6390 BP with an average of about 6040 BP (Clark 1971). Also, the dates for the Nabta Playa grains are not much more recent than radiocarbon dates for the earliest farming sites in southwestern Asia. The earliest radiocarbon date for the Nabta Playa grains is only 1250 years later than the date of the earliest evidence of domesticated grain in the Bus Mordeh phase at Ali Kosh, on the Deh Luran plain of Iranian Khuzistan (Renfrew 1969; Helbaek 1966). Evaluated in the most conservative way, the evidence of grains from Nabta Playa indicates a remarkably rapid dispersal of domesticated cereals. The shortest overland distance between Ali Kosh and Nabta Playa is approximately 2600 km. In a less conservative evaluation, the cereal grains from Nabta Playa raise some interesting questions about the commonly held belief that wheat and barley were domesticated in southwestern Asia. This belief is based on two lines of evidence. The first is the coincidence of early farming sites in southwestern Asia with the present biogeographic ranges of the wild relatives of wheat and barley (Harlan and Zohary 1966). The second is the evidence of both wild and domesticated cereals at some of the early farming sites in southwestern Asia (Renfrew 1969 and 1973). These two lines of evidence are not incontrovertible.

There is some reason to question whether the evidence of wild cereals together with domesticated cereals indicates that these were the earliest farming sites, where the process of cereal domestication was going on. It may be that cereal domestication began much earlier in time and that wild cereals continued to be collected long after cereals were domesticated, as has been pointed out by Zohary (1969). It is also possible to question whether the cereals identified as wild at the southwest Asian sites are truly wild. The criterion used to designate cereals as domesticated has been that several internodes be attached to one another, indicating a nonbrittle rachis, one that does not come apart by formation of abscission zones (Helbaek 1959 and 1966). This criterion is certainly a good indicator of a domesticated cereal, but if this is the only criterion used, it is possible to interpret wrongly a single inflorescence unit or node as wild when it may be from a domesticated plant. Sometimes even this stringent criterion is ignored: *"Hordeum spontaneum"* from the site of Jarmo, for example (Renfrew 1969; Helbaek 1959), is considered wild because it is referred to by the same name as the wild progenitor of domesticated barley. However, the archaeological specimens should be considered as domesticated because, in the words of the investigator who identified the specimens, these cereals "had attained at least a certain degree of toughness . . . to judge by some axis portions consisting of two or three internodes [Helbaek 1959]." According to van Zeist (personal communication), there is evidence of truly wild-type inflorescence fragments, as indicated by smooth abscission zones, in barley specimens from an early Neolithic site in the Damascus area. However, identification of wild einkorn (diploid) wheat from that site is based on grains alone rather than on inflorescence fragments, which are much better indicators of the wild or domesticated status of a cereal.

It is our opinion that the evidence of wild grains from southwestern Asian sites should be reexamined to see if they really should be considered wild. Scanning electron microscopy can help to examine well preserved inflorescence fragments more closely to determine whether they came from plants with a brittle, wild-type inflorescence (as indicated by smooth abscission zones), or whether they came from nonbrittle, domesticated-type inflorescences (as indicated by rough fracture zones on the ends of the fragments).

If we have reason to suspect that cereals may have been domesticated earlier than about 9500 BP, then we must also question the relevance of the coincidence of early southwestern Asian farming sites with the present biogeographic range of wild relatives of wheat and barley. Palynological and paleolimnological evidence (van Zeist 1969; Butzer 1975) suggests that before 8000 BP the climate in the Near East was colder and drier than it is at the present. Such a climate may not have supported populations of wild wheat and barley in the areas where they are now found. If the wild relatives of wheat and barley were not abundant in southwestern Asia before 8000 BP, then perhaps the beginnings of the process of cereal domestication took place elsewhere. Cereal grains from Wadi Kubbaniya, near Aswan in Egypt, dating to about 18,300–17,000 BP, provide further evidence that southwestern Asia may not have been the site of the beginning of the process of domestication of wheat and barley. The results of a scanning electron microscopic study of barley and diploid wheat from Wadi Kubbaniya will be published shortly (Stemler and Falk in press).

ACKNOWLEDGMENTS

We would like to express our thanks to the many people who helped make this study possible. Specimens of wild and domesticated wheats and barley and a great deal of information were supplied by Jack Harlan, Agronomy Department, University of Illinois, Urbana, Illinois, and Charles Schaller, Calvin Qualset, and Pat McGuire of the Agronomy Department, University of California, Davis, California. Ed Risley and Sonia Cook (U.C., Davis) provided much patient technical assistance. A.S. thanks Richard Falk, Kenneth Wells, and Bruce Bonner for their encouragement and for very generously sharing the excellent research facilities of the Botany Department of the University of California at Davis.

REFERENCES

Butzer, K. W.
   1975   Patterns of environmental change in the Near East during late Pleistocene and early Holocene times. In *Problems in prehistory: North Africa and the Levant*, edited by F. Wendorf and A. E. Marks. Dallas: Southern Methodist University Press. Pp. 389–410.

Clark, J. D.
   1971   A re-examination of the evidence for agricultural origins in the Nile Valley. *Proceedings of the Prehistoric Society* 37:34–79.

Harlan, J. R., J. M. J. de Wet, and A. Stemler
   1976   Plant domestication and indigenous African Agriculture. In *Origins of African plant domestication*, edited by J. R. Harlan, J. M. J. de Wet, and A. Stemler. The Hague: Mouton. Pp. 3–19.

Harlan, J. R., and D. Zohary
   1966   Distribution of wild wheats and barley. *Science* 153:1074–1080.

Helbaek, H.
   1959   Domestication of food plants in the Old World. *Science* 130: 365–372.
   1966   Commentary on the phylogenesis of *Triticum* and *Hordeum*. *Economic Botany* 20:350–360.

Renfrew, J. M.
   1969   The archaeological evidence for the domestication of plants: methods and problems. In *The domestication and exploitation of plants and animals*, edited by P. J. Ucko and G. W. Dimbleby. London: Duckworth. Pp. 149–172.
   1973   *Palaeoethnobotany: The prehistoric food plants of the Near East and Europe*. London: Methuen.

Stemler, A. B. L.
in Plant domestication in the Sahara and the Nile. In *The*
press *Sahara and the Nile,* edited by M. A. J. Williams and
H. Fauré. Rotterdam: Balkema.

Stemler, A. B. L., and R. Falk
in A scanning electron microscopic study of cereal grains
press from Wadi Kubbaniya. In *Loaves and fishes: The prehistory of Wadi Kubbaniya,* assembled by F. Wendorf and R. Schild, edited by A. E. Close. Dallas: Department of Anthropology, Institute for the Study of Earth and Man, Southern Methodist University.

Ucko, P. J., and G. W. Dimbleby (Eds.)
1969 *The Domestication and exploitation of plants and animals.* London: Duckworth.

Wendorf, F., R. Schild, R. Said, C. V. Haynes, A. Gautier, and M. Kobusiewicz
1976 The prehistory of the Egyptian Sahara. *Science 193:*103–114.

van Zeist, W.
1969 Reflections on prehistoric environments in the Near East. In *The domestication and exploitation of plants and animals,* edited by P. J. Ucko and G. W. Dimbleby. London: Duckworth, Pp. 35–46.

Zohary, D.
1963 Spontaneous brittle six-row barleys, their nature and origin. *Proceedings of the First International Barley Genetics Symposium, Wageningen.* Pp. 27–31.
1969 The progenitors of wheat and barley in relation to domestication and agricultural dispersal in the Old World. In *The domestication and exploitation of plants and animals,* edited by P. J. Ucko and G. W. Dimbleby. London: Duckworth. Pp. 47–66.

References

Abel, H.
1975 Gerhard Rohlfs' life and work. *Annals of the Geological Survey of Egypt 5:* 17–23.

Abu Al Izz, M. S.
1971 *Landforms of Egypt.* Cairo: American University Press.

Almasy, L. E.
1942 *Unbekannte Sahara.* Leipzig.

Anderson, J. E.
1968 Late Paleolithic skeletal remains from Nubia. In *The prehistory of Nubia,* edited by F. Wendorf. Dallas: Fort Burgwin Research Center and Southern Methodist University Press. Pp. 996–1040.

Arambourg, C.
1948 Observations sur le Quaternaire dans la région du Hoggar. *Travaux de l'Institut de Recherches Sahariennes, Alger 5:* 7–18.
1965 Le gisement moustérien et l'Homme du Jebel Irhoud (Maroc). *Quaternaria 7:* 1–7.

Arambourg, C., and L. Balout
1952 L'ancien lac de Tihodaine et ses gisements préhistoriques. *Actes du Congrès Panafricain de Préhistoire, II Session, Alger, 1952.* Pp. 281–292.

Arkell, A. J.
1949 *Early Khartoum.* London: Oxford University Press.
1953 *Shaheinab.* London: Oxford University Press.

Armelagos, G. J., G. H. Ewing, K. K. Greene, and D. L. Greene
1965 Report of the physical anthropology section, University of Colorado Nubian Expedition. *Kush 13:* 24–27.

Attia, M. J.
1954 Ground water in Egypt. *Bulletin de l'Institut du Désert d'Egypte 4*(1).

Aumassip, G.
1972 Civilisations prénéolithiques des régions sahariennes. In *Actes du Congrès Panafricain de Préhistoire, VI Session, Dakar, 1967.* Pp. 273–278.

Bagnold, R. A.
1931 Journeys in the Libyan Desert, 1929 and 1930. *Geographical Journal 78* (1): 13–39, 524–535.
1933 A further journey through the Libyan Desert. *Geographical Journal 82* (2): 103–129, 211–235.
1939 An expedition to the Gilf Kebir and Uweinat, 1938. I. Narrative of the journey. *Geographical Journal 93* (4): 281–287.
1941 *The physics of blown sand and desert dunes.* London: Methuen.

Bagnold, R. A., W. J. Harding-King, D. Newbold, and W. B. K. Shaw
1931 Journeys in the Libyan Desert, 1929 and 1930. *Geographical Journal 78* (6): 524–535.

Bagnold, R. A., O. H. Myers, R. F. Peel, and H. A. Winkler
1939 An expedition to the Gilf el Kebir and Uweinat, 1938. *Geographical Journal 93* (4): 281–313.

Ball, J.
1900 *Kharga Oasis: Its topography and geology.* Cairo: Geological Survey of Egypt.
1927 Problems of the Libyan Desert. *Geographical Journal 70* (1): 21–28, 105–128, and 209–224.
1933 Further remarks on Kharga Oasis. *Geographical Journal 81* (6): 532.

Balout, L.
1955 *Préhistoire de l'Afrique du Nord. Essai de chronologie.* Paris: Arts et Métiers Graphiques.
1965 Données nouvelles sur le problème du Moustérien en Afrique du Nord. *Actas del V Congreso Panafricano de Prehistoria y de Estudio del Cuatenario, 1, Santa Cruz de Tenerife.* Pp. 137–146.

Barbour, K. M.
1961 *Republic of Sudan, a regional geography.* London: University of London Press.

Barich, B. E.
1974 La serie stratigrafica dell'Uadi Ti-n-Torha (Acacus, Libia). *Origini 8:* 7–184.

Barker, H., R. Burleigh, and N. Meeks
1971 British Museum natural radiocarbon measurements, VII. *Radiocarbon 13* (2): 157–188.

Bar-Yosef, O.
1975 The Epipaleolithic in Palestine and Sinai. In *Problems in prehistory: North Africa and the Levant,* edited by F. Wendorf and A. E. Marks. Dallas: Southern Methodist University Press. Pp. 363–378.

Bar-Yosef, O., F. Burian, and E. Friedman
1974 A Harifan site in the Western Negev. *Mitekufat Haeven* 12: 10–14. (In Hebrew.)

Bar-Yosef, O., and J. L. Phillips (Editors)
1977 Prehistoric investigations in Gebel Maghara, northern Sinai. Jerusalem: *Monographs of the Institute of Archaeology, No. 7.*

Bates, O.
1914 *The Eastern Libyans.* London: Macmillan.

Beadle, L. C.
1975 *The inland waters of tropical Africa.* New York: Longman.

Beadnell, H. J. L.
1909 *An Egyptian oasis: An account of the Oasis of Kharga in the Libyan Desert.* London: John Murray.
1910 The sand dunes of the Libyan Desert. *Geographical Journal 35:* 379–395.
1931 Zerzura. *Geographical Journal 77* (3): 245–250.

Beaudet, G., P. Michel, D. Nahon, P. Oliva, J. Riser, and A. Ruellan
1976 Formes, formations superficielles et variations climatiques récentes du Sahara occidental. *Révue de Géographie Physique et de Géologie Dynamique 18* (2–3): 157–174.

Beucher, F.
1972 Etude palynologique de formations néogènes et quaternaires au Sahara nord-occidental. In *Palaeoecology of Africa,* Vol. 7, edited by E. M. van Zinderen Bakker. Cape Town: A. A. Balkema. Pp. 7–12.

Biberson, P.
1961a Le cadre paléogéographique de la préhistoire du Maroc atlantique. *Publications du Service des Antiquités du Maroc, 16.*
1961b Le Paléolithique inférieur du Maroc atlantique. *Publications du Service des Antiquités du Maroc, 17.*

Binford, L. R.
1968 Post-Pleistocene adaptations. In *New perspectives in archaeology,* edited by S. R. and L. R. Binford. Chicago: Aldine. Pp. 313–341.
1973 Interassemblage variability: The Mousterian and the "functional" argument. In *The explanation of culture change: Models in prehistory,* edited by C. Renfrew. London: Duckworth. Pp. 227–254.

Binford, L. R., and S. R. Binford
1966 A preliminary analysis of functional variability in the Mousterian of Levallois facies. *American Anthropologist 68:* 238–295.

Binford, S. R.
1972 The significance of variability: A minority report. In *The origin of Homo sapiens,* UNESCO Conference 1969, Paris 1972. Pp. 199–210.

Bordes, F.
1953 Essai de classification des industries Moustériennes. *Bulletin de la Société Préhistorique Française 50:* 457–466.
1954 Les limons quaternaires du Bassin de la Seine. *Archives de l'Institut de Paléontologie Humaine,* Paris.
1961 *Typologie du Paléolithique Ancien et Moyen.* Publications de l'Institut de Préhistoire de l'Université de Bordeaux, Mémoire l. Bordeaux: Delmas.
1973 On the chronology and contemporaneity of different Paleolithic cultures in France. In *The explanation of culture change: Models in prehistory,* edited by C. Renfrew. London: Duckworth.

Bordes, F., and M. Bourgon
1951 Le complèxe moustérien: Moustériens, Levalloisien et Tayacien. *L'Anthropologie 55:* 1–23.

Bordes, F., and D. de Sonneville-Bordes
1970 The significance of variability in Paleolithic assemblages. *World Archaeology 2* (1): 61–73.

Boserup, E.
1965 *The conditions of agricultural growth: The economics of agrarian change under population pressure.* Chicago: Aldine.

Bosinski, G.
1969 Eine Variante der Micoque-Technik am Fundplatz Buhlen, Kreis Valdeck. *Jahreschr. für Mitteldeutsche Vorgeschichte 53:* 59–74.

Boulos, L.
1968 The discovery of Medemia palm in the Nubian desert of Egypt. *Bot. Notiser 121:* 117–120.

Bourgon, M.
1957 Les Industries Moustériennes et Pré-Moustériennes du Périgord. *Archives de l'Institut de Paléontologie Humaine, Mémoire 27.* Paris: Masson.

Bovier-Lapièrre, P.
1926 Les gisements paléolithiques de la plaine de l'Abbassieh. *Bulletin de l'Institut d'Egypte 8:* 257–275.

Braidwood, R. J.
1960 The agricultural revolution. *Scientific American 203* (3): 130–152.

Bronson, B.
1972 Farm labour and the evolution of food production. In *Population growth: Anthropological implications,* edited by B. Spooner. Cambridge: M.I.T. Press. Pp. 190–218.
1975 The earliest farming: Demography as cause and consequence. In *Population, ecology and social evolution,* edited by S. Polgar. The Hague: Mouton. Pp. 53–78.

Browne, W. G.
1799 *Travels in Africa, Egypt and Syria, 1792 to 1798.* London.

Butler, B. H.
1974 Skeletal remains from a Late Paleolithic site near Esna, Egypt. In The Fakhurian: A Late Paleolithic industry from Upper Egypt, by D. Lubell. *Papers of the Geological Survey of Egypt,* No. 58. Pp. 176–183.

Butzer, K. W.
1958 Das ökologische Problem der neolithischen Felsbilder der östlichen Sahara. *Abhändlungen der Akademie der Wissenschaften und der Literatur (Mainz) 1:* 20–49.
1961 Climatic changes in arid regions since the Pliocene. *Arid Zone Research (UNESCO) 17:* 31–56.
1964 Pleistocene paleoclimates of the Kurkur Oasis, Egypt. *Canadian Geographer 8* (3): 125–140.
1965 Desert landforms at the Kurkur Oasis. *Annals of the Association of American Geographers 55* (4): 578–591.
1966 Climatic changes in the arid zones of Africa during early to mid-Holocene times. In *World climate from 8,000 to 0 B.C.,* edited by J. S. Sawyer. Proceedings of the International Symposium. London: Royal Meteorological Society. Pp. 72–83.
1971a *Environment and archaeology, an ecological approach to prehistory,* 2nd ed. Chicago: Aldine.
1971b Quartäre Vorzeitklimate der Sahara. In *Die Sahara und ihre Randgebiete,* Vol. I, edited by H. Schiffers. Munich: Weltforum Verlag. Pp. 349–388.
1975 Pleistocene littoral–sedimentary cycles of the Mediterranean Basin: A Mallorquin view. In *After the australopithecines,* edited by K. W. Butzer and G. L. Isaac. The Hague: Mouton. Pp. 25–71.
1976 *Early hydraulic civilization in Egypt.* Chicago: University of Chicago Press.

Butzer, K. W., and C. L. Hansen
1968 *Desert and river in Nubia: Geomorphology and prehistoric environments at the Aswan Reservoir.* Madison: University of Wisconsin Press.
1972 Interrelationships of subsaharan Nilotic deposits and local wadi alluvia in southern Egypt. In *Actes du Congrès Panafricain de Préhistoire, VI session, Dakar, 1967.* Pp. 336–337.

Butzer, K. W., G. L. Isaac. J. L. Richardson, and C. Washbourn-Kamau
1972 Radiocarbon dating of East African lake levels. *Science* 175:1069–1076.

Camps, G.
1955 Le gisement atérien du Camp Franchet d'Esperay. *Libyca* 3:17–56.
1969a Amekni. Néolithique ancien du Hoggar. *Mémoires du Centre de Recherches Anthropologiques, Préhistoriques et Ethnographiques*, No. 10. Paris: Arts et Métiers Graphiques.
1969b Harafin-Ethiopiens. Réflexions sur les origines des négroïdes saharienne. In *Colloque international sur la biologie des populations saharienne*. Alger. Pp. 11–17.
1974a *Les civilisations préhistoriques de l'Afrique du Nord et du Sahara*. Paris: Doin.
1974b Tableau chronologique de la Préhistoire récente du Nord de l'Afrique, Deuxième synthèse des datations absolues obtenues par le carbone 14. *Bulletin de la Société Préhistorique Française* 71 (1):261–278.
1975 The prehistoric cultures of North Africa: Radiocarbon chronology. In *Problems in prehistory: North Africa and the Levant*, edited by F. Wendorf and A. E. Marks. Dallas: Southern Methodist University Press. Pp. 181–192.

Camps-Fabrer, H.
1975 *Un gisement Capsien de faciès sétifien: Medjez II, El Eulma (Algérie)*. Paris: C.N.R.S.

Carlson, R. L.
1967 Excavations at Khor Abu Anga and at sites in Nubia. *Current Anthropology* 8 (4):352.

Carlson, R. L., and J. S. Sigstad
1973 Paleolithic and late Neolithic sites excavated by the Fourth Colorado Expedition. *Kush* 15:51–58.

Caton-Thompson, G.
1952 *Kharga Oasis in prehistory*. London: Athlone Press.

Caton-Thompson, G., and E. W. Gardner
1932 The prehistoric geography of Kharga Oasis. *Geographical Journal* 80 (5):369–406.
1934 *The desert Fayum*. London: Royal Anthropological Institute.

Chamard, Ph. C.
1973a Monographie d'une sebkha continentale du Sud Ouest saharien: La sebkha de Chemchane (Adrar de Mauritanie). *Bulletin de l'Institut Française d'Afrique Noire 35A* (2):207–243.
1973b Paléoclimats du Sud-Ouest saharien au Quaternaire récent. *Colloque Nouakchott sur la désertification au Sud du Sahara, L'Institut Français d'Afrique Noir*

Chamla, M. C.
1968 Les populations anciennes du Sahara et des régions limitrophes. *Mémoires du C.R.A.P.E.*, No. 9. Paris: Arts et Métiers Graphiques.

Chavaillon, J.
1964 Etude stratigraphique des formations quaternaires du Sahara nord-occidental. *Publication du Centre de Recherches sur les zones arides*, No. 5. Paris: C.N.R.S.

Chavaillon, N.
1971 L'Atérien de la Zaouia el Kebira au Sahara nord occidental. (République algérienne). *Libyca* 19:9–51.
1973 L'Atérien de Hassi-Ouchtat dans le Mons d'Ougarta. (Sahara nord occidental). *Libyca* 21:91–138.

Childe, V. G.
1936 *Man makes himself*. London: Watts.

Chmielewski, W.
1968 Early and Middle Paleolithic sites near Arkin, Sudan. In *The prehistory of Nubia*, edited by F. Wendorf. Dallas: Fort Burgwin Research Center and Southern Methodist University Press. Pp. 110–147.

1969 Ensembles Micoque-Prondnikiens en Europe Centrale. *Geographia Polonica* 17:371–386.

Choubert, G., A. Fauré-Muret, and G. C. Maadeveld
1967 Nouvelles dates isotopiques du Quaternaire marocain et leur signification. *Comptes Rendus des Séances de l'Académie des Sciences* 264:434–437.

Clark, J. D.
1971 A re-examination of the evidence for agricultural origins in the Nile Valley. *Proceedings of the Prehistoric Society* 37 (Part II):34–79.
1976 Prehistoric populations and pressures favoring plant domestication in Africa. In *Origins of African plant domestication*, edited by J. R. Harlan, J. M. J. de Wet, and A. B. L. Stemler. The Hague: Mouton. Pp. 67–105.

Clark, J. D., and M. R. Kleindienst
1974 The Stone Age cultural sequence terminology, typology and raw materials. In *Kalambo Falls prehistoric site*, Vol. II, edited by J. D. Clark. Cambridge: Cambridge University Press Pp. 71–106.

Clark, J. D., M. A. J. Williams, and A. B. Smith
1973 The geomorphology and archaeology of Adrar Bous, central Sahara: A preliminary report. *Quaternaria* 17:245–297.

Clayton, P. A.
1933a A reconnaissance of the Gilf Kebir by the late Sir Robert Clayton East Clayton. *Geographical Journal* 18:249–254.
1933b The western side of the Gilf Kebir. *Geographical Journal 81* (3):254–259.
1937 The Southwestern Desert Survey Expedition, 1930–1931. *Bull. Soc. Roy. Géog. d'Egypte 19*:241–265.

Cohen, M. N.
1975 Population pressure and the origins of agriculture: An archaeological example from the coast of Peru. In *Population, ecology, and social evolution*, edited by S. Polgar. The Hague: Mouton. Pp. 79–122.
1977 *The food crisis in prehistory*. New Haven: Yale University Press.

Conrad, G.
1969 *L'évolution continentale post-Hercynienne du Sahara Algérien*. Paris: C.N.R.S.
1972 Les fluctuations climatiques récentes dans l'est du Sahara occidental Algérien. *Actes du Congrès Panafricain de Préhistoire, VI Session, Dakar, 1967*. Pp. 343–349.

Cooke, R. V., and A. Warren
1973 *Geomorphology in deserts*. London: B. T. Batsford.

Cour, P., and D. Duzer
1976 Persistance d'un climat hyperaride au Sahara central et méridional au cours de l'Holocéne. *Révue de Géographie Physique et de Géologie Dynamique 18* (2–3):175–198.

Couvert. M.
1969 Identification de charbons provenant du gisement de Tamar Hat (Algérie). *Libyca* 17:49–52.
1972 Variations paléoclimatiques en Algérie. Traduction climatique des informations paléobotaniques fournies par les charbons des gisements préhistoriques. Note préliminaire. *Libyca 20*:45–48.

Cunnison, I.
1966 *Baggara Arabs: Power and the lineage in a Sudanese nomad tribe*. Oxford: Clarendon.

Dalloni, M.
1955 La station moustérienne de Retaïmia près d'Inkerman (Algérie). *Actes du Congrès Panafricain de Préhistoire, II Session, Alger, 1952*. Pp. 419–427.

Degens, E. T.
1962 Geochemische Untersuchungen von Wässern aus der ägyptischen Sahara. *Geologische Rundschau 52* (2):625–639.

de Heinzelin, J.
1968 Geological history of the Nile Valley in Nubia. In *The prehistory of Nubia,* edited by F. Wendorf. Dallas: Fort Burgwin Research Center and Southern Methodist University Press. Pp. 19–55.

de Heinzelin, J., P. Haesaerts, and F. van Noten
1969 Géologie récente et préhistoire au Jebel Uweinat. *Africa-Tervuren 15* (4):120–126.

De Planhol, X., and P. Rognon
1970 *Les zones tropicales arides et subtropicales.* Paris: A. Collin.

Derricourt, R. M.
1971 Radiocarbon chronology for Egypt and North Africa. *Journal of Near Eastern Studies 30* (4):271–292.

Deuser, W. G., E. H. Ross, and L. S. Waterman
1976 Glacial and pluvial periods: Their relationship revealed by Pleistocene sediments of the Red Sea and Gulf of Aden. *Science 191*:1168–1170.

Diamond, J. M.
1977 Colonization cycles in man and beast. *World Archaeology 8* (3):249–261.

Dorize, L.
1976 L'oscillation climatique actuelle au Sahara. *Révue de Géographie Physique et de Géologie Dynamique 18* (2–3):217–228.

Dyson-Hudson, R., and N. Dyson-Hudson
1969 Subsistence herding in Uganda. *Scientific American 220* (2):76–89.

Ennouchi, E.
1966 Le site du Jebel Irhoud (Maroc). *Actas del V Congreso Panafricano de Prehistoria y le Estudio del Cuaternario, 2, Santa Cruz de Tenerife.* Pp. 53–59.

Evans-Pritchard, E. E.
1940 *The Nuer.* Oxford: Clarendon.

Evernden, J. F., and G. H. Curtis
1965 The potassium–argon dating of Late Cenozoic rocks in East Africa and Italy. *Current Anthropology 6* (4):343–385.

Ezzat, M. A.
1973 Egypt. In *Groundwater resources in Arab countries. Science Monograph 2.* Cairo: Arab League Educational, Cultural and Scientific Organization. Pp. 101–142. (In Arabic.)

Farris, J. C.
1975 Social evolution, population and production. In *Population, ecology and social evolution,* edited by S. Polgar. The Hague: Mouton. Pp. 235–271.

Fauré, H.
1966 Reconnaissance géologique des formations sédimentaires post-paléozoïques du Niger oriental. *Mémoires du Bureau de Recherches Géologiques et Minéralogiques,* No. 47.

Flannery, K. V.
1969 Origins and ecological effects of early domestication in Iran and the Near East. In *The domestication and exploitation of plants and animals,* edited by P. J. Ucko and G. W. Dimbleby. Chicago: Aldine. Pp. 73–100.

Florek, K., J. Lukaszewicz, J. Perkall, H. Steinhaus, and S. Zubrzycki
1951 Sur la liaison et la division des pointes d'un ensemble fin. *Colloquia Mathematica 2*:282–285.

Freeman, L. G.
1975 Acheulian sites and stratigraphy in Iberia and the Maghreb. In *After the australopithecines,* edited by K. W. Butzer and G. L. Isaac. The Hague: Mouton. Pp. 661–743.

Gabriel, B.
1973 Steinplätze: Feuerstellen neolithischer Nomaden in der Sahara. *Libyca 21*:151–168.
1976 Neolithische Steinplätze und Palaökologie in den Ebenen der ostlichen Zentralsahara. *Palaeoecology of Africa,* Vol. 9, edited by E. M. van Zinderen Bakker. Cape Town: A. A. Balkema. Pp. 25–40.
1977a Early and mid-Holocene climate in the eastern central Sahara. In *Drought in Africa,* 2nd ed., edited by D. Dalby, R. J. Harrison Church, and F. Bezzaz. London: International African Institute.
1977b Zum ökologischen Wandel im Neolithikum der östlichen Zentralsahara. *Berliner Geographische Abhandlungen, 27.*

Gardner, E. W.
1932 Some problems of Pleistocene hydrography of Kharga Oasis, Egypt. *Geological Magazine 69*:386–421.
1935 The Pleistocene fauna and flora of Kharga Oasis, Egypt. *Quarterly Journal of the Geological Society of London 91*:479–518.

Gasse, F.
1976 Intérêt de l'étude des Diatomées pour la reconstitution des paléoenvironnements lacustrés. Exemple des lacs d'age Holocéne de l'Afar (Ethiopie et T.F.A.I.) *Révue de Géographie Physique et de Géologie Dynamique 18* (2–3):199–216.

Gautier, A.
1968 Mammalian remains of the northern Sudan and southern Egypt. In *The prehistory of Nubia,* edited by F. Wendorf. Dallas: Fort Burgwin Research Center and Southern Methodist University Press. Pp. 80–99.
n.d. Non-marine mollusks and vertebrate remains from upper Pleistocene deposits and Middle Paleolithic sites at Bir Sahara and Bir Tarfawi, Western Desert, Egypt. Ms.

Geyh, M. A., and D. Jäkel
1974 Spätpleistozäne und holozäne Klimageschichte der Sahara aufgrund zuganglicher 14 C-Daten. *Zeitschrift für Geomorphologie, Neue Folge 18* (1):82–98.

Giegengack, R. F., Jr.
1968 Late Pleistocene history of the Nile Valley in Egyptian Nubia. Ph.D. dissertation, Yale University.

Gilead, D.
1973 Prehistoric finds in the Negev and Sinai. *Mitekufat Haeven 11*:36–42. (In Hebrew.)

Gobert, E. G.
1950 Le gisement paléolithique de Sidi Zin. *Karthago 1*:1–64.

Golachowski, S., B. Kostrubiec, and A. Zagozdzon
1974 *Metody badan geograficzno-osadniczych.* Warsaw: Nauk.

Greenwood, P. H.
1968 Fish remains. In *The prehistory of Nubia,* edited by F. Wendorf. Dallas: Fort Burgwin Research Center and Southern Methodist University Press. Pp. 100–109.

Gruet, M.
1955a Le gisement d'El Guéttar (Tunisie). *Quaternaria 2*:53–68.
1955b Le gisement moustérien d'El Guéttar. *Karthago 5*:1–79.
1958– Le gisement d'El Guéttar et sa flore. *Libyca 6–7*:
1959 79–126.

Guichard, J., and G. Guichard
1965 The Early and Middle Paleolithic of Nubia: A preliminary report. In *Contributions to the prehistory of Nubia,* edited by F. Wendorf. Dallas: Fort Burgwin Research Center and Southern Methodist University Press. Pp. 57–116.
1968 Contributions to the study of the Early and Middle Paleolithic of Nubia. In *The prehistory of Nubia,* edited by F. Wendorf. Dallas: Fort Burgwin Research Center and Southern Methodist University Press. Pp. 148–193.

Harding-King, W. J.
1913 The Libyan Desert from native information. *Geographical Journal 42*:277–283.
1918 Study of a dune belt. *Geographical Journal 51*: 16–33.
1925 *Mysteries of the Libyan Desert.* London.

Harlan, J. R., J. M. J. de Wet, and A. B. L. Stemler
1976 Plant domestication and indigenous African agriculture. In *Origins of African plant domestication,* edited by J. R. Harlan, J. M. J. de Wet, and A. B. L. Stemler. The Hague: Mouton. Pp. 3–19.

Harlan, J. R., and D. Zohary
1966 Distribution of wild wheats and barley. *Science* 153:1074–1080.

Hassan, F. A.
1972 Population dynamics and the beginnings of domestication in the Nile Valley. Paper read at the seventy-first meeting of the American Anthropological Association. Toronto. Mimeographed.
1976 Prehistoric studies of the Siwa Oasis region, northwestern Egypt. *Nyame Akuma,* No. 9. Pp. 18–34.
1978 Archaeological explorations of the Siwa Oasis region, Egypt. *Current Anthropology,* 19 (1):146–148.

Hassan, M. Y.
1956 The place of Zittel's *overwegischichten* in the Upper Senonian stratigraphy with a note on the provincial affinities of its fauna (type area Kharga Oasis). *Bulletin de l'Institut Egypte* 38:77–84.

Hassanein Bey, A. M.
1924 Through Koufra to Darfur. *Geographical Journal* 64:273–291.
1925 *The lost oasis.* London.

Hays, T. R.
1971 The Sudanese Neolithic: A critical analysis. Ph.D. dissertation, Southern Methodist University.
1975 Neolithic settlement of the Sahara as it relates to the Nile Valley. In *Problems in prehistory: North Africa and the Levant,* edited by F. Wendorf and A. E. Marks. Dallas: Southern Methodist University Press. Pp. 193–204.
n.d. Late prehistoric occupation of the Egyptian desert. Unpublished manuscript.

Hebrard, L.
1970 Fichier des ages absolues du Quaternaire d'Afrique au nord de l'équateur. *Bulletin de l'Association Sénégalaise d'Etudes Quaternaires Ouest Africaines* 26:39–56.

Hellstrom, B.
1940 The subterranean water in the Libyan Desert. *Institute of Hydraulics, Royal Institute of Technology, Stockholm.,* Bulletin No. 26.

Hermina, M., M. Ghobrial, and B. Issawi
1961 The geology of the Dakhla area. *Geological Survey of Egypt* 33:1–33.

Hester, J. J., and P. M. Hoebler
1969 Prehistoric settlement patterns in the Libyan Desert. *University of Utah Anthropology Papers,* No. 92.

Hey, R.
1971 Quaternary shorelines of the Mediterranean and Black seas. *Quaternaria* 15:273–284.

Howe, B.
1967 The Paleolithic of Tangier, Morocco, excavations at Cape Ashakar, 1939–1947. *American School of Prehistoric Research Peabody Museum, Harvard Univ.,* Bulletin No. 22.

Howell, F. C., and J. D. Clark
1963 Acheulian hunter–gatherers of sub-Saharan Africa. In *African ecology and human evolution,* edited by F. C. Howell and F. Bourlière. London. Aldine. Pp. 458–533.

Huard, P.
1972 Matériaux archéologiques pour la paléoclimatologie post-glaciaire du Sahara oriental et tchadien. *Actes du Congrès Panafricain de Préhistoire, VI Session, Dakar, 1967.* Pp. 207–217.

Hugot, H. J.
1963 Recherches préhistoriques dans l'Ahaggar nord-occidental, 1950–1957. *Mémoirs du Centre de Recherches Anthropologiques Préhistoriques et Ethnographiques,* No. 1. Paris: Arts et Métiers Graphiques.
1966 Limites méridionales de l'Atérien. *Actas del V Congreso Panafricano de Prehistoria y de Estudio de Cuaternario, 2, Santa Cruz de Tenerife.* Pp. 95–108.

Huzayyin, S. A.
1941 The place of Egypt in prehistory. *Mémoires de l'Institute d'Egypte 43.*

Irwin, H. T., J. B. Wheat, and L. F. Irwin
1968 University of Colorado investigations of Paleolithic and Epipaleolithic sites in the Sudan, Africa. *University of Utah Anthropology Papers,* No. 90.

Issawi, B.
1968 The geology of Kurkur–Dungul area. *Papers of the Geological Survey of Egypt,* No. 46.
1971 Geology of Darb el Arbain, Western Desert, Egypt. *Annals of the Geological Survey of Egypt* 1:53–92.
1973a Geology of the southeastern corner of the Western Desert. *Annals of the Geological Survey of Egypt* 3:25–30.
1973b Quaternary geology of Bir Sahara, Western Desert. Ms.
1977 The geology. In *The prehistory of Dakhla Oasis and adjacent desert,* by R. Schild and F. Wendorf. Wroclaw: Ossolineum. Pp. 11–17.

Jaeger, J. J.
1975 The mammalian faunas and hominid fossils of the middle Pleistocene of the Maghreb. In *After the australopithecines,* edited by K. W. Butzer and G. L. Isaac. The Hague: Mouton. Pp. 399–418.

Jäkel, D., and E. Schultz
1972 Spezielle Untersuchungen an der Mittelterrasse im Enneri Tabi, Tibesti-Gebirge. *Zeitschrift für Geomorphologie, Neue Folge, 15.* Pp. 129–143.

Kassas, M.
1956 Landform and plant cover in the Omdurman Desert. *Bulletin de la Société de Géographie d'Egypte* 29:43–58.
1971 Pflanzenieben in der "östlichen Sahara." In *Die Sahara und ihre Randgebiete,* edited by H. Schiffers. Munich: Weltforum Verlag. Pp. 477–497.

Kemal el Din, H., Prince
1928 L'exploration du Désert Libyque. *La Géographie* 50:171–183, 320–336.

Kemal el Din, H., Prince, and H. Breuil
1928 Les Gravures rupestres du Djebel Ouenat. *Révue Scientifique Illustrée* 66:105–117.

Kleindienst, M. R.
1961 Variability within the Late Acheulian assemblages in Eastern Africa. *South African Archaeological Bulletin* 16:35–52.
1962 Components of the East African Acheulian assemblage: An analytic approach. In *Actes du Congrès Panafricain de Préhistoire et de l'étude du Quaternaire,* edited by G. Mortelmans and J. Nenquin. Pp. 81–112.
1972 Brief observations on some Stone Age sites recorded by the Yale University Prehistoric Expedition to Nubia, 1964–1965. In *Actes du Congrès Panafricain de Préhistoire, VI Session, Dakar, 1967.* Pp. 111–113.

Knetsch, G. A., A. Shata, E. T. Degens, K. O. Münnich, J. C. Vogel, and M. M. El Shazly
1962 Untersuchungen an Grundwässern der Öst-Sahara. *Geologische Rundschau 52* (2):587–610.

Kobusiewicz, M.
1976 Pradzieje pólnocno-wschodniej Afryki miedzy 16 a 5 tysiacleciem P.N.E. *Przegladu Archeologicznego 24:5–102.*

Kostrubiec, B.
1971 Analiza matematyczna zbioru osiedli wojewodztwa opolskiego. In *Strucktury i Procesy Osadnicze,* edited by S. Golachowski. Wroclaw: Opole. Pp. 9–66.

Kowalski, S.
1967a Ciekawsze zabytki paleolityczne z najnowszych badan archeologicznych (1963–1965) w jaskini Ciemnej w Ojcowie, pow. Olkusz. *Materialy Archeologiczne* 8:39–46.
1967b Zagadnienie przejscia od paleolitu srodkowego do gornego na obszarze Polski w aspekcie elementow postepu technicznego. *III Sympozium Paleolityczne,* Vol. I. Pp. 3–7.
1969 Zagadnienie przejscia od paleolitu srodkowego do gornego w Polsce poludniowej w aspekcie postepu technicznego. *Swiatowit* 30:5–21.

Kozlowski, J. K.
1972 On the typologic classification of stone artifacts (contribution to discussion). *Sprawozdania Archeologiczne* 24: 455–467.

Krukowski, S.
1939 Paleolit. In *Prahistoria ziem Polskich,* Warsaw. Pp. 1–117.

Krzyzaniak, L.
1978 New light on early food-production in the central Sudan. *Journal of African History* 19 (3).

Leigh, E. G., Jr.
1968 Fossil Mollusca from the Kurkur Oasis. In *Desert and river in Nubia,* edited by K. W. Butzer and C. L. Hansen. Madison: University of Wisconsin Press. Pp. 513–514.

Leroi-Gourhan, A.
1957 Note sur les possibilités qu'apporte l'analyse pollinique aux études climatologiques en Afrique du Nord. *Bulletin de la Société Préhistorique Française.* 54:524–525.

Libby, W. F.
1952 *Radiocarbon dating.* Chicago: University of Chicago Press.

Lubell, D., J. L. Ballais, A. Gautier, F. A. Hassan, A. E. Close, C. Chippindale, J. Elmendorf, and G. Aumassip
1975 The prehistoric cultural ecology of Capsian escargotières. *Libyca* 23:43–121.

Lubell, D., F. A. Hassan, A. Gautier, and J. L. Ballais
1976 The Capsian escargotières. *Science* 191:910–920.

Lubin, V. P.
1965 Kvoprosu o metodike izutshenia nijniepaleolititsheskih kamennyh orudii. In *Paleolit i Neolit SSSR,* Vol. 5. Moscow–Leningrad: Nauka. Pp. 7–75.
1969 Rannij Paleolit Kabkaza. In *Priroda i Razvitie Piervobitnovo Obshtshestva na Teritorii Evropeisuoi Tshasti SSSR.* Moscow: Nauka. Pp. 154–168.
1977 *Musterskije kultury Kaukaza.* Leningrad: Nauka.

Maley, J.
1973 Mécanismes des changements climatiques aux bases latitudes. *Paleogeography, Paleoclimatology, Paleoecology* 14 (3):193–227.
1976 Essai sur le rôle de la zone tropicale dans les changements climatiques: l'exemple africain. *Comptes Rendus de l'Académie des Sciences, Paris* 283 (Series D):337–340.
1977a Analyses polliniques et paleoclimatologiques des douze derniers millénaires du Bassin du Tchad (Afrique Centrale). *Rech. Françaises sur le Quaternaire (I.N.Q.U.A., 1977),* Supplement au Bulletin de l'Association Française d'Etudes Quaternaires, 1977-1, No. 50. Pp. 187–197.
1977b Paleoclimates of central Sahara during the early Holocene. *Nature* 269:573–578.

Marks, A. E.
1968a The Halfan industry. In *The prehistory of Nubia,* edited by F. Wendorf. Dallas: Fort Burgwin Research Center and Southern Methodist University Press. Pp. 392–460.
1968b The Khormusan: An upper Pleistocene industry in Sudanese Nubia. In *The prehistory of Nubia,* edited by F. Wendorf. Dallas: Fort Burgwin Research Center and Southern Methodist University Press. Pp. 315–391.
1968c The Mousterian industries of Nubia. In *The prehistory of Nubia,* edited by F. Wendorf. Dallas: Fort Burgwin Research Center and Southern Methodist University Press. Pp. 194–314.
1968d The Sebilian industry of the Second Cataract. In *The prehistory of Nubia,* edited by F. Wendorf. Dallas: Fort Burgwin Research Center and Southern Methodist University Press. Pp. 461–531.
1973 The Harif point: A new tool type from the Terminal Epipaleolithic of the central Negev, Israel. *Paléorient* 1:97–99.
1975 An outline of prehistoric occurrences and chronology in the central Negev, Israel. In *Problems in prehistory: North Africa and the Levant,* edited by F. Wendorf and A. E. Marks. Dallas: Southern Methodist University Press. Pp. 351–362.

Marks, A. E., and T. R. Scott
1976 Abu Salem: Type site of the Harifian industry of the southern Levant. *Journal of Field Archaeology* 3:(1):43–60

Marks, A. E., J. L. Shiner, and T. R. Hays
1968 Survey and excavations in the Dongola Reach, Sudan. *Current Anthropology* 9(4):319–323.

Marmier, F., and G. Trécolle
1968 Stratigraphie du gisement d'Hassi-Mouillah. Région de Ouargla (Algérie). *Bulletin de la Société Préhistorique Française, comptes rendus des séances mensuelles* 65(4):121–127.

McBurney, C. B. M.
1960 *The Stone Age of northern Africa.* Harmondsworth: Penguin.
1967 *The Haua Fteah (Cyrenaïca) and the Stone Age of the southeast Mediterranean.* Cambridge: Cambridge University Press.
1975 Current status of the Lower and Middle Paleolithic of the entire region from the Levant through North Africa. In *Problems in prehistory: North Africa and the Levant,* edited by F. Wendorf and A. E. Marks. Dallas: Southern Methodist University Press. Pp. 411–425.

McBurney, C. B. M., and R. W. Hey
1955 *Prehistory and Pleistocene geology in Cyrenaican Libya.* Cambridge: Cambridge University Press.

McHugh, W. P.
1971 Late prehistoric cultural adaptation in the southeastern Libyan Desert. Ph.D. dissertation, Department of Anthropology, University of Wisconsin, Madison.
1974 Cattle pastoralism in Africa. A model for interpreting archaeological evidence from the Eastern Sahara Desert. In *Arctic Anthropology* 11(Suppl.):236–244.
1975 Some archaeological results of the Bagnold–Mond expedition to the Gilf Kebir and Gebel Uweinat, southern Libyan Desert. *Journal of Near Eastern Studies* 34(1):31–62.

Mellars, P. A.
1970 Some comments on the notion of "functional variability" in stone-tool assemblages. *World Archaeology* 2(1):74–80.

Messerli, B.
1972 Formen und Formungsprozesse in des Hochgebirgsregion des Tibesti. *Hochgebirgsforschung,* No. 2. Munich: University of Innsbruck Press. Pp. 23–86.

Michel, P., P. Elouard, and H. Fauré
1968 Nouvelles recherches sur le Quaternaire récent de la région de Saint-Louis (Sénégal). *Bulletin de l'Institut Français d'Afrique Noire, 30A,* Series A (1):1–38.

Mori, F.
1965a Contribution to the study of the prehistoric pastoral

people of the Sahara. Chronological data from the excavations in the Acacus. In *Miscalena en homenaje el abate Breuil (1877–1961)*, Vol. 2. Barcelona. Pp. 172–179.

1965b *Tadrart Acacus, Arte rupestre e culture del Sahara prehistorico.* Turin: G. Einaudi.

Motts, W. S.
1965 Hydrologic types of playas and closed valleys and some relations of hydrology to playa geology. In *Geology, mineralogy and hydrology of U.S. playas*, edited by J. T. Neal. Air Force Cambridge Research Laboratories Environmental Research Paper, No. 96. (AFCRL 65-266). Pp. 73–104.

Munnich, K. O., and J. C. Vogel
1962 Untersuchungen an Pluvialen Wässern der Öst-Sahara. *Geologische Rundschau* 52(2):611–624.

Murray, G. W.
1939 The road to Chephren's quarries. *Geographical Journal* 94:97–111.
1952 The water beneath the Egyptian Western Desert. *Geographical Journal* 118(4):443–452.

Myers, O. H.
1939 The Sir Robert Mond Expedition of the Egypt Explorations Society. *Geographical Journal* 93:287–291.

Nicolaisen, J.
1963 *Ecology and culture of the pastoral Tuareg with particular reference to the Tuareg of Ahaggar and Ayr.* National Museum of Copenhagen, Etnografisk Raekke IX.

Niethammer, G.
1971 Die Fauna der Sahara. In *Die Sahara und ihre Randgebiete*, Vol. 2, edited by H. Schiffers. Munich: Weltforum Verlag. Pp. 499–588.

Nordström, H.-A.
1972 Neolithic and A-Group sites. *The Scandinavian Joint Expedition to Sudanese Nubia*, Vol. 3, Parts 1 and 2. Stockholm: Scandinavian University Press.

Noy, T., A. J. Legge, and E. S. Higgs
1973 Recent excavations at Nahal Oren, Israel. *Proceedings of the Prehistoric Society* 39:75–99.

Parmenter, C., and D. W. Folger
1974 Eolian biogenic detritus in deep sea sediments: A possible index of equatorial ice age aridity. *Science* 185:695–698.

Peake, H.
1928 *The origins of agriculture.* London: Benn.

Peel, R. F.
1939 Rock-paintings from the Libyan Desert. *Antiquity* 13:389–402.
1941 Denudational landforms of the central Libyan Desert, *Journal of Geomorphology* 4(1):3–23.

Peel, R. F., and R. A. Bagnold
1939 Archaeology: Additional notes. *Geographical Journal* 93(4):291–295.

Penderel, H. W. G. J.
1934 The Gilf Kebir. *Geographical Journal* 83:449–456.

Perkal, J.
1961 *Matematyka dla przyodnikow i rolnikow*, Vol. II. Warsaw: Nauk.

Phillips, J. L.
1973 Two Final Paleolithic sites in the Nile Valley and their external relations. *Papers of the Geological Survey of Egypt* No. 57.

Pias, J.
1970 Les formations sédimentaires Tertiaires et Quaternaires de la cuvette tchadienne et les sols qui en derivent. *Mémoires de l'O.R.S.T.O.M.*, No. 43.

Polgar, S.
1975 Population evolution and theoretical paradigm. In *Population, ecology, and social evolution*, edited by S. Polgar. The Hague: Mouton. Pp. 1–25.

Ramendo, L.
1963 Les galets aménagés de Reggan (Sahara). *Libyca* 11:43–74.

Reed, C. A.
1964 A natural history study of Kurkur Oasis, Libyan Desert, Egypt. Part I: Introduction. *Postilla*, No. 84.
1966 The Yale University Prehistoric Expedition to Nubia, 1962–1965. *Discovery* 1(2):16–23.
1977 Origins of agriculture: Discussion and some conclusions. In *Origins of agriculture*, edited by C. A. Reed. The Hague: Mouton. Pp. 879–953.

Reygasse, M.
1935 Découverte d'ateliers de technique acheuléenne dans le Tassili des Ajjers (Erg Tihodäine). *Bulletin de la Société Préhistorique Française* 32(6):358–362.

Rhotert, H.
1952 *Libysche Felsbilder.* Darmstadt: L. C. Wittich.

Roche, J.
1972 Les industries paléolithiques de la Grotte de Taforalt (Maroc Oriental). *Actes du Congrès Panafricain de Préhistoire, VI Session, Dakar, 1967.* Pp. 102–108.
1976 Cadre chronologique de l'Epipaléolithique marocain. *IX Congrès U.I.S.P.P., Colloque II, Nice.* Pp. 153–167.

Rognon, P.
1976 Essai d'interprétation des variations climatiques au Sahara depuis 40,000 ans. *Révue de Géographie Physique et Géologie Dynamique* 18(2–3):251–282.

Rognon, P., and M. A. J. Williams
1977 Late Quaternary climatic changes in Australia and North Africa: A preliminary interpretation. In *Paleogeography, paleoclimatology, and paleoecology* 21(4):285–327.

Rohlfs, G.
1875 *Drei Monate in der Libyschen Wüste.* Kassel.

Ronen, A., D. Kaufman, R. Gophna, N. Bakler, P. Smith, and A. Amiel
1975 The Epi-Paleolithic site Hefziba, central coastal plain of Israel. *Quartär* 26:53–72.

Roubet, F. E.
1947 Quelques nouveaux gisements préhistoriques. *Bulletin de la Société de Géographie et d'Archéologie d'Oran* 70:115–126.
1966 Présentation comparative d'un gisement côtier des environs de Berard, a l'ouest d'Alger, Etude stratigraphique sur l'Atérien. *Actes du Congrès Préhistoire de France, VIII Session, Ajaccio.* Pp. 109–128.
1972 Recherches récentes sur la stratigraphie du littoral, a l'ouest d'Alger, l'Atérien et les formations de la côte entre Berard et Tipasa. *Actes du Congrès Panafricain de Préhistoire, VI Session, Dakar, 1967.* Pp. 144–145.

Ruhlmann, A.
1952 The Moroccan Aterian and its subdivisions. *Proceedings 1st Panafrican Congress of Prehistory, Nairobi, 1947.* Oxford: Blackwell.

Said, R.
1962 *The geology of Egypt.* Amsterdam–New York: Elsevier.
1969 Pleistocene geology of the Dungul region, southern Libyan Desert, Egypt. In Prehistoric settlement patterns in the Libyan Desert, edited by J. J. Hester and P. M. Hoebler. *University of Utah Anthropology Papers*, No. 92. Pp. 7–18.
1975 The geological evolution of the River Nile. In *Problems in prehistory: North Africa and the Levant*, edited by F. Wendorf and A. E. Marks. Dallas: Southern Methodist University Press. Pp. 7–44.

Said, R., and B. Issawi
1965 Preliminary results of a geological expedition to Lower Nubia and to Kurkur and Dungul Oasis, Egypt. In *Contributions to the prehistory of Nubia*, edited by F. Wendorf. Dallas: Southern Methodist University Press. Pp. 1–28.

Sandford, K. S.
1933 Past climate and early man in the southern Libyan Desert. *Geographical Journal* 82(2):219–222.

Sandford, K. S., and A. J. Arkell
1939 Paleolithic man and the Nile Valley in Lower Egypt. *University of Chicago Oriental Institute Publication,* No. 46.

Saxon, E. C., A. E. Close, C. Cluzel, V. Morse, and N. J. Shackleton
1974 Results of recent investigations of Tamar Hat. *Libyca* 22:49–91.

Schild, R.
1969 Proba ustalenia listy form zwiazanych z procesem przygotowania oblupni i rdzeniowaniem w cyklu mazowszanskim. *III Sympozium Paleolityczne* 2:3–15.

Schild, R., M. Chmielewska, and H. Wieckowska
1968 The Arkinian and Shamarkian industries. In *The prehistory of Nubia,* edited by F. Wendorf. Dallas: Fort Burgwin Research Center and Southern Methodist University Press. Pp. 651–767.

Schild, R., and F. Wendorf
1975 New explorations in the Egyptian Sahara. In *Problems in prehistory: North Africa and the Levant,* edited by F. Wendorf and A. E. Marks. Dallas: Southern Methodist University Press. Pp. 65–112.
1977a Kulkuletti und Gademotta—"Platz der Teufel." *Das Altertum,* Vol. I. Pp. 12–19.
1977b *The prehistory of Dakhla Oasis and adjacent desert.* Wroclaw: Ossolineum.

Schultz, E.
1976 Aktueller Pollenniederschlag in der zentralen Sahara und Interpretationen—möglichkeiten quartärer pollenspektren. In *Palaeoecology of Africa,* Vol. 9, edited by E. M. van Zinderen Bakker. Cape Town: A. A. Balkema, Pp. 8–14.

Servant, M.
1970 Nouvelles données stratigraphiques sur le Quaternaire supérieur et récent au nord-est du lac Tchad. *Cah. O.R.S.T.O.M.,* sér. Géol. 2(1):95–114.
1973 Séquences continentales et variations climatiques: évolution du bassin du Tchad au Cénozoïque supérieur. Thesis, University of Paris.

Servant, M., and S. Servant-Vildary
1972 Nouvelles données pour une interprétation paléoclimatique de séries continentales du Bassin Tchadien (Pleistocéne récent, Holocéne). In *Palaeoecology of Africa,* Vol. 6, edited by E. M. van Zinderen Bakker. Cape Town: A. A. Balkema, Pp. 87–92.

Shackleton, N. J.
1975 The stratigraphic record of deep-sea cores and its implications for the assessment of glacials, interglacials, stadials and interstadials in the Mid-Pleistocene. In *After the australopithecines,* edited by K. W. Butzer and G. L. Isaac. The Hague: Mouton. Pp. 1–24.

Shata, A., G. Knetsch, E. T. Degens, O. Munnich, and M. M. El Shazly
1962 The geology, age and origin of the ground water supplies in some desert areas of the U.A.R. *Bulletin de l'Institut du Egypte* 12(2):61–124.

Shaw, B. D.
1976 Climate, environment and prehistory in the Sahara. *World Archaeology* 8(2):133–149.

Shaw, W. B. K.
1945 *Long-range desert group.* Toronto: Collins.

Shiner, J. L.
1968a The Cataract tradition. In *The prehistory of Nubia,* edited by F. Wendorf. Dallas: Fort Burgwin Research Center and Southern Methodist University Press. Pp. 535–629.
1968b The Khartoum Variant industry. In *The prehistory of Nubia,* edited by F. Wendorf. Dallas: Fort Burgwin Research Center and Southern Methodist University Press. Pp. 768–790.
1968c Miscellaneous sites. In *The prehistory of Nubia,* edited by F. Wendorf. Dallas: Fort Burgwin Research Center and Southern Methodist University Press. Pp. 630–650.

Shiner, J. L., A. E. Marks, W. Chmielewski, J. de Heinzelin, and T. R. Hays
1971 *The prehistory and geology of northern Sudan.* Report to the National Science Foundation.

Simon, H. A.
1969 *The sciences of the artificial.* Cambridge: M.I.T. Press.

Simons, P.
1973 Der Osten der Sahara, B. Die Nilwüste. In *Die Sahara und ihre Randgebiete,* Vol. III, edited by H. Schiffers. Munich: Weltforum Verlag. Pp. 433–535.

Smith, P. E. L.
1972 Changes in population pressure in archaeological explanation. *World Archaeology* 4(1):5–18.
1976 Stone-Age man on the Nile. *Scientific American* 235(2):30–38.

Smith, P. E. L., and T. C. Young
1972 The evolution of early agriculture and culture in Greater Mesopotamia: A trial model. In *Population growth: Anthropological implications,* edited by B. J. Spooner, Cambridge. M.I.T. Press. Pp. 1–59.

Spooner, B. J. (Editor)
1972 *Population growth: Anthropological implications.* Cambridge: M.I.T. Press.

Stearns, Ch. E.
1967 Pleistocene geology of Cape Ashakar and vicinity. In *The Paleolithic of Tangier, Morocco,* edited by B. Howe. American School of Prehistoric Research, Peabody Museum, Harvard University, Bulletin No. 22. Pp. 6–35.
1970 The Ouljian Stage, Atlantic Coast of Morocco. *Geological Society of America, 1970 Abstracts, Annual Meeting* 2(7):694.

Stearns, Ch. E., and D. L. Thurber
1965 $Th^{230}–U^{234}$ dates of the late Pleistocene marine fossils from the Mediterranean and Moroccan littorals. *Quaternaria* 7:29–43.

Strouhal, E.
1972 Une contribution à la question du caractère de la population préhistorique de la Haute-Egypte. *Actes du Congrès Panafricain de Prèhistoire, VI Session, Dakar, 1967.* Pp. 510–512.

Terell, J.
1977 Biology, biogeography of man. *World Archaeology* 8(3):237–248.

Thompson, B. W.
1965 *The climate of Africa.* London: Oxford University Press.

Tixier, J.
1955 Les abris sous roche de Dakhlat es-Saâdane (Commune mixte de Bou-Saâda). *Libyca* 3:81–128.
1960 Les industries Lithiques d'Aïn Fritissa (Maroc Oriental). *Bulletin d'Archéologie Marocaine* 3:107–248.
1963 Typologie de l'Epipaléolithique du Maghreb. *Mémoires du Centre de Recherches Anthropologiques, Préhistorique et Ethnographiques,* No. 2. Paris: Arts et Métiers Graphiques.
1967 Procédés d'analyse et questions de terminologie concernant l'études des ensembles industriels du Paléolithique récent et de l'Epipaléolithique dans l'Afrique du Nord-Ouest. In *Background to evolution in Africa,* edited by W. W. Bishop and J. D. Clark. Chicago: University of Chicago Press. Pp. 771–820.

Van Campo, M.
1958 Analyse pollinique des dépôts wurmiens d'el Guéttar

(Tunisie). *Veroffentlich. d. Geobotanische Inst. Rubel, Zurich* 34:133–135.

1975 Pollen analyses in the Sahara. In *Problems in prehistory: North Africa and the Levant,* edited by F. Wendorf and A. E. Marks. Dallas: Southern Methodist University Press. Pp. 45–64.

Van Campo, M., and R. Coque
1960 Palynologie et géomorphologie dans le sud Tunisien. *Pollen et Spores* 2(2):275–284.

Van Campo, M., Ph. Guinet, and J. Cohen
1968 Fossil pollen from Late Tertiary and middle Pleistocene deposits of the Kurkur Oasis. In *Desert and river in Nubia,* edited by K. W. Butzer and C. L. Hansen, Madison: University of Wisconsin Press. Pp. 515–520.

van Zinderen Bakker, E. M.
1972 Late Quaternary lacustrine phases in the southern Sahara and East Africa. In *Palaeoecology of Africa,* Vol. 6, edited by E. M. van Zinderen Bakker. Cape Town: A. A. Balkema. Pp. 15–27.

van Zinderen Bakker, E. M., and J. A. Coetzee
1972 A re-appraisal of late Quaternary climatic evidence from tropical Africa. In *Palaeoecology of Africa,* Vol. 7, edited by E. M. van Zinderen Bakker, Pp. 151–181.

Vaufrey, R.
1955 *Préhistoire de l'Afrique, Tome I:Le Maghreb.* Paris: Masson.

Vermeersch, P. M.
1976 Trois nouveaux sites épipaléolithiques à Elkab (Haute-Egypte). *L'Anthropologie* 80(3):509–514.

Vermeersch, P. M., E. Paulissen, and G. Gijselings
1977 Prospection préhistorique entre Asyut et Nag'Hammadi (Egypte). *Bulletin de la Société Royale Belge d'Anthropologie et de Préhistoire* 88:117–124.

Vita-Finzi, C., and R. A. Kennedy
1965 Seven Saharan sites. *Journal of the Royal Anthropological Institute* 95(2):195–213.

Wendorf, F. (Editor)
1961 Paleoecology of the Llano Estacado. *Fort Burgwin Research Center, Publication No. 1.* Santa Fe: Museum of New Mexico Press.

1968 *The prehistory of Nubia,* 2 vols. and atlas. Dallas: Fort Burgwin Research Center and Southern Methodist University Press.

Wendorf, F., R. L. Laury, C. C. Albritton, R. Schild, C. V. Haynes, P. E. Damon, M. Shafiqullah, and R. Scarborough
1975 Dates for the Middle Stone Age of East Africa. *Science* 187:740–742.

Wendorf, F., and R. Schild.
1974 *A Middle Stone Age sequence from the central Rift Valley, Ethiopia.* Warsaw: Institute of the History of Material Culture, Polish Academy of Sciences.
1976a The Middle Paleolithic of northeastern Africa: new data

and concepts. *IX Congrès U.I.S.P.P., Colloque III, Nice.* Pp. 8–34.
1976b *Prehistory of the Nile Valley.* New York: Academic Press.
1976c The use of ground grain during the Late Paleolithic of the Lower Nile Valley, Egypt. In *Origins of African Plant Domestication,* edited by J. R. Harlan, J. M. J. de Wet, and A. B. L. Stemler. The Hague: Mouton. Pp. 269–288.

Wendorf, F., R. Schild, and A. E. Close
in press *Loaves and fishes: the prehistory of Wadi Kubbaniya* Dallas: Department of Anthropology, Institute for the Study of Earth and Man, Southern Methodist University.

Wendorf, F., R. Schild, N. El Hadidi, A. E. Close, M. Kobusiewicz, H. Wieckowska, B. Issawi, and H. Haas
1979 The use of barley in the Egyptian Late Paleolithic. *Science* 205:1341–1347.

Wendorf, F., R. Schild, R. Said, C. V. Haynes, M. Kobusiewicz, A. Gautier, N. El Hadidi, H. Wieckowska, and A. E. Close
1977 Late Pleistocene and Recent climatic changes in the Egyptian Sahara. *Geographical Journal* 143(2):211–234.

Wetzel, R., and G. Bosinski
1969 *Die Bocksteinschmiede im Lonetal,* 2 vols. Stuttgart.

Wiercinski, A.
1963 Analiza struktury rasowej ludnosci Egiptu w epoce predynastycznej (The analysis of the racial structure of Egyptian population in the Predynastic period, with English summary). *Materialy i Prace Antropologicene 56.* Wroclaw.

Williams, M. A. J., and D. A. Adamson
1973 The physiography of the central Sudan. *Geographical Journal* 139(3):498–508.
1974 Late Pleistocene desiccation along the White Nile. *Nature* 248: 584–586.

Williams, M. A. J., and J. D. Clark
1976 Prehistory and Quaternary environments in the central Sudan. In *Palaeoecology of Africa,* Vol. 9, edited by E. M. van Zinderen Bakker. Pp. 52–53.

Williams, M. A. J., J. D. Clark, D. A. Adamson, and R. Gillespie
1975 Recent Quaternary research in central Sudan. *Bulletin de l'Association Sénégalaise d'Etudes Quaternaires Ouest Africaines,* No. 46. Pp. 75–86.

Winkler, H.
1938– *Rock drawings of southern Upper Egypt,* Vols. I and
39 II. London: Oxford University Press.

Zittel, A. K.
1883 Beiträge zur Geologie und Paläontologie der Libyschen Wüste und der angrenzenden Gebiete von Aegypten. *Paläontographica* 30(1):1–112.

Subject Index